Instructor's Solutions Manual to accompany

PHYSICS

for Scientists and Engineers

THIRD EDITION

Includes complete solutions to all new problems

VOLUME ONE

by

RAYMOND A. SERWAY

James Madison University

STEVE VAN WYK

Chapman College

RALPH V. McGREW

Broome Community College

LOUIS H. CADWELL

Providence College

SAUNDERS COLLEGE PUBLISHING

Harcourt Brace Jovanovich College Publishers

Fort Worth Philadelphia San Diego New York Orlando Austin
San Antonio Toronto Montreal London Sydney Tokyo

Serway–Cadwell–Van Wyk: Instructor's Solution's Manual to accompany
PHYSICS FOR SCIENTISTS & ENGINEERS, 3/E
UPDATED VERSION, VOLUME ONE

ISBN 0–03–096033–9

234 021 987654321

PREFACE

This Instructor's Solutions Manual has been written to accompany the updated third edition of the textbooks **Physics for Scientists and Engineers** and **Physics for Scientists and Engineers with Modern Physics**, both by Raymond A. Serway. The manual includes the following:

(1) Detailed solutions to all end–of–chapter problems, with boxed answers.

(2) Answers to even–numbered problems are included at the end of this volume. (Answers to odd–numbered problems are included in the textbooks.)

Because of its large size the manual has been split into two volumes. Volume I contains solutions and answers to problems in Chapter 1 through 22. Volume II contains solutions and answers to problems found in Chapters 23 through 47. As the title of this work implies, this manual was prepared for the convenience of instructors who are teaching this course. Particularly since we have included solutions to all of the problems in the text, we strongly urge that instructors exercise precautionary measures to keep their manuals secure. While we recognize that instructors may post solutions to selected problems, we request that the entire solutions manual not be made available to students as a courtesy to other instructors who wish to use these problems on exams.

This updated third edition contains about 670 new problems which are identified with an asterisk (*) in front of the solution problem number. In almost all cases, the new problems have replaced an "old" problem so that the remaining problems' and their numbers, are identical to those in the third edition.

Please note that a Student Study Guide is available, which includes answers to selected end–of–chapter problems, as well as detailed solutions to approximately ten of the odd–numbered problems per chapter. As a convenience to the instructor, these problem numbers are listed at the beginning of this manual. The Student Study Guide also contains answers to many of the end–of–chapter questions and other features such as objectives, skills, notes from selected sections, equations and concepts, programmed exercises, and a selection of nineteen computer modules. For additional information about the other ancillary items, please see the Preface of the textbooks.

A great deal of time and effort has been devoted to checking the accuracy of the solutions and preparing this manual. If you should find any errors, omissions, or inconsistencies, despite our efforts, please notify us* and we will attempt to correct them in future printings. We also welcome your comments on the solutions, as well as suggestions for alternate solutions.

Raymond A. Serway
Steve Van Wyk
Ralph McGrew

* Please send your corrections to Prof. Steven Van Wyk, Chapman College, P.O. Box 2285, Bremerton, WA 98310.

ACKNOWLEDGEMENTS

A number of people have made valuable contributions to this enormous project and deserve our sincere thanks and appreciation.

First, we thank John R. Gordon, Lawrence H. Hmurcik, and the late Henry Leap for their fine work on the solutions manual for the second edition of the Serway textbooks. Many of the solutions contained in this manual were taken from this work. We are most grateful to Charles D. Teague for carefully checking solutions to most new problems, and Jeffrey J. Braun for organizing and reviewing the problems as they are presented in the textbooks. Many of the new problems were provided by Ron Canterna, Paul Feldker, Roger Ludin, Richard Reimann, Jill Rugare, Stan Shepard, Som Tyagi, and James Walker. We thank Mary Toscano and Nancy Toscano of M&N TOSCANO, Somerville, Massachusetts and Sue Jarrett and Judy Sarver of Mustard Seed Word Processing, Bremerton, Washington, for their excellent assistance in computer typesetting of this manuscript. Finally, we owe much appreciation to Ellen Newman, Senior Developmental Editor, who coordinated all phases of the project and followed it diligently through its completion.

Serway's Summary of New Problems for PSE Updated Third Edition

Chapter 1

Problems 4, 7, 16, 17, 26, 31, 34, 35, 38, 39, 40, 45, 46, 47, 60, 61, 62, 63

Chapter 2

Problems 9, 12, 14, 18, 20, 24, 32, 35, 36, 40, 41, 44, 46, 64

Chapter 3

Problems 6, 22, 23, 32, 33, 34, 51, 52, 55, 56, 57, 58, 64, 67, 71, 72, 73, 74, 75

Chapter 4

Problems 3, 4, 13, 14, 16, 18, 26, 29, 36, 45, 59, 60, 68, 75, 76, 87

Chapter 5

Problems 16, 17, 19, 22, 27, 29, 35, 36, 47, 49, 51, 56, 61, 62, 63, 64, 68, 72, 76, 77, 82, 89, 90

Chapter 6

Problems 7, 8, 10, 16, 18, 23, 27, 37, 51, 53

Chapter 7

Problems 9, 19, 30, 31, 39, 40, 41, 59, 65, 73, 77, 78, 87, 88, 89

Chapter 8

Problems 15, 21, 30, 32, 36, 49, 50, 54, 62, 63, 68

Chapter 9

Problems 3, 4, 12, 20, 25, 30, 31, 33, 34, 39, 46, 47, 55, 65

Chapter 10

Problems 8, 10, 12, 18, 30, 32, 36, 37, 40, 44, 49, 50, 53

Chapter 11

Problems 5, 8, 14, 16, 19, 26, 28, 43, 47, 53, 55

Chapter 12

Problems 1, 18, 21, 22, 23, 24, 28, 30, 31, 32, 46, 50, 52, 53, 54

Chapter 13

Problems 6, 11, 16, 20, 22, 24, 27, 28, 34, 56, 58, 59, 64

Chapter 14

Problems 5, 6, 7, 9, 10, 14, 18, 19, 27, 28, 30, 32, 34, 46, 47, 56, 59, 60, 62, 68

Chapter 15

Problems 6, 26, 28, 29, 32, 38, 39, 59, 60, 62, 63, 64, 66, 69, 70, 74

Chapter 16

Problems 5, 11, 14, 23, 28, 31, 32, 33, 50, 51, 54

Chapter 17

Problems 25, 28, 30, 31, 35, 38, 40, 46, 52, 54, 58

Chapter 18

Problems 6, 22, 25, 28, 29, 34, 39, 50, 56, 59, 63, 68

Chapter 19

Problems 9, 18, 21, 23, 26, 28, 35, 36, 37, 38, 39, 43, 63

Chapter 20

Problems 5, 10, 12, 16, 17, 22, 23, 26, 27, 32, 48, 51, 53, 54, 57, 59, 60, 61, 63, 65, 70, 71, 82, 83

Chapter 21

Problems 3, 4, 10, 11, 66, 70, 73, 74, 75, 76, 77

Chapter 22

Problems 4, 5, 9, 17, 18, 34, 43, 44, 47, 50, 54, 56, 59, 60, 65, 66

Chapter 23

Problems 2, 6, 11, 12, 13, 14, 21, 46, 58, 62, 65, 66, 70, 74, 77, 78

Chapter 24

Problelms 12, 14, 16, 19, 24, 44, 53, 63, 64

Chapter 25

Problems 8, 24, 26, 45, 46, 64, 70, 71, 74, 75, 76, 77, 87

Chapter 26

Problems 16, 24, 26, 36, 37, 46, 47, 60, 61, 62, 63, 70, 74, 75, 76, 77, 78, 79

Chapter 27

Problems 8, 14, 21, 26, 27, 28, 32, 34, 38, 49, 50, 52, 55, 56, 59, 62, 65, 66, 73

Chapter 28

Problems 6, 9, 11, 12, 13, 22, 23, 28, 29, 30, 33, 36, 38, 41, 56, 57, 70, 71, 72, 75, 87, 88, 89, 90, 91

Chapter 29

Problems 18, 26, 30, 40, 41, 46, 52, 56, 60, 62, 63, 64, 72

Chapter 30

Problems 12, 13, 16, 17, 32, 62, 74, 75, 76, 87, 88, 89

Chapter 31

Problems 44, 54, 56, 58, 60, 61, 67, 69, 71, 72, 73

Chapter 32

Problems 10, 35, 36, 37, 44, 71, 72, 73, 76, 79, 80, 84, 85, 86

Chapter 33

Problems 34, 37, 38, 46, 48, 49, 58, 66, 68, 69, 70, 72, 75, 77, 78, 80, 83, 87

Chapter 34

Problems 8, 11, 12, 14, 17, 20, 26, 27, 28, 30, 51, 52, 59, 60, 61, 62, 63

Chapter 35

Problems 16, 17, 32, 33, 48, 50, 54, 55, 56, 57, 58

Chapter 36

Problems 4, 20, 28, 30, 37, 58, 62, 66, 67, 68, 74, 76, 77, 78

Chapter 37

Problems 4, 6, 8, 10, 28, 35, 38, 39, 40, 41, 43, 44, 46, 48, 52, 54, 58, 62, 68, 70, 71, 72

Chapter 38

Problems 10, 12, 13, 14, 22, 23, 24, 28, 30, 31, 32, 61, 66, 69, 74

Chapter 39

Problems 9, 10, 16, 17, 18, 22, 36, 40, 47, 51, 52

Chapter 40

Problems 8, 24, 28, 32, 40, 46, 58, 65, 67, 68, 69, 70, 72

Chapter 41

Problems 8, 20, 22, 30, 52, 53, 54, 62, 67, 68, 72

Chapter 42

Problems 16, 18, 20, 30, 32, 38, 42, 44, 45, 50, 51, 54

Chapter 43

Problems 4, 6, 7, 31, 32, 34, 36

Chapter 44

Problems 9, 10, 17

Chapter 45

Problems 9, 12, 14, 28, 30, 32, 34, 40, 42, 43, 46, 47, 50, 52, 61, 62, 68, 70, 72, 77, 78, 82, 83, 84

Chapter 46

Problems 6, 7, 17, 23, 32, 33, 34, 37, 38

Chapter 47

Problems 27, 28, 29, 30

SOLUTIONS FROM THE STUDENT STUDY GUIDE

Chapter 1	Chapter 2	Chapter 3	Chapter 4	Chapter 5
1.5	2.3	3.5	4.7	5.18
1.6	2.5	3.7	4.9	5.20
1.10	2.11	3.9	4.15	5.24
1.15	2.13	3.17	4.23	5.33
1.23	2.15	3.25	4.33	5.39
1.25	2.29	3.39	4.37	5.50
1.27	2.33	3.47	4.49	5.55
1.41	2.43	3.53	4.55	5.57
1.43	2.45	3.59	4.66	5.65
1.49	2.51	3.69	4.79	5.69
1.51				5.73
1.53				5.74
				5.75
				5.83
				5.87

Chapter 6	Chapter 7	Chapter 8	Chapter 9	Chapter 10
6.5	7.7	8.7	9.5	10.7
6.13	7.11	8.11	9.11	10.11
6.21	7.17	8.23	9.19	10.13
6.25	7.29	8.33	9.35	10.17
6.29	7.37	8.39	9.37	10.31
6.33	7.49	8.47	9.55	10.33
6.39	7.61	8.57	9.59	10.39
6.45	7.75	8.59	9.67	10.41
	7.81	8.61	9.79	10.43
			9.81	

Chapter 11	Chapter 12	Chapter 13	Chapter 14	Chapter 15
11.3	12.3	13.5	14.3	15.3
11.11	12.7	13.15	14.17	15.11
11.25	12.33	13.23	14.25	15.27
11.39	12.37	13.33	14.31	15.37
11.49	12.41	13.47	14.39	15.45
11.59	12.43	13.51	14.41	15.57
	12.49	13.53	14.55	15.61
	12.56	13.65	14.63	15.67
			14.67	15.73
			14.69	15.75

CHAPTER 1

1.1 $\rho = \dfrac{M}{L^3} = \dfrac{350\text{ g}}{(5\text{ cm}^3)} = \boxed{2.8\text{ g/cm}^3}$

1.2 $\rho = M/V$ where $V = 4\pi R^3/3$;

Thus, $R = (3M/4\pi\rho)^{1/3} = [3 \times 475/4\pi(8.93)]^{1/3} = \boxed{2.33\text{ cm}}$

1.3

$$V_{cu} = V_0 - V_i = \frac{4}{3}\pi(r_0^3 - r_i^3)$$

$$V_{cu} = \frac{4}{3}\pi[(5.75\text{ cm})^3 - (5.70\text{ cm})^3]$$

$$V_{cu} = 20.6\text{ cm}^3$$

$$\rho = \frac{m}{V}$$

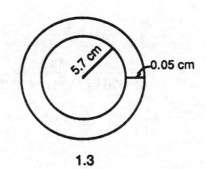

1.3

$$m = \rho V = (8.92\text{ g/cm}^3)(20.6\text{ cm}^3) = \boxed{184\text{ g}}$$

*1.4

$$\frac{\rho_J}{\rho_E} = \frac{M_J/\frac{4}{3}\pi R_J^3}{M_E/\frac{4}{3}\pi R_E^3} = \frac{M_J}{M_E}\left(\frac{R_E}{R_J}\right)^3$$

$$= 317.4\left(\frac{1}{10.95}\right)^3 = \boxed{0.242}$$

1.5 Use $m = $ atomic weight$/N_A$ and $1\text{ u} = 1.66 \times 10^{-24}$ g

(a) For He, $m = 4/6.02 \times 10^{23} = \boxed{6.64 \times 10^{-24}\text{ g} = 4\text{ u}}$

(b) For Fe, $m = 56/6.02 \times 10^{23} = \boxed{9.30 \times 10^{-23}\text{ g} = 56\text{ u}}$

(c) For Pb, $m = 207/6.02 \times 10^{23} = \boxed{3.44 \times 10^{-22}\text{ g} = 207\text{ u}}$

1.6 (a) $M = \rho L^3 = (7.86\text{ g/cm}^3)(5 \times 10^{-6}\text{ cm})^3 = \boxed{9.83 \times 10^{-16}\text{ g}}$

(b) $N = M(\dfrac{N_A}{\text{Atomic Weight}}) = (9.83 \times 10^{-16})(6.02 \times 10^{23}/56) = \boxed{1.06 \times 10^7\text{ atoms}}$

*1.7 (a) $\dfrac{30 \text{ gal}}{420 \text{ s}} = \boxed{7.14 \times 10^{-2} \text{ gal/s}}$

(b) $\left(\dfrac{30 \text{ gal}}{420 \text{ s}}\right)\left(\dfrac{3.786 \times 10^{-3} \text{ m}^3}{1 \text{ gal}}\right) = \boxed{2.7 \times 10^{-4} \text{ m}^3/\text{s}}$

(c) $\left(\dfrac{1 \text{ m}^3}{2.7 \times 10^{-4} \text{ m}^3/\text{s}}\right)\left(\dfrac{1 \text{ h}}{3600 \text{ s}}\right) = \boxed{1.03 \text{ h}}$

1.8 From Table 1.5, the density of copper is $\rho = 8.93 \times 10^3 \text{ kg/m}^3$

$$m = \rho V \qquad (\text{Eq.1.1})$$

$$V = \pi r^2 \Delta h$$

$$\Delta h = \frac{m}{\rho(\pi r^2)} = \frac{62 \text{ kg}}{(8930 \text{ kg/m}^3)\pi \times (0.243 \text{ m})^2}$$

$$\Delta h = 3.74 \times 10^{-2} \text{ m} = \boxed{3.74 \text{ cm}}$$

1.9 $[x] = L; \ [v] = L/T; \ [a] = L/T^2$

$$x = vt + (1/2)at^2$$

$$[L] = [L/T][T] + (1/2)[L/T^2][T]^2$$

$$[L] = [L] + [L]$$

so the expression is dimensionally correct.

1.10 $[s] = L; \ [a] = LT^{-2}; \ [t] = T$

$$s = ka^m t^n$$

$$[s] = [a]^m[t]^n = (LT^{-2})^m T^n = L^m T^{-2m+n}$$

$$L = L^m T^{(-2m+n)} \text{ so } \boxed{m = 1}$$

$$-2m + n = 0 \text{ so } \boxed{n = 2m = 2}$$

$$s = kat^2$$

Since k is dimensionless, its value cannot be determined by dimensional analysis.

1.11 $[v^2] = L^2/T^2, [a] = L/T^2$ and $[s] = L$

Given $v^2 = ka^m s^n$, it follows from an analysis of dimensions that $m = n = 1$.

1.12 $[v(m/s)]^2 = [v_0(m/s)]^2 + 2[a(m/s^2)][x(m)]$

All terms are in m^2/s^2. Therefore the equation is dimensionally correct.

1.13   (a) is incorrect since $[ax] = m^2/s^2$, while $[v] = m/s$.
(b) is correct since $[y] = m$, and $\cos(k, x)$ has no dimensions if $[k] = m^{-1}$.

1.14 $T = \sqrt{\dfrac{L}{L/T^2}} = \sqrt{T^2} = T$

1.15 $[s] = L; \ [t] = T$

$c = \dfrac{s^3}{t}$ so $[c] = [s]/[t^3] = L/T^3 = \boxed{LT^{-3}}$

The dimensions of c are LT^{-3}

*1.16 $V(\text{ft}^3) = 1.5 \times 10^6 \left(\frac{\text{ft}^3}{\text{mo}}\right) t + 0.008 \times 10^6 \left(\frac{\text{ft}^3}{\text{mo}^2}\right) t^2$

$V(\text{ft}^3) = \dfrac{1.5 \times 10^6 (\text{ft}^3)}{2.59 \times 10^6 \text{ s}} t(s) + \dfrac{800 \text{ ft}^3}{(2.59 \times 10^6 \text{ s})^2} t^2(s^2)$

$V(\text{ft}^3) = \left(0.579 \dfrac{\text{ft}^3}{\text{s}}\right) t + \left(1.19 \times 10^{-9} \dfrac{\text{ft}^3}{\text{s}^2}\right) t^2$

*1.17 $\left(\dfrac{\text{kg} \cdot \text{m}}{\text{s}^2}\right) = \dfrac{G(\text{kg})^2}{(\text{m}^2)}$

Cross-multiplying, the units of G are found to be $\dfrac{\text{m}^3}{\text{kg} \cdot \text{s}^2}$.

1.18 $V = 8.50 \text{ in}^3; 1 \text{ in} = 2.54 \text{ cm}; 1 \text{ cm} = 10^{-2} \text{ m}$

$V = 8.50 \text{ in}^3 \times (2.54 \text{ cm/in})^3 \times (10^{-2} \text{ m/cm})^3$

$V = 8.50 \times (2.54)^3 \times 10^{-6} \text{ m}^3 = \boxed{1.39 \times 10^{-4} \text{ m}^3}$

1.19 $\text{Area} = 100.0 \text{ ft} \times 150.0 \text{ ft} = 1.500 \times 10^4 \text{ ft}^2$

$= (1.500 \times 10^4 \text{ ft}^2)(0.0929 \text{ m}^2/\text{ft}^2) = \boxed{1.39 \times 10^2 \text{ m}^2}$

1.20 $h = 2.0 \text{ in}; w = 3.5 \text{ in}; \ell = 6.5 \text{ in}; 1 \text{ in} = 2.54 \times 10^{-2} \text{ m}$

$V = h \times w \times \ell = 2.0 \text{ in} \times 3.5 \text{ in} \times 6.5 \text{ in}$

$= 45.5 \text{ in}^3 = 45.5 \text{ in}^3 \times (2.54 \times 10^{-2} \text{ m/in})^3$

$= \boxed{7.46 \times 10^{-4} \text{ m}^3}$

1.21   Speed is determined by use of known conversion factors:

$v = (5 \text{ furlong/fortnight}) (220 \text{ yd/furlong})(\text{fortnight/14 day})$

$\times (\text{day/24 h})(\text{h/3600 s}) \times (\text{m/1.097 yd})$

$v = \boxed{8.3 \times 10^{-4} \text{ m/s}}$

1.22 $1 \text{ acre} = \dfrac{1}{640} \text{ mi}^2$

$= (\dfrac{1}{640} \text{ mi}^2)(1.609 \dfrac{\text{km}}{\text{mi}})^2(1000 \dfrac{\text{m}}{\text{km}})^2 = \boxed{4045 \text{ m}^2}$

1.23 $M = 23.94 \text{ g} = 23.94 \times 10^{-3} \text{ kg}$

$V = 2.10 \text{ cm}^3 = 2.10 \times 10^{-6} \text{ m}^3$

$\rho = \dfrac{M}{V} = \dfrac{23.94 \times 10^{-3} \text{ kg}}{2.10 \times 10^{-6} \text{ m}^3} = \boxed{1.14 \times 10^4 \text{ kg/m}^3}$

1.24 $S^3 = V$

$$S = \sqrt[3]{V} = \sqrt[3]{1 \text{ qt}[\frac{1 \text{ gal}}{4 \text{ qt}}][\frac{3.786 \text{ liter}}{1 \text{ gal.}}][\frac{10^3 \text{ cm}^3}{1 \text{ liter}}]} = \boxed{9.82 \text{ cm}}$$

1.25 $T = 1.3 \times 10^{17}$ s; Since 1 year $= 3.16 \times 10^7$ s

$$T = \frac{1.3 \times 10^{17} \text{ s}}{3.16 \times 10^7 \text{ s/y}} = \boxed{4.1 \times 10^9 \text{ y}}$$

*1.26 $N_{\text{atoms}} = \dfrac{M_{\text{sun}}}{M_{\text{atom}}} = \dfrac{2 \times 10^{30} \text{ kg}}{1.67 \times 10^{-27} \text{ kg}} = \boxed{1.2 \times 10^{57}}$

1.27 $t = 1$ h; $v = 3 \times 10^8$ m/s

1 mi = 1609 m; 1 h = 60 min; 1 min = 60 s

$s = vt = 3 \times 10^8$ m/s $\times$ 1 h

$s = (3 \times 10^8 \text{ m/s})(60 \text{ s/min})(60 \text{ min/h})(1 \text{ h})(1 \text{ mi}/1609 \text{ m})$

$s = \boxed{6.71 \times 10^8 \text{ mi}}$

1.28 Each wall is 12×8 ft^2 in area

There are four walls, $A = 4 \times 12 \times 8 = \boxed{384 \text{ ft}^2}$

Since 1 m = 3.281 ft, $A = 384/(3.281)^2 = \boxed{35.7 \text{ m}^2}$

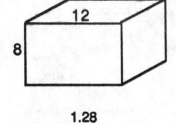

1.28

1.29 1 mi = 1609 m = 1609 km

(a) To go from mi/h to km/h, multiply by 1.609

(b) 55 mi/h = 88.5 km/h

(c) 65 mi/h = 104.6 km/h; $\Delta v = \boxed{16.1 \text{ km/h}}$

1.30   (a) $(86{,}400 \text{ s/day}) \times (365\frac{1}{4} \text{ days/y})$

$$1 \text{ y} = \boxed{3.156 \times 10^7 \text{ s}}$$

(b) $V_{\text{sphere}} = \frac{4}{3}\pi r^3 = \frac{4}{3}\pi(\frac{10^{-6}}{2} \text{ m})^3 = 5.235 \times 10^{-19} \text{ m}^3$

$$T = \frac{1 \text{ m}^3}{5.236 \times 10^{-16} \text{ m}^3/\text{s}} = 1.9 \times 10^{18} \text{ s} = \boxed{6 \times 10^{10} \text{ y}}$$

*1.31 $At = V$

$$\therefore \quad t = \frac{V}{A} = \frac{3.78 \times 10^{-3} \text{ m}^3}{25 \text{ m}^2} = \boxed{1.51 \times 10^{-4} \text{ m}}$$

1.32 $h = 481 \text{ ft} = 146.6 \text{ m}$

$B = 566280 \text{ ft}^2 = 52{,}600 \text{ m}^2$

$V = \frac{1}{3}Bh = \frac{1}{3}(52{,}600)(146.6) = \boxed{2.57 \times 10^6 \text{ m}^3}$

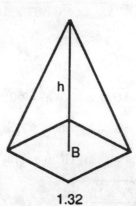

1.32

1.33 $W = (2.5 \text{ tons})(2 \times 10^6) = 5 \times 10^6 \text{ tons}$

$$\boxed{W = 10^{10} \text{ pounds}}$$

*1.34 $$\frac{d_{\text{star}}}{dia_{\text{sun}}} = \frac{x}{7 \text{ mm}}$$

The scaled distance $x = 7 \text{ mm}\left(\dfrac{d_{\text{star}}}{dia_{\text{sun}}}\right)$

$$x = 7 \text{ mm}\left(\frac{4 \times 10^{16} \text{ m}}{1.4 \times 10^9 \text{ m}}\right) = 2 \times 10^8 \text{ mm} = \boxed{200 \text{ km}}$$

*1.35
$$\frac{d_{\text{galaxy}}}{dia_{\text{Milky Way}}} = \frac{x}{25 \text{ cm}}$$

The scaled distance $x = 25 \text{ cm} \left(\frac{d_{\text{galaxy}}}{dia_{\text{Milky Way}}} \right)$

$$x = 25 \text{ cm} \left(\frac{2 \times 10^6 \text{ ly}}{10^5 \text{ ly}} \right)$$

$$x = 500 \text{ cm} = \boxed{5 \text{ m}}$$

1.36 (a) $\dfrac{\text{Area of earth}}{\text{Area of moon}} = \dfrac{4\pi R_e^2}{4\pi R_m^2} = \dfrac{R_e^2}{R_m^2}$

$$= \frac{(6.37 \times 10^6 \text{ m})^2}{(1.74 \times 10^6 \text{ m})^2} = \boxed{13.4}$$

(b) $\dfrac{\text{Volume of earth}}{\text{Volume of moon}} = \dfrac{R_e^3}{R_m^3} = \left(\dfrac{6.37}{1.74}\right)^3 = \boxed{49.1}$

1.37 $\rho = \dfrac{m}{V} \qquad V = \dfrac{4}{3}\pi r^3$

$$m = \rho\left(\frac{4}{3}\pi r^3\right) = (5.5 \times 10^3 \frac{\text{kg}}{\text{m}^3})(\frac{4}{3}\pi)(6.37 \times 10^6 \text{ m})^3 = \boxed{5.95 \times 10^{24} \text{ kg}}$$

*1.38 $At = V$

$$A = \frac{V}{t} = \frac{1 \text{ m}^3}{10^{-6} \text{ m}} = \boxed{10^6 \text{ m}^2}$$

*1.39 $\rho_{\text{Al}} V_{\text{Al}} = \rho_{\text{Fe}} V_{\text{Fe}}$

$$\rho_{\text{Al}} \left(\frac{4}{3}\pi r_{\text{Al}}^3 \right) = \rho_{\text{Fe}} \left(\frac{4}{3}\pi r_{\text{Fe}}^3 \right)$$

$$\left(\frac{r_{\text{Al}}}{r_{\text{Fe}}} \right)^3 = \frac{\rho_{\text{Fe}}}{\rho_{\text{Al}}}$$

$$r_{\text{Al}} = \sqrt[3]{\frac{\rho_{\text{Fe}}}{\rho_{\text{Al}}}}(r_{\text{Fe}}) = \sqrt[3]{\frac{7.86}{2.7}}(2 \text{ cm}) = \boxed{2.86 \text{ cm}}$$

*1.40   # Heartbeats $= (70 \text{ y}) \left(\dfrac{365 \text{ da}}{1 \text{ y}}\right) \left(\dfrac{24 \text{ h}}{1 \text{ da}}\right) \left(\dfrac{60 \text{ min}}{1 \text{ h}}\right) \left(\dfrac{60 \text{ heartbeats}}{1 \text{ min}}\right)$

$\qquad\qquad\qquad = \boxed{2.21 \times 10^9}$

1.41   A ping-pong ball is about 3 cm in diameter and can be thought of as occupying a cube about $3 \times 3 \times 3$ cm^3. That is, $V_{\text{Ball}} = 27$ cm^3

Take a typical room (my living room) as 12 ft. $\times$ 15 ft. $\times$ 8 ft.

1 ft $\cong$ 30 cm, so $V_{\text{Room}} = 12 \times 15 \times 8$ ft$^3 = (30 \text{ cm}/1 \text{ ft})^3 \approx 3.9 \times 10^7$ cm^3.

The number of ping-pong balls which can fill the room is

$$N \equiv \frac{V_{\text{Room}}}{V_{\text{Ball}}} \approx \frac{(4 \times 10^7 \text{ cm}^3)}{(27 \text{ cm}^3)} = 1.5 \times 10^6$$

Therefore a typical room can hold about

$\boxed{10^6}$ ping-pong balls.

1.42   There are about 100 million cars. There are about 10,000 $\dfrac{\text{mi/y}}{\text{car}}$

(10^8) cars $(10^4 \dfrac{\text{mi/y}}{\text{car}}) = 10^{12} \dfrac{\text{mi}}{\text{y}}$

distance between changes is about 5,000 miles. Number of changes is about
$(10^{12}\dfrac{\text{mi}}{\text{y}})(\dfrac{1 \text{ change}}{5,000 \text{ mi}}) \cong 2 \times 10^8 \dfrac{\text{changes}}{\text{y}}$

Amount of oil $\cong 2 \times 10^8 \dfrac{\text{changes}}{\text{y}} [\dfrac{5 \text{ qts.}}{\text{change}}] \cong 10^9 \dfrac{\text{qts.}}{\text{y}}$

Cost of oil $\cong 10^9 \dfrac{\text{qts.}}{\text{y}}$ [$1/qt] $\cong \boxed{\$1 \text{ Billion}}$

1.43   Assuming two 6-packs per week per family and four people per family, we estimate 30 billion cans per year. Taking the mass of one can as 5 g, we estimate a total mass of 1.5×10^8 kg, corresponding to about 10^5 tons.

1.44   1 acre $= 4.36 \times 10^4$ ft^2 $= 6.28 \times 10^6$ in^2.

Volume of rain $= 6.28 \times 10^6$ in^3 (for a 1 in. rainfall).

Estimating the radius of a raindrop to be 0.1 in., the volume is estimated to be $4\pi R^3/3 \approx 4 \times 10^{-3}$ in^3. Hence the # of raindrops is $= 6.28 \times 10^6/4 \times 10^{-3} \approx \boxed{10^9}$.

*1.45 $2d = vt$

$$d = \frac{vt}{2} = \frac{(3 \times 10^8 \text{ m/s})(2.56 \text{ s})}{2} = \boxed{3.84 \times 10^8 \text{ m}}$$

*1.46 $\dfrac{\ell_{\text{barrels}}}{d_{\text{USA}}} = \dfrac{6 \times 10^9 \text{ m}}{4 \times 10^6 \text{ m}} = \boxed{1500 \text{ times larger}}$

*1.47 $2\pi r = 150$ m

$\qquad r = 23.9$ m

$\qquad \dfrac{h}{r} = \tan 55°$

$\qquad h = (23.9 \text{ m})(\tan 55°) = \boxed{34.1 \text{ m}}$

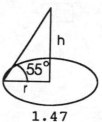

1.47

1.48   (162 games) $\times$ (2 pitchers) $\times$ (120 pitches/pitcher/game).

Approximately $\boxed{40{,}000 \text{ pitches}}$

1.49   Assume: Total population $= 10^7$; one out of every 100 people has a piano; one tuner can serve about 1,000 pianos (about 4 per day for 250 weekdays, assuming each piano is tuned once per year). Therefore

$$\text{\# tuners} = \left(\frac{1 \text{ tuner}}{1000 \text{ pianos}}\right)\left(\frac{1 \text{ piano}}{100 \text{ people}}\right)(10^7 \text{people}) = \boxed{100}$$

1.50   30. (a) $\boxed{2}$ (b) $\boxed{4}$ (c) $\boxed{3}$ (d) $\boxed{2}$

1.51   (a) $C = 2\pi r = 2\pi(3.5 \text{ cm}) = 21.99115 \text{ cm}$

Round off to 2 significant digits (i.e., the radius has only 2 significant digits).
Therefore $\boxed{C = 22 \text{ cm}}$

(b) $A = \pi r^2 = 3.14159(4.65 \text{ cm})^2 = 67.92903 \text{ cm}^2$

r has the least number of significant digits (3), so round off to 3 digits:

$\boxed{A = 67.9 \text{ cm}^2}$

1.52   (a) $756 + 27.3 + 0.83 + 2.5 = \boxed{797}$

(b) $3.2 \times 3.563 = \boxed{11}$

(c) $5.6 \times \pi = \boxed{18}$

1.53   Referring to the sketch we have

$$A = \ell w = (15.30 \pm 0.05)(12.80 \pm 0.05) \text{ cm}^2$$

$$A = [(15.30)(12.80) \pm (15.30)(0.05) \pm (0.05)(12.80)]$$

$$= \boxed{(195.8 \pm 1.4) \text{ cm}^2}$$

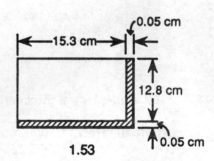

1.53

In the above we have our area $\pm$ an error term. However, we neglected the term $(0.05)(0.05)$ or $(\text{error})^2$. From the sketch, it is clearly insignificant.

1.54 $r = (6.50 \pm 0.20) \text{ cm} = (6.50 \pm 0.20) \times 10^{-2} \text{ m}$

$m = (1.85 \pm 0.02) \text{ kg}$

$\rho = m(\frac{4}{3})\pi r^3$ also,

$\dfrac{\delta\rho}{\rho} = \dfrac{\delta m}{m} + \dfrac{3\delta r}{r}.$

In other words, the percentages of error are cumulative.

Therefore $\dfrac{\delta\rho}{\rho} = \dfrac{0.02}{1.85} + \dfrac{3(0.20)}{6.50} = 0.103,$

$\rho = \dfrac{1.85}{(\frac{4}{3})\pi(6.5 \times 10^{-2} \text{ m})^3} = \boxed{1.61 \times 10^3 \text{ kg/m}^3}$

and $\rho \pm \delta\rho = (1.61 \pm 0.167) \times 10^3 \text{ kg/m}^3$

1.55   (a) $\boxed{3}$ (b) $\boxed{4}$ (c) $\boxed{3}$ (d) $\boxed{2}$

1.56   Perimeter $= 2(38.44 \text{ m}) + 2(19.5 \text{ m}) = \boxed{115.9 \text{ m}}$

1.57 $V = 2V_1 + 2V_2 = 2(V_1 + V_2)$

$V_1 = (17.0 \text{ m} + 1.0 \text{ m} + 1.0 \text{ m})(1.0 \text{ m})(0.90 \text{ m})$

$\quad = 1.70 \text{ m}^3$

$V_2 = (10.0 \text{ m})(1.0 \text{ m})(0.090 \text{ m}) = 0.900 \text{ m}^3$

$V = 2(1.70 \text{ m}^3) + 2(0.900 \text{ m}^3) = \boxed{5.2 \text{ m}^3}$

$\delta\ell_1 = (0.1 \text{ m} + 0.01 \text{ m} + 0.01 \text{ m}) = 0.12 \text{ m}$

$\left.\begin{array}{l} \dfrac{\delta\ell_1}{l_1} = \dfrac{0.12 \text{ m}}{19.0 \text{ m}} = 0.0063 \\[2mm] \dfrac{\delta w_1}{w_1} = \dfrac{0.01 \text{ m}}{1.0 \text{ m}} = 0.010 \\[2mm] \dfrac{\delta t_1}{t_1} = \dfrac{0.1 \text{ cm}}{9.0 \text{ cm}} = 0.011 \end{array}\right\}$ $\begin{array}{l} \dfrac{\delta V}{V} = 0.006 + 0.010 + 0.011 \\[2mm] \quad = 0.027 = \boxed{2.7\%} \end{array}$

1.57

1.58 $\displaystyle\sum_{i=1}^{4}(2i+1)=3+5+7+9=\boxed{24}$

1.59 $\displaystyle\sum_{i=1}^{4}i^2=1^2+2^2+3^2+4^2=30$

$\displaystyle(\sum_{i=1}^{4}i)^2=(1+2+3+4)^2=(10)^2=100$

The expressions are not equal.

*1.60

θ	$\tan\theta$	$\sin\theta$	diff
15	0.268	0.259	3 %
20	0.364	0.342	6 %
25	0.466	0.423	10.3 %
24	0.445	0.407	9.5 %
24.4	0.454	0.413	9.8 %
24.5	0.456	0.415	9.9 %
24.6	0.458	0.416	10.0 %

$\boxed{24.6°}$

*1.61 $\displaystyle\frac{\pi\times10^7-(365.25)(86400)}{(365.25)(86400)}=\boxed{0.449\ \%}$

*1.62 # gallons saved

$\displaystyle=\ (50\times10^6)\left(10^4\frac{\text{mi}}{\text{y}}\right)\left(\frac{1\ \text{gal}}{20\ \text{mi}}\right)-(50\times10^6)\left(10^4\frac{\text{mi}}{\text{y}}\right)\left(\frac{1\ \text{gal}}{25\ \text{mi}}\right)$

$\displaystyle=\ \boxed{5\times10^9\ \text{gallons}}$

*1.63   (a) $m = \dfrac{10^{-3}\text{ kg}}{1\text{ cm}^3} = \dfrac{10^{-3}\text{ kg}}{10^{-6}\text{ m}^3} = 1000\text{ kg/m}^3$

(b) $m_{\text{cell}} = \rho V = \left(1000\ \dfrac{\text{kg}}{\text{m}^3}\right)\left(\dfrac{4}{3}\pi\right)(0.5 \times 10^{-6}\text{ m})^3 = 5 \times 10^{-16}\text{ kg}$

$m_{\text{kidney}} = \left(1000\ \dfrac{\text{kg}}{\text{m}^3}\right)\left(\dfrac{4}{3}\pi\right)(4 \times 10^{-2}\text{ m})^3 = 300\text{ g}$

$m_{\text{fly}} = \left(1000\ \dfrac{\text{kg}}{\text{m}^3}\right)(4 \times 10^{-3}\text{ m})^2 \cong 0.01\text{ g}$

*1.64 $\rho = \dfrac{M}{V} = \dfrac{M}{\pi f^2 \ell}$ for a cylinder.

(a) $\rho_{\text{Al}} = 2.75\text{ g/cm}^3$

(b) $\rho_{\text{Cu}} = 9.36\text{ g/cm}^3$

(c) $\rho_{\text{Brass}} = 8.91\text{ g/cm}^3$

(d) $\rho_{\text{Sn}} = 7.68\text{ g/cm}^3$

(e) $\rho_{\text{Fe}} = 7.88\text{ g/cm}^3$

CHAPTER 2

2.1   (a) $d = \sqrt{(x_2 - x_1)^2 + (y_2 - y_1)^2} = \sqrt{(2 - [-3])^2 + (-4 - 3)^2}$

$\qquad = \sqrt{25 + 49} = \boxed{8.60 \text{ m}}$

(b) $r = \sqrt{2^2 + (-4)^2} = \sqrt{20} = \boxed{4.47 \text{ m}}$

$\qquad \theta_1 = \tan^{-1}(-\frac{4}{2}) = -63.4°$

$\qquad r_2 = \sqrt{(-3)^2 + 3^2} = 18^{1/2} = \boxed{4.24 \text{ m}}$

$\qquad \theta_2 = 135°$ measured from $+\,x$ axis

2.2 $(x, y) = (-3.0, 5.0)$ m, $x = r\cos\theta$, $y = r\sin\theta$, and $r = \sqrt{x^2 + y^2}$, thus

$r = \sqrt{(-3)^2 + (5)^2} = \sqrt{34} = 5.83$ m and $\cos\theta = \dfrac{x}{r} = -\dfrac{3.0}{5.83} = -0.515$,

therefore $\theta = 121°$ and $(r, \theta) = \boxed{(5.83 \text{ m}, 121°)}$

2.3 $x = r\cos\theta = (5.50 \text{ m})\cos 240° = (5.50 \text{ m})(-0.5) = \boxed{-2.75 \text{ m}}$

$y = r\sin\theta = (5.50 \text{ m})\sin 240° = (5.50 \text{ m})(-0.866) = \boxed{-4.76 \text{ m}}$

2.4   (a) $x = r\cos\theta$ and $y = r\sin\theta$, therefore

$\qquad x_1 = (2.50 \text{ m})\cos 30°, y_1 = (2.50 \text{ m})\sin 30°$, and $(x_1, y_1) = (2.17, 1.25)$ m

$\qquad x_2 = (3.80 \text{ m})\cos 120°, y_2 = (3.80 \text{ m})\sin 120°$, and $(x_2, y_2) = (-1.9, 3.29)$ m

(b) $d = \sqrt{(\Delta x)^2 + (\Delta y)^2} = \sqrt{16.56 + 4.16} = \boxed{4.55 \text{ m}}$

2.5 $d = \sqrt{(\Delta x)^2 + (\Delta y)^2} = \sqrt{5} \text{ m} = \boxed{2.236 \text{ m}}$

2.6 $r = \boxed{\sqrt{5} \text{ m}}$, $\theta = \tan^{-1}\dfrac{1}{2} = \boxed{26.5°}$

2.7 $x = (2.5 \text{ m})\cos 35° = \boxed{2.04 \text{ m}}$

$y = (2.5 \text{ m})\sin 35° = \boxed{1.43 \text{ m}}$

2.8   Four possible answers $\boxed{25 \text{ m@} \pm 37°}$ or $\boxed{61.8 \text{ m@} \pm 14°}$ (The 90° turns are indeterminate)

*2.9 $\tan 35° = \dfrac{x}{100 \text{ m}}$

$x = (100 \text{ m})(\tan 35°) = \boxed{70 \text{ m}}$

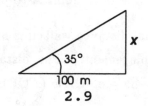

2.9

2.10 $R = \sqrt{(13 \text{ km})^2 + (6 \text{ km})^2} = \boxed{14.3 \text{ km}}$

$\theta = \tan^{-1}\left(\dfrac{13}{6}\right) = \boxed{65.2° \text{ N of } E}$

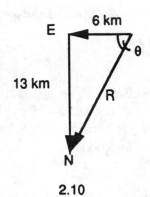

2.10

2.11

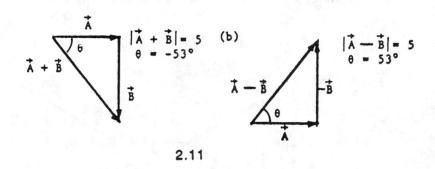

2.11

*2.12   (a) Using graphical methods, place the tail of vector **A** at the head of vector **B** . The new vector **A** + **B** has a magnitude of <u>6.1</u> <u>at 112 °</u> from the x-axis.

(b) The vector difference **A** − **B** is found by placing the negative of vector **B** at the head of vector **A** . The resultant vector **A** − **B** has magnitude <u>14.8</u> units at an <u>angle of 22.5 °</u> from the +x-axis.

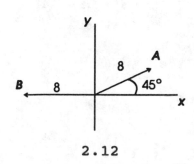

2.12

2.13   See the sketch on right

(a) $|\ d\ | = |\ -10i\ | = \boxed{10\ \text{m}}$ since the displacement is a straight line from point A to point B.

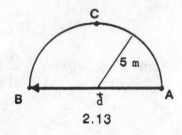

2.13

(b) The actual distance walked is not equal to the straight-line displacement. The distance follows the curved path of the semi-circle (ACB). $s = (\frac{1}{2})(2\pi r) = 5\pi = \boxed{15.7\ \text{m}}$.

(c) If the circle is complete, d begins and ends at point A. Hence $|\ d\ | = 0$.

*2.14   Find the resultant $F_1 + F_2$ graphically by placing the tail of F_2 at the head of F_1. The resultant force vector $F_1 + F_2$ is of magnitude <u>9.54 N</u> and at an angle of 57° above the x-axis.

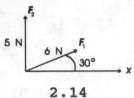

2.14

2.15   To find these vector expressions graphically, we draw each set of vectors as indicated by the drawings below. Measurements of the results are taken using a ruler and protractor.

(a)   (b)   (c)   (d)

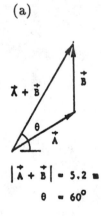

$|\vec{A} + \vec{B}| = 5.2$ m
$\theta = 60°$

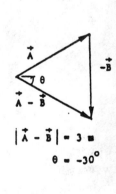

$|\vec{A} - \vec{B}| = 3$ m
$\theta = -30°$

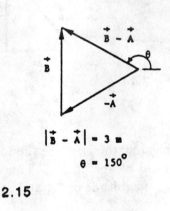

$|\vec{B} - \vec{A}| = 3$ m
$\theta = 150°$

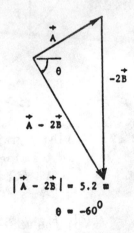

$|\vec{A} - 2\vec{B}| = 5.2$ m
$\theta = -60°$

2.15

2.16   East x, $\sum x = 8.2 \cos 30° - 15 = -7.9$

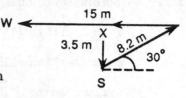

2.16

North y, $\sum y = -3.5 + 8.2 \sin 30° = +0.6$.

Displacement of puppy $= d = \sqrt{(7.9)^2 + (0.6)^2} = 7.92$ m

@ $\theta = \tan^{-1} \dfrac{0.6}{-7.92 \text{ m}} = 4.3°$ N of W

2.17   horizontal x vertical y

$$\sum x = 200 + 135 \cos 30° + 135 \cos(-40°) = \boxed{420 \text{ ft.}}$$

$$\sum y = 0 + 135 \sin 30° + 135 \sin(-40°) = \boxed{-19 \text{ ft.}}$$

$$d = \sqrt{x^2 + y^2} = 421 \text{ ft.}$$

$$\theta = \tan^{-1}\left(\frac{-19}{420}\right) = -2.6°$$

*2.18

x	y
0 km	3 km
1.41	1.41
-4	0
-2.12	-2.12
-4.71	2.29

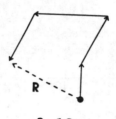

2.18

$$R = \sqrt{|x|^2 + |y|^2} = 5.24 \text{ km}$$

$$\theta = \tan^{-1}\frac{y}{x} = 154°$$

2.19   Coordinates of super-hero are: $x = (100 \text{ m}) \cos(-30°) = 86.6 \text{ m}$

$y = (100 \text{ m}) \sin(-30°) = -50.0 \text{ m}$

*2.20   (a) 7 blocks

(b) R = 5 blocks @ 143°

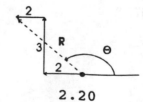

2.20

2.21   Coordinates of final point,

$$x = -175\cos(15°) = -169 \text{ m}$$

$$y = +175\sin(15°) = 45.3 \text{ m}$$

unknown vector is $K_2 = (-69i + 45.3j)$ m

displacement is $\sqrt{69^2 + 45.3^2} = \boxed{82.5 \text{ m}}$

at $\theta = \tan^{-1}\dfrac{45.3}{-69} = \boxed{147°}$ from East.

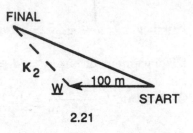

2.21

2.22 $+x$ East, $+y$ North

$$\sum x = 250 + 125\cos 30° = 358 \text{ m}$$

$$\sum y = 75 + 125\sin 30° - 150 = -12.5 \text{ m}$$

$$d = \sqrt{x^2 + y^2} = \sqrt{358^2 + 12.5^2} = \boxed{358.2 \text{ m}}$$

from cave entrance.

2.23 $A_x = -25 \qquad A_y = 40$

$$A = \sqrt{A_x^2 + A_y^2} = \sqrt{(-25)^2 + 40^2} = 47.2 \text{ units}$$

From the triangle, we find that $|\phi| = 58°$, so that $\theta = 122°$

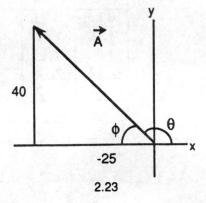

2.23

*2.24 $B = B_x i + B_y j + B_z k$

$$B = 4i + 6j + 3k$$

$$|B| = \sqrt{4^2 + 6^2 + 3^2} = \boxed{7.81}$$

$$\alpha = \cos^{-1} 4/7.81 = 59.2°$$

$$\beta = \cos^{-1} 6/7.81 = 39.8°$$

$$\gamma = \cos^{-1} 3/7.81 = 67.4°$$

2.25

Quadrant	I	II	III	IV
x component	+	−	−	+
y component	+	+	−	−

2.26 $x = d\cos\theta = (50\ \text{m})\cos(120)$

$\qquad = \boxed{-25\ \text{m}}$

$\quad y = d\sin\theta = (50\ \text{m})\sin(120)$

$\qquad = \boxed{43.3\ \text{m}}$

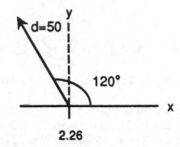

2.26

2.27 $d = \sqrt{(x_1 + x_2 + x_3)^2 + (y_1 + y_2 + y_3)^2}$

$\qquad = \sqrt{(3 - 5 + 6)^2 + (2 + 3 + 1)^2} = \sqrt{52} = \boxed{7.21\ \text{m}}$

$\quad \theta = \tan^{-1}\left(\dfrac{6}{4}\right) = \boxed{56.3°}$

2.28 $A = -8.7i + 15j \qquad B = 13.2i - 6.6j$

$A - B + 3C = 0$

$3C = B - A = 21.9i - 21.6j$

$C = 7.3i - 7.2j \quad$ or

$C_x = \boxed{7.3\ \text{cm}} \quad C_y = \boxed{-7.2\ \text{cm}}$

2.29   (a) $(A + B) = (3i - 2j) + (-i - 4j) = \boxed{2i - 6j}$

(b) $(A - B) = (3i - 2j) - (-i - 4j) = \boxed{4i + 2j}$

(c) $\mid A + B \mid = \sqrt{2^2 + 6^2} = \boxed{6.32}$

(d) $\mid A - B \mid = \sqrt{4^2 + 2} = \boxed{4.47}$

(e) $\theta \mid A + B \mid = \tan^{-1}\left(-\dfrac{6}{2}\right) = \boxed{-71.6°} = 288.4°$

$\qquad \theta \mid A - B \mid = \tan^{-1}\left(\dfrac{2}{4}\right) = \boxed{26.6°}$

2.30   (a) $R = A + B + C = (i + 3j) + (2i - j) + (3i + 5j) = 6i + 7j$

   (b) $R = \sqrt{R_x^2 + R_x^2} = \sqrt{6^2 + 7^2} = \sqrt{36 + 49} = \sqrt{85} = \boxed{9.22}$

   $\tan\theta = \dfrac{R_y}{R_x} = \dfrac{7}{6} = 1.17$, thus $\theta = \tan^{-1}\left(\dfrac{7}{6}\right) = \boxed{49.4°}$

2.31 $x = r\cos\theta$ and $y = r\sin\theta$, therefore:

   (a) $x = 12.8\cos 150°, y = 12.8\sin 150°$, and $(x, y) = (-11.1i + 6.4j)$ m

   (b) $x = 3.3\cos 60°, y = 3.3\sin 60°$, and $(x, y) = (1.65i + 2.86j)$ cm

   (c) $x = 22\cos 215°, y = 22\sin 215°$, and $(x, y) = (-18i - 12.6j)$ in

*2.32   (a) $D = A + B + C = 2i + 4j$

   $|D| = \sqrt{2^2 + 4^2} = \underline{4.47}$ at $\theta = 63.4°$

   (b) $E = -A - B + C = -6i + 6j$

   $|E| = \sqrt{6^2 + 6^2} = \underline{8.49}$ at $\theta = 135°$

2.33 $d_1 = -3.5j; \quad d_2 = 8.2\cos(45)i + 8.2\sin(45)j = 5.8i + 5.8j$

   $d_3 = -15i$

   $R = d_1 + d_2 + d_3 = (-15 + 5.8)i + (5.8 - 3.5)j = -9.2i + 2.3j$

or 9.2 m west and 2.3 m north

2.34   Refer to the sketch:

$$R = A + B + C = -10i - 15j + 50i = 40i - 15j$$

$$|R| = [40^2 + (-15)^2]^{1/2} = \boxed{42.7 \text{ yards}}$$

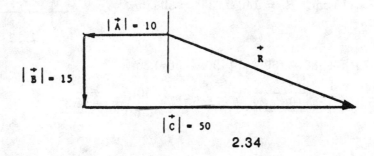

2.34

*2.35 $V = V_xi + V_yj = (300 + 100\cos 30°)i + (100\sin 30°)j$

$$V = (386.6i + 50j) \text{ mph}$$

$$|V| = \underline{390 \text{ mph}} \; at \; 7.37° \; N \; of \; E$$

*2.36

x	y
0 m	4.0 m
1.41	1.41
-.50	-0.866
+.91	4.54

$$|R| = \sqrt{|x|^2 + |y|^2} = \underline{4.65 \text{ m}} \; at \; 78.6° \text{ N of E.}$$

2.37 $A = 3 \text{ m}, \; \theta_A = 30°, \; B = 3 \text{ m}, \; \theta_B = 90°$

$$A_x = A\cos\theta_A = 3\cos 30° = 2.60 \text{ m}, \quad A_y = A\sin\theta_A = 3\sin 30° = 1.50 \text{ m}$$

so, $A = A_xi + A_yj = (2.60i + 1.50j) \text{ m.}$

$$B_x = 0, B_y = 3 \text{ m} \quad \text{so } B = 3j \text{ m}$$

$$A + B = (2.061i + 1.50j) + 3j = \boxed{(2.60i + 4.50j) \text{ m}}$$

2.38 Refer to the sketch:

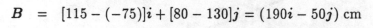

We have $B = R - A$

$$A_x = 150\cos 120° = -74 \text{ cm}, \quad A_y = 150\sin 120° = 130 \text{ cm}$$

$$R_x = 140\cos 35° = 115 \text{ cm}, \quad R_y = 140\sin 35° = 80 \text{ cm}$$

Therefore

$$B = [115 - (-75)]i + [80 - 130]j = (190i - 50j) \text{ cm}$$

$$|B| = [190^2 + (50)^2]^{1/2} = \boxed{196 \text{ cm}}, \quad \theta = \tan^{-1}\left(-\frac{50}{196}\right) = \boxed{-14.3°}$$

2.39 (a) $A = 8i + 12j - 4k$

(b) $B = \dfrac{A}{4} = 2i + 3j - k$

(c) $C = -3A = -24i - 36j + 12k$

*2.40 (a) $C = A + B = 0i + 1j - 2k$

$|C| = \sqrt{1^2 + 2^2} = \underline{2.24}$

(b) $D = A - B = 4i + 5j - 6k$

$|D| = \sqrt{4^2 + 5^2 + 6^2} = \underline{8.77}$

*2.41 (a) $C = A + B = 5i - j - 3k$

$|C| = \sqrt{5^2 + 1^2 + 3^2} = \underline{5.92}$

(b) $D = 2A - B = 4i + 11j - 15k$

$|D| = \sqrt{4^2 + 11^2 + 15^2} = \underline{19.0}$

2.42 $\quad A_x \;=\; 4, A_y = -2, A = \sqrt{A_x^2 + A_y^2} = \sqrt{4^2 + (-2)^2} = \sqrt{20}$

$\qquad R \;=\; 3A = 3(20)^{1/2} = 13.4 \;(\text{Magnitude})$

Since R is along y, $R_x = 0, R_y = 13.4$

$\qquad R \;=\; A + B, \text{ or } 13.4j = (4i - 2j) + B, \text{ so we find}$

$\qquad B \;=\; \boxed{-4i + 15.4j}$

2.43 $\quad A_x = -3, \quad A_y = 2$

(a) $A = A_x i + A_y j = \boxed{-3i + 2j}$

(b) $|A| \;=\; \sqrt{A_x^2 + A_y^2} = \sqrt{(-3)^2 + (2)^2} = \boxed{3.61}$

$\qquad \tan\theta \;=\; \dfrac{A_y}{A_x} = \dfrac{2}{(-3)} = -0.667, \; \theta = \tan^{-1}(-0.667) = -33.7°$

$\qquad \theta$ is in the 2nd quadrant, so $\theta = 180° + (-33.7°) = \boxed{146.3°}$

(c) $R_x \;=\; 0, R_y = -4, \;\; R = A + B \text{ thus } B = R - A \text{ and}$

$\qquad B_x \;=\; R_x - A_x = 0 - (-3) = 3, \;\; B_y = R_y - A_y = -4 - 2 = -6$

$\qquad$ Therefore, $B = \boxed{3i - 6j}$

*2.44

x	y
300	0
175	303
0	150
475	453

$\qquad \theta \;=\; \tan^{-1}\dfrac{y}{x} = 43.6° \text{ N of E}$

$\qquad |R| \;=\; \sqrt{x^2 + y^2} = \underline{656 \text{ km}}$

2.45 $\quad D_x \;=\; -5 \text{ m} \qquad D_y = 3 \text{ m}$

$\qquad D \;=\; \sqrt{D_x^2 + D_y^2} = \sqrt{(-5)^2 + 3^2} = \sqrt{34} = \boxed{5.83 \text{ m}}$

$\qquad \phi \;=\; \left|\tan^{-1}\left(\dfrac{D_y}{D_x}\right)\right| = 31°$

$\qquad \theta \;=\; 180 - \phi = \boxed{149°}$

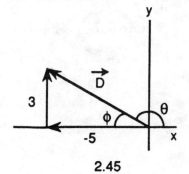

2.45

*2.46 Taking components along **i** and along **j** , we get two equations

$$6a - 8b + 26 \;=\; 0$$

$$-8a + 3b + 19 \;=\; 0$$

Solving simultaneously, a = 5, b = 7.

Therefore, $5\boldsymbol{A} + 7\boldsymbol{B} + \boldsymbol{C} = 0$.

2.47 Refer to the sketch:

(a) $R_x \;=\; 40\cos 45° - 30\cos 45° = \boxed{49.5 \text{ N}}$

      $R_y \;=\; 40\sin 45° - 30\sin 45° + 20 = \boxed{2.71 \text{ N}}$

(b) $|\boldsymbol{R}| \;=\; \sqrt{(49.4)^2 + (27.1)^2}$

         $=\; \boxed{56.4 \text{ N}}$

      $\theta \;=\; \tan^{-1}\!\left(\dfrac{27.1}{49.5}\right) = \boxed{28.7°}$

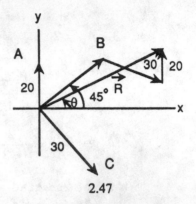

2.47

2.48 (a) $R_x = \boxed{2}$, $R_y = \boxed{1}$, $R_z = \boxed{3}$,

(b) $|\boldsymbol{R}| = \sqrt{R_x^2 + R_y^2 + R_z^2} = \sqrt{4 + 1 + 9} = \sqrt{14} = \boxed{3.74}$

(c) $\cos\theta_x \;=\; \dfrac{R_x}{|\boldsymbol{R}|} \Rightarrow \theta_x = \cos^{-1}\!\left(\dfrac{R_x}{|\boldsymbol{R}|}\right) = \boxed{57.7° \text{ from } + x}$

      $\cos\theta_y \;=\; \dfrac{R_y}{|\boldsymbol{R}|} \Rightarrow \theta_y = \cos^{-1}\!\left(\dfrac{R_y}{|\boldsymbol{R}|}\right) = \boxed{74.5° \text{ from } + y}$

      $\cos\theta_z \;=\; \dfrac{R_z}{|\boldsymbol{R}|} \Rightarrow \theta_z = \cos^{-1}\!\left(\dfrac{R_z}{|\boldsymbol{R}|}\right) = \boxed{36.7° \text{ from } + z}$

2.49 $d_1 = 100\boldsymbol{i}$ $d_2 = -300\boldsymbol{j}$

$d_3 = -150\cos(30)\boldsymbol{i} - 150\sin(30)\boldsymbol{j} = -130\boldsymbol{i} - 75\boldsymbol{j}$

$d_4 = -200\cos(60)\boldsymbol{i} + 200\sin(60)\boldsymbol{j} = -100\boldsymbol{i} + 173\boldsymbol{j}$

$\boldsymbol{R} = d_1 + d_2 + d_3 + d_4 = -130\boldsymbol{i} - 202\boldsymbol{j}$

$|\boldsymbol{R}| = [(-130)^2 + (-202)^2]^{1/2} = 240 \text{ m}$

$\phi = \tan^{-1}\!\left(\dfrac{202}{130}\right) = 57°$

$\theta = 180 + \phi = 237°$

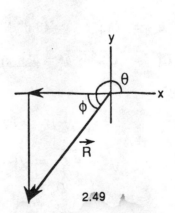

2.49

2.50 (a) $F = F_1 + F_2$

$\qquad = 120\cos(60)i + 120\sin(60)j - 80\cos(75)i + 80\sin(75)j$

$\qquad = 60i + 104j - 21i + 77j = 39i + 181j$

$\qquad |F| = \sqrt{39^2 + 181^2} = 185$ N; $\theta = \tan^{-1}\left(\dfrac{181}{39}\right) = 77.8°$

(b) $F' = -F = -39i - 181j$

2.51 (a) Write vector expressions for the position vectors in unit-vector form for these two points.

(b) What is the displacement vector?

(a) $r_1 = x_1 i + y_1 j = \boxed{(-3i - 5j)\ \text{m}}$

$\qquad r_2 = x_2 i + y_2 j = \boxed{(-i + 8j)\ \text{m}}$

(b) Displacement is $\Delta r = r_2 - r_1$

$\qquad \Delta r = (x_2 - x_1)i + (y_2 - y_1)j = [-1 - (-3)]i + [8 - (-5)]j = \boxed{(2i + 13j)\ \text{m}}$

2.52 (a) From the sketch $R_1 = ai + bj$; $\ |R_1| = \sqrt{a^2 + b^2}$

(b) $R_2 = ai + bj + ck$ and $|R_2| = \sqrt{a^2 + b^2 + c^2}$

The above relations can also be found by using the Pythagorean theorem.

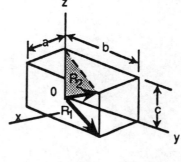

2.52

2.53   Displacement is invariant under a rotation of

coordinates.

Therefore $r = r'$ or $r^2 = (r')^2$

$$x^2 + y^2 = (x')^2 + (y')^2 \tag{1}$$

Also $\theta' = \theta - \alpha$

$$\tan^{-1}\left(\frac{y'}{x'}\right) = \tan^{-1}\left(\frac{y}{x}\right) - \alpha$$

$$\left(\frac{y'}{x'}\right) = \frac{\left[\frac{y}{x} - \tan\alpha\right]}{\left[1 + \left(\frac{y}{x}\right)\tan\alpha\right]} \tag{2}$$

Solving (1) and (2) simultaneously gives

$$x' = x\cos\alpha + y\sin\alpha \text{ and } y' = -x\sin\alpha + y\cos\alpha$$

2.54   Vector identities.

CHAPTER 3

3.1 (a) $\bar{v} = \dfrac{\Delta x}{\Delta t} = \dfrac{2.3\ \text{m}}{1.0\ \text{s}} = \boxed{2.3\ \text{m/s}}$

(b) $\bar{v} = \dfrac{\Delta x}{\Delta t} = \dfrac{57.5\ \text{m} - 9.2\ \text{m}}{3\ \text{s}} = \boxed{16.1\ \text{m/s}}$

(c) $\bar{v} = \dfrac{\Delta x}{\Delta t} = \dfrac{57.5\ \text{m} - 0\ \text{m}}{5\ \text{s}} = \boxed{11.5\ \text{m/s}}$

3.2 (a) Displacement $= (8.5 \times 10^4\ \text{m/h})(\dfrac{35}{60}\ \text{h}) + 130 \times 10^3\ \text{m}$

$= (49.6 + 130) \times 10^3\ \text{m} = \boxed{180\ \text{km}}$

(b) Average velocity $= \dfrac{\text{displacement}}{\text{time}} = \dfrac{180\ \text{km}}{[\frac{(35+15)}{60} + 2]\text{h}} = \boxed{63.4\ \text{km/h}}$

(c)

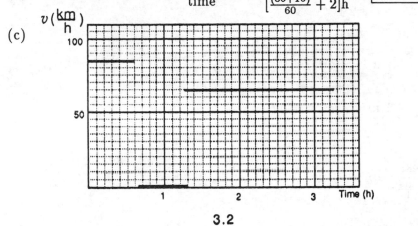

3.2

From the graph, displacement $=$ area under the curve

$= \dfrac{(85\ \text{km})}{\text{h}}(\dfrac{35}{60}\ \text{h}) + (\dfrac{65\ \text{km}}{\text{h}})(2\ \text{h}) = \boxed{180\ \text{km}}$

3.3 (a) $v_{av} = \dfrac{x}{t} = \dfrac{10\ \text{m}}{2\ \text{s}} = \boxed{5\ \text{m/s}}$

(b) $v_{av} = \dfrac{5\ \text{m}}{4\ \text{s}} = \boxed{1.25\ \text{m/s}}$

(c) $v_{av} = \dfrac{x_2 - x_1}{t_2 - t_1} = \dfrac{5\ \text{m} - 10\ \text{m}}{4\ \text{s} - 2\ \text{s}} = \boxed{-2.5\ \text{m/s}}$

(d) $v_{av} = \dfrac{x_2 - x_1}{t_2 - t_1} = \dfrac{-5\ \text{m} - 5\ \text{m}}{7\ \text{s} - 4\ \text{s}} = \boxed{-3.3\ \text{m/s}}$

(e) $v_{av} = \dfrac{x_2 - x_1}{t_2 - t_1} = \dfrac{0 - 0}{8 - 0} = \boxed{0\ \text{m/s}}$

3.4   (a) $d = vt$; $d_1 = (5 \text{ m/s})(4 \text{ min})(60 \text{ s/min}) = 1200 \text{ m}$

$d_2 = (4)(3)(60) = 720 \text{ m}$; $d_T = d_1 + d_2 = \boxed{1920 \text{ m}}$

(b) $\bar{v} = \dfrac{v_1 t_1 + v_2 t_2}{t_1 + t_2} = \dfrac{(5)(4) + (4)(3)}{4 + 3} = \boxed{\dfrac{32}{7} \text{ m/s}}$

3.5   (a) $v = \dfrac{d}{t} = \dfrac{50}{20} = \boxed{2.50 \text{ m/s}}$

(b) $v = \dfrac{50}{22} = \boxed{-2.27 \text{ m/s}}$

(c) Since the displacement is zero for the round trip, $\bar{v} = 0$.

*3.6 $x = 10t^2$

For $t(\text{s}) = $ 2   2.1   3

    $x(\text{m}) = $ 40   44.1   90

(a) $\bar{v} = \dfrac{\Delta x}{\Delta t} = \dfrac{50 \text{ m}}{1 \text{ s}} = \boxed{50 \text{ m/s}}$

(b) $\bar{v} = \dfrac{\Delta x}{\Delta t} = \dfrac{4.1 \text{ m}}{0.1 \text{ s}} = \boxed{41 \text{ m/s}}$

3.7 $t_1 = \dfrac{d}{v_1} = \dfrac{200 \text{ km}}{40 \, \frac{\text{km}}{\text{h}}} = 5 \text{ h}$

We have

$t_2 = t_1 - 1 = 4 \text{ h}$

$\bar{v}_2 = \dfrac{d}{t_2} = \dfrac{200 \text{ km}}{4 \text{ h}} = \boxed{50 \text{ km/h}}$

3.8   (a) $\bar{v} = \dfrac{\Delta x}{\Delta t} = \dfrac{x_5 - x_2}{5 - 2}$

$\bar{v} = \dfrac{1.2 \text{ m} - 3.0 \text{ m}}{3.0 \text{ s}}$

$\bar{v} = \boxed{-0.60 \text{ m/s}}$

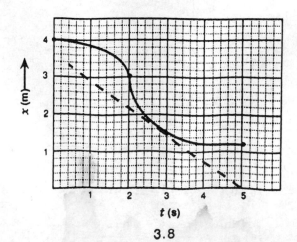

3.8

(b) $v \cong -\dfrac{2.2 \text{ m}}{2.8 \text{ s}} \cong \boxed{-0.8 \text{ m/s}}$

3.9 (a) at $t_i = 1.5$ s, $x_i = 8$ m (Point A)

at $t_f = 4$ s, $x_f = 2$ m (Point B)

$$v = \frac{x_f - x_i}{t_f - t_i} = \frac{(2 - 8)}{(4 - 1.5)} = -\frac{6}{2.5} = \boxed{-2.4 \text{ m/s}}$$

(b) The slope of the tangent line is found from points C and D.

$(t_c = 1 \text{ s}, x_c = 9 \text{ m})$ and $(t_D = 3.5 \text{ s}, x_D = 1 \text{ m})$, $v \cong \boxed{-3.2 \text{ m/s}}$

(c) The velocity is zero when x is a minimum. This is at $t \approx \boxed{4 \text{ s}}$

3.10 $v_{(2.0 \text{ s})} = 9.2$ m/s

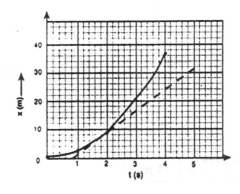

3.10

3.11 (a) Constant velocity indicates a straight line graph determined by points

$(1, -3)$ and $(6,5)$

(b) $v = \text{slope} = \dfrac{5 - (-3)}{(6 - 1)} = \dfrac{8}{5} = \boxed{1.6 \text{ m/s}}$

a

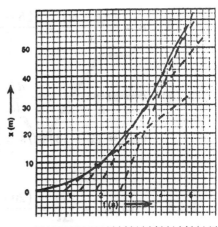

3.12 (b) At $t = 5.0$ s the slope is $v \cong \dfrac{58 \text{ m}}{2.3 \text{ s}} \cong 25$ m/s

At $t = 4.0$ s, the slope is $v \cong \dfrac{53 \text{ m}}{3 \text{ s}} \cong 18$ m/s

At $t = 3.0$ s, the slope is $v \cong \dfrac{45 \text{ m}}{3.6 \text{ s}} \cong 13$ m/s

b

At $t = 2.0s$ the slope is $v \cong \dfrac{31 \text{ m}}{4.1 \text{ s}} \cong 7.6$ m/s

(c) $\bar{a} = \dfrac{\Delta v}{\Delta t} \cong \dfrac{17.4 \text{ m/s}}{3.0 \text{ s}} \cong 5.8 \text{ m/s}^2$

(d) Initial velocity of car was zero.

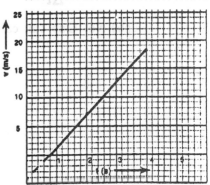

3.12

3.21 $x = 2 + 3t - t^2$, $v = \dfrac{dx}{dt} = 3 - 2t$, $a = \dfrac{dv}{dt} = -2$, at $t = 3$ s

  (a) $x = (2 + 9 - 9)$ m $= \boxed{2 \text{ m}}$

  (b) $v = (3 - 6)$ m/s $= \boxed{- \text{ 3 m/s}}$

  (c) $a = \boxed{- \text{ 2 m/s}^2}$

*3.22 $\bar{a} = \dfrac{\Delta v}{\Delta t} = \dfrac{31 \text{ m/s}}{0.00117 \text{ s}} = \boxed{26,500 \text{ m/s}^2}$

*3.23   (a) $a = \dfrac{\Delta v}{\Delta t} = \dfrac{8 \text{ m/s}}{6 \text{ s}} = \boxed{\dfrac{4}{3} \text{ m/s}^2}$

  (b) Maximum positive acceleration is at $t = 3$ s, and is approximately $\boxed{2 \text{ m/s}^2}$

  (c) $a = 0$ at $\boxed{t = 6 \text{ s}}$, and also for $\boxed{t \geq 10 \text{ s}}$

  (d) Maximum negative acceleration is at t = 8 s, and is approx. $\boxed{-1.5 \text{ m/s}^2}$.

3.24   (a) $a_{av} = \boxed{0 \text{ m/s}^2}$

  (b) $a = \dfrac{(80 - 50)}{5} = \boxed{6 \text{ m/s}^2}$

  (c) $d_1 = (50 \text{ m/s})(10 \text{ s}) = 500$ m, $d_2 = 50(5) + \dfrac{6(5)^2}{2} = 325$ m

   $d_T = 500 + 325 = \boxed{825 \text{ m}}$

  (d) $v_{av} = \dfrac{(80 + 50)}{2} = \boxed{65 \text{ m/s}}$

3.25   Given $v_0 = 12$ cm/s when $x_0 = 3$ cm (t = 0), and at $t = 2$ s, x = −5 cm

  $\Delta x = v_0 t + (\dfrac{1}{2})at^2$;

  $\Rightarrow x - x_0 = v_0 t + (\dfrac{1}{2})at^2$; $-5 - 3 = 12(2) + (\dfrac{1}{2})a(2)^2$; $\Rightarrow -8 = 24 + 2a$

  $a = -\dfrac{32}{2} = \boxed{- \text{ 16 cm/s}^2}$

3.26 $v_0 = 60 \text{ m/s} \quad v_f = 85 \text{ m/s}$

$t = 12 \text{ s.} \qquad \therefore a = \dfrac{\Delta v}{\Delta t} = \dfrac{25}{12} \text{ m/s}^2$

$x = v_0 t + \dfrac{1}{2} a t^2$

$x = [(60)(12) + \dfrac{1}{2}(\dfrac{25}{12})(12)^2] \text{ m} = \boxed{870 \text{ m}}$

3.27   (a) $v_0 = -2 \times 10^5 \text{ m/s} \qquad a = 4.2 \times 10^{14} \text{ m/s}^2 \qquad v^2 = v_0^2 + 2ax = 0$

$x = -\dfrac{v_0^2}{2a} = -\dfrac{(-2 \times 10^5 \text{ m/s})^2}{2(4.2 \times 10^{14} \text{ m/s}^2)} = \boxed{-4.76 \times 10^{-5} \text{ m}}$

(b) $x = v_0 t + \dfrac{1}{2} a t^2$

$0.05 = -2 \times 10^5 t + 2.1 \times 10^{14} t^2$

$t = \dfrac{2 \times 10^5 \pm \sqrt{4 \times 10^{10} + 4.2 \times 10^{13}}}{4.2 \times 10^{14}} = \boxed{15.9 \times 10^{-9} \text{ s}}$

3.28   (a) Total distance = area under the (v,t) curve

$= (\frac{1}{2})(50 \text{ m/s})(15 \text{ s}) + (50 \text{ m/s})(40 - 15)\text{s} + (\frac{1}{2})(50 \text{ m/s})(10 \text{ s}) = \boxed{1875 \text{ m}}$

(b) From $t = 10 \text{ s}$ to $t = 40 \text{ s}$, distance $= \frac{1}{2}(50 + 33)(5) + (50)(25) = \boxed{1457 \text{ m}}$

(c) $a = \dfrac{\Delta v}{\Delta t} = \dfrac{50 - 0}{15} = 3.3 \text{ m/s}^2; \quad 0 \le t \le 15 \text{ s}$

$a = 0 \qquad\qquad\qquad\quad 15 < t < 50 \text{ s}$

(d) $x_1 = 1.67 t^2; \ x_2 = 50 t - 375; \ x_3 = 50 t - 2.5 t^2 - 1625$

(e) 37.5 m/s

3.29 $v_0 = 5.2 \text{ m/s}$

(a) $v(t = 2.5) = v_0 + at = 5.2 + (3)(2.5) = \boxed{12.7 \text{ m/s}}$

(b) $v(t = 2.5) = v_0 + at = 5.2 + (-3)(2.5) = \boxed{-2.3 \text{ m/s}}$

3.30   (a) $v^2 = v_0^2 + 2ax$

$0 = 3^2 + 400a \quad \boxed{a = -2.25 \times 10^{-2} \text{ m/s}^2}$

(b) $v = v_0 + at; \quad t = -\dfrac{v_0}{a} = -\dfrac{3}{(-2.25 \times 10^{-2})} = \boxed{133 \text{ s}}$

(c) $v^2 = v_0^2 + 2ax = 3^2 - (2)(2.25 \times 10^{-2})(150) = 2.25 \text{ m}^2/\text{s}^2 \quad \boxed{v = 1.5 \text{ m/s}}$

3.31 $v_0 = 100$ m/s, $a = -5.0$ m/s^2

$v^2 = v_0^2 + 2ax$ $0 = (100)^2 - 2(5.0)x$

$x = \boxed{1000 \text{ m}}$, and $t = \boxed{20 \text{ s}}$

No, at this acceleration the plane would overshoot the runway.

*3.32   Distance travelled by car $= v_0 t - \frac{1}{2}at^2 + \frac{1}{2}at^2 = (25 \text{ m/s})(10 \text{ s}) = 250$ m.

Distance travelled by train $= v_0 t = (25 \text{ m/s})(10 \text{ s} + 45 \text{ s} + 10 \text{ s}) = 1625$ m.

The train leads the car by $\boxed{1375 \text{ m}}$

*3.33   (a) $x = \frac{1}{2}at^2$ (Eq. 3.10)

$400 \text{ m} = \frac{1}{2}(10 \text{ m/s}^2)t^2$

$t = \boxed{8.94 \text{ s}}$

(b) $v = at$ (Eq. 3.7)

$v = (10 \text{ m/s}^2)(8.94 \text{ s}) = \boxed{89.4 \text{ m/s}}$

*3.34 $x = \bar{v}t = \left(\dfrac{26 + 0}{2} \text{m/s}\right)(18 \text{ s}) = \boxed{234 \text{ m}}$

3.35   (a) $\Delta x = v_0 t + (\frac{1}{2})at^2$

$a = 2\dfrac{(\Delta x - v_0 t)}{t^2} = 2\dfrac{(2 \text{ m} - 0)}{(3 \text{ s})^2} = \boxed{0.444 \text{ m/s}^2}$

(b) $v = v_0 + at = 0 + (0.44 \text{ m/s}^2)(3 \text{ s}) = \boxed{1.32 \text{ m/s}}$

(c) $t = \sqrt{\dfrac{2(\Delta x - v_0 t)}{a}} = \sqrt{\dfrac{2(1 \text{ m} - 0)}{0.44 \text{ m/s}^2}} = \boxed{2.13 \text{ s}}$

(d) $v = v_0 + at = 0 + (0.444 \text{ m/s}^2)(2.13 \text{ s}) = \boxed{0.943 \text{ m/s}}$

3.36 $\quad a = \dfrac{\Delta v}{\Delta t}; \quad \Delta v = 160 \text{ km/h} = 44.44 \text{ m/s}$

$\quad\quad \Delta x = \bar{v}\Delta t = 2 \text{ km} = 2000 \text{ m}$

$\quad\quad \Delta t = \dfrac{\Delta x}{\bar{v}} = \dfrac{2000 \text{ m}}{22.22 \text{ m/s}} = 90 \text{ s}$

(a) $a = \dfrac{44.44 \text{ m/s}}{90.0 \text{ s}} = \boxed{0.494 \text{ m/s}^2}$

(b) After 300 s, the lead train is $\quad x_1 = 2000 \text{ m} + (44.44)(210) \text{ m}$

$$= \boxed{11.33 \text{ km ahead}}$$

(c) During the next 90 seconds, as the second engine comes up to speed, the lead engine will travel another $(44.44)(90)$ m. Therefore, after $6\frac{1}{2}$ minutes, the two trains will be $x_2 = 11,330 + 4,000 - 2,000 = \boxed{13.33 \text{ km}}$ apart.

3.37 $\quad$ (a) $v_0 = 16 \text{ m/s} \quad\quad x = 4.0 \text{ m} \quad\quad v = 0.$

$\quad\quad x = \left(\dfrac{v + v_0}{2}\right)t$

$\quad\quad t = \dfrac{2x}{v + v_0} = \dfrac{80 \text{ m}}{16 \text{ m/s}} = 5 \text{ s}$

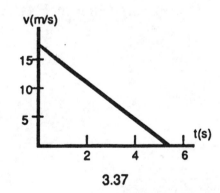

3.37

$\quad$ Acceleration $= \dfrac{\Delta v}{\Delta t} = -\dfrac{16}{5} = \boxed{-3.2 \text{ m/s}^2}$

(b) $\boxed{t = 5 \text{ s}}$

3.38 $t_1 = \dfrac{d}{v} = \dfrac{50}{5} = 10$ s

$v = (v_0^2 + 2as)^{1/2} = 5^{1/2}; \quad t = \dfrac{v - v_0}{a} = \dfrac{\sqrt{5} - 5}{0.2} = 13.8$ s

$t_{\text{total}} = t_1 + t_2 = 10$ s $+ 13.8$ s $= \boxed{23.8 \text{ s}}$

3.39 $v_0 = 30$ m/s, $x_0 = 0$, $a = -2$ m/s^2

(a) $x = x_0 + v_0 t + \dfrac{1}{2}at^2$ or $x = 0 + 30t - 1t^2 = 30t - t^2$

$v = v_0 + at$ or $\boxed{v = 30 - 2t}$

(b) $x = maximum$ when $v = 0$; $\quad v = 30 - 2t = 0 \Rightarrow t = 15$ s

$x = 30t - t^2 = 30(15) - 15^2 = \boxed{225 \text{ m}}$

3.40   (a) $t = \dfrac{v - v_0}{a} = \dfrac{5.4 \times 10^5 \text{ m/s} - 3.0 \times 10^5 \text{ m/s}}{8.0 \times 10^{14} \text{ m/s}^2} = \boxed{3 \times 10^{-10} \text{ s}}$

(b) $x = v_0 t + \dfrac{1}{2}at^2$

$x = (3.0 \times 10^5 \text{ m/s})(3 \times 10^{10} \text{ s}) + \dfrac{1}{2}(8 \times 10^{14} \text{ m/s}^2)(3 \times 10^{-10} \text{ s})^2$

$x = \boxed{1.26 \times 10^{-4} \text{ m}}$

3.41

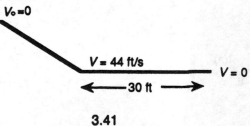

3.41

$\Delta x = \overline{v}\Delta t$

30 ft $= (22$ ft/s$)(\Delta t)$

Time to stop car is $\Delta t = \dfrac{30}{22}$ s $= 1.36$ s

Acceleration $= a = \dfrac{\Delta v}{\Delta t} = \dfrac{-44 \text{ ft/s}}{1.36 \text{ s}} = -32.3$ ft/s^2

3.42 (a) $a = \dfrac{v^2 - v_0^2}{2x} = \dfrac{(280 \text{ m/s})^2 - (420 \text{ m/s})^2}{2(0.1 \text{ m})} = \boxed{-4.9 \times 10^5 \text{ m/s}^2}$

(b) $t = \dfrac{0.10}{350} + \dfrac{0.02}{280} = \boxed{3.57 \times 10^{-4} \text{ s}}$

(c) $v_0 = 420 \text{ m/s}, \quad v = 0 \quad a = -4.9 \times 10^5 \text{ m/s}^2 \quad v^2 = v_0^2 + 2ax$

$$x = \dfrac{v^2 - v_0^2}{2a} = -\dfrac{v_0^2}{2a} = -\dfrac{(420 \text{ m/s})^2}{(-2 \times 4.9 \times 10^5 \text{ m/s}^2)}$$

$$= 0.18 \text{ m} = N(0.10 \text{ m})$$

$$N = \boxed{1.8 \text{ thickness}}$$

3.43 (a) $a = \dfrac{v - v_0}{t} = -\dfrac{632(5280/3600)}{1.4} = \boxed{-662 \text{ ft/s}^2}$

(b) $x = v_0 t + \dfrac{1}{2}at^2 = (632)(5280/3600)(1.4) - \dfrac{1}{2}662(1.4)^2 = \boxed{649 \text{ ft}}$

3.44 (a) Player A has: $t_A = t$; $a_A = 4$; $v_{A_0} = 0$

Player B has: $t_B = (3 + t)$ $a_B = 0$ (uniform velocity),

$$v_{B0} = v_B = 12 \text{ m/s}$$

$$\Delta x_A = \Delta x_B$$

$$\frac{1}{2}a_A t^2 = v_{B0} t_B$$

$$\frac{1}{2}(4)t^2 = (12)(t + 3) \text{ or } t = \boxed{8.2 \text{ s}}$$

(b) $\Delta x_A = \left(\frac{1}{2}\right)(4)(8.2)^2 = \boxed{134 \text{ m}}$

3.45 $s = 144 \text{ ft} = \dfrac{1}{2}gt^2 = 16t^2 \quad t_{\text{fall}} = \sqrt{\dfrac{144}{16}} = 3 \text{ s}$

(a) $v = gt = (32 \text{ ft/s}^2)(3 \text{ s}) = \boxed{96 \text{ ft/s}}$ DOWN

(b) Acceleration $a = \dfrac{\Delta v}{\Delta t} = \dfrac{-96 \text{ ft/s}}{0.312 \text{ s}} = \boxed{-3076 \text{ ft/s}^2}$

(c) Time to crush box $\Delta t = \dfrac{\Delta x}{v} = \dfrac{1.5 \text{ ft}}{48 \text{ ft/s}} = \boxed{0.031 \text{ s}}$

3.46 We have

$$y = -\frac{1}{2}gt^2 + v_0 t + y_0$$

$$0 = -(4.9 \text{ m/s}^2)t^2 - (8 \text{ m/s})t + 30 \text{ m}$$

Solving for t, $t = \dfrac{8 \pm \sqrt{64 + 588}}{-9.8}$

Using only the positive value for t, we find $\boxed{t = 1.79 \text{ s}}$

3.47   (a) $y = v_0 t + \dfrac{1}{2}at^2$

   $4 = (1.5)v_0 - (4.9)(1.5)^2$ and $\boxed{v_0 = 10.0 \text{ m/s}}$

   (b) $v = v_0 + at = 10.0 - (9.8)(1.5) = -4.68 \text{ m/s}$

   $v = \boxed{4.68 \text{ m/s downward}}$

3.48   (a) $v_0 = +5.0 \text{ m/s} \quad a = -9.8 \text{ m/s}^2 \quad y = -2.10 \text{ m}$

   $y = v_0 t + \dfrac{1}{2}at^2 - 21.0 = (5.0)t - 4.9t^2 - 21 \quad 4.9t^2 - 5.0t - 21 = 0$

   $t = \dfrac{5.0 \pm \sqrt{(5.0)^2 + (4)(21)(4.9)}}{9.8} = \dfrac{5.0 \pm 20.9}{9.8} = \boxed{2.64 \text{ s}}$

   (b) $v = v_0 - gt = \boxed{-20.9 \text{ m/s}}$

   (c) $v_0 = -5.0 \text{ m/s} \quad a = 9.8 \text{ m/s}^2 \quad y = -21 \text{ m}$

   $y = v_0 t + \dfrac{1}{2}at^2$

   $-21 = -5t - 4.9t^2, \quad t = \boxed{1.62 \text{ s}}$

3.49 $v_0 = 15 \text{ m/s}$

   (a) $v = v_0 - gt = 0$

   $t = \dfrac{v_0}{g} = \dfrac{15 \text{ m/s}}{9.8 \text{ m/s}^2} = \boxed{1.53 \text{ s}}$

   (b) $h = v_0 t - \dfrac{1}{2}gt^2 = \dfrac{v_0^2}{2g} = \dfrac{225}{19.6} \text{ m} = \boxed{11.5 \text{ m}}$

   (c) At $t = 2 \text{ s}$

   $v = v_0 - gt = 15 - 19.6 = \boxed{-4.61 \text{ m/s}}$

   $a = -g = \boxed{-9.8 \text{ m/s}^2}$

3.50 Time to top $= 10$ s. $v = v_0 - gt$

(a) At the top, $v = 0$.   Then, $t = \dfrac{v_0}{g} = 10$ s. $\boxed{v_0 = 98 \text{ m/s}}$

(c) $h = v_0 t - \dfrac{1}{2} g t^2$

At $t = 10$ s, $h = (98)(10) - \dfrac{1}{2}(9.8)(10)^2 = \boxed{490 \text{ m}}$

*3.51 (a) $\quad v = v_0 - gt \quad$ (Eq 3.12)

$\quad v = 0$ when t $= 3$ s, $g = 9.8$ m/s^2,

$\quad \therefore \; v_0 = gt = (9.8 \text{ m/s}^2)(3 \text{ s}) = \boxed{29.4 \text{ m/s}}$

(b) $y = \dfrac{1}{2}(v + v_0)t^2 = \dfrac{1}{2}(29.4 \text{ m/s})(3 \text{ s})^2 = \boxed{44.1 \text{ m}}$

*3.52 On moon, $1 \text{ m} = \frac{1}{2}(1.62 \text{ m/s}^2)t^2$; $\; t = 1.11$ s

On earth, $1 \text{ m} = \frac{1}{2}(9.8 \text{ m/s}^2)t^2$; $\; t = 0.45$ s

Time to fall 1 m on moon is 2.46 times longer

3.53 $v = -18.8$ m/s, $a = -9.8$ m/s^2, $y = -18$ m

(a) $v^2 = v_0^2 + 2ay, \quad v_0^2 = v^2 - 2ay$

$\quad v_0^2 = (18.8)^2 - 2(-9.8)(-18)$

$\quad v_0 = \boxed{0.8 \text{ m/s}}$

(b) Measured from ground level, $h = \dfrac{v^2}{2g} = \dfrac{(18.8)^2}{19.6}$ m $= \boxed{18.0 \text{ m}}$

3.54 $\quad y = \frac{1}{2}gt_1^2 \quad y = v_0 t_2 + \frac{1}{2}gt_2^2 \quad t_1 = 2 + t_2$

$$\frac{1}{2}g(2 + t_2)^2 = v_0 t_2 + \frac{1}{2}gt_2^2$$

$$\frac{1}{2}g[4 + 4t_2 + t_2^2] = v_0 t_2 + \frac{1}{2}gt_2^2$$

$$2g + 2gt_2 + \frac{1}{2}gt_2^2 = v_0 t_2 + \frac{1}{2}gt_2^2$$

$$2g = t_2[v_0 - (2\ s)(9.8\ \text{m/s}^2)]$$

$$t_2 = \frac{(2)(9.8\ \text{m/s}^2)}{30\ \text{m/s} - 19.6\ \text{m/s}}$$

$$t_2 = 188\ \text{s}, \ t_1 = 3.88\ \text{s}$$

$$y = \frac{1}{2}(9.8\ \text{m/s}^2)(3.88\ \text{s})^2 = \boxed{73.9\ \text{m}}$$

*3.55 Time to fall 3 m is found from Eq. 3.14

$\quad 3\ \text{m} = \frac{1}{2}(9.8\ \text{m/s}^2)t^2; \ t = 0.782\ \text{s}$

(a) With the horse galloping at 10 m/s, the horizontal distance is $vt = \boxed{7.82\ \text{m}}$

(b) $t = \boxed{0.782\ \text{s}}$

*3.56 $\quad x = \int_{t=0}^{10} v\,dt = \int_0^{10}(2.4t + 30)dt$

$$= \left(\frac{2.4t^2}{2} + 30t\right)\Big|_0^{10} = \boxed{420\ \text{m}}$$

*3.57 $\quad y = 7t - 4.9t^2$

$\quad\quad v = \frac{dy}{dt} = 7 - 9.8t$

(a) $v_0 = \boxed{7\ \text{m/s}}$

(b) $v(1.26\ \text{s}) = 7 - (9.8\ \text{m/s}^2)(1.26\ \text{s}) = \boxed{-5.35\ \text{m/s}}$

(c) $a = \frac{dv}{dt} = \boxed{-9.8\ \text{m/s}^2}$

*3.58 $a = 3t + 5$

$$v = \int_0^t (3t + 5)dt = \frac{3}{2}t^2 + 5t$$

$$x = \int_0^t (1.5t^2 + 5t)dt = \frac{1.5t^3}{3} + \frac{5t^2}{2}$$

$$x(2\text{ s}) = 0.5(2)^3 + 2.5(2)^2 = \boxed{14.0\text{ m}}$$

3.59 $v = (5 + 10t)\text{ m/s}$, $x_0 = 20\text{ m}$

(a) $a = \dfrac{dv}{dt} = \boxed{10\text{ m/s}^2}$

(b) $x - x_0 = \displaystyle\int_{t=0}^t v\,dt = 5t + 5t^2$

$$\boxed{x = (20 + 5t + 5t^2)\text{ m}}$$

(c) At $t = 0$, $\boxed{v = 5\ \text{m/s}}$

3.60 $a = \dfrac{dv}{dt} = -3v^2$, $v_0 = 1.5\text{ m/s}$

Solving for v, $\dfrac{dv}{dt} = -3v^2$

$$\int_{v=v_0}^v v^{-2}\,dv = -3\int_{t=0}^t dt$$

$$-\frac{1}{v} + \frac{1}{v_0} = -3t$$

$$\text{or } 3t = \frac{1}{v} - \frac{1}{v_0}$$

$$\text{When } v = \frac{v_0}{2},\quad t = \frac{1}{3v_0} = \boxed{0.22\text{ s}}$$

3.61 $x(t) = \frac{1}{4}at^2 + 2bt$

where $a = 1$ m/s^2 and $b = 1$ m/s, evaluate the average velocity $\bar{v}$ during elapsed time intervals starting at $t_a = 2$ s for which $\Delta t = 1$ s, 0.5 s, 0.1 s, 0.01 s, and 0.001 s.

Solution:

Evaluating $x(t_a) = x(2 \text{ s})$, we find

$x(2 \text{ s}) = \frac{1}{4}(1 \text{ m/s})^2(2 \text{ s})^2 + 2(1 \text{ m/s})(2 \text{ s}) = 5$ m. Then, using Eq. 3.1 for $\bar{v}$, we have

$$\bar{v} = \frac{x(2 \text{ s} + \Delta t) - (5 \text{ m})}{\Delta t}$$

For $\Delta t = 1$ s, $\bar{v} = \frac{x(3 \text{ s}) - (5 \text{ m})}{1 \text{ s}} = \frac{\frac{9}{4} + 6 - 5}{1}$ m/s $= 3.250$ m/s.

Substituting the remaining values of Δt, we obtain the following results for $\bar{v}$:

Δt(s)	1	0.5	0.1	0.01	0.001
$\bar{v}$(m/s)	3.250	3.125	3.025	3.0025	3.00025

From these values for $\bar{v}$ it appears that in the limit $\Delta t \to 0$, we have $v = 3$ m/s. We can see the dependence of $\bar{v}$ on Δt if we write

$$\begin{aligned}
\Delta x &= x(t_a + \Delta t) - x(t_a) \\
&= [\frac{1}{4}a(t_a + \Delta t)^2 + 2b(t_a + \Delta t)] - [\frac{1}{4}at_a^2 + 2bt_a] \\
&= [\frac{1}{4}at_a^2 + \frac{1}{2}at_a\Delta t + \frac{1}{4}a(\Delta t)^2 + 2bt_a + 2b\Delta t] - [\frac{1}{4}at_a^2 + 2bt_a] \\
&= (\frac{1}{2}at_a + 2b)\Delta t + \frac{1}{4}a(\Delta t)^2
\end{aligned}$$

Then $\bar{v} = \frac{\Delta x}{\Delta t} = \frac{1}{2}at_a + 2b + \frac{1}{4}a\,\Delta t$

For $t_a = 2s, a = 1$ m/s^2, and $b = 1$ m/s, we find

$$\bar{v}(2 \text{ s}) = (3 + \frac{1}{4}\Delta t) \text{ m/s}$$

and the dependence of $\bar{v}$ on Δt for this case is exhibited explicitly. It is easy to verify that this expression leads to the values of $\bar{v}$ listed in the table above. It is also clear that in the limit $\Delta t \to 0$ the velocity at $t = 2$ s is indeed exactly 3 m/s. The instantaneous velocity at $t = 2$ s can also be obtained by differentiating $s(t)$ and evaluating the result at $t = 2$ s. We find

$$v(t) = \frac{dx}{dt} = \frac{d}{dt}x(t) = \frac{1}{2}at + 2b$$

so that $v(2 \text{ s}) = \frac{1}{2}(1 \text{ m/s}^2)(2 \text{ s}) + 2(1 \text{ m/s}) = 3$ m/s

3.62 (a) $v_0 = 18.0$ m/s $x = 38.0$ m.

If the reaction time is zero, the time to travel 38.0 m is given by $t = \dfrac{2x}{v_0}$

$$t = \frac{(2)(38.0 \text{ m})}{18 \text{ m/s}} = 4.22 \text{ s}$$

Distance traveled in 4.22 s is given by

$$x = v_0 t + \frac{1}{2}at^2$$

$$= (18 \text{ m/s})(4.22 \text{ s}) - (\frac{4.5}{2}\text{m/s}^2)(4.22 \text{ s})^2 = 35.9 \text{ m}$$

If the reaction time is t_1 then a distance of 38.0 m - 35.9 m must be traveled at 18 m/s in time t_1. Then $v = \dfrac{x}{t_1}$ and $t_1 = \dfrac{x}{v} = \dfrac{2.11 \text{ m}}{18 \text{ m/s}} = \boxed{0.117 \text{ s}}$

(b) In 0.30 s, the distance traveled at 18 m/s is $x = v_0 t_1 = (18.0 \text{ m/s})(0.3) = 5.4$ m.

The distance traveled at an acceleration - 4.5 m/s² is $38 - 5.4 = 32.6$ m.

$$v^2 = v_0^2 + 2ax = (18.0 \text{ m/s})^2 - 2(4.5 \text{ m/s}^2)(32.6 \text{ m}) = 30.6 \text{ m}^2/\text{s}^2$$

$$v = \sqrt{30.6} = \boxed{5.53 \text{ m/s}}$$

3.63 (a) $y = v_{0_1} t + \dfrac{1}{2}at^2 = 50 = 2t + \dfrac{1}{2}(9.80)t^2$

$t = \boxed{2.99 \text{ s}}$ after the first stone is thrown.

(b) $y = v_{0_2} t + \dfrac{1}{2}at^2$ and $t = 2.99 - 1 = 1.99$ s

substitute $50 = v_{0_2}(1.99) + \dfrac{1}{2}(9.80)(1.99)^2$

$v_{0_2} = \boxed{15.4 \text{ m/s}}$ downward

(c) $v_1 = v_{0_1} + at = -2 + (-9.80)(2.99) = \boxed{-31.3 \text{ m/s}}$

$v_2 = v_{0_2} + at = -15.4 + (-9.80)(1.99) = \boxed{-34.9 \text{ m/s}}$

*3.64 $v = 30t - 0.5t^2$

$$t(s) = 0 \quad 1 \quad 5 \quad 6$$

$$v(m/s) = 0 \quad 29.5 \quad 137.5 \quad 162$$

(a) $a = \dfrac{\Delta v}{\Delta t} = \dfrac{29.5 \text{ m/s}}{1 \text{ s}} = \boxed{29.5 \text{ m/s}^2}$

(b) $a = \dfrac{\Delta v}{\Delta t} = \dfrac{24.5 \text{ m/s}}{1 \text{ s}} = \boxed{24.5 \text{ m/s}^2}$

3.65   (a) $v^2 = v_0^2 + 2a\Delta x = 0 + (2)(-9.80 \text{ m/s}^2)(2 \text{ m})$

$$v = \boxed{-6.26 \text{ m/s}}$$

(b) Here v_0 is velocity with which ball leaves the ground and

$$v = 0 \text{ at top of path, so}$$

$$v_0^2 = v^2 - 2a\Delta x = 0 - 2(-9.80 \text{ m/s}^2)(1.85 \text{ m})$$

$$v_0 = \boxed{6.02 \text{ m/s}}$$

(c) $t_{\text{total}} = t_1 + t_2 = \dfrac{\Delta v_1}{a} + \dfrac{\Delta v_2}{a}$

$$t_{\text{total}} = \dfrac{(-6.26 \text{ m/s})}{(-9.8 \text{ m/s}^2)} + \dfrac{(-6.02 \text{ m/s})}{(-9.8 \text{ m/s}^2)} = \boxed{1.25 \text{ s}}$$

3.66   (a) Using Eq. 3.11, $v^2 - v_0^2 = 2a(x - x_0)$

$$(125 \text{ km/h})^2 = 2a(250 \text{ m}) = (34.7 \text{ m/s})^2 \quad \boxed{a = 2.41 \text{ m/s}^2}$$

(b) Using Eq. 3.7, $v = at + v_0$ $34.7 \text{ m/s} = (2.41 \text{ m/s}^2)t$

$$\boxed{t = 14.4 \text{ s}} \ .$$

(c) Again, using Eq. 3.7,

$$v = (2.41 \text{ m/s}^2)(25 \text{ s}) = \boxed{60.25 \text{ m/s}}$$

*3.67 $100 \text{ m} - \dfrac{100 \text{ m}}{10.8 \text{ s}}(10.3 \text{ s}) = \boxed{4.63 \text{ m}}$

3.68 Let the velocity upon hitting the ground be v_2 and let the velocity be v_1 at the time $\Delta t = 1.50$ s earlier. Then, with the *downward* direction positive (so that $a = +g$), we have

$$v_2 = v_1 + g\Delta t = v_1 + (9.80 \text{ m/s}^2)(1.50 \text{ s}) \tag{1}$$

$$= v_1 + 14.70 \text{ m/s}$$

We also know that the distance Δy fallen during the time Δt can be related to the *average* velocity by

$$\Delta y = \frac{1}{2}(v_1 + v_2)\Delta t \tag{2}$$

$$\text{so} \quad v_1 + v_2 = \frac{2(30 \text{ m})}{(1.50 \text{ s})} = 40 \text{ m/s}$$

Adding Eqs. (1) and (2), we find

$$2v_2 = (40 + 14.70) \text{ m/s}$$

$$\text{or} \quad v_2 = \frac{1}{2}(54.70 \text{ m/s}) = 27.35 \text{ m/s}$$

Finally, solving Eq. 3.15 for h, we have

$$h = \frac{v_2^2}{2g} = \frac{(27.35 \text{ m/s})^2}{2(9.80 \text{ m/s}^2)} = \boxed{38.16 \text{ m}}$$

3.69 (a) We require $x_s = x_k$ when $t_s = t_k + 1$

$$x_s = \frac{1}{2}(12 \text{ ft/s}^2)(t_k + 1)^2 = \frac{1}{2}(16 \text{ ft/s}^2)(t_k)^2 = x_k$$

$$t_k = \boxed{6.46 \text{ s}}$$

(b) $x_k = \dfrac{1}{2}(16 \text{ ft/s}^2)(6.47 \text{ s})^2 = \boxed{334 \text{ ft}}$

(c) $v_k = (16 \text{ ft/s}^2)(6.47 \text{ s}) = \boxed{103 \text{ ft/s}}$

$$v_s = (12 \text{ ft/s}^2)(7.47 \text{ s}) = \boxed{89.5 \text{ ft/s}}$$

3.70 Consider the motion of the puck in two increments: constant velocity, v_0 for a distance of 10 ft., following acceleration by the stick; and constant acceleration of -20 ft/s².

(a) While on the rough ice, we have

$$v^2 = v_0^2 + 2a_2\Delta x \quad \text{or}$$

$$v_0^2 = v^2 - 2a_2\Delta x = (40 \text{ ft/s})^2 - (2)(-20 \text{ ft/s}^2)(90 \text{ ft})$$

$$v_0 = 72.1 \text{ ft/s}$$

The average acceleration given the puck by the stick is then

$$a_1 = \frac{\Delta v}{\Delta t} = \frac{(72.1 \text{ ft/s})}{(0.01 \text{ s})} = \boxed{7210 \text{ ft/s}^2}$$

(b) $x_{\text{total}} = x_1 + x_2 = 10 \text{ ft} + x_2$ where

$$x_2 = \frac{(v^2 - v_0^2)}{2a_2} = \frac{0 - (72.1 \text{ ft/s})^2}{2(-20 \text{ ft/s}^2)} = 130 \text{ ft} \quad \text{and}$$

$$x_{\text{total}} = \boxed{140 \text{ ft}}$$

(c) $t_{\text{total}} = t_1 + t_2$, where $t_1 = \frac{x_1}{v_0} = \frac{10 \text{ ft}}{72.1 \text{ ft/s}} = 0.139 \text{ s}$ and

$$t_2 = \frac{v - v_0}{a_2} = \frac{0 - 72.1 \text{ ft/s}}{-20 \text{ ft/s}^2} = 3.61 \text{ s} \qquad t_{\text{total}} = \boxed{3.75 \text{ s}}$$

* 3.71 $v = \dfrac{\Delta x}{\Delta t} = \dfrac{325 \times 10^3 \text{ m}}{20 \times 10^6 \text{ y}} = \boxed{1.62 \text{ cm/y}}$

*3.72 Distance travelled by motorist $= (15 \text{ m/s})t$

Distance travelled by policeman $= \frac{1}{2}(2 \text{ m/s}^2)t^2$

(a) Intercept occurs when $15t = t^2$

$$t = \boxed{15 \text{ s}}$$

(b) $v(\text{officer}) = (2 \text{ m/s}^2)t = \boxed{30 \text{ m/s}}$

(c) $x(\text{officer}) = \frac{1}{2}(2 \text{ m/s}^2)t^2 = \boxed{225 \text{ m}}$

*3.73 (a) $v = \dfrac{26 \text{ mi} + \frac{385}{1760} \text{ mi}}{\left(2 + \frac{13}{60} + \frac{9}{3600}\right) \text{ h}} = \dfrac{26.22 \text{ mi}}{2.22 \text{ h}} = \boxed{11.8 \text{ mph}}$

$\qquad\qquad v = \left(\dfrac{\text{mi}}{11.8 \text{ h}}\right)\left(\dfrac{1609 \text{ m/mi}}{3600 \text{ s/h}}\right) = \boxed{5.28 \text{ m/s}}$

(b) The time to do the last 5.22 mi was, for Boileau,

$$t = \frac{d}{v} = \frac{5.22 \text{ mi}}{11.8 \text{ mi/h}} = 0.442\text{h} = 26.5 \text{ min}$$

Assuming that Boileau was ahead by 2.5 min. when he crossed the 21-mi mark, the second-place finisher was then $(29 \text{ min.})\left(\dfrac{11.8 \text{ mi/h}}{60 \text{ min /h}}\right) = 5.7$ miles from the finish-line. At this time, the second-place runner had a velocity $v_0 = 5.28$ m/s.

If Boileau finished the race 0.5 min. ahead, then the second-place finisher covered the last 5.7 miles in 27.0 min. This is an average velocity of 12.67 mi/h = 5.66 m/s.

Assuming a constant acceleration, the final velocity of the second-place runner is found from

$$\bar{v} = \tfrac{1}{2}(v_0 + v_f) = 5.66 \text{ m/s},$$

with $v_0 = 5.28$ m/s

$\qquad\quad v_f = 6.04$ m/s

And the average acceleration of the second-place runner was

$$a = \frac{v_f - v_0}{\Delta t} = \frac{6.04 \text{ m/s} - 5.28 \text{ m/s}}{(27 \text{ min})(60 \text{ s/min})} = \boxed{4.7 \times 10^{-4} \text{ m/s}^2}$$

*3.74 (a) $d = \tfrac{1}{2}(9.8)t_1^2, \quad d = 336t_2$

$\qquad\quad t_1 + t_2 = 2.40$

$\qquad\quad 336t_2 = 4.9(2.40 - t_2)^2$

$\qquad\quad 4.9t_2^2 - 359.5t_2 + 28.22 = 0$

$$t_2 = \frac{359.5 \pm \sqrt{(359.5)^2 - 4(4.9)(28.22)}}{9.8}$$

$$t_2 = \frac{359.5 \pm 358.75}{9.8}$$

$\qquad \therefore \ d = 336t_2 = \boxed{26.4 \text{ m}}$

(b) Ignoring the sound travel time, $d = \tfrac{1}{2}(9.8)(2.4)^2 = 28.22$ m, an error of 6.88%.

*3.75 $s = \frac{1}{2}at^2$

$2 = \frac{1}{2}a(0.63)^2$

$a = \frac{4}{(0.63)^2} = \boxed{10.4 \text{ m/s}^2}$

3.76   Let path (#1) correspond to the motion of the rocket accelerating under its own power. Path (#2) is the motion of the rocket under the influence of gravity with the rocket still rising. Path (#3) is the motion of the rocket under the influence of gravity, but with the rocket falling. The data in the table that is circled is found from the uncircled data given in each column.

(# 1): $v^2 - (80)^2 = 2(4)(1000)$; therefore $v = 120$

$120 = 80 + (4)t$ giving $t = 10$ s

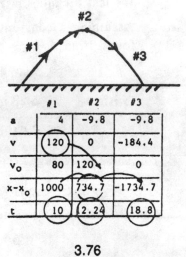

(# 2): $0 - (120)^2 = 2(-9.80)\Delta x$ giving $\Delta x = 734.7$ m

$0 - 120 = -9.8t$ giving $t = 12.24$ s

(# 3): $v^2 - 0 = 2(-9.80)(-1734.7)$ giving $v = -184.4$

$-184.4 - 0 = (-9.8)t$ giving $t = 18.8$ s

	#1	#2	#3
a	4	-9.8	-9.8
v	120	0	-184.4
v_0	80	120	0
$x-x_0$	1000	734.7	-1734.7
t	10	2.24	18.8

3.76

(a) $t_{total} = 10 + 12.24 + 18.8 = \boxed{41 \text{ s}}$

(b) $\Delta x_{total} = \boxed{1734.7 \text{ m}}$

(c) $v = \boxed{-184 \text{ m/s}}$

3.77 (a) Let x be the distance traveled at acceleration a until maximum speed v is reached. If this is achieved in time t we can use the following three equations:

$$x = \frac{(v + v_0)}{2}t_1, \qquad 100 - x = v(10.2 - t_1) \quad \text{and} \quad v = v_0 + at_1$$

with $v_0 = 0$ these become $x = \frac{vt_1}{2}$, $100 - x = (10.2 - t_1)v$ and $v = at_1$.

The first two given $100 = (10.2 - \frac{1}{2}t_1)v = (10.2 - t_{1/2})at_1 \quad a = \frac{200}{(20.4 - t_1)t_1}$.

For Maggie $a = \frac{200}{(18.4)2} = \boxed{5.43 \text{ m/s}^2}$

For Judy $a = \frac{200}{(17.4)(3)} = \boxed{3.84 \text{ m/s}^2}$

(b) $v = at_1$

Maggie: $v = (5.43)(2) = \boxed{10.86 \text{ m/s}}$

Judy: $v = (3.84)(3) = \boxed{11.5 \text{ m/s}}$

(c) At the second mark $x = \frac{1}{2}at_1^2 + v(6 - t_1)$

Maggie: $x = \frac{1}{2}(5.43)(2)^2 + (10.86)(4) = 54.3 \text{ m}$

Judy: $x = \frac{1}{2}(3.84)(3)^2 + (10.5)3 = 51.8 \text{ m}$

Maggie is ahead by $\boxed{2.5 \text{ m}}$

3.78 (a)

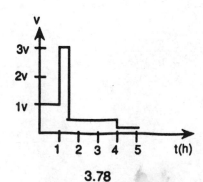

3.78

(b) $d = \sum_{i=1}^{4} v_i t_i = v + \frac{3v}{2} + \frac{3}{2} \cdot \frac{v}{2} + 2\frac{v}{3} = \boxed{3.92v}$

(c) $\bar{v} = \frac{d}{T} = \frac{3.92v}{5} = \boxed{0.784v}$

3.79 $a_1 = 0.1 \text{ m/s}^2$, $a_2 = -0.5 \text{ m/s}^2$

$$x = 1000 \text{ m} = \frac{1}{2}a_1 t_1^2 + v_1 t_2 + \frac{1}{2}a_2 t_2^2$$

$t_1 + t_2$ and $v_1 = a_1 t_1 = -a_2 t_2$

$$1000 = \frac{1}{2}a_1 t_1^2 + a_1 t_1 (-\frac{a_1 t_1}{a_2}) + \frac{1}{2}a_2(\frac{a_1 t_1}{a_2})^2$$

$$1000 = \frac{1}{2}a_1(1 - \frac{a_1}{a_2})t_1^2$$

$$t_1 = \sqrt{\frac{20,000}{1.2}} = \boxed{129 \text{ s}}$$

$$t_2 = \frac{a_1 t_1}{-a_2} = \frac{12.9}{0.5} \approx 26 \text{ s}$$

Total time $= t = \boxed{155 \text{ s}}$

3.80   (a) In walking a distance Δx, in a time Δt the length of rope ℓ is only increased by $\Delta x \sin \theta$.

∴ The pack lifts at a rate $\dfrac{\Delta x}{\Delta t} \sin \theta$.

$$v = \frac{\Delta x}{\Delta t}\sin\theta = v_0 \frac{x}{\ell} = v_0 \frac{x}{\sqrt{x^2 + h^2}}$$

(b) $a = \dfrac{dv}{dt} = v_0 \dfrac{\frac{dx}{dt}}{\ell} + v_0 x \dfrac{d}{dt}(\dfrac{1}{\ell})$

   $a = v_0 \dfrac{v_0}{\ell} - v_0 x \dfrac{\frac{d\ell}{dt}}{\ell^2}$, but $\dfrac{d\ell}{dt} = v$

∴ $a = \dfrac{v_0^2}{\ell}(1 - \dfrac{x^2}{\ell^2}) = \dfrac{v_0^2}{\ell}\dfrac{h^2}{\ell^2} = \dfrac{h^2 v_0}{(x^2 + h^2)^{3/2}}$

(c) $\dfrac{v_0^2}{h}$, 0   (d) v_0,   0

3.81 $x^2 + y^2 = L^2$

Differentiating this expression with respect to time, we find

$$2x\frac{dx}{dt} + 2y\frac{dy}{dt} = 0$$

or, $\dfrac{dy}{dt} = -\dfrac{x}{y}\dfrac{dx}{dt}$

Therefore; $\dfrac{dy}{dt} = \dfrac{x}{y}v = v\,\text{ctn}\,\alpha$

When $\alpha = 60°$, $\text{ctn}\,\alpha = \dfrac{1}{\sqrt{3}}$, and we have

$$\frac{dy}{dt} = \frac{v}{\sqrt{3}}$$

3.82   (a) $v = v_0\dfrac{x}{\sqrt{x^2 + h^2}}$, $x = v_0 t$, $h = 6$ m, $v_0 = 2$ m/s.

(b) $a = h^2\dfrac{v_0^2}{(x^2 + h^2)^{3/2}}$, $x = v_0 t$, $h = 6$ m, $v_0 = 2$ m/s.

3.83 $a = \dfrac{\Delta v}{\Delta t}$, $\Delta x = \bar{v}\Delta t$, $x_1 = x_0 + \Delta x$

t	v	Δv	a	$\bar{v}$	Δx	x
0.5	1.0	1.0	2	0.50	0.25	0.25
1.0	3.0	2.0	4	2.00	1.000	1.25
1.5	4.5	1.5	3	3.75	1.875	3.12
2.0	7.0	2.5	5	5.75	2.875	6.00
2.5	9.5	2.5	5	8.25	4.120	10.12
3.0	10.5	1.0	2	10.00	5.000	15.12
3.5	12.0	1.5	3	11.25	5.620	20.75
4.0	14.0	2.0	4	13.00	6.500	27.25
4.5	15.0	1.0	2	14.50	7.250	34.50

3.84 $a_0 = 3 \text{ m/s}^2,\quad v_0 = 0,\quad x_0 = 0.$

Let $\Delta t = 0.1$ s

t	$a_0 e^{-x}$	$\Delta v = a\Delta t$	$v = v + \Delta v$	$\Delta x = \overline{v}t$	$x = x + 1$
0.00	3.00	0.00	0.00	0.00	0.0000
0.01	$3e^{-0}$	3(0.01)	0.03	(0.015)(0.01)	0.0001
0.02	$3e^{-0.00015}$	3(0.01)	0.06	(0.03)(0.01)	0.0004
0.03	$3e^{-0.00045}$	3(0.01)	0.09	etc.	
$\vdots$					

3.85   Assume $v_0 = 0$ and $x_0 = 0$

$$a = \sqrt{3 + t^2}\ \text{m/s}^2$$

$$v = \sum_i a_i \Delta t_i$$

$$x = \sum_i \overline{v}_i \Delta t_i$$

$$v(5.7) \cong 19.8\ \text{m/s}$$

$$x(5.7) \cong 44.3\ \text{m}$$

CHAPTER 4

4.1 $\Delta\mathbf{r} = [x(3) - x(1)]\mathbf{i} + [y(3) - y(1)]\mathbf{j}$

Now,

$$x(3) = 9a + 3b \qquad y(3) = 3c + d$$

$$x(1) = a + b \qquad y(1) = c + d$$

Hence,

$$\Delta\mathbf{r} = (8a + 2b)\mathbf{i} + 2c\mathbf{j}$$

4.2   (a) For the average velocity, we have

$$\begin{aligned}
\bar{\mathbf{v}} &= (\frac{x(4) - x(2)}{4\,\text{s} - 2\,\text{s}})\mathbf{i} + (\frac{y(4) - y(2)}{4\,\text{s} - 2\,\text{s}})\mathbf{j} \\
&= (\frac{5\,\text{m} - 3\,\text{m}}{2\,\text{s}})\mathbf{i} + (\frac{3\,\text{m} - 1.5\,\text{m}}{2\,\text{s}})\mathbf{j} \\
&= (\mathbf{i} + 0.75\mathbf{j})\,\text{m/s}
\end{aligned}$$

(b) For the velocity components, we have

$$\begin{aligned}
v_x &= \frac{dx}{dt} = a = 1\,\text{m/s} \\
v_y &= \frac{dy}{dt} = 2ct = (\frac{1}{4}\,\text{m/s}^2)t
\end{aligned}$$

Therefore,

$$\mathbf{v} = v_x\mathbf{i} + v_y\mathbf{j} = (1\,\text{m/s})\mathbf{i} + (\frac{1}{4}\,\text{m/s}^2)t\mathbf{j}$$

$$\mathbf{v}(2) = (1\,\text{m/s})\mathbf{i} + (0.5\,\text{m/s})\mathbf{j}$$

and the speed is

$$|v|_{t=2\,\text{s}} = \sqrt{(1\,\text{m/s})^2 + (0.5\,\text{m/s})^2} = \boxed{1.12\,\text{m/s}}$$

*4.3

x	y
0	-3600
-3000	0
$\underline{-1273}$	$\underline{1273}$
-4273 m	-2327 m

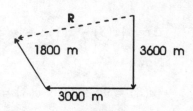

4.3

(a) Net displacement = $\boxed{4.87 \text{ km}}$ @ 209° from East

(b) Average speed $= \dfrac{(20 \text{ m/s})(180 \text{ s}) + (25 \text{ m/s})(120 \text{ s}) + (30 \text{ m/s})(60 \text{ s})}{(180 \text{ s} + 120 \text{ s} + 60 \text{ s})}$

$= \boxed{23.3 \text{ m/s}}$

(c) Average velocity $= \dfrac{4870 \text{ m}}{360 \text{ s}} = \boxed{13.5 \text{ m/s}}$ along **R**

*4.4

(a) $\mathbf{r} = 18t\mathbf{i} + (4t - 4.9t^2)\mathbf{j}$

(b) $\mathbf{v} = (18 \text{ m/s})\mathbf{i} + [4 \text{ m/s} - (9.8 \text{ m/s}^2)t]\mathbf{j}$

(c) $\mathbf{a} = (-9.8 \text{ m/s}^2)\mathbf{j}$

(d) $\mathbf{r}(3 \text{ s}) = (54 \text{ m})\mathbf{i} - (32.1 \text{ m})\mathbf{j}$

(e) $\mathbf{v}(3 \text{ s}) = (18 \text{ m/s})\mathbf{i} - (25.4 \text{ m/s})\mathbf{j}$

(f) $\mathbf{a}(3 \text{ s}) = (-9.8 \text{ m/s}^2)\mathbf{j}$

4.5

(a) $\mathbf{v} = \mathbf{v}_0 + \mathbf{a}t$; $\mathbf{a} = (\mathbf{v} - \mathbf{v}_0)t = [(9\mathbf{i} + 7\mathbf{j}) - (3\mathbf{i} - 2\mathbf{j})]/3 = \boxed{(2\mathbf{i}+3\mathbf{j}) \text{ m/s}^2}$

(b) $\mathbf{r} = \mathbf{r}_0 + \mathbf{v}_0 t + \dfrac{1}{2}\mathbf{a}t^2 = (3\mathbf{i} - 2\mathbf{j})t + \dfrac{1}{2}(2\mathbf{i} + 3\mathbf{j})t^2$;

$x = (3t + t^2)$ m and $y = (1.5t^2 - 2t)$ m

4.6

(a) $\mathbf{v} = \mathbf{v}_0 + \mathbf{a}t = (2\mathbf{i} + 4\mathbf{j})t$ m/s; $v_x = \boxed{2t \text{ m/s}}$ and $v_y = \boxed{4t \text{ m/s}}$

(b) $\mathbf{r} = \mathbf{r}_0 + \mathbf{v}_0 t + \dfrac{1}{2}\mathbf{a}t^2 = \dfrac{1}{2}(2\mathbf{i} + 4\mathbf{j})t^2$ m; $x = t^2$ m and $y = 2t^2$ m

(c) $v = \sqrt{v_x^2 + v_y^2} = \sqrt{4t^2 + 16t^2} = \sqrt{20}t = \boxed{4.47t \text{ m/s}}$

4.7 $\mathbf{v_0} = (4\mathbf{i} + \mathbf{j})$ m/s and $\mathbf{v}(20) = (20\mathbf{i} - 5\mathbf{j})$ m/s.

(a) $a_x = \dfrac{\Delta v_x}{\Delta t} = \dfrac{20 - 4}{20}$ m/s^2 = $\boxed{0.8 \text{ m/s}^2}$

$a_y = \dfrac{\Delta v_y}{\Delta t} = \dfrac{-5 - 1}{20}$ m/s^2 = $\boxed{-0.3 \text{ m/s}^2}$

(b) $\theta = \tan^{-1}[\dfrac{-0.3}{0.8}] = -20.6° = \boxed{339.4° \text{ from } +x \text{ axis}}$

(c) At $t = 25$ s,

$$x = x_0 + v_{x0}t + \frac{1}{2}a_x t^2 = 10 + 4(25) + \frac{1}{2}(0.8)(25)^2 = \boxed{360 \text{ m}}$$

$$y = y_0 v_{y0}t + \frac{1}{2}a_y t^2 = -4 + 1(25) + \frac{1}{2}(-0.3)(25)^2 = \boxed{-72.7 \text{ m}}$$

$$\theta = \tan^{-1}(\frac{v_y}{v_x}) = \tan^{-1}(\frac{-6.5}{24}) = \boxed{-15°}$$

4.8 (a) $v = \dfrac{dr}{dt} = (\dfrac{d}{dt})(3\mathbf{i} - 6t^2\mathbf{j}) = -12t\,\mathbf{j}$ m/s;

$a = \dfrac{dv}{dt} = (\dfrac{d}{dt})(-12t\mathbf{j}) = -12\mathbf{j}$ m/s^2

(b) $\mathbf{r} = (3\mathbf{i} - 6\mathbf{j})$ m; $\mathbf{v} = -12\mathbf{j}$ m/s

4.9 $\mathbf{a} = 3\mathbf{j}$ m/s^2; $\mathbf{v_0} = 5\mathbf{i}$ m/s; $\mathbf{r_0} = 0\mathbf{i} + 0\mathbf{j}$

(a) $\mathbf{r} = \mathbf{r_0} + \mathbf{v_0}t + \dfrac{1}{2}\mathbf{a}t^2 = [5t\mathbf{i} + \dfrac{1}{2}3t^2\mathbf{j}]$ m

$\mathbf{v} = \mathbf{v_0} + \mathbf{a}t = (5\mathbf{i} + 3t\mathbf{j})$ m/s

(b) $t = 2$ s, $r = (5)2\mathbf{i} + \dfrac{1}{2}(3)(2)^2\mathbf{j} = (10\mathbf{i} + 6\mathbf{j})$ m so $x = \boxed{10 \text{ m}}$, $y = \boxed{6 \text{ m}}$

$v = 5\mathbf{i} + 3(2)\mathbf{j} = (5\mathbf{i} + 6\mathbf{j})$ m/s

$v = |v| = \sqrt{v_x^2 + v_y^2} = \sqrt{5^2 + 6^2} = \boxed{7.81 \text{ m/s}}$

4.10 $x(t) = v_0 t, \quad z(t) = h - \frac{1}{2}gt^2$

When the stone lands on the beach, we have $z = 0$, so that the corresponding time t' is

$$t' = \sqrt{\frac{2h}{g}} = \sqrt{\frac{2(50 \text{ m})}{9.80 \text{ m/s}^2}} = \boxed{3.19 \text{ s}}$$

On impact,

$$v_z = \frac{dz}{dt} = -gt' = -(9.80 \text{ m/s}^2)(3.19 \text{ s}) = -31.26 \text{ m/s}$$

$$v_x = \frac{dx}{dt} = v_0 = 18 \text{ m/s}.$$

Therefore, the speed is

$$v = \sqrt{v_x^2 + v_z^2} = \sqrt{(31.26 \text{ m/s})^2 + (18 \text{ m/s})^2} = \boxed{36.1 \text{ m/s}}$$

Also, $\tan\beta = \dfrac{v_z}{v_x} = \dfrac{-31.26 \text{ m/s}}{18 \text{ m/s}}$ so that $\beta = \boxed{-60.1°}$.

4.11 (a) The mug leaves the counter horizontally with a velocity v_{x0} (say). If time to elapses before it hits the ground, then, since there is no horizontal acceleration, $x = v_{x0}t$. i.e., $t = \dfrac{x}{v_{x0}} = \dfrac{(1.4 \text{ m})}{v_{x0}}$. In the same time it falls a distance

0.86 m with acceleration downward of 9.8 m/s^2. Then using

$$y = y_0 + v_{y0}t + \frac{1}{2}a_y t^2 \text{ we have}$$

$$0 = 0.86 \text{ m} - \frac{1}{2}(9.8 \text{ m/s}^2)(\frac{1.4 \text{ m}}{v_{x0}})^2$$

$$\text{i.e.,} \quad v_{x0} = \sqrt{\frac{(4.9 \text{ m/s}^2)(1.96 \text{ m}^2)}{0.86 \text{ m}}} = \boxed{3.34 \text{ m/s}}$$

(b) The vertical velocity component with which it hits the floor is

$$v_y = v_{y0} + a_y t = -(9.8 \text{ m/s}^2)(\frac{1.4 \text{ m}}{3.34 \text{ m/s}}) = \boxed{-4.11 \text{ m/s}}$$

Hence, the angle θ at which the mug strikes the floor is given by

$$\theta = \tan^{-1}(\frac{v_y}{v_x}) = \tan^{-1}(\frac{-4.11}{3.34}) = \boxed{-50.9°}$$

4.12 (a) (b) Since the shot leaves the gun horizontally, the time it takes to reach the target is $t = \dfrac{x}{v_0}$. The vertical distance traveled in this time is

$$y = \frac{1}{2}gt^2 = \frac{g}{2}\left(\frac{x}{v_0}\right)^2 = Ax^2 \text{ where } A = \frac{g}{2v_0^2}$$

(c) If $x = 3$ m, $y = 0.21$ m, then $A = \dfrac{0.21}{9} = 0.023$

$$v_0 = \sqrt{\frac{g}{2A}} = \sqrt{\frac{9.8}{0.046}} \text{ m/s} = \boxed{14.6 \text{ m/s}}$$

*4.13 $240 \text{ m} = \dfrac{1}{2}(9.8 \text{ m/s}^2)t^2$

$$t = \boxed{7.00 \text{ s}}$$

$$v = \frac{1000 \text{ m}}{7 \text{ s}} = \boxed{143 \text{ m/s}}$$

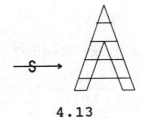

4.13

*4.14 With no air friction, the time-of-flight is

$$t = \frac{2v_0\sin\theta}{g}$$

$$R = (v_0\cos\theta)t = \frac{2v_0^2\sin\theta_0\cos\theta_0}{g}$$

$$283 \text{ m} = \frac{\sin2\theta}{g}v_0^2$$

$$v_0 = \boxed{74.5 \text{ m/s}}$$

4.15 $x_0 = 0; \quad y_0 = 35 \text{ m}; \quad v_{x0} = v_0; \quad v_{y0} = 0; \quad a_x = 0; \quad a_y = 9.80 \text{ m/s}^2$

(a) When $x = 80$ m, $y = 0$.

$$y = y_0 + v_{y0}t - \frac{1}{2}gt^2 = 35 - 4.9t^2 = 0; \quad \text{thus } t^2 = \frac{35}{4.90} \text{ and}$$

$$t = \sqrt{\frac{35}{4.90}} = \boxed{2.67 \text{ s}}$$

(b) $x = x_0 + v_{x0}t = v_0t; \quad 80 = v_0 \times 2.67 \text{ thus } v_0 = \dfrac{80}{2.67} = \boxed{29.9 \text{ m/s}}$

(c) $v_x = v_{x0} = \boxed{29.9 \text{ m/s}}$

$$v_y = v_{y0} - gt = 0 - 9.80t = -9.80 \times 2.67 = \boxed{-26.2 \text{ m/s}}$$

*4.16   To determine Beamon's time-of-flight, use Eq.3.11, where at maximum height $v_y = 0$, and

$$0^2 - v_{yo}^2 = 2(-9.8)(0.9)$$

$$v_{yo} = 4.2 \text{ m/s}$$

$$t_{up} = \frac{0.9 \text{ m}}{2.1 \text{ m/s}} = \underline{0.429 \text{ s}}$$

The time to fall 1.75 m is found from Eq. 3.14

$$1.75 = \frac{1}{2}(9.8)t^2$$

$$t_{down} = 0.598 \text{ s}$$

(a) Time of flight T= $(0.428 + 0.598)$ s = $\boxed{1.03 \text{ s}}$

(b) $v_x = \dfrac{8.90 \text{ m}}{1.03 \text{ s}} = \boxed{8.67 \text{ m/s}}$

$v_y = \boxed{4.2 \text{ m/s}}$

(c) $\theta = \tan^{-1} \dfrac{v_y}{v_x} = \boxed{25.8°}$

4.17   (a) We use the equation

$$y = x \tan \theta_0 - \frac{gx^2}{2v_0^2 \cos^2 \theta_0} \quad \text{with } x = 36 \text{ m, } v_0 = 20.0 \text{ m/s, and } \theta = 53°.$$

So,

$$y = (36 \text{ m})(\tan 53°) - \frac{(9.8 \text{ m/s}^2)(36 \text{ m})^2}{(2)(20 \text{ m/s})^2 \cos^2 53°} = 47.77 - 43.83 = 3.94 \text{ m}$$

The ball clears the bar by $(3.94 - 3.05)$ m = 0.89 m.

(b) The time the ball takes to reach the maximum height is

$$t_1 = \frac{v_0 \sin \theta_0}{g} = \frac{(20 \text{ m/s})(\sin \ 53°)}{9.8 \text{ m/s}^2} = 1.63 \text{ s}$$

The time to travel 36 m horizontally is $t_2 = \dfrac{x}{v_{ox}}$

$$t_2 = \frac{36 \text{ m}}{(20 \text{ m/s})(\cos 53°)} = 3.0 \ \text{s}$$

Since $t_2 > t_1$ the ball clears the goal on its way down.

*4.18 $(40 \text{ m/s})(\cos 30°)t = 50 \text{ m}$. (Eq. 4.12)

The stream of water takes $t = 1.44$ s to reach the building, which it strikes at a height

$$y = v_{y0}t - \frac{1}{2}gt^2$$

$$= (40\sin 30°)t - \frac{1}{2}(9.8)t^2$$

$$= (40)\left(\frac{1}{2}\right)(1.44) - 4.9(1.44)^2 = \boxed{18.7 \text{ m}}$$

4.19   (a) To find the minimum speed, we take the range $R = 75$ m

to be the *maximum* range, which occurs at $\theta_0 = 45°$. Thus,

$$R = \frac{v_0^2 \sin^2 \theta_0}{g} \quad \text{and} \quad R_{\max} = \frac{v_0^2}{g}$$

Solving for v_0 we find:

$$v_0 = \sqrt{R_{\max}g} = \sqrt{75(9.80)} = \boxed{27.1 \text{ m/s}}$$

(b) $R = v_{x0}t = (v_0 \cos \theta_0)t \implies t = \dfrac{R}{(v_0 \cos \theta_0)}$

$$t = \frac{75}{(27.1)(\cos 45°)} = \boxed{3.91 \text{ s}}$$

4.20 $v_{x0} = 500$ m/s $v_{y0} = 0$; $x_f = 200$ m; $x_0 = y_0 = 0$.

(a) Find y when $x = 200$ m.

$$x = x_0 + v_{x0}t = 500t = 200 \text{ m}, \text{ so that } t = 0.4 \text{ s}.$$

$$y = y_0 + v_{y0}t - \frac{1}{2}gt^2 = -(4.9 \text{ m/s}^2)t^2 = -(4.9 \text{ m/s}^2)(0.40)^2 = 0.784 \text{ m}.$$

The bullet strikes the target $\boxed{0.784 \text{ m}}$ below the center

(b) The range $R = \dfrac{v_0^2}{g} \sin 2\theta_0$, so $\sin 2\theta_0 = \dfrac{Rg}{v_0^2}$

$$\theta = \frac{1}{2}\sin^{-1}\left(\frac{Rg}{v_0^2}\right) = \frac{1}{2}\sin^{-1}\left[\frac{(200 \text{ m})(9.8 \text{ m/s}^2)}{(500 \text{ m/s})^2}\right]$$

$\boxed{\theta = 0.225°}$ above the horizontal.

4.21   (a) The range R is given by

$$R = \frac{v_0^2}{g} \sin 2\theta_0 = \frac{(1.7 \times 10^3 \text{ m/s}^2)}{9.8 \text{ m/s}^2} \sin 110° = 2.77 \times 10^5 \text{ m} = \boxed{277 \text{ km}}$$

(b) If the time in the air is t then t is given from $v_{0x} \equiv v_0 \cos\theta_0 = \dfrac{R}{t}$

$$t = \frac{R}{v_0 \cos\theta_0} = \frac{2.77 \times 10^5 \text{ m}}{(1700 \text{ m/s}) \cos 55°} = 284 \text{ s} = \boxed{4.74 \text{ min}}$$

4.22   Assume ball hit from near ground at home plate. $R = \dfrac{v_0^2(\sin 2\theta_0)}{g}$

$$v_0 = \sqrt{\frac{Rg}{(\sin 2\theta_0)}},\ R = 150 \text{ m when } \theta_0 = 45° \text{ so } v_0 = \boxed{38.3 \text{ m/s}}$$

When $\theta_0 = 20°$, $R = \dfrac{(3.83)^2(\sin 40°)}{9.80} = \boxed{96.4 \text{ m}}$

4.23 $h = \dfrac{v_0^2 \sin^2\theta_0}{2g}$; $R = \dfrac{v_0^2(\sin 2\theta_0)}{g}$; $3h = R$;

so $\dfrac{3v_0^2 \sin^2\theta_0}{2g} = \dfrac{v_0^2 \sin 2\theta_0}{g}$ or

$\dfrac{2}{3} = \dfrac{\sin^2\theta_0}{\sin 2\theta_0} = \dfrac{\tan\theta_0}{2}$

thus $\theta_0 = \tan^{-1}\left(\dfrac{4}{3}\right) = \boxed{53.1°}$

4.24   (a) For the maximum horizontal distance R we have $R = \dfrac{v_0^2}{g}\sin 2\theta_0$

where $\theta_0 = 45°$

Then $R = \dfrac{v_0^2}{g} = \dfrac{2gh}{g} = 2h$

(b) Let t_1, t_2 be the times spent in the air for the purely vertical motion and the vertical–horizontal motion respectively. Using

$v = v_0 + at$ gives

$-v_0 = v_0 - gt_1$

$t_1 = \dfrac{2v_0}{g} = \dfrac{2\sqrt{2gh}}{g} = \boxed{2\sqrt{\dfrac{2h}{g}}}$

For t_2 we use $v_{0x} = \dfrac{x}{t_2}$

i.e., $t_2 = \dfrac{x}{v_{0x}} = \dfrac{R}{v_{0x}} = \dfrac{2h}{\sqrt{2gh}\cos 45°} = \dfrac{2}{\frac{1}{\sqrt{2}}}\sqrt{\dfrac{h}{2g}} = \boxed{2\sqrt{\dfrac{h}{g}}}$

4.25   Maximum distance occurs when $\theta_0 = 45°$.

Then $R = \dfrac{v_0^2}{g'}\sin 2\theta_0 = \dfrac{v_0^2}{g'}$ (Eq. 4.18)

Solving for $g' = \dfrac{v_0^2}{R} = \dfrac{81}{30} = \boxed{2.7 \text{ m/s}^2}$

*4.26   (a) $x = v_{x_0}t = (8\cos -20°)(3) = \boxed{22.6 \text{ m}}$

(b) Taking y positive downwards,

$y = v_{y_0}t + \dfrac{1}{2}gt^2$

$= 8(\cos 20°)3 + \dfrac{1}{2}(9.8)(3)^2 = \boxed{52.3 \text{ m}}$

(c) $10 = 8\cos 20° t + \dfrac{1}{2}(9.8)t^2$

Write as a quadratic,

$4.9t^2 + 2.74t - 10 = 0$

$t = \dfrac{-2.74 \pm \sqrt{(2.74)^2 + 196}}{9.8} = \boxed{1.18 \text{ s}}$

4.27 Centripetal acceleration (Eq. 4.22) $\quad a_r = \dfrac{v^2}{r} = \dfrac{(8 \text{ m/s})^2}{2 \text{ m}} = \boxed{32 \text{ m/s}^2}$

4.28   (a) $v = r\omega$

At 8 revs/s $\quad v = (0.6 \text{ m})(8 \text{ rev/s})(2\pi \text{ rad/rev}) = 30.2 \text{ m/s} = 9.6\pi \text{ m/s}$

At 6 revs/s $\quad v = (0.9 \text{ m})(6 \text{ rev/s})(2\pi \text{ rad/rev}) = 33.9 \text{ m/s} = 10.8\pi \text{ m/s}$

$\boxed{6 \text{ rev/s}}$ gives the larger linear speed.

(b) Acceleration $= \dfrac{v^2}{r} = \dfrac{(9.6\pi \text{ m/s})^2}{0.6 \text{ m}} = \boxed{1.52 \times 10^3 \text{ m/s}^2}$

(c) At 6 rev/s, acceleration $= \dfrac{(10.8\pi \text{ m/s})^2}{0.9 \text{ m}} = \boxed{1.28 \times 10^3 \text{ m/s}^2}$

*4.29 $\quad a_r = \dfrac{v^2}{r} = \dfrac{(20 \text{ m/s})^2}{(1.06 \text{ m})} = \boxed{377 \text{ m/s}^2}$

4.30 $\quad a = \dfrac{v^2}{R} \qquad T = (24 \text{ h})(\dfrac{3600 \text{ s}}{\text{h}}) = 86400 \text{ s}$

$v = \dfrac{2\pi R}{T} = \dfrac{2\pi(6.37 \times 10^6 \text{ m})}{86400 \text{ s}} = 2910.6 \text{ m/s}$

$a = \dfrac{(2910.6 \text{ m/s})^2}{6.37 \times 10^6 \text{ m}} = \boxed{0.0337 \text{ m/s}^2}$ (directed toward the center of the Earth.)

4.31   (a) $v = \dfrac{\Delta x}{\Delta t} = \dfrac{2\pi(3.84 \times 10^8 \text{ m})}{[(27.3 \text{ d})(24 \text{ h/d})(3600 \text{ s/h})} = \boxed{1.02 \times 10^3 \text{ m/s}}$

(b) Since v is constant and only direction changes,

$a = \dfrac{v^2}{r} = \dfrac{(1.02 \times 10^3)^2}{(3.84 \times 10^8)} = \boxed{2.72 \times 10^{-3} \text{ m/s}^2}$

4.32 $\quad v = r\omega = (0.30 \text{ m})(630 \text{ rev/min})(2\pi \text{ rad/rev})/(60 \text{ s/ min}) = \boxed{19.8 \text{ m/s}}$

4.33   (a) $r = 0.4$ m

The particle travels a distance $2\pi r = 2\pi(0.4)$ m in each revolution. Therefore, since it makes 5 rev each second, it travels a distance of $5(2\pi)(0.4)$ m each second. Hence,

$$v = \frac{5(2\pi)(0.4) \text{ m}}{1 \text{ s}} = \boxed{12.6 \text{ m/s}}$$

(b) $a = \dfrac{v^2}{r} = \dfrac{(12.6 \text{ m/s})^2}{(0.4 \text{ m})} = \boxed{395 \text{ m/s}^2}$ directed towards the center of the circle.

4.34 $r = 0.5$ m; $v_t = (200 \text{ rev/min})(1 \text{ min}/60 \text{ s})(2\pi r/\text{rev}) = \boxed{10.47 \text{ m/s}}$

$$a = \frac{v^2}{r} = \frac{(10.47)^2}{0.5} = \boxed{219 \text{ m/s}^2 \text{ (inward)}}$$

4.35 $r = 2.5$ m, $a = 15$ m/s^2

(a) $a_r = a \cos 30° = (15 \text{ m/s}^2) \cos 30° = \boxed{13.0 \text{ m/s}^2}$

(b) $a_r = \dfrac{v^2}{r}$,   so $v^2 = r a_r = (2.5 \text{ m})(13.0 \text{ m/s}^2) = 32.5 \text{ m}^2/\text{s}^2$

$$v = \sqrt{32.5} \text{ m/s} = \boxed{5.70 \text{ m/s}}$$

(c) $a^2 = a_t^2 + a_r^2$ so

$$a_t = \sqrt{a^2 - a_r^2} = \sqrt{(15 \text{ m/s}^2)^2 - (13 \text{ m/s})^2} = \boxed{7.48 \text{ m/s}^2}$$

*4.36   (a) $a_t = \boxed{0.6 \text{ m/s}^2}$

(b) $a_r = \dfrac{v^2}{r} = \dfrac{(4 \text{ m/s})^2}{20 \text{ m}} = \boxed{0.8 \text{ m/s}^2}$

(c) $a = \sqrt{a_t^2 + a_r^2} = \boxed{1.0 \text{ m/s}^2}$

at $\theta = \tan^{-1}\dfrac{a_r}{a_t} = 53.1°$ inward from path

4.37 $a_r = \dfrac{v^2}{r} = 1.29 \text{ m/s}^2$

$a_T = \dfrac{\Delta v}{\Delta t} = \dfrac{(-40 \frac{m}{km})(10^3 \frac{m}{km})(\frac{1 m}{3600 s})}{15 \text{ s}} = -0.741 \text{ m/s}^2$

$a = \sqrt{a_r^2 + a_t^2} = \sqrt{(1.29 \text{ m/s}^2)^2 + (-0.741 \text{ m/s}^2)^2} = \boxed{1.48 \text{ m/s}^2}$

4.38   (a) $a_r = \dfrac{v^2}{r} = \dfrac{(5 \text{ m/s})^2}{1 \text{ m}} = \boxed{25 \text{ m/s}^2}$ $a_T = g = 9.8 \text{ m/s}^2$

(b)

4.38

(c) $a = \sqrt{a_r^2 + a_t^2} = \sqrt{(25 \text{ m/s}^2)^2 + (9.8 \text{ m/s})^2} = \boxed{26.8 \text{ m/s}^2}$

$\phi = \tan^{-1}\left(\dfrac{a_t}{a_r}\right) = \tan^{-1}\dfrac{9.8 \text{ m/s}^2}{25 \text{ m/s}^2} = \boxed{21.4°}$

4.39 $a_{\text{top}} = \dfrac{v^2}{r} = \dfrac{(4.3 \text{ m/s})^2}{0.6 \text{ m}} = \boxed{30.8 \text{ m/s}^2 \text{ down}}$

$a_{\text{bottom}} = \dfrac{v^2}{r} = \dfrac{(6.5 \text{ m/s})^2}{0.6} = \boxed{70.4 \text{ m/s}^2 \text{ upward}}$

4.40 $r = 2$ m; $v = 8$ m/s

(a) $a_r = \dfrac{v^2}{r} = \dfrac{8^2}{2} = \boxed{32 \text{ m/s}^2}$

$a_r = a \cos 60°$ (1); $a_t = a \sin 60°$ (2)

Divide (2) by (1) $\dfrac{a_t}{a_r} = \dfrac{\sin 60°}{\cos 60°} = \tan 60°$

(b) $a_t = a_r \tan 60° = (32 \text{ m/s}^2) \tan 60° = \boxed{55.4 \text{ m/s}^2}$

(c) $a = \dfrac{a_r}{\cos 60°} = \dfrac{32 \text{ m/s}^2}{\cos 60°} = \boxed{64 \text{ m/s}^2}$

4.41 (a) $u = v - v' = -50 - 60 = -110$ km/h or 110 km/h north

(b) $u = v - v' = 60 - (-50) = 110$ km/h or 110 km/h south

4.42 (a) We define the velocities as follows:

v = vel of motorist with respect to the road = 80 km/h

u = vel of police car with respect to the road = 95 km/h

v' = vel of motorist with respect to the police car.

Then $v' = v - u = 80$ km/h $- 95$ km/h $= -15$ km/h.

(b) Velocity of police car with respect to the motorist is $-v' = +15$ km/h. West

4.43 Total time in still water $t = \dfrac{d}{v} = \dfrac{2000}{1.2} = \boxed{1.67 \times 10^3 \text{ s}}$

Total time = time upstream and time downstream

$t_{\text{up}} = \dfrac{1000}{(1.2 - 0.5)} = 1429$ s, $t_{\text{down}} = \dfrac{1000}{(1.2 + 0.5)} = 588$ s

$t_{\text{total}} = 1429 + 588 = 2017$ s $= \boxed{2.02 \times 10^3 \text{ s}}$

4.44 v = river speed; v_0 = canoe speed in still water;

$v_0 + v = 2.9$ m/s; $v - v_0 = -1.2$ m/s

Adding and dividing by 2 gives $v = \boxed{0.85 \text{ m/s}}$

*4.45 $v_{\text{Shadow}} = v_{\text{Hawk}} \cos 60° = 5 \cos 60° = \boxed{2.5 \text{ m/s}}$

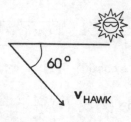

4.45

4.46   The key to solving problems of this type is to identify carefully the selection of the observers (and frames), S and S'. In this case, it is convenient to take the shore observer to be S and to consider a *hypothetical observer S'* drifting with the river, as shown in the diagram. The "particle" being observed is the boat.

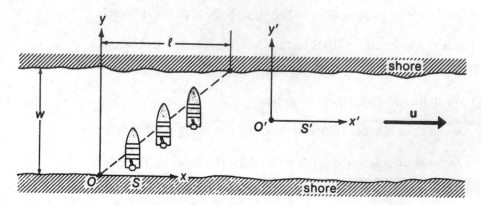

We are given that the river's velocity components are $u_x = 1.5$ m/s, $u_v = 0$, and those of the boat are $v'_x = 2$ m/s. $v'_x = 0$. Therefore, taking components of Eq. 4.40, we have

$$v_x = u_x + v'_x = 1.5 \text{ m/s}$$

$$v_y = u_y + v_y = 2 \text{ m/s}$$

which give the velocity components as seen by the shore observer. The time to cross the river can be found using v_y :

$$t = \frac{w}{v_y} = \frac{160 \text{ m}}{2 \text{ m/s}} = 80 \text{ s}$$

Then we obtain for ℓ, the distance to the downstream landing point,

$$\ell = v_x t = (1.5 \text{ m/s})(80 \text{ s}) = \boxed{120 \text{ m}}$$

4.47 $v = (150^2 + 30^2)^{1/2} = \boxed{153 \text{ km/h}}$

$\theta = \tan^{-1}\left(\dfrac{30}{150}\right) = \boxed{11.3^\circ}$ north of west

4.48   Let v_{pg} = velocity of the plane relative to the ground,

v_{ag} = velocity of the air relative to the ground, and

v_{pa} = velocity of the plane relative to the air. The velocities are related as shown in the following equation and vector addition diagram:

$v_{pg} = v_{pa} + v_{ag}$

   (a) The heading direction is

$\theta = \sin^{-1}\left(\dfrac{v_{ag}}{v_{pa}}\right) = \sin^{-1}\left(\dfrac{50}{200}\right) = \boxed{14.5^\circ}$ N of W

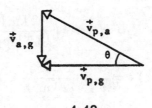

4.48

   (b) $|v_{pg}| = \sqrt{|v_{pa}|^2 - |v_{ag}|^2} = \sqrt{(200)^2 - (50)^2}$ km/h

$= \boxed{194 \text{ km/h}}$

4.49   Let v_{rg} = velocity of the rain relative to ground,

v_{rc} = velocity of rain relative to the car, and

v_{cg} = velocity of the car relative to ground. These vectors are

related as shown in the following equation and vector addition

diagram: $v_{rg} = v_{rc} + v_{cg}$. Therefore

   (a) $v_{rc} = \dfrac{v_{cg}}{\cos 30^\circ} = \dfrac{50 \text{ km/h}}{\cos 30^\circ} = \boxed{57.7 \text{ km/h}}$

   (b) $v_{rg} = v_{cg}\tan 30^\circ = (50 \text{ km/h})(\tan 30^\circ) = \boxed{28.9 \text{ km/h}}$ downward

4.50 $\alpha =$ Heading with respect to the shore

$\beta =$ Angle of boat with respect to the shore

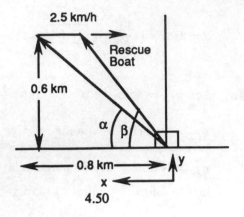

(a) The boat should always head

for the child at heading

$$\alpha = \tan^{-1} \frac{0.6}{0.8} = \boxed{36.9°}$$

(b) $v_x = 20 \cos \alpha - 2.5 = 13.5$ km/h

$v_y = 20 \sin \alpha = 12$ km/h

$$\beta = \tan^{-1} \left(\frac{12 \text{ km/h}}{13.5 \text{ km/h}} \right) = \boxed{41.6°}$$

(c) $t = \dfrac{d}{v} = \dfrac{0.6 \text{ km}}{12 \text{ km/h}} = 0.05$ h $= \boxed{3 \text{ min}}$

4.51 (a) To an observer at rest in the train car the bolt accelerates
downward and toward the rear of the train.

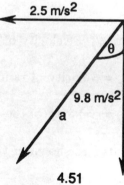

$$a = \sqrt{(2.5 \text{ m/s})^2 + (9.8 \text{ m/s})^2} = \boxed{10.1 \text{ m/s}^2}$$

$$\tan \theta = \frac{2.5 \text{ m/s}^2}{9.8 \text{ m/s}^2} = 0.255$$

$$\theta = 14.3° \text{ to the south from the vertical}$$

(b) $a = 9.8$ m/s^2, vertically downward.

4.52

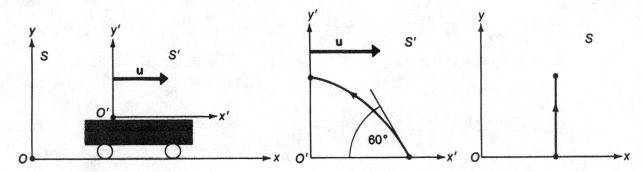

Solution:

Identify the student as the S' observer and the professor as the S observer. For the initial motion in S', we have

$$\frac{v'_y}{v'_x} = \tan 60° = \sqrt{3}$$

Then, because there is no x-motion in S, we can write $v_x = v'_x + u = 0$

so that $v'_x = -u = -10$ m/s

Hence, the ball is thrown backwards in S'. Then,
$$v_y = v'_y = \sqrt{3}|v'_x| = 10\sqrt{3} \text{ m/s}$$

Using $v_y^2 = 2gh$ (from Eq. 4.17), we find

$$h = \frac{(10\sqrt{3} \text{ m/s})^2}{2(9.80 \text{ m/s}^2)} = \boxed{15.3 \text{ m}}$$

The motion of the ball as seen by the student in S' is shown in diagram(b). The view of the professor in S is shown in diagram(c).

4.53   (a) $v_x = 2t$ and $v_y = 0$, so $v = \boxed{2t i \text{ m/s}}$

(b) $6 - 3t = 0$ so $t = 2$ s thus $x = 2t^2/2 = t^2 = \boxed{4 \text{ m/s}}$ and

$$y = 6t - 3t^2/2 = \boxed{6 \text{ m}}$$

4.54 To catch up to the ball, the velocity of the boy must be $v = v_0 \cos \alpha$

$$\cos \alpha = \frac{v}{v_0} = (\frac{20 \text{ m}}{3 \text{ s}})(\frac{1}{20 \text{ m/s}}) = 0.33 \quad \text{or} \quad \alpha = 70.5°$$

$$v_{0y} = v_0 \sin \alpha = 18.9 \text{ m/s}$$

Using Eq. 4.17, we find

$$y_m = \frac{(v_0 \sin \alpha)^2}{2g} = \frac{(18.9 \text{ m/s})^2}{19.6 \text{ m/s}^2} = \boxed{18.2 \text{ m}}$$

4.55   (a) While on the incline:

$$v^2 - v_0^2 = 2a\Delta x \qquad v - v_0 = at$$

$$v^2 - 0 = 2(4)(50) \quad 20 - 0 = 4t$$

$$v = \boxed{20 \text{ m/s}} \qquad t = \boxed{5 \text{ s}}$$

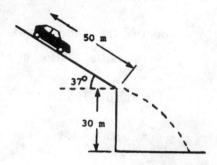

4.55

(b) Initial free-flight conditions give us

$$v_{0x} = 20 \cos 37 = 16 \text{ m/s}; \quad v_{y0} = -20 \sin 37 = -12 \text{ m/s}$$

$$v_x = v_{x0} \quad \text{since } a_x = 0;$$

$$v_y = -(2a_y \Delta y - v_{y0}^2)^{1/2} = -[2(-9.80)(-30) - (-12)^2]^{1/2} = -27 \text{ m/s}$$

$$v = (v_x^2 + v_y^2)^{1/2} = [16^2 + (-27)^2]^{1/2} = \boxed{31 \text{ m/s}}$$

(c) $t_1 = 5 \text{ } s; \quad t_2 = \frac{(v_y - v_{y0})}{a_y} = \frac{(-27 + 12)}{(-9.80)} = 1.55 \text{ s}$

$$t = t_1 + t_2 = \boxed{6.55 \text{ s}}$$

(d) $\Delta x = v_{x0}t_1 = (16)(1.5) = \boxed{24 \text{ m}}$

4.56 $x = (v_0 \cos 30°)t$

$y = (v_0 \sin 30°)t - \dfrac{1}{2}gt^2$

$40 \text{ m} = v_0(8.66)t$

$t = \dfrac{40 \text{ m}}{0.866v_0} = \dfrac{46.2 \text{ m}}{v_0}$

$t^2 = \dfrac{2133 \text{ m}^2}{v_0^2}$

$-20 \text{ m} = v_0(0.50)(\dfrac{46.2 \text{ m}}{v_0}) - 4.9 \text{ m/s}^2(\dfrac{2133 \text{ m}^2}{v_0^2})$

$v_0^2(43.1 \text{ m}) = 10453 \text{ m}^2/\text{s}^2$

$v_0^2 = 243 \text{ m}^2/\text{s}^2$

$v_0 = \boxed{15.6 \text{ m/s}}$

4.57 $R = 60 \text{ m}$ $R = \dfrac{v_0^2}{g}\sin 2\alpha$ (Eq. 4.18)

$\sin 2\alpha = \dfrac{Rg}{v_0^2}$ where $\alpha = 10.8°$

Using Eq. 4.14,

$y = -(\dfrac{g}{2v_0^2 \cos^2 \alpha})x^2 + (\tan \alpha)x + 1$ m

At $x = 45$ m, $y = \boxed{3.16 \text{ m}}$

4.58 $v_0 = 200$ m/s, $R = 2$ km

    (a) $R = \dfrac{v_0^2 \sin 2\theta_0}{g}$,   thus

$$\sin 2\theta_0 = \frac{Rg}{v_0^2} = \frac{(2000 \text{ m})(9.80 \text{ m/s}^2)}{(200 \text{ m/s})^2} = 0.49$$

    Therefore $2\theta_0 = 29.3°$ or $150.7°$ and $\theta_0 = \boxed{14.7°}$ or $\boxed{75.3°}$

    (b) $R = v_{x0}t = v_0 \cos \theta_0 t$ thus $t = \dfrac{R}{(v_0 \cos \theta)}$.

$$\text{For } \theta_0 = 14.7°, \, t = \frac{2000 \text{ m}}{200 \ \cos 14.7°} = \boxed{10.3 \text{ s}}$$

$$\text{For } \theta_0 = 75.4°, \, t = \frac{2000 \text{ m}}{200 \ \cos 75.4} = \boxed{39.6 \text{ s}}$$

*4.59   At $t = 2$ s, $v_x \; = \; 4$ m/s

$$v_y \; = \; -8 \text{ m/s}$$

$$v \; = \; \sqrt{v_x^2 + v_y^2} = \boxed{8.94 \text{ m/s}}$$

$$\theta \; = \; \tan^{-1}\frac{v_y}{v_x} = \boxed{-63°} \text{ below horizontal}$$

*4.60 $x = 2 \text{ m} + (3 \text{ m/s})t; \quad y = x - (5 \text{ m/s}^2)t^2$

    (a) At $t \; = \; 0$, $\; x = 2$ m, $\; y = 2$ m

$$r \; = \; \sqrt{x^2 + y^2} = \boxed{2.83 \text{ m}}$$

    (b) At $t \; = \; 2$, $\; x = 8$ m, $\; y = -12$ m

$$r \; = \; \sqrt{x^2 + y^2} = \boxed{14.4 \text{ m}}$$

4.61 The vertical height of the stone when released from A is

$$y_0 = (1.5 + 1.2 \sin 30°) \text{ m} = 2.1 \text{ m}$$

(a) The equations of motion are

$$v_y = v_0 \sin 60° - gt = (1.3 - 9.8t) \text{ m/s}.$$

$$v_x = v_0 \cos 60° = 0.75 \text{ m/s}$$

$$y = (2.1 + 1.3t - 4.9t^2) \text{ m}.$$

$$x = (0.75t) \text{ m}$$

$$y = 0 \quad \text{when } t = \frac{-1.3 \pm \sqrt{1.69 + 41.16}}{-9.8} = 0.8 \text{ s}$$

Then $x_A = (0.75)(0.8) \text{ m} = \boxed{0.6 \text{ m}}$

(b) The equations of motion are

$$v_y = v_0(-\sin 60°) - gt = (-1.3 - 9.8t) \text{ m/s}$$

$$v_x = v_0(\cos -60°) = 0.75 \text{ m/s}$$

$$y = (2.1 - 1.3t - 4.9t^2) \text{ m}$$

$$x = (0.75t) \text{ m}$$

$$y = 0 \quad \text{when } t = \frac{1.3 \pm \sqrt{1.69 + 41.16}}{-9.8} = 0.535 \text{ s}$$

Then $x_B = (0.75)(0.535) \text{ m} = \boxed{0.4 \text{ m}}$

(c) $a_c = \dfrac{v^2}{r} = \dfrac{(1.5 \text{ m/s})^2}{1.2 \text{ m}} = \boxed{1.87 \text{ m/s}^2}$

(d) After release $a = g$

4.62   Find the time that it will take the truck to move 20 meters.

$v_{truck} = 10$ m/s, $d = 20$ m, $d = vt$ therefore $t = d/v = 20/10 = 2$ s

Time up $=$ Time down $= t/2 = 1$ s

(a) The ball will be thrown with vertical velocity thus $\phi = 0°$ from vertical

(b) $v_y = v_{y0} - gt$ therefore $v_{y0} = gt = (9.80 \text{ m/s}^2)(1 \text{ s}) = \boxed{9.80 \text{ m/s}}$

(c) The boy will see straight line motion along the vertical.

(d) The observer will see the ball move with a component of velocity $v_{x0} = 10$ m/s
to the north as well as above accelerated motion in the vertical direction with
$v_{y0} = \boxed{9.80 \text{ m/s}}$. Therefore the angle from the vertical is

$$\phi = \tan^{-1} \frac{v_{x0}}{v_{y0}} = \tan^{-1} \frac{10}{9.80} = \boxed{45.6° \text{ north of the vertical}} \text{ and}$$
$$v_0 = \sqrt{v_{y0}^2 + v_{x0}^2} = \sqrt{(9.80)^2 + (10)^2} = \boxed{14 \text{ m/s}}$$

An observer in the fixed frame will see the path of the ball as a parabola.

4.63   Find initial velocity of dart when shot *at rest*, horizontally, one meter above the
ground. $v_{y0} = 0$; $y = -1$ m; $x_r = 5$ m.

$y = v_{y0}t - \frac{1}{2}gt^2$ thus $t = \sqrt{-2y/g}$ and $x = v_{x0}t$

thus $v_{x0} = \frac{x}{t} - \frac{x}{\sqrt{-2y/g}} = x\sqrt{\frac{g}{-2y}} = 5\sqrt{\frac{9.80}{2}} = \boxed{11.1 \text{ m/s}}$

How far will the dart go if it is shot horizontally at one meter above the ground
while sliding down the board at 2 m/s?

$y = v_{y0}t - \frac{1}{2}gt^2$ thus

$0 = \frac{gt^2}{2} - v_{y0}t + y = 4.9t^2 - 2(0.707)t - 1$ and thus

$t = -\frac{1.414 \pm \sqrt{(1.414)^2 + 4(4.90)1}}{2(4.90)} = 0.32995$ s

$x = v_{0x}t = [11.07 + 2(0.707)](0.32995) = \boxed{4.12 \text{ m}}$

4.64 Consider the rocket's trajectory in 3 parts as shown in the sketch.

Our initial conditions give:

$a_y = 30 \sin 53° = 24 \text{ m/s}^2$; $a_x = 30 \cos 53° = 18 \text{ m/s}^2$

$v_{y0} = 100 \sin 53° = 80 \text{ m/s}$; $v_{x0} = 100 \cos 53° = 60 \text{ m/s}$

In the table below, circled data is derived from known (i.e., uncircled) data.

	#1	#2	#3
a_y	24	-9.8	-9.80
a_x	18	0.0	0.00
v_y	152	0.0	-173.00
v_x	114	114.0	114.00
v_{y0}	80	152.0	0.00
x_{x0}	60	114.0	114.00
Δy	348	1179.0	-1527.00
Δx	261	1768.0	2012.00
t	3	15.5	17.65

Path #1: $v_y - 80 = (24)(3)$ or $v_y = 152 \text{ m/s}$

$v_x - 60 = (18)(3)$ or $v_x = 114 \text{ m/s}$

$\Delta y = (80)(3) + \frac{1}{2}(24)(3)^2 = 348 \text{ m}$

$\Delta x = (60)(3) + \frac{1}{2}(3)^2 = 261 \text{ m}$

Path #2: $a_x = 0$, $v_x = v_{x0} = 114 \text{ m/s}$

$0 - 152 = -(9.80)t$ or $t = 15.5 \text{ s}$

$\Delta x = (114)(15.5) = 1768 \text{ m}$;

$\Delta y = (152)(15.5) - \frac{1}{2}(9.80)(15.5)^2 = 1179 \text{ m}$

Path #3: $(v_y)^2 - 0 = 2(-9.80)(-1527)$

or $v_y = -173 \text{ m/s}$

$v_x = v_{x0}$ since $a_x = 0$

$-173 - 0 = -(9.80)t$ or $t = 17.65 \text{ s}$

$\Delta x = (114)(17.65) = 2012 \text{ m}$

(a) $\Delta y(\text{max}) = \boxed{1530 \text{ m}}$

(b) $t(net) = 3 + 15.5 + 17.65 = \boxed{36.2 \text{ s}}$

(c) $\Delta x(net) = 261 + 1768 + 2012 = \boxed{4040 \text{ m}}$

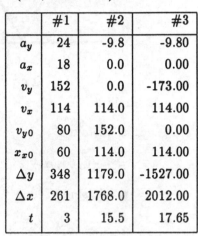

4.64

4.65

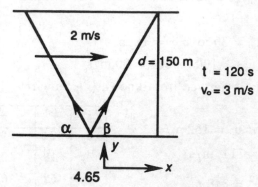

2 m/s

$d = $ 150 m

$t = 120$ s

$v_0 = 3$ m/s

α β

y

x

4.65

At angle α

$v_y = v_0 \sin \alpha$ $\qquad\qquad y = (v_0 \sin \alpha)t = 150$ m

$v_x = -v_0 \cos \alpha + 2$ $\qquad x = (-v_0 \cos \alpha + 2)t$

$y = (3 \sin \alpha)120 = 150$ m

$\alpha = \sin^{-1} \dfrac{15}{36} = 24.6°$

$x = (-3 \cos \alpha + 2)(120) = \boxed{87.3 \text{ m upstream}}$

At angle β $\quad v_y = v_0 \sin \beta; \quad y = (v_0 \sin \beta)t = 150$ m

$v_x = v_0 \cos \beta + 2; \quad x = (v_0 \cos \beta + 2)t$

$y = (3 \sin \beta)120 = 150$ m

$\beta = \sin^{-1} \dfrac{15}{36} = 24.6°$

$x = (3 \cos \beta + 2)(120) = \boxed{567.3 \text{ m downstream}}$

Physics for Scientists and Engineers

4.66 Refer to the sketch:

(a) & (b) $\Delta x = v_{x0}t$;   substitution yields $130 = (v_0 \cos 35)t$

$\Delta y = v_{y0}t + \dfrac{1}{2}at^2$ substitution yields

$20 = (v_0 \sin 35)t + \dfrac{1}{2}(-9.80)t^2$

Solving the above gives $t = \boxed{3.81 \text{ s}}$ $v_0 = \boxed{41.7 \text{ m/s}}$

(c) $v_y = v_0 \sin\theta_0 - gt$

$v_x = v_0 \cos\theta_0$

At $t = 3.81$ s, $v_y = 41.7 \sin 35° - (9.8)(3.81) = -13.4$ m/s

$v_x = (41.7 \cos 35°) = 34.1$ m/s

$v = \sqrt{v_x^2 + v_y^2} = \boxed{36.6 \text{ m/s}}$

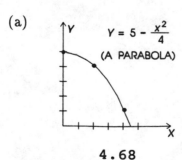

4.66

4.67 $R = \dfrac{v_0^2 \sin(2\theta)}{g} = 63.8$ m.

Therefore the net is 13.8 m short of the landing position.

$\Delta x = v_{x0}t = (25 \cos 45)t = 13.8$ m and

$h = \Delta y = v_{y0}t + \frac{1}{2}a_y t^2 = (25 \sin 45)t + \frac{1}{2}(-9.80)t^2$

By solving the above 2 equations, we eliminate t and find $h = \boxed{10.8 \text{ m}}$

*4.68 $\mathbf{r} = (2t)\mathbf{i} + (5 - t^2)\mathbf{j}$

$x = 2t$, $y = 5 - t^2 = 5 - \dfrac{x^2}{4}$

(a)

$Y = 5 - \dfrac{x^2}{4}$

(A PARABOLA)

4.68

(b) $\mathbf{v} = \dfrac{d\mathbf{r}}{dt} = 2\mathbf{i} - (2t)\mathbf{j}$

(c) $\mathbf{r} \cdot \mathbf{v} = 0$ when $\mathbf{r} \perp \mathbf{v}$.   This occurs when

$0 = (2t)(2) + (5 - t^2)(-2t)$

$0 = 4t - 10t + 2t^3$

$2t(t^2 - 3) = 0$

With roots $t = -1.73$ s, 0, $+1.73$ s.

$\mathbf{v} \perp \mathbf{r}$ at $\boxed{t = 0 \text{ s and } 1.73 \text{ s.}}$

4.69 (a) $y = -\frac{1}{2}gt^2$; $x = v_0 t$. Combine the equations eliminating t.

$$y = -\frac{1}{2} g\left(\frac{x^2}{v_0^2}\right) \text{ from this } x^2 = \left(-\frac{2y}{g}\right)v_0^2$$

thus $x = v_0\sqrt{\dfrac{-2y}{g}} = 275\sqrt{\dfrac{2(3000)}{9.80}} = \boxed{6804 \text{ m}}$

(b) The plane has the same velocity as the bomb in the x direction.

Therefore the plane will be 2000 m directly above the bomb when it hits the ground.

(c) $\tan\theta = \dfrac{x}{y}$; therefore $\theta = \tan^{-1}\dfrac{x}{y} = \tan^{-1}\left(\dfrac{6804}{3000}\right) = \boxed{66.2°}$

4.70 The football travels a distance

$$R = \frac{v_0^2 \sin(2\theta)}{g} = \frac{(20)^2 \sin(60)}{9.80} = 35.4 \text{ m}$$

Time of flight of the ball is

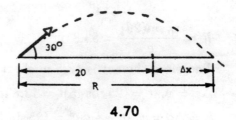

4.70

$$T = \frac{2v_0 \sin\theta}{g} = \frac{2(20)\sin 30}{9.80} = 2.04 \text{ s}$$

The receiver is Δx away from where the ball lands and $\Delta x = 35.4 - 20 = 15.4$ m.

To cover this distance in 2.04 s, he travels with

velocity $v = \dfrac{15.4}{2.04} = \boxed{7.52 \text{ m/s}}$

4.71   Find the velocity at 10 cm.

$$v = (0.5556 \text{ rev/s})(2\pi)\frac{10 \text{ cm}}{1 \text{ rev}} = \boxed{34.9 \text{ cm/s}}$$

Find the time to jump 5 cm and land

$$y = -\frac{1}{2}gt^2 \quad \text{time up or down} = \sqrt{\frac{2y}{g}}$$

$$\text{total time} = 2\sqrt{\frac{2y}{g}} = 2\sqrt{\frac{2(5)}{980}} = \boxed{0.202 \text{ s}}$$

(a) Find the linear displacement $y = vt = (34.9 \text{ cm/s})(0.202 \text{ s}) = \boxed{7.05 \text{ cm}}$

(b) Find how far record rotates during time of jump

$$\text{Revs} = (0.5556 \text{ rev/s})(0.2025 \text{ s}) = 0.1122 \text{ rev}; \quad 1 \text{ rev} = 360°$$

$$\theta_A = (0.1122 \text{ rev})(360°/1 \text{ rev}) = \boxed{40.39°}$$

position of point A is given by

$$R_A = 10 \text{ cm and } \theta_A = 40.39° \text{ below the } x-\text{axis}$$

(c) Find the angular direction of landing point θ_B

$$\tan\theta_B = \frac{y}{R_A}. \quad \text{Therefore } \theta_B = \tan^{-1}\left(\frac{y}{R_A}\right) = \tan^{-1}\left(\frac{7.05}{10}\right) = \boxed{35.18°}$$

Find the radial position to the landing point

$$R_B = (y^2 + R_A^2)^{1/2} = [(7.05)^2 + 10^2]^{1/2} = \boxed{12.24 \text{ cm}}$$

The position of point B is given by

$$R_B = 12.24 \text{ cm and } \theta_B = 35.18° \text{ below the } x-\text{axis.}$$

4.72

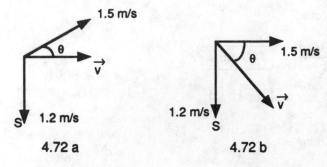

4.72 a   **4.72 b**

(a) $1.5 \sin \theta = 1.2$, therefore $\theta = \sin^{-1}\left(\frac{1.2}{1.5}\right) = 53.1°$

$v = \frac{50}{t} = 1.5 \cos(53)$; Solve for t and find $t = \boxed{55.5 \text{ s}}$

(b) $v = \sqrt{(1.2)^2 + (1.5)^2} = 1.92$ m/s and $\theta = \tan^{-1}\frac{1.2}{1.5} = 38.7°$

The distance traveled is $d = \frac{5}{\cos(38.7)} = 64.1$ m

Therefore $t = \frac{d}{v} = \frac{6.41 \text{ m}}{1.92 \text{ m/s}} = \boxed{33.4 \text{ s}}$

4.73   (a) Let v_0 be the initial speed of the bullet.

The maximum range is given by $R_{\text{max}} = \frac{v_0^2}{g}$

So $v_0 = \sqrt{R_{\text{max}} g} = \sqrt{(500 \text{ m})(9.9 \text{ m/s}^2)} = 70$ m/s

If $R = 350$ m and the angle of projection of the bullet is θ_0 then

$$R = \frac{v_0^2}{g} \sin 2\theta_0$$

$$\sin 2\theta_0 = \frac{gR}{v_0^2} = \frac{(9.8 \text{ m/s}^2)(350 \text{ m})}{(70 \text{ m/s})^2} = 0.7$$

$$2\theta_0 = 44.4° \text{ and } \theta_0 = \boxed{22.2°}$$

$$\text{or } 2\theta_0' = 180° - 44.4° \text{ and } \theta_0' = \boxed{67.8°}$$

(Note complementary angles give the same range).

(b) $R = \frac{(70)^2}{g} \sin 28° = \boxed{235 \text{ m}}$

(c) $R = \frac{(70)^2}{g} \sin 152° = \boxed{235 \text{ m}}$ (same)

4.74   Using hint: $t(log) = t(boat)$

$\boxed{\text{LOG:}}$ $\Delta x = vt$; $1000 = vt$, where v = river's speed

$\boxed{\text{BOAT:}}$ Let V = boat's speed in still water = 13.6 m/s

therefore $d = (V - v)t_1$; $(d + 1000) = (V + v)t_2$ and $t = t_1 + t_2$

Combining the above gives

$$\frac{1000}{v} = \frac{d}{(V - v)} + d + \frac{1000}{(V + v)}$$

Also $d = (V - v)(3600)$ [i.e., convert 1 h to 3600 s]

Substitution gives $v = \boxed{0.139 \text{ m/s}}$

*4.75 $\mathbf{C} = v_x\mathbf{i} + v_y\mathbf{j}$

$\quad\quad$ 6.12 sin60°$\quad\quad\quad\quad$ 6.12 cos60°

$\quad\quad$ $\underline{-4 \sin 40°}$$\quad\quad\quad\quad$ $\underline{4 \; \cos 40°}$

$\quad$ $v_x = 2.73$ km/h$\quad$ $v_y = -0.00417$ km/h

The velocity of the current is

$\mathbf{C} = (2.73 \text{ km/h})\mathbf{i} - (4.17 \text{ m/h})\mathbf{j}$

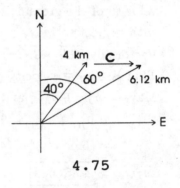

4.75

*4.76   (a) If the sailor is 4 km east of his original position after 2 hours, then

$$C = \frac{4 \text{ km}}{2 \text{ hr}} = \boxed{2 \text{ km/h, due East.}}$$

(b) The resultant of $\mathbf{v}_1 + \mathbf{C}$ is

$\quad$ $\mathbf{v} = (2\mathbf{i} + 3\mathbf{j}) + (2\mathbf{i}) = 4\mathbf{i} + 3\mathbf{j}$.

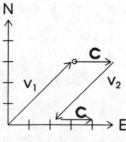

Note: $\mathbf{v}_1 = -\mathbf{v}_2$

4.76

4.77   (a) Let A, B be the positions of Mary and Jane respectively at time t when
$AB = 25$ m. They both start from point O, so
$OA = v_{MG}t = (4.0 \text{ m/s})t$ and
$OB = v_{JG}t = (5.4 \text{ m/s})t$
The cosine formula for triangle OAB gives
$(AB)^2 = (OB)^2 + (OA)^2 - 2(OA)(OB)\cos 60°$
i.e.,

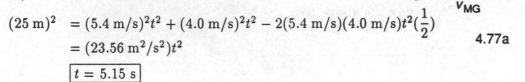

$$(25 \text{ m})^2 = (5.4 \text{ m/s})^2 t^2 + (4.0 \text{ m/s})^2 t^2 - 2(5.4 \text{ m/s})(4.0 \text{ m/s})t^2(\tfrac{1}{2})$$
$$= (23.56 \text{ m}^2/\text{s}^2)t^2$$

4.77a

$$\boxed{t = 5.15 \text{ s}}$$

(b) OB, BA, represent the
velocities of respectively Jane with respect
to the ground and Mary
with respect to the ground.
Then $BC \equiv -BA$ is the
velocity of the ground
with respect to Mary.
Vectorially, $\overrightarrow{OB} + \overrightarrow{BC} = \overrightarrow{OC}$.
That is $v_{JM} \equiv$ velocity of Jane with respect to
Mary $= v_{JG} + v_{MG}$ and has magnitude v_{JM} where

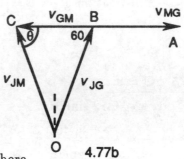

4.77b

$$v_{JM}^2 = v_{JG}^2 + v_{MG}^2 - 2v_{JG}v_{MG}\cos 60°$$
$$= (5.4 \text{ m/s})^2 + (4.0 \text{ m/s})^2 - (5.4 \text{ m/s})(4 \text{ m/s})$$

$v_{JM} = \boxed{4.85 \text{ m/s}}$

This result may also be obtained by dividing the distance they are apart
(25 m) by the time 5.15 s. The direction is obtained by finding the angle
$OCB = \theta$ in the figure above using the sine rule.

$$\cos \theta = \frac{\sin \theta}{v_{JG}} = \frac{\sin 60°}{v_{JM}}$$

i. e., $\quad \sin \theta = \dfrac{v_{JG}\sin 60°}{v_{JM}} = \dfrac{(5.4 \text{ m/s})(\sin 60°)}{4.85 \text{ m/s}}$

$\qquad \theta = 74.6° = \boxed{15.46°} \text{ W of N}$

(c) We go back to the figure in (a).
At $t = 4.05$ s $\quad OA = (4 \text{ m/s})(4 \text{ s}) = 16.0$ m

$OB = v_{JG}t = (5.4 \text{ m/s})(4 \text{ s}) = 21.6$ m.

$AB^2 = (OB)^2 + (OA)^2 - 2(OA)(OB)\cos 60° = (21.6 \text{ m})^2 + (21.6 \text{ m})(16 \text{ m})$

$AB = $ the distance between Mary and Jane $= \boxed{19.4 \text{ m}}$

4.78 (a) At the edge of the roof

$$v_0 = \sqrt{2a\Delta x} = \sqrt{2(5)8} = 8.94 \text{ m/s}.$$

Therefore $v_{x0} = 8.94 \cos 37 = 7.14$ m/s and

$v_{y0} = -8.94 \sin 37 = -5.38$ m/s.

Since $a_x = 0,\quad v_x = v_{x0} = \boxed{7.14 \text{ m/s}}$

$$\begin{aligned} v_y &= -\sqrt{v_{y0}^2 - 2g\Delta y} \\ &= -\sqrt{(5.38)^2 + (19.6)(6)} = \boxed{-12.1 \text{ m/s}} \end{aligned}$$

4.78

(b) On the roof: $t_1 = \dfrac{\Delta v}{a} = \dfrac{8.94}{5} = 1.79$ s

In the air:
$$t_2 = \frac{(v_y - v_{y0})}{a_y} = \frac{-12.1 - (-5.38)}{(-9.80)} = 0.686 \text{ s}$$

Therefore $t = \boxed{2.47 \text{ s}}$

(c) $\Delta x = v_{x0}t_2 = (7.14 \text{ m/s})(0.686 \text{ s}) = \boxed{4.90 \text{ m}}$

4.79 (a) $\Delta x = v_{x0}t,\quad \Delta y = v_{y0}t + \dfrac{1}{2}gt^2,$

$d \cos 50 = (10 \cos 15)t$, and

$d \sin 50 = (10 \sin 15)t + \dfrac{1}{2}(-9.80)t^2$

Solving the above gives

$d = \boxed{43.2 \text{ m}} \quad t = \boxed{2.87 \text{ s}}$

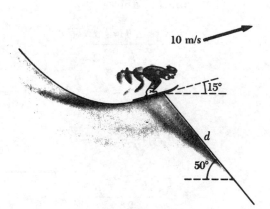

4.79

(b) Since $a_x = 0$,

$v_x = v_{x0} = 10 \cos 15 = \boxed{9.66 \text{ m/s}}$

$v_y = v_{y0} + a_y t = (10 \sin 15) - (9.80)(2.87)$

$\quad = \boxed{-25.5 \text{ m/s}}$

Air resistance would decrease the values of the range and maximum height. As an air foil he can overcome much friction and increase his distance.

4.80   (a) If the ball hits the tree while traveling horizontally the distance from the point of projection of the ball to the tree is half the range, and the height of the tree to the point where it is hit is the maximum height. Using $y = x \tan \theta - \dfrac{gx^2}{2v_0^2 \cos^2 \theta}$

i.e., $h = b \tan \theta - \dfrac{gb^2}{2v_0^2 \cos^2 \theta}$

Also the range $R = \dfrac{v_0^2 \sin 2\theta}{g}$

i.e., $2b = \dfrac{2v_0^2 \sin \theta \cdot \cos \theta}{g}$ (1)

or $\dfrac{g}{2v_0^2 \cos \theta} = \dfrac{\sin \theta}{2b}$

Then, $h = b \tan \theta - \left(\dfrac{b^2}{\cos \theta}\right) \cdot \dfrac{\sin \theta}{2b}$

$h = b \tan \theta - \dfrac{b \tan \theta}{2} = \dfrac{b \tan \theta}{2}$

Therefore, $\boxed{\tan \theta = \dfrac{2h}{b}}$

(b) From (1) above

$b = \dfrac{v_0^2 \sin \theta \cos \theta}{g}$

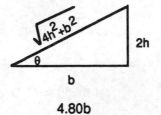

4.80b

Since $\tan \theta = \dfrac{2h}{b}$, $\sin \theta = \dfrac{2h}{\sqrt{4h^2 + b^2}}$ and

$\cos \theta = \dfrac{b}{\sqrt{4h^2 + b^2}}$ $b = v_0^2 \dfrac{2hb}{(4h^2 + b^2)g}$

$v_0^2 = \dfrac{(4h^2 + b^2)g}{2h}$ and $\boxed{v_0 = \sqrt{\dfrac{(4h^2 + b^2)g}{2h}}}$

4.81

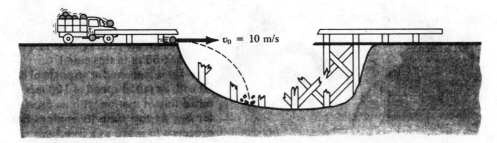

4.81

(1) Equation of bank   (2) and (3) are the equations of motion

(1) $y^2 = 16x$ (2) $x = v_0 t$ (3) $y = -\frac{1}{2}gt^2$

Substitute for t from (2) into (3) $y = -\frac{1}{2}(\frac{x^2}{v_0^2})$

Equate y from the bank equation to y from the equations of motion:

$$16x = -[-\frac{1}{2}g(\frac{x^2}{v_0^2})]^2 \implies \frac{g^2 x^4}{4v_0^4} - 16x = x(\frac{g^2 x^3}{4v_0^4} - 16) = 0$$

From this $x = 0$ or $x^3 = \frac{64v_0^4}{g^2}$ and $x = 4(\frac{10^4}{9.80^2})^{1/3} = \boxed{18.8 \text{ m}}$

Also $y = -\frac{1}{2}g(\frac{x^2}{v_0^2}) = \frac{1}{2}\frac{(9.80)(18.8)^2}{10^2} = \boxed{-17.3 \text{ m}}$

4.82

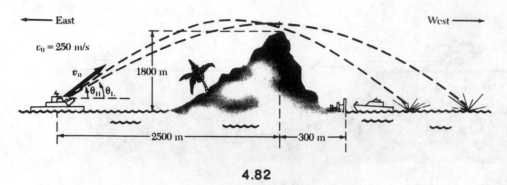

4.82

Find the highest elevation θ_H that will clear the mountain peak, this will yield the range of the closest point of bombardment. Next find the lowest elevation θ_L that will clear the mountain peak, this will yield the maximum range under these conditions if both θ_H and θ_L are $> 45°$: $x = 2500$ m, $y = 1800$ m, $v_0 = 250$ m/s.

$$y = y_{y0}t - \frac{1}{2}gt^2 = v_0(\sin\theta)t - \frac{1}{2}gt^2; \quad x = v_{x0}t - v_0(\cos\theta)t$$

Thus $t = \dfrac{x}{v_0\cos\theta}$

Substitute into the expression for y

$$y = v_0(\sin\theta)\frac{x}{v_0\cos\theta} - \frac{1}{2}g\left(\frac{x}{v_0\cos\theta}\right)^2 = x\tan\theta - \frac{gx^2}{2v_0^2\cos^2\theta}$$

but $\dfrac{1}{\cos^2\theta} = \tan^2\theta + 1$ thus $y = x\tan\theta - \dfrac{gx^2}{2v_0^2}(\tan^2\theta + 1)$ and

$$0 = \frac{gx^2}{2v_0^2}\tan^2\theta - x\tan\theta + \frac{gx^2}{2v_0^2} + y$$

Substitute values, use the quadratic formula and find

$\tan\theta = 3.905$ or 1.197 which gives $\theta_H = 75.6°$ and $\theta_L = 50.1°$

Range (at θ_H) $= \dfrac{v_0^2\sin 2\theta_H}{g} = \boxed{3065 \text{ m}}$ from enemy ship

3065 - 2500 - 300 = 265 m from shore

Range (at θ_L) $= \dfrac{v_0^2\sin 2\theta_L}{g} = \boxed{6276 \text{ m}}$ from enemy ship

6276 - 2500 - 200 = 3476 m from shore

Therefore safe distance is $\boxed{< 265 \text{ m}}$ or $\boxed{> 3476 \text{ m}}$ from the shore.

4.83   (a) $v = \dfrac{\Delta d}{\Delta t} = \dfrac{\sqrt{(197)^2 + (43)^2}}{4.34}$

             $v = \boxed{46.5 \text{ m/s}}$

      (b) $\alpha = \tan^{-1}\left(\dfrac{-197}{43.4}\right) = \boxed{-77.6°}$

      (c) $197 = \dfrac{1}{2}gt^2$ $\boxed{t = 6.34 \text{ s}}$

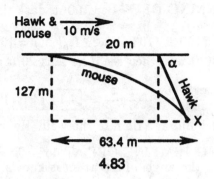

4.83

4.84   (a) *Coyote:* $\Delta x = \dfrac{1}{2}at^2$; $70 = \dfrac{1}{2}(15)t^2$

         Roadrunner: $\Delta x = v_0 t$; $70 = v_0 t$

         Solving the above, we get $v_0 = \boxed{22.9 \text{ m/s}}$ and $t = \boxed{3.06 \text{ s}}$

      (b) At the edge of the cliff $v_{x0} = at = 15(3.06) = 45.9$ m/s

         $\Delta y = \dfrac{1}{2}a_y t^2$ substituting we find - $100 = \dfrac{1}{2}(-9.80)t^2$

         $\Delta x = v_{x0}t + \dfrac{1}{2}a_x t^2 = (45.9)t + \dfrac{1}{2}(15)t^2$

         Solving the above gives $\Delta x = \boxed{360 \text{ m}}$ $t = \boxed{4.52 \text{ s}}$

      (c) $v_x = v_{x0} + a_x t = 45.9 + (15)(4.52) = \boxed{114 \text{ m/s}}$

          $v_y = a_y t = (-9.80)(4.52) = \boxed{-44.3 \text{ m/s}}$

4.85 RUNNING OFF - Use 100 m dash time to find his horizontal velocity.

$v = (100 \text{ m}/103.\text{s})(3.28 \text{ ft}/1 \text{ m}) = \boxed{31.8 \text{ ft/s}}$ Using this value to find the time to go 30 ft and then see if he falls 20 ft or more in this time since

$t = \dfrac{x}{v_0}, \quad y = -\dfrac{1}{2}g\dfrac{x^2}{v_0^2} = \boxed{-14.14 \text{ ft}}$ He falls 14.24 ft in the time to traverse 30 ft to next building. He hits the wall. He will not make it this way.

LONG JUMPING OFF AT 45° - Since his range is known on the horizontal and the angle the angle of elevation is known, his initial velocity may be found. This result is used to find the time to traverse 30 ft. Use this time to find his height when he makes it to the next building.

$R = \dfrac{v_0^2 \sin 2\theta}{g}$ thus $v_0 = \sqrt{Rg} = \sqrt{25.5(32)} = \boxed{28.6 \text{ ft/s}}$

Also $v_{x0} = v_{y0} = v_0 \cos\theta = v_0/\sqrt{2}$

$x = v_{x0}t$ thus $t = \dfrac{x}{v_{x0}} = \dfrac{30}{(2.86)/\sqrt{2}} = \boxed{1.48 \text{ s}}$

$y = v_{y0}t - \dfrac{1}{2}gt^2 = (\dfrac{28.6}{\sqrt{2}})(1.48) - \dfrac{1}{2}(32)(1.48)^2 = \boxed{-5 \text{ ft}}$

By using the long jump technique he will be only five feet below his take off height, therefore he will make it to safety this way.

*4.87

$$\mathbf{r}_1 = 4\mathbf{i} + 2\mathbf{j} - 4.9t^2\mathbf{j}$$

$$\mathbf{r}_2 = (6\cos20°t))\mathbf{i} + (6\sin20°t)\mathbf{j} - 4.9t^2\mathbf{j}$$

$$|\Delta\mathbf{r}|^2 = (4 - 6\cos20°t)^2 + (2 - 6\sin20°t)^2$$

$$= 20 - 48\cos20°t - 24\sin20°t + 36\cos^2 20°t^2 + 36\sin^2 20°t^2$$

$$= 20 - (48\cos20° + 24\sin20°)t + 36t^2$$

$$|\Delta\mathbf{r}|^2 = 20 - 53.3t + 36t^2$$

(b) Minimum separation occurs when

$$\dfrac{d(\Delta r)^2}{dt} = 0 = -53.3 + 72t, \text{ or when } \boxed{t = 0.74 \text{ s.}}$$

The minimum separation is

$$\Delta r = \sqrt{20 - 53.3(0.74) + 36(0.74)^2}$$

(a) $\boxed{\Delta r = 0.511 \text{ m}}$

CHAPTER 5

5.1 For the same force F, acting on different masses

$F = m_1 a_1$ and $F = m_2 a_2$

(a) $\dfrac{m_1}{m_2} = \dfrac{a_2}{a_1} = \dfrac{1}{3}$ (Eq. 5.1)

(b) $F = (m_1 + m_2)a = m_1 a_2 = 3\,\text{N}$

$\boxed{a = 0.75\ \text{m/s}^2}$

5.2   (a) $m = 6$ kg, $a = 2$ m/s^2, $|\Sigma F| = ma = 6\ \text{kg} \times 2\ \text{m/s}^2 = \boxed{12\ \text{N}}$

(b) $\Sigma F = ma$, $m = 4$ kg, $|\Sigma f| = 12$ N,

$a = \dfrac{|\Sigma F|}{m} = \dfrac{12\ \text{N}}{4\ \text{kg}} = \boxed{3\ \text{m/s}^2}$

5.3 $F = 10$ N, $m = 2$ kg

(a) $a = \dfrac{F}{m} = \dfrac{10\ \text{N}}{2\ \text{kg}} = \boxed{5\ \text{m/s}^2}$

(b) $W = mg = (2\ \text{kg})(9.80\ \text{m/s}^2) = \boxed{19.6\ \text{N}}$

(c) $a = \dfrac{2F}{m} = \dfrac{2(10\ \text{N})}{2\ \text{kg}} = \boxed{10\ \text{m/s}^2}$

5.4 For a constant force (constant acceleration)

the distance traveled, starting from rest, is $x = \dfrac{1}{2}\,at^2$ (Eq. 3.10)

$x = 4$ m, $t = 2$ s, $\therefore a = 2$ m/s^2

$F = ma = (3\ \text{kg})(2\ \text{m/s}^2) = \boxed{6\ \text{N}}$

5.5 $m = 0.005$ kg, $v = 320$ m/s, $v_o = 0$, $x = 0.82$ m

$\overline{F} = m\overline{a} = m\dfrac{\Delta v}{\Delta t}$ (Eq. 3.4)

Find Δt from Eq. 3.1 $\Delta t = \dfrac{\Delta x}{\overline{v}} = \dfrac{0.82 \text{ m}}{160 \text{ m/s}} = 0.0051$ s

$\therefore$ $\overline{F} = (0.005 \text{ kg})\dfrac{(320 \text{ m/s})}{(0.0051 \text{ s})} = \boxed{314 \text{ N}}$

5.6 $W = mg = 1.4$ N, $m = 0.143$ kg

$v = 32$ m/s, $v_o = 0$, $\Delta t = 0.09$ s

$\overline{v} = 16$ m/s $\overline{a} = \dfrac{\Delta v}{\Delta t} = 355$ m/s^2

(a) Distance $x = \overline{v}t = (16 \text{ m/s})(0.09 \text{ s}) = \boxed{1.44 \text{ m}}$

(b) Average force $\overline{F} = m\overline{a} = (0.143 \text{ kg})\,(355 \text{ m/s}^2) = \boxed{50.8 \text{ N}}$

5.7 $m = 3$ kg, $a = (2i + 5j)$ m/s^2 $F = ma = (6i + 15j)$ N

$|F| = \sqrt{6^2 + 15^2}$ N $= \boxed{16.15 \text{ N}}$

5.8   From MKS to CGS and English units:

(a) $1 \text{ N} = 1 \text{ kg} \cdot \text{m/s}^2 = (10^3 \text{ g})(10^2 \text{ cm})/\text{s}^2 = \boxed{10^5 \text{ dynes}}$

(b) $1 \text{ N} = 1 \text{ kg} \cdot \text{m/s}^2 = (\dfrac{2.2}{32} \text{ sl})\,(3.281 \text{ ft})/\text{s}^2 = \boxed{0.225 \text{ lb}}$

(For conversion tables, see inside cover of text.)

5.9   (a) $W = mg = 120 \text{ lb} = (4.448 \dfrac{\text{N}}{\text{lb}})(120 \text{ lb}) = \boxed{533.76 \text{ N}}$

(b) $m = \dfrac{W}{g} = \dfrac{533.76 \text{ N}}{9.81 \text{ m/s}^2} = \boxed{54.4 \text{ kg}}$

5.10 $W = (0.072)(25) \text{ N} = \boxed{1.8 \text{ N}}$

5.11 $W_{\text{moon}} = mg_{\text{moon}} = 115 \text{ N}$

$m = \dfrac{115 \text{ N}}{1.63 \text{ m/s}^2} = \boxed{70.5 \text{ kg}}$

5.12 $W = mg = 900 \text{ N}$

$m = \dfrac{900 \text{ N}}{9.81 \text{ m/s}^2} = 91.74 \text{ kg}$

$W_{\text{on Jupiter}} = (91.74 \text{ kg})(25.9 \text{ m/s}^2) = \boxed{2376 \text{ N}}$

5.13 $W_B = mg_B = 27 \text{ N}$

$m = \dfrac{27 \text{ N}}{(1.6)(9.81) \text{ m/s}^2} = 1.72 \text{ kg}$

$g_x = \dfrac{10 \text{ N}}{1.72 \text{ kg}} = \boxed{5.81 \text{ m/s}^2}$

5.14 (a) Hand pulls on spring. Spring, though it stretches, pulls back with equal force. Spring pulls on wall. Wall pulls back with equal force.

(b) For constant velocity, all forces are in balance.

(c) During the acceleration phase, the foot exerts a force $F = m_{\text{ball}}a$, on the football and the football exerts a force $F = m_{\text{ball}}a$ on the foot of the kicker.

(d) Equal and opposite forces. Note that the acceleration of the large mass is very much less than the acceleration of the small mass.

5.15

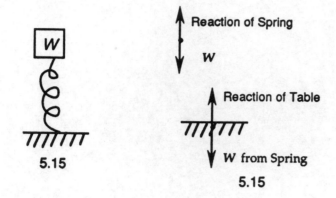

5.15   **W** from Spring

5.15

*5.16 $F = \sqrt{20^2 + 5^2} = 20.6$ N

$a = \dfrac{F}{m}$

$a = \boxed{5.15 \text{ m/s}^2 \text{ at } 14° \text{ S of E}}$

5.16

*5.17 $F = m_1 a_1 = (2 \text{ kg})(3 \text{ m/s}^2) = \boxed{6 \text{ N, East}}$

$m_2 = \dfrac{F}{a_2} = \dfrac{6 \text{ N}}{1 \text{ m/s}^2} = \boxed{6 \text{ kg}}$

5.18   (a) $\Sigma F = F_1 + F_2 = (20i + 15j)$ N

$\Sigma F = ma$, $20i + 15j = 5a$

$a = (4i + 3j)$ m/s^2 or $\boxed{a = 5 \text{ m/s}^2}$

$\theta = 36.9°$

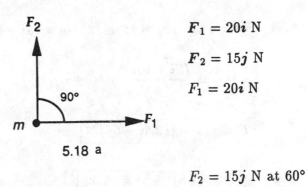

$F_1 = 20i$ N

$F_2 = 15j$ N

$F_1 = 20i$ N

5.18 a

(b) $F_{2x} = 15 \cos 60° = 7.5$ N

$F_2 = 15j$ N at $60°$

$F_{2y} = 15 \sin 60° = 13$ N

$F_2 = (7.5i + 13j)$ N

$\Sigma F = F_1 + F_2$

$\quad = (27.5i + 13j)$ N $= ma = 5a$

$a = (5.5i + 2.6j)$ m/s^2

or $\boxed{a = 6.08 \text{ m/s}^2}$ $\theta = 25.3°$

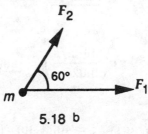

5.18 b

*5.19   (a) $a = \dfrac{\Delta v}{\Delta t} = \dfrac{(4-3) \text{ m/s}}{0.5 \text{ s}} = \boxed{2 \text{ m/s}^2}$

(b) $F = ma = (80 \text{ kg})(2 \text{ m/s}^2) = \boxed{160 \ \text{N}}$

(c) $a_2 = \dfrac{F}{m_2} = \dfrac{160 \text{ N}}{50 \text{ kg}} = \boxed{3.2 \text{ m/s}^2}$

5.20 $\Sigma F = ma$ $m = 9$ kg, $a = 2$ m/s^2 $\Sigma F = 18$ N (to the right)

$\Sigma F = F_1 + F_2$ $\therefore$ $F_2 = \boxed{7 \text{ N to the left}}$

5.21 $m = 4$ kg, $v_0 = 3i$ m/s, $v_8 = (8i + 10j)$ m/s, $t = 8$ s.

$$a = \frac{v}{t} = \frac{(5i + 10j)}{8} \text{ m/s}^2$$

$$F = ma = \boxed{(2.5i + 5j) \text{ N}}$$

$$F = \sqrt{(2.5)^2 + 5^2} = \boxed{5.59 \text{ N}}$$

*5.22 $F = ma = (0.5 \text{ kg})\left(\dfrac{30 \text{ m/s}}{0.025 \text{ s}}\right) = \boxed{600 \text{ N}}$

5.23 $a = 3$ ft/s^2, $(mg)_{\text{truck}} = 4000$ lb, $(mg)_{\text{trailer}} = 10,000$ lb

$$m = \frac{14,000}{32} \text{ sl}, \quad F = ma = \frac{42,000}{32} \text{ lb.} = \boxed{1312 \text{ lb}}$$

If $m = \dfrac{34,000}{32}$ sl, $a = \dfrac{F}{m} = \dfrac{42,000/32}{34,000/32} = \boxed{1.23 \text{ ft/s}^2}$

5.24 (a) $F = ma$ and $v^2 = v_0^2 + 2ax$ or $a = \dfrac{v^2 - v_o^2}{2x}$

Therefore

$$F = m\frac{(v^2 - v_o^2)}{2x}$$

$$= (9.1 \times 10^{-31} \text{ kg})\frac{[(7 \times 10^5 \text{ m/s})^2 - (3 \times 10^5 \text{ m/s})^2]}{(2)(0.05 \text{ m})} = \boxed{3.6 \times 10^{-18} \text{ N}}$$

(b) The weight of the electron is

$$W = mg = (9.1 \times 10^{-31} \text{ kg})(9.8 \text{ m/s}^2) = \boxed{8.9 \times 10^{-30} \text{ N}}$$

The accelerating force is approximately 4×10^{11} times the weight of the electron.

5.25 (a) $\boxed{15 \text{ lb}}$ (b) $\boxed{5 \text{ lb}}$ (c) $\boxed{0}$

5.26 (a) First construct a free body diagram for the 5 kg mass as shown in the figure to the right. Since the mass is in static equilibrium we can require $T_3 - 49\ \text{N} = 0$ or $T_3 = 49\ \text{N}$. Next construct a free body diagram for the knot as shown in the figure to the right. Again since the system is stationary, $a = 0$ and applying Newton's second law in component form gives $\Sigma F_x = T_2 \cos 50° - T_1 \cos 40° = 0$ $\Sigma F_y = T_2 \sin 50° + T_1 \sin 40° - 49\ \text{N} = 0.$ Solving the above equations simultaneously for T_1 and T_2 gives $\boxed{T_1 = 31.5\ \text{N}}$ and $\boxed{T_2 = 37.5\ \text{N}}$ and above we found $\boxed{T_3 = 49\ \text{N}}$

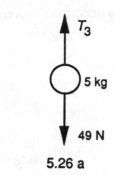

5.26 a

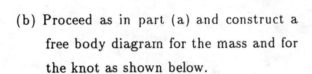

(b) Proceed as in part (a) and construct a free body diagram for the mass and for the knot as shown below.

Applying Newton's second law in each case (for a stationary system) we find:

$T_3 - 98\ \text{N} = 0$

$T_2 - T_1 \cos 60° = 0$

$T_1 \sin 60° - T_3 = 0$

Solving this set of equations we find:

$\boxed{T_1 = 113\ \text{N}}$ $\boxed{T_2 = 56.6\ \text{N}}$

and $\boxed{T_3 = 98\ \text{N}}$

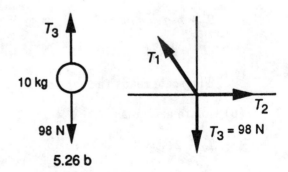

5.26 b

*5.27 Choosing a coordinate system with **i** East and **j** North,

$(5\ N)\mathbf{j} + \mathbf{F_2} = 10\ N\ \angle 30° = (5\ N)\mathbf{j} + (8.66\ N)\mathbf{i}$

$\therefore\ \mathbf{F_2} = 8.66\ N\ (East)$

5.28 $2F \sin 10° = 200\ N$

(a) $F = 575.8\ N$ each.

(b) No. An ∞ force is required.

*5.29

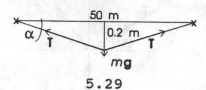

$$
\begin{aligned}
m &= 1\ kg \\
mg &= 9.8\ N \\
\tan\alpha &= \frac{0.2}{25}
\end{aligned}
$$

5.29

Balancing forces,

$2T \sin\alpha = mg$

$$T = \frac{9.8\ N}{2 \sin\alpha} = \boxed{613\ N}$$

5.30 (a) Isolate either mass

$\mathbf{T} + \mathbf{mg} = m\mathbf{a} = 0$

$|\mathbf{T}| = |\mathbf{mg}|$

The scale reads the tension T, so $T = mg = 5\ kg \times 9.8\ m/s^2 = \boxed{49\ N}$

(b) Isolate each mass

$\mathbf{T_2} + 2\mathbf{T_1} = 0$

$T_2 = 2|T_1| = 2mg = \boxed{98\ N}$

(c) $\Sigma \mathbf{F} = \mathbf{N} + \mathbf{T} + \mathbf{mg} = 0$

Take the x component

$N_x + T_x + mg_x = 0$ or $0 + T - mg \sin 30° = 0$

$T = mg \sin 30° = \dfrac{mg}{2} = \dfrac{(5)(9.80)}{2} = \boxed{24.5\ N}$

5.31 $T_1 \sin \theta + T_2 \sin \theta_2 = W$ (1)

$T_2 \cos \theta_1 = T_2 \cos \theta_2$ (2)

(a) Eliminate T_2 and solve for T_1.

$$\frac{T_1(\sin \theta_1 \cos \theta_2 + \cos \theta_1 \sin \theta_2)}{\cos \theta_2} = W$$

Solution follows from trigonometric identity.

(b) $T_3 = \boxed{200 \text{ N}}$ $T_1 = T_3 \dfrac{\cos 25°}{\sin 35°} = \boxed{316 \text{ N}}$ $T_2 = T_1 \dfrac{\cos 10°}{\cos 25°} = \boxed{343 \text{ N}}$

5.32 $m_{\text{suitcase}} = 20$ kg, $F = 35$ N

(a) $F \cos \theta = 20$ N

$$\cos \theta = \frac{20}{35} = 0.5714, \boxed{\theta = 55.15°}$$

(b) $N = W - F \sin \theta = [196 - 35(0.820)]$ N

$$\boxed{N = 167.3 \text{ N}}$$

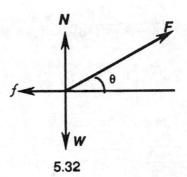

5.32

5.33 $W = 8820$ N, $g = 9.80$ m/s^2, $v_o = 55$ m/s, $v_f = 0$, $x_f - x_o = 1000$ m

$$m = \frac{W}{g} = \frac{8820 \text{ N}}{9.80 \text{ m/s}^2} = \boxed{900 \text{ kg}}$$

$\Sigma F = ma$

$v_f^2 = v_o^2 + 2a(x - x_o)$, $0 = 55^2 + 2a(1000)$ $a = -1.51$ m/s^2

$\Sigma F = ma = (900 \text{ kg})(-1.51 \text{ m/s}^2) = \boxed{-1.36 \times 10^3 \text{ N}}$

The minus sign means that the force is a retarding force.

5.34 $m = 0.12$ kg, $v_o = 400$ m/s, $x = 0.15$ m, $v_{\text{final}} = 0$

$$x = \overline{v}t, \quad a = \frac{\Delta v}{\Delta t}, \quad f = ma.$$

$$t = \frac{x}{\overline{v}} = \frac{0.15}{200} = 0.00075 \text{ s}$$

$$a = \frac{400 \text{ m/s}}{0.00075 \text{ s}} = -533,333 \text{ m/s}^2$$

$f = (0.012)(-533,333) \text{ N} = \boxed{-6400 \text{ N}}$ (acting to slow the bullet.)

*5.35   At constant deceleration, the time necessary to stop the car is dist/avg velocity:

$$t = \frac{80 \text{ m}}{10 \text{ m/s}} = 8 \text{ s}$$

(a) Therefore, the (negative) acceleration of the car is

$$a = \frac{\Delta v}{\Delta t} = \frac{-20 \text{ m/s}}{8 \text{ s}} = \boxed{-2.5 \text{ m/s}^2}$$

(b) The magnitude of the force is $F = ma = \left|(1000\text{kg})(-2.5 \text{ m/s}^2)\right| = \boxed{2500 \text{ N}}$, opposite to **v**.

*5.36 $R = \sqrt{(390)^2 + (180)^2} = 429.5 \text{ N}$

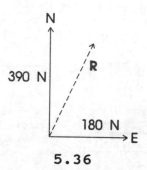

at $\theta = \tan^{-1}\left(\dfrac{390}{180}\right) = 65.2°$ North of East.

The acceleration of the boat is

$$a = \frac{R}{m} = \frac{429.5 \text{ N}}{270 \text{ kg}} = \boxed{1.59 \text{ m/s}^2} \text{ at } 65.2° \text{ N of E.}$$

5.36

5.37 $T - m_1 g = m_1 a$ (1)   Forces acting on 2 kg block

$F_x - T = m_2 a$ (2)   Forces acting on 8 kg block

(a) Eliminate T and solve for a.

$$a = \frac{F_x - m_1 g}{m_1 + m_2} \quad a > 0 \text{ for } F_x > m_1 g$$

(b) Eliminate a and solve for T.

$$T = \frac{m_1}{m_1 + m_2}(F_x + m_2 g) \quad T = 0 \text{ for } F_x < -m_2 g$$

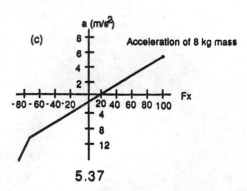

5.37

5.38   Applying Newton's second law to each block (motion along the x−axis.)

For $m_2 : \Sigma F = F - T = m_2 a$.   For $m_1 : \Sigma F = T = m_1 a$

Solving these equations for a and T we find

$$a = \frac{F}{m_1 + m_2} \quad \text{and} \quad T = \frac{F m_1}{m_1 + m_2}$$

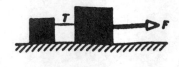

5.38

5.39 $m_1 = 3$ kg, $m_2 = 5$ kg

$T - m_1 g = m_1 a \qquad m_2 g - T = m_2 a$

(a) Eliminate a, solve for $\boxed{T = 36.8 \text{ N}}$

(b) Eliminate T, solve for $\boxed{a = 2.45 \text{ m/s}^2}$

(c) $x = \dfrac{1}{2}at^2$, At $t = 1$ s, $\boxed{x = 1.23 \text{ m}}$

5.40 The two forces acting on the block are the normal force, N and the weight, mg. If the block is considered to be a point mass and the x-axis is chosen to be parallel to the plane then the free body diagram will be as shown in the figure to the right. The angle θ is the angle of inclination of the plane. Applying Newton's second law for the accelerating system (and taking the direction of motion as the positive direction) we have

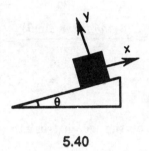

5.40

$\Sigma F_y = N - mg \cos \theta = 0; \quad N = mg \cos \theta$

$\Sigma F_x = mg \sin \theta = ma; \quad a = g \sin \theta$

(a) When $\theta = 15°$ $a = \boxed{2.54 \text{ m/s}^2}$

(b) Starting from rest

$v^2 = v_o^2 + 2ax$

$v = \sqrt{(2ax)} = \sqrt{(2)(2.54\text{m/s}^2)(2\text{m})} = \boxed{3.18 \text{ m/s}}$

5.41 $v^2 = v_o^2 + 2ax$

Taking $v = 0$, $v_o = 5$ m/s, and $a = -g\sin(20)$ gives

$0 = 5^2 - 2(9.80)\sin(20)x$ or,

$x = \dfrac{25}{2(9.80)\sin(20)} = \boxed{3.73 \text{ m}}$

5.41

5.42 Following Example 5.5, and using Equations (5) and (6) with $m_1 = 2$ kg, $m_2 = 6$ kg and $\theta = 55°$ gives

(a) $a = \dfrac{m_2 g \sin\theta - m_1 g}{m_1 + m_2} = \boxed{3.57 \text{ m/s}^2}$ (down the incline)

(b) $T = \dfrac{m_1 m_2 g(1 + \sin\theta)}{m_1 + m_2} = \boxed{26.7 \text{ N}}$

(c) Since $v_o = 0$, $v = at = (3.57 \text{ m/s}^2)(2 \text{ s}) = \boxed{7.14 \text{ m/s}}$

5.43 Let F_N be the weight registered by the scale.

(a) Before the elevator moves it registers

$F_N = mg = (72 \text{ kg})(9.8 \text{ m/s}^2) = \boxed{706 \text{ N}}$.

(b) During the first 0.8 s: $F = ma$, i. e. $F_N - mg = ma$

$a = \dfrac{v - v_o}{t} = \dfrac{1.2 \text{ m/s}}{0.8 \text{ s}} = 1.5 \text{ m/s}^2$

and $F_N = m(g + a) = (72 \text{ kg})(9.8 \text{ m/s}^2 + 1.5 \text{ m/s}^2) = \boxed{814 \text{ N}}$

(c) At constant speed,

$F_N - mg = ma = 0$. so $F_N = mg = \boxed{706 \text{ N}}$.

(d) While slowing down the acceleration is given by

$v = v_o + at$ or $a = \dfrac{v - v_o}{t} = \dfrac{0 - 1.2}{1.5} = -0.8 \text{ m/s}^2$

$F = ma$ i. e. $F_N - mg = ma$

$F_N - 706 \text{ N} = -(72)(0.8)$

$F_N = \boxed{648 \text{ N}}$

5.44 $\quad v_x = \dfrac{dx}{dt} = 5(2t), \quad v_y = \dfrac{dy}{dt} = 3(3t^2)$

$\quad a_x = \dfrac{dv_x}{dt} = 10 \quad, a_y = \dfrac{dv_y}{dt} = 18t$

At $t = 2.0$ s, $\quad a_x = 10$ m/s^2, $\quad a_y = 36$ m/s^2

$F_x = ma_x = (3 \text{ kg})(10 \text{ m/s}^2) = 30$ N

$F_y = ma_y = (3 \text{ kg})(36 \text{ m/s}^2) = 108$ N

$F = \sqrt{F_x^2 + F_y^2} = \boxed{112 \text{ N}}$

5.45 $\quad a_x = \dfrac{F_x}{m} = 2.5 + t^3 \qquad a_x = \dfrac{dv_x}{dt}$

$\Delta v_x = \displaystyle\int_0^t a_x dt = \int_0^4 (2.5 + t^3)dt$

$\Delta v_x = 2.5t \big|_0^4 + \dfrac{1}{4}t^4 \big|_0^4 = 74$ m/s

Since $v_o = 0, \quad v_f = \boxed{74 \text{ m/s}}$

5.46   (a) Pulley P has acceleration a_2.

Since m_1 moves *twice* the distance P does in the same time it has twice the acceleration of P.   i. e. , $a_1 = 2a_2$

(b) From the figure, and using $F = ma$:

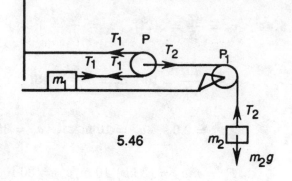

5.46

$$m_2g - T_2 = m_2a_2 \qquad\qquad (1)$$

$$T_1 = m_1a_1 = 2m_1a_2 \qquad\qquad (2)$$

$$T_2 - 2T_1 = 0. \qquad\qquad (3)$$

Eq. (1) becomes $m_2g - 2T_1 = m_2a_2$

This equation, combined with Eq. (2) yields

$$\frac{2T_1}{m_1}(m_1 + m_2) = m_2g$$

$$T_1 = \frac{m_1 m_2}{2m_1 + \frac{1}{2}m_2}g \quad \text{and} \quad T_2 = \frac{m_1 m_2}{m_1 + \frac{1}{4}m_2}g$$

(c) From the values of T_1 and T_2 we find that

$$a_1 = \frac{T_1}{m_1} = \frac{m_2g}{2m_1 + \frac{1}{2}m_2}$$

$$a_2 = \frac{1}{2}a_1 = \frac{m_2g}{4m_1 + m_2}$$

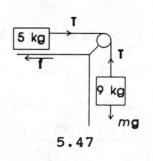

5.47

$$T - F_f = 5a \quad \text{(for 5 kg mass)}$$
$$mg - T = 9a \quad \text{(for 9 kg mass)}$$

[ADD THESE EQUATIONS]

$$9(9.8) - 0.2(5)(9.8) = 14a$$
$$a = 5.6 \text{ m/s}^2$$
$$\therefore T = 5(5.6) + 0.2(5)(9.8) = \boxed{37.8 \ N}$$

5.47

5.48   For equilibrium: $f = F$ and $N = W$.

Also $f = \mu N$

i. e. $\mu = \dfrac{f}{N} = \dfrac{F}{W}$

$$\mu_s = \frac{75 \text{ N}}{(25)(9.8) \text{ N}}, \quad \text{and} \quad \mu_k = \frac{60 \text{ N}}{(25)(9.8) \text{ N}}$$

$$\mu_s = \boxed{0.306} \qquad\qquad \mu_k = \boxed{0.245}$$

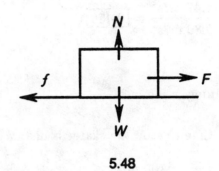

5.48

*5.49 $F = ma = \mu mg$ (acceleration comes from the tires pushing against the road.)

If $\mu = 1$, then $a = g = 9.8 \text{ m/s}^2$ and, from Eq. 3.11,

$$v^2 - 0^2 = 2ax = 2(9.8)(400)$$
$$\therefore v = \boxed{88.5 \text{ m/s}} \quad \text{(about 200 mph)}$$

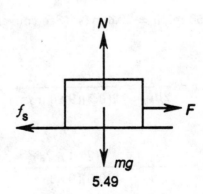

5.49

5.50 $F = \mu N = ma$ and in this case the normal force $N = mg$ therefore

$F = \mu mg = ma$ or $\mu = \dfrac{a}{g}$

The acceleration is found from

$a = \dfrac{(v - v_o)}{t} = \dfrac{(80 \text{ mi/h})(0.447 \text{ m/s/mi/h})}{8 \text{ s}} = 4.47 \text{ m/s}^2$

Substituting this value into the expression for μ we find

$\mu = \dfrac{4.47 \text{ m/s}^2}{9.80 \text{ m/s}^2} = \boxed{0.456}$

*5.51 $f = \mu mg = ma = m\dfrac{\Delta v}{\Delta t}$

The time to stop the skater is distance/avg velocity:

$t = \dfrac{100 \text{ m}}{5 \text{ m/s}} = 20 \text{ s.}$

$\therefore \mu = \dfrac{\Delta v}{g\Delta t} = \dfrac{10 \text{ m/s}}{(9.8 \text{ m/s}^2)(20 \text{ s})} = \boxed{0.051}$

5.52 $v = 50 \text{ mi/h} = 22.4 \text{ m/s}$. (See conversions in back of text.) Following Example 5.9,

(a) $x = \dfrac{v_0^2}{2\mu_k g} = \dfrac{(22.4 \text{ m/s})^2}{2(0.1)(9.80 \text{ m/s}^2)} = \boxed{256 \text{ m}}$

(b) $x = \dfrac{v_0^2}{2\mu_k g} = \dfrac{(22.4 \text{ m/s})^2}{2(0.6)(9.80 \text{ m/s}^2)} = \boxed{42.7 \text{ m}}$

(c) Since $\mu_s > \mu_k$, you would want to take advantage of 'static' friction to bring the car to rest. Slamming the brakes causes the wheels to lock, so that kinetic friction will prevail.

5.53 $W = 60$ N

$\theta = 15°$

$\phi = 35°$

$F = 2.5$ N

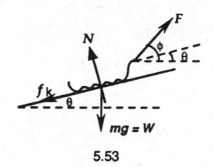

5.53

(a) The sled is in equilibrium on the plane.

Resolving along the plane: $F\cos(\phi - \theta) = mg\sin\theta + f_k$.

Resolving $\perp$ plane: $N + F\sin(\phi - \theta) = mg\cos\theta$. Also $f_k = \mu_k N$

$F\cos(\phi - \theta) - mg\sin\theta = \mu_k[mg\cos\theta - F\sin(\phi - \theta)]$

$2.5\cos 20° - 60\sin 15° = \mu_k(60\cos 15° - 2.5\sin 20°)$ $\mu_k = \boxed{0.161}$

(b) Resolving $\perp$ to the plane: $N = mg\cos\theta$ Along the plane we have $F = ma$

$mg\sin\theta - f_k = ma = \dfrac{W}{g}a$. Also $f_k = \mu_k N = \mu_k mg\cos\theta$. So along the plane

we have $mg\sin\theta - \mu_k\, mg\cos\theta = ma$

$a = g(\sin\theta - \mu_k\cos\theta) = (9.8\text{ m/s}^2)(\sin 15° - 0.16\cos 15°) = \boxed{1.01\text{ m/s}^2}$

5.54   (a) ΣF (along incline) $= 15 - W\cos(45°) - f_k = 0$ (1)

ΣF (perpendicular to incline) $=\ N - W\sin(45°) = 0$

Also, $f_k = \mu_k N = (0.3)W\sin(45°) = 0.212W$

Using this in Eq. (1) gives

$15 - 0.707W - 0.212W = 0$ $W = \boxed{16.3\text{ N}}$

(b) ΣF (along incline) $= F - W\cos(45) + f_k = 0$ or

$F = 16.3\cos(45°) - 0.212(16.3) = \boxed{8.07\text{ N}}$

5.55 (a) $\Sigma F_x(m_1) = T - f_1 = m_1 a \quad \Sigma F_x(m_2) = 50 - T - f_2 = m_2 a$

$\Sigma F_y(m_1) = N_1 - m_1 g = 0 \quad \Sigma F_y(m_2) = N_2 - m_2 g = 0$

$f_1 = \mu_1 N_1 = (0.1)(10 \text{ kg})(9.80 \text{ m/s}^2) = 9.80 \text{ N}$

$f_2 = \mu_2 N_2 = (0.1)(20 \text{ kg})(9.80 \text{ m/s}^2) = 19.6 \text{ N}$

$T - 9.8 = 10a, \quad 50 - T - 19.6 = 20a$

Adding $50 - 29.4 = 30a,$

$a = \boxed{0.687 \text{ m/s}^2} \qquad T = 10a + 9.80 = \boxed{16.7 \text{ N}}$

*5.56 The child accelerates by pushing against the ice with a force

$F = \mu m g = m a$

$a = \mu g = (0.05)(9.8) = 0.49 \text{ m/s}^2$

The time to traverse 12 m at this acceleration is found from

$x = \frac{1}{2} a t^2$

$12 \text{ m} = \frac{1}{2}(0.49)t^2$

$\boxed{t = 7.0 \text{ s}}$

5.57 $m = 3 \text{ kg}, \quad \theta = 30°, \quad x = 2 \text{ m}, \quad t = 1.5 \text{ s}$

(a) $x = \frac{1}{2} a t^2 \quad 2 \text{ m} = \frac{1}{2} a (1.5 \text{ s})^2 \longrightarrow a = \frac{4}{1.5^2} = \boxed{1.78 \text{ m/s}^2}$

$\Sigma F = N + f + mg = ma$

$x: \quad 0 - f + mg \sin 30° = ma \longrightarrow f = m(g \sin 30° - a)$

$y: \quad N + 0 - mg \cos 30° = 0 \longrightarrow N = mg \cos 30°$

(b) $\mu_k = \frac{f}{N} = \frac{m(g \sin 30° - a)}{mg \cos 30°} = \tan 30° - \frac{a}{g(\cos 30°)} = \boxed{0.368}$

(c) $f = m(g \sin 30° - a) = (3)(9.80 \sin 30° - 1.78) = \boxed{9.37 \text{ N}}$

(d) $v^2 = v_o^2 + 2a(x - x_o)$ where $x - x_o = 2 \text{ m}$

$v^2 = 0 + 2(1.78)(2) = 7.11 \text{ m}^2/\text{s}^2 \longrightarrow v = \sqrt{7.11 \text{ m}^2/\text{s}^2} = \boxed{2.67 \text{ m/s}}$

5.58 (a) ΣF (along incline) $= Mg\sin\theta - f_k = Ma$ (1)

ΣF (perpendicular to incline) $= Mg\cos\theta - N = 0$

Also, $f_k = \mu_k N = \mu_k Mg\cos\theta$.   Hence, (1) becomes

$Ma = Mg\sin\theta - \mu_k Mg\cos\theta$

$a = g(\sin\theta - \mu_k\cos\theta)$

(b) In this case, (1) becomes $Mg\sin\theta + f_k = -Ma$

and we find $a = -g(\sin\theta + \mu_k\cos\theta)$

(The negative sign for a indicates that the block is decelerating.)

5.59 Following Example 5.8, we have

$\mu_s = \tan\theta_c = \tan(36) = \boxed{0.727}$

$\mu_k = \tan\theta_{c'} = \tan(30) = \boxed{0.577}$

5.60 (a) The crate is in equilibrium.

Let the normal force acting on it be N and the friction force, f_s.

Resolving vertically : $N = W + F\sin\phi$

Horizontally : $F\cos\phi = f_s$

But $f_s \le \mu_s N$

i. e. , $F\cos\phi \le \mu_s(W + F\sin\phi)$

or $F(\cos\phi - \mu_s\sin\phi) \le \mu_s W$

Divide by $\cos\phi$: $F(1 - \mu_s\tan\phi) \le \mu_s W\sec\phi$

Then $F_{(minimum)} = \dfrac{\mu_s W\sec\phi}{1 - \mu_s\tan\phi}$

(b) $F = \dfrac{0.4(100\ N)\sec\phi}{1 - 0.4\tan\phi}$

ϕ	$F(N)$
0°	40
15°	46.4
30°	60.1
45°	94.3
60°	260.4

*5.61 $mg\ \cos 30° - f = ma$

$mg\ \cos 30° = \mu mg \sin 30° = m\frac{g}{2}$

$\cos 30° - \mu\ \sin 30° = \frac{1}{2}$

$\mu = \left(\cos 30° - \frac{1}{2}\right)/(\sin 30°) = \boxed{0.732}$

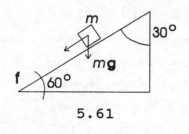

5.61

*5.62   The crate, of mass m, does not slide until $ma \geq \mu mg$. If $\mu = 0.4$, then the deceleration of the truck may not exceed $a = (0.4)(9.8) = 3.92$ m/s^2, and the distance travelled is $x = v_0 t - \frac{1}{2}at^2$ where $t = \frac{v_0}{a} = 3.82$ s.

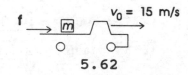

5.62

$\therefore\ x = \frac{v_0^2}{2a} = \frac{(15\ \text{m/s})^2}{2(3.92\ \text{m/s}^2)} = \boxed{28.7\ \text{m}}$

*5.63 $mg\ \sin 30° - \mu\ mg \cos 30° = ma$

If $\mu = 0.74$, then $a = g \sin 30° - 0.74 g \cos 30° = -1.38$ m/s^2

At constant deceleration, the distance travelled down the slope is

$$x\ =\ \bar{v}t$$

where $t\ =\ \dfrac{v_0}{a} = \dfrac{20\ \text{m/s}}{1.38\ \text{m/s}^2} = 14.49$ s.

$\therefore\ x\ =\ \bar{v}t = (10\ \text{m/s})(14.5\ \text{s}) = \boxed{145\ \text{m}}$

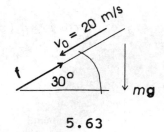

5.63

*5.64 Using Eq. 3.11, with $a = \dfrac{F_f}{m} = \dfrac{\mu mg}{m} = \mu g$

For car # 1

$$0^2 - (20 \text{ m/s})^2 = 2(0.75)(9.8 \text{ m/s}^2)x_1$$

$$x_1 = 27.21 \text{ m}$$

For car # 2, while braking

$$0^2 - (30 \text{ m/s})^2 = 2(0.75)(9.8 \text{ m/s}^2)x_2$$

$$x_2 = 61.22 \text{ m}$$

Because car # 2 has a 0.1 s delay, the total distance travelled by # 2 is

$x_2 + (30 \text{ m/s})(.1 \text{ s}) = 64.22 \text{ m}$

$\Delta x = (64.22 - 27.21)\text{m} = \boxed{37.0 \text{ m}}$ is the minimum separation.

5.65 Draw free body diagrams and apply Newton's 2nd law.

$\Sigma F = 0 = T_5 - mg, \quad T_5 = mg$

Assume frictionless pulleys

$T_1 = T_2 = T_3 \quad \Sigma F = 0 = T_2 + T_3 - T_5$

$2T_2 = T_5 \quad T_2 = \dfrac{T_5}{2} \quad T_1 = T_2 = T_3 = \dfrac{mg}{2}$

$F_A = T_1 = \dfrac{mg}{2}$

$\Sigma F = 0 = T_4 - T_1 - T_2 - T_3$

$T_4 = T_1 + T_2 + T_3 = \dfrac{3mg}{2}$

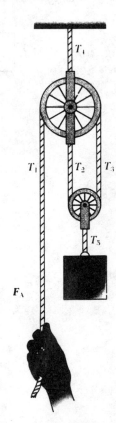

5.65

5.66 $\Sigma F = 0 = T_A - 3T$

$T_A = 3T$

$T_A = 3W$

Maximum T_A can be is 240 lb

$3W = 1200$ lb

"Big" Al cannot raise the safe.

The maximum weight "Big" Al can raise is slightly less than

$W = \dfrac{T_A}{3} = \boxed{80 \text{ lb}}$

5.67 $v_f^2 = 2ax = 2x(\dfrac{F}{m})$

$F = \dfrac{mv_f^2}{2x} = \boxed{1.66 \times 10^6 \text{ N}}$

*5.68   Resistance to sliding is $f = \mu mg$

and the weight $W = Mg$

At the point of slipping, $\mu mg = Mg$, $\boxed{\mu = \dfrac{M}{m}}$

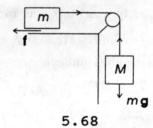

5.68

5.69   (a) $F = ma$; $18 = (2 + 3 + 4)a$; $a = \boxed{2 \text{ m/s}^2}$

(b) The force on each block can be found by knowing mass and

acceleration:

$$F_1 = m_1 a = 2(2) = \boxed{4 \text{ N}}$$

$$F_2 = m_2 a = 3(2) = \boxed{6 \text{ N}}$$

$$F_3 = m_3 a = 4(2) = \boxed{8 \text{ N}}$$

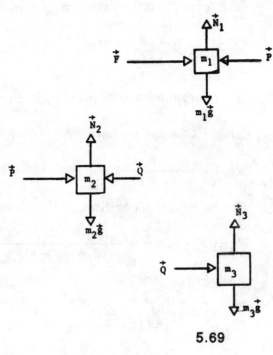

(c) The force on each block is the

resultant of all contact forces.

Therefore $F_1 = 4 \text{ N} = F - P$

$$P = \boxed{14 \text{ N}}$$

$$F_2 = 6 \text{ N} = P - Q$$

$$Q = \boxed{8 \text{ N}}$$

5.69

5.70   (a) $F - \mu mg = ma$

$$18 - (2 + 3 + 4)(9.8)(0.1) = (2 + 3 + 4)a$$

therefore $a = \boxed{1.02 \text{ m/s}^2}$

(b) $F_1 = m_1 a = \boxed{2.04 \text{ N}}$

$$F_2 = m_2 a = \boxed{3.06 \text{ N}}$$

$$F_3 = m_3 a = \boxed{4.08 \text{ N}}$$

(c) $18 - F_{12} - 2(9.80)(0.1) = 2.04$ $F_{12} = \boxed{14 \text{ N}}$

$$F_{12} - F_{23} - 3(9.80)(0.1) = 3.06$$ $F_{23} = \boxed{8 \text{ N}}$

5.71 (a) Force exerted on tractor by ground is F. The reaction to the force that the tractor exerts on the ground, is a force of magnitude F, directed to the right.

(b) Normal force on each driving wheel $N = \frac{1}{3}Mg$

The force of static friction $= \frac{F}{2} \leq \mu_s N$ i. e., $F \leq 2\mu_s \frac{Mg}{3}$ so that

$$\mu_s \leq g\mu_s \geq \frac{3}{2}\frac{F}{Mg}.$$

Therefore the least values of μ_s is $\frac{3F}{2Mg}$

(c) Using $F_{\text{net}} = ma$ we have $F = (M + m_1 + m_2 + m_3)a$ or

$$a = \frac{F}{M + m_1 + m_2 + m_3}$$

(d) $F = ma$ for M alone gives $F - T_3 = Ma$ (1)

$$T_3 = F - Ma = F - \frac{MF}{M + m_1 + m_2 + m_3}$$

$$T_3 = \frac{F(m_1 + m_2 + m_3)}{M + m_1 + m_2 + m_3}$$

On m_3: $T_3 - T_2 = m_3 a$ or $T_2 = T_3 - m_3 a = F$

From Eq. (1) this becomes

$$T_2 = F - Ma - m_3 a = F - \frac{(M + m_3)F}{M + m_1 + m_2 + m_3} = \frac{(m_1 + m_2)F}{M + m_1 + m_2 + m_3}$$

Similarly; for $m_1, T_1 = m_1 a$

$$T_1 = \frac{m_1 F}{M + m_1 + m_2 + m_3}$$

(e) The net force on m_2 is $T_2 - T_1$

$$T_2 - T_1 = \frac{(m_1 + m_2)F - m_1 F}{M + m_1 + m_2 + m_3} = \frac{m_2 F}{M + m_1 + m_2 + m_3}$$

*5.72 It is impossible.

By Newton's third law, as you pull harder on the rope, you push harder on the platform.

5.73   (a) The force of static friction between the blocks
accelerates the 2 kg block.

(b) $\Sigma F = ma$,

$F - \mu N_2 = ma$,

$F - (0.2)[(5+2)(9.80)] = (5+2)3$

therefore $F = \boxed{34.7 \text{ N}}$

(c) $f = \mu_1(2)(9.80) = m_1 a = 2(3)$

therefore $\mu = \boxed{0.306}$

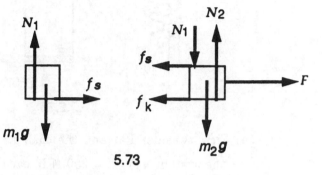

5.73

5.74   (a)

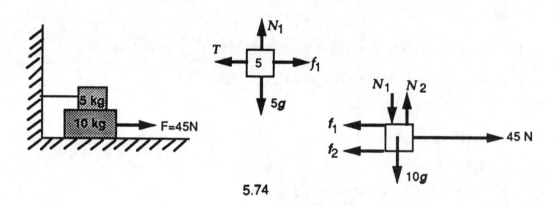

5.74

(b) 5 kg : $\Sigma F_x = ma$ $N_1 = 5g = 5(9.80) = 49 \text{ N}$ $f_1 - T = 0$

$T = f_1 = \mu mg = (0.2)(5)(9.80) = \boxed{9.8 \text{ N}}$

10 kg : $\Sigma F_x = ma$ $\Sigma F_y = 0$

$45 - f_1 - f_2 = 10a$ $N_2 - N_1 - 10g = 0$

$f_2 = \mu N_2 = \mu(N_1 + 10g) = (0.2)(49 + 98) = 29.4 \text{ N}$

$45 - 9.8 - 29.4 = 10a$

$a = \boxed{0.58 \text{ m/s}^2}$

5.75 (a)

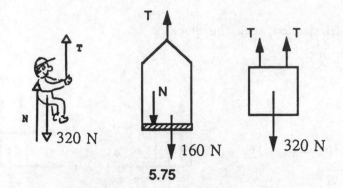

320 N   160 N   320 N

5.75

(b) First consider Pat and the chair as the system. Note that *two* ropes support the system, and $T = 250$ N in each rope. Applying $\Sigma F = ma$

$2T - 480 = ma$ where $m = \dfrac{480}{9.80} = 49.0$ kg

Solving for a gives $a = \dfrac{(500 - 480)}{49} = \boxed{0.408 \text{ m/s}^2}$

(c) $\Sigma F(\text{on Pat}) = N + T - 320 = ma$ where $m = \dfrac{320}{9.80} = 32.7$ kg

$N = ma + 320 - T = 32.7(0.408) + 320 - 250 = \boxed{83.3 \text{ N}}$

*5.76 The forces acting on the sled are

(a) $\quad T - F_f = ma$

$T - 500 \text{ N} = (100 \text{ kg})(1 \text{ m/s}^2)$

$T = \boxed{600 \text{ N}}$

(b) Frictional force pushes the horse forward.

$T_{\text{horse}} - T = m_{\text{horse}}a$

$f - 600 \text{ N} = (500 \text{ kg})(1 \text{ m/s}^2)$

$f = \boxed{1110 \text{ N}}$

(c) $f - F_f = 600 \text{ N}$

$\sum m = 100 \text{ kg} + 500 \text{ kg}$

$a = \dfrac{\sum F}{\sum m} = \dfrac{600 \text{ N}}{600 \text{ kg}} = \boxed{1 \text{ m/s}^2}$

*5.77 $mg \sin 45° - \sigma x(mg)\cos 45° = ma$

$$a = \frac{dv}{dt} = g\sin 45° - g\sigma x\cos 45°$$

$$\frac{dv}{dt} = \frac{dv}{dx}\frac{dx}{dt} = v\frac{dv}{dx} = 0.707g - 0.707g\sigma x$$

Integrating,

$$\int_{v=0}^{v} v\,dv = \int_{x=0}^{x} 0.707g\,dx - 0.707\int_{x=0}^{x} g\sigma x\,dx$$

$$\frac{v^2}{2} = 0.707g\left[x - \sigma\frac{x^2}{2}\right]$$

(a) $v = 0$ when $x = \dfrac{2}{\sigma} = \boxed{4\text{ m}}$

(b) v is maximum when $a = 0$, when $0.707g = 0.707g\sigma x$, when $x = 2$ m.

At that point,

$$v_{max}^2 = 1.404\,g[2 - 1]$$

$$v_{max} = \boxed{3.72\text{ m/s}}$$

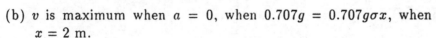

5.77

5.78

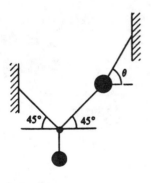

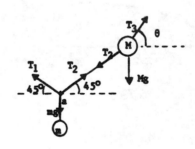

5.78

At point a:

$\Sigma F_x = 0;\quad T_2\cos 45 - T_1\cos 45 = 0$

$\Sigma F_y = 0;\quad (T_1 + T_2)\sin 45 - mg = 0$

At point b:

$\Sigma F_x = 0;\quad -T_2\cos 45 + T_3\cos\theta = 0$

$\Sigma F_y = 0;\quad T_3\sin\theta - Mg - T_2\sin 45 = 0$

Solving the above gives $T_2 = T_1 = \dfrac{mg}{2\sin 45°}$

$\tan\theta = 1 + \dfrac{Mg}{T_2\cos 45°} = 1 + \dfrac{2M}{m}$ since $\cos 45° = \sin 45°$.

5.79   (a) Let T be the tension in the wire. Then

since the wire is continuous, $T = W$. For

equilibrium $T\cos\phi + F\sin\theta = W$ and

$T\sin\phi = F\cos\theta$. Since $T = W$ these

equations give

$$\frac{F}{W} = \frac{1 - \cos\phi}{\sin\theta} = \frac{\sin\phi}{\cos\theta}$$

$$\cos\theta = \cos\theta\cos\phi + \sin\theta\sin\phi = \cos(\phi - \theta)$$

i. e. , $\theta = \phi - \theta \quad 2\theta = \phi.$

(b) $F = \dfrac{W\sin\phi}{\cos\theta} = \dfrac{W\sin\phi}{\cos\phi/2}$

$$= \frac{2W\sin\frac{\phi}{2}\cos\frac{\phi}{2}}{\cos\frac{\phi}{2}} = 2W\sin\frac{\phi}{2}$$

(c)

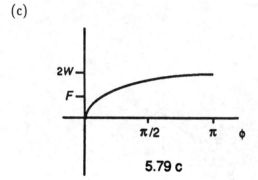

5.79 c

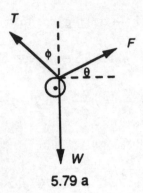

5.79 a

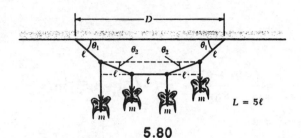

5.80

5.80

Apply Newton's 2nd law to two points where butterflies are attached on either half of mobile (other half redundant)

(1) $T_2 \cos\theta_2 - T_1 \cos\theta_1 = 0$

(2) $T_1 \sin\theta_1 - T_2 \sin\theta_2 - mg = 0$

(3) $T_2 \cos\theta_2 - T_3 = 0$

(4) $T_2 \sin\theta_2 - mg = 0$

Substitute (4) into (2) for $T_2 \sin\theta_2$ $T_1 \sin\theta_1 - mg - mg = 0$

then $T_1 = \dfrac{2mg}{\sin\theta_1}$

Substitute (3) into (1) for $T_2 \cos\theta_2$ $T_3 - T_1 \cos\theta_1 = 0$, $T_3 = T_1 \cos\theta_1$

Substitute value of T_1; $T_3 = 2mg\dfrac{\cos\theta_1}{\sin\theta_1} = \dfrac{2mg}{\tan\theta_1}$

From Eq. (4), $T_2 = \dfrac{mg}{\sin\theta_2}$

(b) We must find θ_2 and substitute for $\theta_2 : T_2 = \dfrac{mg}{\sin[\tan^{-1}(1/2\tan\theta_1)]}$

divide (4) by (3);

$\dfrac{T_2 \sin\theta_2}{T_2 \cos\theta_2} = \dfrac{mg}{T_3} \implies \tan\theta_2 = \dfrac{mg}{T_3}$

Substitute value of $T_3 \implies \tan\theta_2 = \dfrac{mg\tan\theta_1}{2mg}$

$\theta_2 = \tan^{-1}(\dfrac{\tan\theta_1}{2})$

(c) D is the total horizontal displacement of each string

$D = 2l \cos\theta_1 + 2l \cos\theta_2 + l$ and $L = 5l$

$D = \dfrac{L}{5}\{2\cos\theta_1 + 2\cos[\tan^{-1}(\dfrac{1}{2}\tan\theta_1)] + 1\}$

5.81   (a) $\Sigma \mathbf{F} = \mathbf{F}_1 + \mathbf{F}_2 = (-9\mathbf{i} + 3\mathbf{j})$ N

Acceleration $\mathbf{a} = a_x\mathbf{i} + a_y\mathbf{j} = \dfrac{\mathbf{F}}{m} = \dfrac{(-9\mathbf{i} + 3\mathbf{j}) \text{ N}}{2 \text{ kg}} = (-4.5\mathbf{i} + 1.5\mathbf{j}) \text{ m/s}^2.$

Velocity $\mathbf{v} = v_x\mathbf{i} + v_y\mathbf{j} = \mathbf{v}_o + \mathbf{a}t = \mathbf{a}t$

$\mathbf{v} = (-4.5\mathbf{i} + 1.5\mathbf{j})(\text{m/s}^2)(10 \text{ s}) = \boxed{(-45\mathbf{i} + 15\mathbf{j}) \text{ m/s}}$

(b) The direction of motion makes angle θ with the

x–direction. $\theta = \tan^{-1}(\dfrac{v_y}{v_x}) = \tan^{-1}(-\dfrac{15 \text{ m/s}}{45 \text{ m/s}})$

$\theta = -18.4° + 180° = \boxed{162° \text{ from } +x \text{ axis}}$

(c) Displacement: $x - displacement$

$= x - x_o = v_{ox}t + \dfrac{1}{2}a_x t^2 = (\dfrac{1}{2})(-4.5 \text{ m/s}^2)(10s)^2 = -225 \text{ m}$

$y - displacement = y - y_o = v_{yo}t + \dfrac{1}{2}a_y t^2 = \dfrac{1}{2}(+1.5 \text{ m/s}^2)(10 \text{ s})^2 = +75 \text{ m}$

$\Delta r = \boxed{(-225i + 75j) \text{ m}}$

(d) Position: $\equiv r = r_1 + \Delta r$

$r = (-2i + 4j) + (-225i + 75j) = (-227i + 79j) \text{ m}$

*5.82 $a' = g \sin \theta = (9.8 \text{ m/s}^2)\left(\dfrac{1.774}{127.1}\right) = 13.7 \text{ cm/s}^2$

a is found from $\dfrac{x}{\sin \theta} = \dfrac{1}{2}at^2$

$\boxed{\bar{a}_{\text{AVG}} = 14.4 \text{ cm/s}^2}$

$\boxed{a' = 13.7 \text{ cm/s}^2}$

the % difference is 6.1%.

5.83 Note that m_2 should be in *contact* with the cart.

$\Sigma F = ma$

For $m_1 : T = m_1 a \qquad a = \dfrac{m_2 g}{m_1}$

For $m_2 : T - m_2 g = 0$

For all 3 blocks : $F = (M + m_1 + m_2)a = (M + m_1 + m_2)(\dfrac{m_2 g}{m_1})$

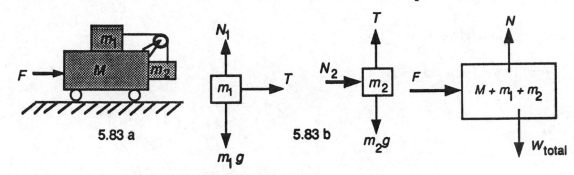

5.83 a   **5.83 b**

5.84 (1) $m_1(a - A) = T \Longrightarrow a = T/m_1 + A$

(2) $MA = R_x = T \Longrightarrow A = T/M$

(3) $m_2 a = m_2 g - T \Longrightarrow T = m_2(g - a)$

(a) Substitute the value for a from (1) into (3) and solve for T;

$T = m_2[g - (T/m_1 + A)]$

Substitute for A from (2);

$T = m_2[g - (\dfrac{T}{m_1} + \dfrac{T}{M})] = m_2 g[\dfrac{m_1 M}{m_1 M + m_2(m_1 + M)}]$

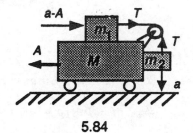

5.84

(b) Solve (3) for a and substitute value of T

$a = \dfrac{m_2 g(M + m_1)}{m_1 M + m_2(M + m_1)}$

(c) From (2), $A = T/M$;   Substitute the value of T

$A = \dfrac{m_1 m_2 g}{m_1 M + m_2(m_1 + M)}$

(d) $a - A = \dfrac{M m_2 g}{m_1 M + m_2(m_1 + M)}$

5.85 $\Sigma F = ma$, where a has the same magnitude for all blocks:

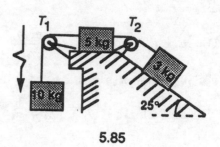

5.85

 10 kg block : $T_1 - 10(9.80) = -10(2)$

 5 kg block : $T_2 - T_1 + f_5 = -5(2)$

 3 kg block : $T_2 - 3(9.80)\sin 25 - f_3 = +3(2)$

where $f_5 = \mu m_5 g = \mu(5)(9.80)$

and $f_3 = \mu m_3 g \cos\theta = \mu(3)(9.80)\cos 25°$

Solving these gives $T_1 = \boxed{78 \text{ N}}$

$T_2 = \boxed{35.9 \text{ N}}$ $\mu = \boxed{0.655}$

5.86   (a)   (b)

5.86

(b) & (c) $\Sigma F = ma$, therefore

#1: $T_1 - \mu m_1 g = m_1 a$

   $T_1 - (0.3)(2)(9.8) = 2a$

#2: $T_2 - T_1 - \mu m_1 g = m_2 a$

   $T_2 - T_1 - 2(9.8)(0.3) = 3a$

#3: $m_3 g - T_2 = m_3 a$

   $10(9.8) - T_2 = 10a$

Solving the above gives: $T_1 = \boxed{17.4 \text{ N}}$ $T_2 = \boxed{40.5 \text{ N}}$ and $a = \boxed{5.75 \text{ m/s}^2}$

5.87 Since it has a larger mass, we expect the 7 kg block to move down the plane. The acceleration for both blocks should have the same magnitude since they are joined together by a non–stretching string.

$$\Sigma F_1 = m_1 a_1 \quad -m_1 g \sin 35° + T = m_1 a$$

$$\Sigma F_2 = m_2 a_2 \quad -m_2 g \sin 35° + T = -m_2 a$$

and

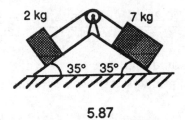

5.87

$$-(2)(9.80) \sin 35 + T = 2a$$

$$-(7)(9.80) \sin 35 + T = -7a$$

$$T = \boxed{17.5 \text{ N}} \qquad a = \boxed{3.12 \text{ m/s}^2}$$

5.88 $\quad \Sigma F_1 = m_1 a_1 \quad -F(gravity) - F(friction) + T = m_1 a$

$\quad\quad\quad \Sigma F_2 = m_2 a_2 \quad -F(gravity) + F(friction) + T = -m_2 a$

$$-2(9.80) \sin 35 - 2(9.80)\mu \cos 35 + T = 2(1.5)$$

$$-7(9.80) \sin 35 + 7(9.80)\mu \cos 35 + T = -7(1.5)$$

Solving the above gives $\mu = \boxed{0.202} \quad T = \boxed{17.5 \text{ N}}$

*5.89 $\quad mg\sin\theta \;=\; m(5 \text{ m/s}^2)$

$$\theta \;=\; \boxed{30.7°}$$

$$mg\cos\theta \;=\; T$$

$$T \;=\; \boxed{0.843 \text{ N}}$$

5.89

*5.90   If all the weight is on the rear wheels,

(a) $F = ma$ $mg\mu_s = ma$

But $s = \dfrac{at^2}{2} = \dfrac{g\mu_s t^2}{2}$,   so $\mu_s = \dfrac{2s}{gt^2}$

$\mu_s = \dfrac{2(0.25 \text{ mi})(1609 \text{ m/mi})}{(9.8 \text{ m/s}^2)(4.96 \text{ s})^2} = \boxed{3.34}$

(b) Time would increase, as the wheels would skid and only kinetic friction would act; or perhaps the car would flip over.

5.91 $a_{\text{mug}} = \dfrac{f}{m} = 0.5 \text{ m/s}^2$

$x_{\text{mug}} = \dfrac{1}{2}a_{\text{mug}}t^2 = \dfrac{1}{2}(0.5 \text{ m/s}^2)t^2$

$x_{\text{mug}} = (0.25 \text{ m/s}^2)t^2, \quad t^2 = \dfrac{x}{0.25 \text{ m/s}^2}$

The edge of the cloth moves 30 cm$+ x$

$0.30 \text{ m} + x = \dfrac{1}{2}a_{\text{cloth}}t^2$

$0.30 \text{ m} + x = \dfrac{1}{2}(3.0 \text{ m/s}^2)(\dfrac{x}{0.25 \text{ m/s}^2})$

$0.30 + x = 6.0x$

$5x = 0.30 \text{ m}$

$x = \boxed{0.06 \text{ m}} = 6.0 \text{ cm}$

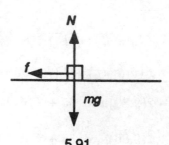

5.91

CHAPTER 6

6.1   (a) Average speed $= v_{av} = \dfrac{200 \text{ m}}{25 \text{ s}} = \boxed{8.0 \text{ m/s}}$

(b) $F = \dfrac{mv^2}{r}$ where $r = \dfrac{200 \text{ m}}{2\pi} = 31.83 \text{ m}$

$F = \dfrac{(1.5 \text{ kg})(8.0 \text{ m/s})^2}{31.83 \text{ m}} = \boxed{3.02 \text{ N}}$

6.2   Neglecting relativistic effects. $F = ma_c = \dfrac{mv^2}{r}$

$F = (2 \times 1.661 \times 10^{-27} \text{ kg})\dfrac{(2.998 \times 10^7 \text{ m/s})^2}{(0.48 \text{ m})} = \boxed{6.22 \times 10^{-12} \text{ N}}$

6.3 $F = \dfrac{mv^2}{r} = \dfrac{(1.5 \text{ kg})(4.0 \text{ m/s})^2}{(0.4 \text{ m})} = \boxed{60.0 \text{ N}}$

6.4 $F = m\dfrac{v^2}{r}$

$v = \sqrt{\dfrac{rF}{m}} = \sqrt{\dfrac{(5.3 \times 10^{-11} \text{ m})(8.2 \times 10^{-8} \text{ N})}{9.11 \times 10^{-31} \text{ kg}}} = 2.18 \times 10^6 \text{ m/s}$

frequency $= (2.18 \times 10^6 \text{ m/s})[\dfrac{1 \text{ rev}}{2\pi(5.3 \times 10^{-11} \text{ m})}] = \boxed{6.56 \times 10^{15} \text{ rev/s}}$

6.5 $m = 3 \text{ kg} : r = 0.8 \text{ m}$. The string will break if the tension exceeds the weight corresponding to 25 kg, so $T_{max} = Mg = 25 \times 9.80 = 245 \text{ N}$. When the 3 kg mass rotates in a horizontal circle, the tension provides the centripetal force, so $T = \dfrac{mv^2}{r} = \dfrac{3v^2}{0.8}$.

Then $v^2 = \dfrac{rT}{m} = \dfrac{0.8T}{3} \leq \dfrac{(0.8T_{max})}{3} = \dfrac{0.8 \times 245}{3} = 65.3 \text{ m}^2/\text{s}^2$

and $0 < v < \sqrt{65.3}$ or $\boxed{0 < v < 8.08 \text{ m/s}}$

6.6   (a) We require that $\dfrac{GmM_e}{r^2} = \dfrac{mv^2}{r}$ but $g = \dfrac{M_e G}{R_e^2}$

In this case $r = 2R_e$, therefore $\dfrac{g}{4} = \dfrac{v^2}{2R_e}$ or $v = \sqrt{\dfrac{gR_e}{2}}$

$$v = \sqrt{\frac{(9.8 \text{ m/s}^2)(6.37 \times 10^6 \text{ m})}{2}} = \boxed{5.59 \times 10^3 \text{ m/s}}$$

(b) $T = \dfrac{2\pi r}{v} = \dfrac{(2\pi)(2)(6.37 \times 10^6 \text{ m})}{5.59 \times 10^3 \text{ m/s}} = \boxed{239 \text{ min}}$

(c) $F = \dfrac{GmM_e}{(2R_e)^2} = \dfrac{mg}{4} = \dfrac{(300 \text{ kg})(9.80 \text{ m/s}^2)}{4} = \boxed{735 \text{ N}}$

* 6.7   The orbit radius is $r = (1.7 \times 10^6 \text{ m} + 10^5 \text{ m})$

$\qquad\qquad\qquad\qquad = 1.8 \times 10^6 \text{ m}.$

Now using the information in Example 6.5,

$$\frac{GM_m m_s}{r^2} = \frac{m_s 2^2 \pi^2 r^2}{rT^2} = m_s a$$

(a) $a = \dfrac{GM_m}{r^2} = \dfrac{(6.67 \times 10^{-11})(7.4 \times 10^{22})}{(1.8 \times 10^6 \text{ m})^2} = \boxed{1.52 \text{ m/s}^2}$

(b) $a = \dfrac{v^2}{r}, \quad v = \sqrt{(1.52 \text{ m/s}^2)(1.8 \times 10^6 \text{ m})} = \boxed{1660 \text{ m/s}}$

(c) $v = \dfrac{2\pi r}{T}, \quad T = \dfrac{2\pi(1.8 \times 10^6)}{1.66 \times 10^3} = \boxed{6820 \text{ s}}$

* 6.8   To cancel the gravity force requires a velocity v such that

$$\frac{mv^2}{r} = mg$$

$$v = \sqrt{rg} = \sqrt{(18 \text{ m})(9.8 \text{ m/s}^2)} = \boxed{13.3 \text{ m/s}}$$

6.9 $N = mg$ since $a_y = 0$

The centripetal force is the frictional force f.

From Newton's second law

$$f = ma_r = \frac{mv^2}{r}$$

But the friction condition is

$$f \leq \mu_s N$$

i. e. , $\dfrac{mv^2}{r} \leq \mu_s mg$

$$v \leq \sqrt{\mu_s r g} = \sqrt{(0.6)(35\ \text{m})(9.8\ \text{m/s}^2)}$$

$$v \leq \boxed{14.3\ \text{m/s}}$$

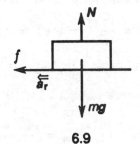

6.9

* 6.10 $\mu mg = \dfrac{mv^2}{r}$

$$\mu = \frac{v^2}{gr} = \frac{(12\ \text{m/s})^2}{(9.8\ \text{m/s}^2)(52\ \text{m})} = \boxed{0.283}$$

6.11   (a) Tension $= F = mg = (1.0\ \text{kg})(9.80\ \text{m/s}^2) = \boxed{9.80\ \text{N}}$

(b) Centripetal force $= F_1 = mg = \boxed{9.80\ \text{N}}$

(c) $\dfrac{m_1 v^2}{r} = F_1$;   so $v = \sqrt{\dfrac{r F_1}{m_1}}$

$$v = \sqrt{\frac{(1.0\ \text{m})(9.8\ \text{N})}{0.25\ \text{kg}}} = \boxed{6.26\ \text{m/s}}$$

6.12   (a) Speed = distance/time.

If the radius of the hand of the clock is r then

$$v = \frac{2\pi r}{T} \implies vT = 2\pi r$$

$$r_m = r_s \qquad \therefore T_m v_m = T_s v_s$$

where $v_m = 1.75 \times 10^{-3}$ m/s, $T_m = (60 \times 60)$ s and $T_s = 60$ s.

$$v_s = (\frac{T_m}{T_s})v_m = (\frac{60^2\ s}{60\ s})(1.75 \times 10^{-3}\ m/s) = \boxed{0.105\ m/s}$$

(b) $v = \frac{2\pi r}{T}$ for the second hand, $r = \frac{vT}{2\pi} = \frac{(0.105\ m/s)(60\ s)}{2\pi} = 1.003 m$

Then $a_c = \frac{v^2}{r} = \frac{(0.105\ m/s)^2}{1.003\ m} = \boxed{1.11 \times 10^{-2}\ m/s^2}$

6.13   (a) static friction

(b) $ma = f + N + mg, \quad \Sigma F_y = 0 = N - mg$, thus

$N = mg$ and $\Sigma F_r = m\frac{v^2}{r} = f = \mu N = \mu mg$

Then $\mu = \frac{v^2}{rg} = \frac{(50\ cm/s)^2}{(30\ cm)(980\ cm/s^2)} = \boxed{0.0850}$

6.14   (a) The reaction force N_1 represents

the apparent weight of the woman

$F = ma$.

i. e. $mg - N_1 = \frac{mv^2}{r}$, so $N_1 = mg - \frac{mv^2}{r}$

$N_1 = 600 - (\frac{600}{9.8})\frac{(9)^2}{11} = \boxed{149\ N}$

6.14

(b) If $N_1 = 0$, $mg = \frac{mv^2}{r}$

This gives $v = \sqrt{rg} = \sqrt{(11.0\ m)(9.80\ m/s^2)} = \boxed{10.4\ m/s}$

6.15 $\Sigma F_x = \frac{mv^2}{r} = mg + N$; But $N = 0$ at this minimum speed condition, so

$\frac{mv^2}{r} = mg \implies v = \sqrt{gr} = \sqrt{(9.80\ m/s^2)(1\ m)} = \boxed{3.13\ m/s}$

* 6.16   (a) $a_r = \dfrac{v^2}{r} = \dfrac{(4 \text{ m/s})^2}{12 \text{ m}} = \boxed{1.33 \text{ m/s}^2}$

   (b) $a = \sqrt{a_r^2 + a_T^2}$

   $= \sqrt{(1.33)^2 + (1.2)^2} = \boxed{1.79 \text{ m/s}^2}$

   at an angle $\theta = \tan^{-1}\left(\dfrac{a_r}{a_T}\right) = 48°$ inward

6.16

6.17 $M = 40$ kg, $R = 3$ m, $T = 350$ N

   (a) $\Sigma F = 2T - Mg = \dfrac{Mv^2}{R}$; $v^2 = (2T - Mg)(\dfrac{R}{M})$

   $v^2 = [700 - (40)(9.8)](\dfrac{3}{40})] = 23.1 (\text{m}^2/\text{s}^2)$; $\boxed{v = 4.81 \text{ m/s}}$

   (b) $N - Mg = F = \dfrac{Mv^2}{R}$

   $N = Mg + \dfrac{Mv^2}{R} = 40(9.8 + \dfrac{23.1}{3}) = \boxed{700 \text{ N}}$

* 6.18 At the top of the vertical circle,

   $T = \dfrac{mv^2}{r} - mg$

   $= m\omega^2 r - mg = (0.4)(8)^2(0.5) - (0.4)(9.8) = \boxed{8.88 \text{ N}}$

6.19 $\Sigma F_y = ma_y = \dfrac{mv^2}{R}$

   $N - mg = -\dfrac{mv^2}{R}$

   $N = m[g - \dfrac{v^2}{r}] = 2.87$ N

6.19

6.20   (a) $v = 20$ m/s, N = force of track on roller coaster, and $R = 10$ m.

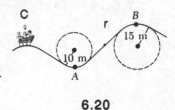

$$\Sigma F = \frac{Mv^2}{R} = N - Mg : \text{ From this we find}$$

$$N = Mg + \frac{Mv^2}{R} = (500 \text{ kg})(9.80 \text{ m/s}^2) + \frac{(500 \text{ kg})(20 \text{ m/s}^2)}{(10 \text{ m})}$$

$$N = 4900 \text{ N} + 20{,}000 \text{ N} = \boxed{2.49 \times 10^4 \text{ N}}$$

6.20

(b) At B, $N - Mg = -\dfrac{Mv^2}{R}$. The max speed at B corresponds to $N = 0$

$$-Mg = -\frac{Mv_{\max}^2}{R} \implies v_{\max} = \sqrt{Rg} = \sqrt{15(9.80)} = \boxed{12.1 \text{ m/s}}$$

6.21   Let the tension at the lowest point be T.

$F = ma$

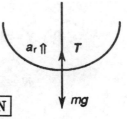

$$T - mg = ma_r = \frac{mv^2}{r}$$

$$T = m(g + \frac{v^2}{r}) = (85 \text{ kg})[9.8 \text{ m/s}^2 + \frac{(8 \text{ m/s})^2}{10 \text{ m}}] = \boxed{1.38 \text{ kN} > 1000 \text{ N}}$$

He doesn't make it across the river because the rope breaks.   6.21

6.22   (a) $a_r = \dfrac{v^2}{r}$, $r = \dfrac{v^2}{a_r} = \dfrac{(13 \text{ m/s})^2}{2(9.8 \text{ m/s}^2)} = \boxed{8.62 \text{ m}}$

(b) Let F be the force exerted by the rail.

Newton's law gives $Mg + F = \dfrac{Mv^2}{r}$

$F = M(\dfrac{v^2}{r} - g) = M(2g - g) = \boxed{Mg, \text{ downward}}$

(c) $a_r = \dfrac{v^2}{r} = \dfrac{(13 \text{ m/s})^2}{20 \text{ m}} = \boxed{8.45 \text{ m/s}^2}$

(d) If the force by the rail is F_1, then

$F_1 + Mg = \dfrac{Mv^2}{r} = Ma_r$

$F_1 = M(a_r - g)$ which is < 0, since $a_r = 8.45 \text{ m/s}^2$

Thus, the normal force must point away from the center of the curve for F_1 to be positive $a_r > g$

i. e. $\dfrac{v^2}{r} > g$ or $v > \sqrt{rg} = \sqrt{(20 \text{ m})(9.8 \text{ m/s}^2)}$

$\boxed{v > 14 \text{ m/s}}$

* 6.23 $v = \dfrac{2\pi r}{T} = \dfrac{2\pi(3 \text{ m})}{(12 \text{ s})} = 1.57 \text{ m/s}$

(a) $a = \dfrac{v^2}{r} = \dfrac{(1.57 \text{ m/s})^2}{(3 \text{ s})} = \boxed{0.822 \text{ m/s}^2}$

(b) For no motion,

$F_f = ma = (45 \text{ kg})(0.822 \text{ m/s}^2) = \boxed{37.0 \text{ N}}$

(c) $F_f = \mu mg$, $\mu = \dfrac{37 \text{ N}}{(45 \text{ kg})(9.8 \text{ m/s}^2)} = \boxed{0.084}$

6.24   The net force in the direction of motion is

$$\Sigma F = T \sin \theta = ma, \text{ where } T \text{ is the tension in the string.}$$

But $T = \dfrac{mg}{\cos \theta}$ (since the vertical forces equal zero).

Therefore $a = \dfrac{T \sin \theta}{m} = (\dfrac{mg}{\cos \theta})(\dfrac{\sin \theta}{m}) = g \tan \theta.$

When the string is 25 cm long and the mass is deflected by 6 cm,

$$\tan \theta = \frac{6}{\sqrt{(25)^2 - (6)^2}} = 0.247 \text{ and } a = g(0.247) = \boxed{2.42 \ \text{m/s}^2}$$

in the forward direction.

6.25 $\Sigma F_x = ma_x = T \sin \theta$ \qquad (1)

$\Sigma F_y = 0 = T \cos \theta - mg$ \quad or

$mg = T \cos \theta$ \qquad (2)

(a) Divide (1) by (2) $\Longrightarrow \dfrac{a_x}{g} = \tan \theta$

$$\theta = \tan^{-1}(\frac{a_x}{g}) = \tan^{-1}(\frac{3}{9.8}) = \boxed{17.0°}$$

(b) From (1), $T = \dfrac{ma_x}{\sin \theta} = \dfrac{(0.5 \ \text{kg})(3 \ \text{m/s}^2)}{\sin 17°} = \boxed{5.12 \ \text{N}}$

6.26   (a)

$$\Sigma F_x = Ma, \quad a = \frac{T}{M} = \frac{18 \ \text{N}}{5 \ \text{kg}} = \boxed{3.60 \ \text{m/s}^2} \text{ to the right.}$$

(b) If $v = $ const, $a = 0$, so $T = \boxed{0}$ (This is also an equilibrium situation.)

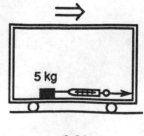

6.26

(c) Someone in the car (noninertial observer) claims that the forces on the mass along x are T and a fictitious force $(-Ma)$. Someone at rest outside the car (inertial observer) claims that T is the only force on M in the $x-$direction.

* 6.27 $F_{\text{max}} = W + ma = 591$ N

$F_{\text{min}} = W - ma = 391$ N

(a) Adding, $2W = 982$ N, $\boxed{W = 491 \text{ N}}$

(b) Since $W = mg$, $m = \dfrac{491 \text{ N}}{9.8 \text{ m/s}^2} = \boxed{50.1 \text{ kg}}$

(c) Subtracting the above equations,

$2ma = 300$ N $\therefore$ $\boxed{a = 2 \text{ m/s}^2}$

6.28 $a_c = \left(\dfrac{4\pi^2 R_e}{T^2}\right)\cos 35° = 0.0226 \text{ m/s}^2$

$(a_{\text{net}})_y = 9.8 - (a_c)_y = 9.78 \text{ m/s}^2$

$(a_{\text{net}})_x = 0.016 \text{ m/s}^2$

$\boxed{\theta = \arctan \dfrac{a_x}{a_y} = 0.0927°}$

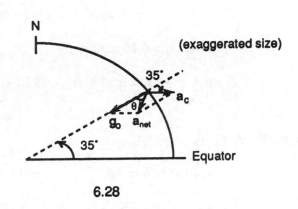

6.28

6.29 $m = 80$ kg, $v_t = 50$ m/s

(a) At $v = 30$ m/s, $a = g - \dfrac{(C\rho A/2)v^2}{m} = 9.8 - \dfrac{(0.314)(30)^2}{80}$

$= \boxed{6.27 \text{ m/s}^2 \text{ downward}}$

(b) At $v = 50$ m/s, terminal velocity has been reached.

$\Sigma F_y = 0 = mg - R$

$\Rightarrow R = mg = (80 \text{ kg})(9.80 \text{ m/s}^2) = \boxed{784 \text{ N directed up}}$

Also $R = \dfrac{C\rho Av^2}{2} \Rightarrow \dfrac{C\rho A}{2} = \dfrac{R}{v^2} = \dfrac{784}{(50)^2} = 0.314 \text{ kg} \cdot \text{s}^2/\text{m}$

(c) At $v = 30$ m/s, $\dfrac{C\rho Av^2}{2} = (0.314)(30)^2 = \boxed{283 \text{ N}}$

6.30   (a) $a = g - bv$ When $v = v_t$, $a = 0$ and $g = bv_t$.

$$b = \frac{g}{v_t}$$

The styrofoam falls 1.5 m at constant speed

v_t in 5.0 s. Thus $v_t = \dfrac{y}{t} = \dfrac{1.5 \text{ m}}{5.0 \text{ s}} = 0.3 \text{ m/s}$

Then $b = \dfrac{9.8 \text{ m/s}^2}{0.3 \text{ m/s}} = \boxed{32.8 \text{ s}^{-1}}$

(b) At $t = 0$, $v = 0$ and $a = g = \boxed{9.80 \text{ m/s}^2}$

(c) When $v = 0.15$ m/s,

$$a = g - bv = 9.80 \text{ m/s}^2 - (32.7 \text{ s}^{-1})(0.15 \text{ m/s}) = \boxed{4.90 \text{ m/s}^2}$$

6.31   (a) $v(t) = v_0 e^{-ct}$

$v(20 \text{ s}) = 5 = v_0 e^{-20c}$ $v_0 = 10 \text{ m/s}$

So $5 = 10 e^{-20c}$, and $-20c = \ln\left(\dfrac{1}{2}\right)$

$$c = -\frac{\ln\left(\frac{1}{2}\right)}{20} = \boxed{3.47 \times 10^{-2} \text{ s}^{-1}}$$

(b) At $t = 40$ s, $v = (10 \text{ m/s})e^{-40c} = (10 \text{ m/s})(0.25) = \boxed{2.50 \text{ m/s}}$

(c) $v = v_0 e^{-ct}$

$$a = \frac{dv}{dt} = -cv_0 e^{-ct} = \boxed{-cv}$$

6.32   (a) $\rho = \dfrac{m}{V}$; $A = 0.0201 \text{ m}^2$; $D = \dfrac{1}{2}\rho A C_{D}itv^2 = mg$

$$m = \rho V = (0.83 \text{ g/cm}^3)[\tfrac{4}{3}\pi(8.0 \text{ cm})^3] = 1.78 \text{ kg}$$

$$v_t = \sqrt{\frac{2(1.78 \text{ kg})(9.8 \text{ m/s}^2)}{0.5(1.29 \text{ kg/m}^3)(0.0201 \text{ m}^2)}} = \boxed{51.7 \text{ m/s}}$$

(b) $v^2 = v_0^2 + 2gh$; $h = \dfrac{v^2}{2g} = \dfrac{(51.7 \text{ m/s})^2}{2(9.8 \text{ m/s}^2)} = \boxed{137 \text{ m}}$

6.33 (a) $v = v_t(1 - e^{-bt/m})$; from this we find $\dfrac{dv}{dt} = \dfrac{v_t b}{m} e^{-bt/m}$

From the stated conditions $a = \dfrac{dv}{dt} = g$ when $t = 0$.

Substituting these values into the expressions for dv/dt, we have

$$g = \frac{v_t b}{m} \text{ or } b = \frac{mg}{v_t} = \frac{(0.003)(9.80)}{(0.02)} = \boxed{1.47 \text{ N} \cdot \text{s/m}}$$

(b) Take the ln of each side of Eq. 6.16, where $v = 0.63 v_t$ to find

$$t = -\frac{m}{b} \ln(1 - 0.63) = -\frac{0.003}{1.47} \ln(0.37) = \boxed{2.04 \times 10^{-3} \text{ s}}$$

(c) $F = ma = m \dfrac{dv}{dt}$ and from part (a)

$$F = m(\frac{v_t b}{m}) = v_t b = (0.02 \text{ m/s})(1.47 \text{ kg/s}) = \boxed{2.94 \times 10^{-2} \text{ N}}$$

6.34 $a_r = \dfrac{v^2}{r}$, $\quad v = (30 \dfrac{\text{rev}}{\text{min}})(\dfrac{1 \text{ min}}{60 \text{ s}})(\dfrac{2\pi(0.05\text{m})}{\text{rev}}) = 0.157 \text{ m/s}$

$$a_r = \frac{(0.157 \text{ m/s})^2}{0.05 \text{ m}} = \boxed{0.493 \text{ m/s}^2}$$

$$a_t = \frac{\Delta v}{\Delta t} = \frac{0 - 0.157 \text{ m/s}}{0.3 \text{ s}} = \boxed{-0.524 \text{ m/s}^2}$$

$$a = \sqrt{a_t^2 + a_r^2} = \boxed{0.720 \text{ m/s}^2}$$

6.34

6.35 (a) $F = \dfrac{mv^2}{r} = \dfrac{(9.11 \times 10^{-31} \text{ kg})(2.2 \times 10^6 \text{ m/s})^2}{0.53 \times 10^{-10} \text{ m}} = \boxed{8.32 \times 10^{-8} \text{ N}}$

(b) $a = \dfrac{v^2}{r} = \dfrac{(2.2 \times 10^6 \text{ m/s})^2}{0.53 \times 10^{-10} \text{ m}} = \boxed{9.13 \times 10^{22} \text{ m/s}^2}$

(c) 1 rev $= 2\pi r = 2\pi(0.53 \times 10^{-10} \text{ m}) = 3.33 \times 10^{-10} \text{ m}$

$$(2.2 \times 10^6 \text{ m/s})\frac{1 \text{ rev}}{3.33 \times 10^{-10} \text{ m}} = \boxed{6.61 \times 10^{15} \text{ rev/s}}$$

6.36 $\Sigma F_y = ma_y$

$$T - mg = m\frac{v^2}{r}$$

$$T = m(g + \frac{v^2}{r}) = [(0.40 \text{ kg})(9.8 \text{ m/s}^2 + \frac{(8.2 \text{ m/s})^2}{0.80 \text{ m}})] = \boxed{37.5 \text{ N}}$$

* 6.37 $F\cos 5° = mg = (80 \text{ kg})(9.8 \text{ m/s}^2)$

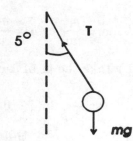

   (a) $T = 787$ N

$$\boxed{\mathbf{T} = (68.6 \text{ N})\mathbf{i} + (784 \text{ N})\mathbf{j}}$$

   (b) $T\sin 5° = ma_r$, $\boxed{a_r = 0.857 \text{ m/s}^2}$

                                                                                   6-37

6.38   (a) $F = ma$; in this case, the force of friction causes the centripetal

   acceleration of the mass. Therefore, $\mu mg = m(\omega^2 R)$ and

$$\omega^2 = \frac{\mu mg}{R} = \frac{(0.3)(9.80)}{(0.2)} = 14.7 \text{ rad}^2/\text{s}^2 \text{ so}$$

$$\omega = 3.83 \text{ rad/s} \text{ and } f = \frac{\omega}{2\pi} = \boxed{0.610 \text{ rev/s}}$$

   (b) $v = R\omega = (0.2)(3.83) = \boxed{0.766 \text{ m/s}}$

   $a = R\omega^2 = (0.2)(3.83)^2 = \boxed{2.93 \text{ m/s}^2}$

6.39   (a) Since the centripetal acceleration on a person is outward

   (up from the earth), it is equivalent to the effect of a falling

   elevator. Therefore, $W' = W - \frac{mv^2}{r}$ or $\boxed{W > W'}$

   (b) At the poles, $v = 0$, and $W' = W = mg = 75(9.80) = \boxed{735 \text{ N}}$

   At the equator, $W' = W - 75(0.034) = \boxed{732 \text{ N}}$

6.40 (a) The putty when dislodged rises in time t. To find t we use

$$v = v_0 + at : \text{ i. e. }, \ -v = v - gt$$

or $t = \dfrac{2v}{g}$ where v is the speed of the wheel.

If R is the radius of the wheel $v = \dfrac{2\pi R}{t}$

so $t = \dfrac{2\pi R}{v} = \dfrac{2v}{g}$

Thus $v^2 = \pi R g$ and $v = \boxed{\sqrt{\pi R g}}$

(b) The putty is dislodged when F, the force holding it to

the wheel $= \dfrac{mv^2}{R}$.

$$F = \frac{mv^2}{R} = \boxed{m\pi g}$$

6.41 $\Sigma F_x = \dfrac{mv^2}{r} = N \sin\theta \quad (1)$

$\Sigma F_y = 0 = mg - N \cos\theta$

$mg = N \cos\theta \qquad (2)$

Divide (1) by (2)

$\dfrac{v^2}{rg} = \tan\theta$ and $v = \sqrt{rg\tan\theta} = \sqrt{(400 \text{ m})(9.80 \text{ m/s}^2)\tan(6°)} = \boxed{20.3 \text{ m/s}}$

6.42   (a) If the car is about to slip *down* the plane,

$$-mg\sin\theta + f = \frac{mv^2}{r}\cos\theta \quad \text{where} \quad f = \mu[mg\cos\theta + m\frac{v^2}{r}\sin\theta]$$

From the above we find $v_{min} = \sqrt{\dfrac{Rg(\tan\theta - \mu)}{1 + \mu\tan\theta}}$

If the car slips up the plane then $-mg\sin\theta - f = \dfrac{mv^2}{r}\cos\theta$ and

$$v_{max} = \sqrt{\frac{Rg(\tan\theta + \mu)}{1 - \mu\tan\theta}}$$

(b) $v_{min} = 0 = \sqrt{\dfrac{Rg(\tan\theta - \mu)}{1 - \mu\tan\theta}}$ therefore $\mu = \tan\theta$

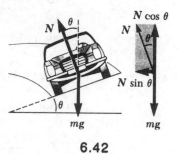

(c) $v_{min} = \sqrt{\dfrac{(100\text{ m})(9.8\text{ m/s}^2)(\tan 10° - 0.1)}{1 + 0.1\tan 10°}} = \boxed{8.57 \text{ m/s}}$

6.42

$$v_{max} = \sqrt{\frac{(100\text{ m})(9.8\text{ m/s}^2)(\tan 10° + 0.1)}{1 - 0.1\tan 10°}} = \boxed{16.6 \text{ m/s}}$$

6.43 $\Sigma F_y = L_y + T_y + W_y = L\cos 20° - T\sin 20° - 7.35 = ma_y = 0$

$\Sigma F_x = L_x + T_x + W_x = L\sin 20° + T\cos 20° + 0 = m\dfrac{v^2}{r}$

$m\dfrac{v^2}{r} = (0.75)\dfrac{(35\text{ m/s})^2}{56.4\text{ m}} = 16.3\text{ N}$

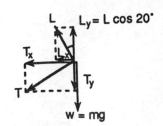

$\therefore L\sin 20° + T\cos 20° = 16.3\text{ N}$

$L\cos 20° - T\sin 20° = 7.35\text{ N}$

$L + T\dfrac{\cos 20°}{\sin 20°} = \dfrac{16.3}{\sin 20°}$

$L = 60\text{ m}$

$L - T\dfrac{\sin 20°}{\cos 20°} = \dfrac{7.35}{\cos 20°}$

$r = L\cos 20°$
$\quad = 56.4\text{ m}$

$T(\cot 20° + \tan 20°) = \dfrac{16.3}{\sin 20°} - \dfrac{7.35}{\cos 20°}$

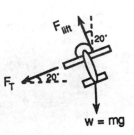

$T(3.111) = 39.82$

$T = \boxed{12.8\text{ N}}$

6.43

6.44   Let the angle the wedge makes with the horizontal be θ. The equations for the mass m are

$$g = N\cos\theta \quad \text{and} \quad N\sin\theta = \frac{mv^2}{r}$$

where $r = L\cos\theta$.

Eliminating N gives $\dfrac{N\sin\theta}{N\cos\theta} = \tan\theta = \dfrac{mv^2}{mg\,L\cos\theta}$

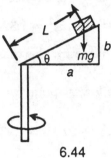

Therefore $v^2 = Lg\cos\theta\tan\theta = Lg\sin\theta$

6.44

$$\boxed{v = \sqrt{gL\sin\theta}}$$

6.45   (a) $v = 300\,\text{mph}[(88\,\text{ft/s})/(60\,\text{mph})] = 440\,\text{ft/s}$

At the lowest point, his seat exerts an upward force,

therefore his weight seems to increase. His apparent weight is

$$W' = W + ma = 160 + (\frac{160}{32})\frac{(440)^2}{1200} = \boxed{967\,\text{lb}}$$

6.45 a

(b) At the highest point, the force of the seat on the pilot is

directed away from the pilot and $W' = W - ma = \boxed{-647\ \text{lb}}$

Since $W' < 0$, the pilot must be strapped down.

6.54 b

(c) When $W' = 0$, then $W = ma = \dfrac{mv^2}{R}$. If we can vary R and v such

that the above is true, then the pilot feels weightless.

6.46 r is the distance from the axis and

θ is the angle between the strings and axis.

$r = 2^2 - (1.5)^2 = 1.32$ m and $\theta = \cos^{-1}(\frac{1.5}{2}) = 41.4°$

By symmetry, the tensions in each string are equal.

(a) At the lowest point we have $- mg + 2T \sin \theta = \dfrac{mv^2}{r}$

$-4(9.8) + 2T \sin(41.4°) = 4\dfrac{(4)^2}{1.32},$ thus $T = \boxed{66.3 \ \text{N}}$

(b) In the horizontal position $2T \sin \theta = m\dfrac{v^2}{R}$, thus $T = \boxed{36.6 \ \text{N}}$

Note: gravity does not enter into the above since it acts at

an angle of 90° to T.

(c) At the highest point, $-2T \sin \theta - mg = -\dfrac{mv^2}{r}$, thus $T = \boxed{6.96 \ \text{N}}$

6.47   From problem 46: $\theta = 41.4°$, $r = 1.32$ m.

The tensions in each string are no longer equal.

For the y direction: $T_1 \cos \theta - T_2 \cos \theta = mg$

For the x direction: $(T_1 + T_2) \sin \theta = \dfrac{mv^2}{r}$

Solving these we get

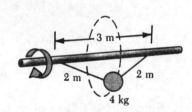

6.46   **and**   6.47

$T_1 = m(\dfrac{v^2}{r})\dfrac{\cos \theta}{(2 \cos \theta \sin \theta)} + g \sin \theta$

$T_1 = \dfrac{(4)(6)^2}{1.32}\dfrac{\cos(41.4°)}{2 \cos(41.4°) \sin(41.4°)} + (9.80) \sin(41.4°) = \boxed{108 \ \text{N}}$

and $T_2 = \boxed{55.7 \ \text{N}}$

6.48 (a) While the car negotiates the curve the accelerometer is at the angle θ.

Vertically: $T\cos\theta = mg$

Horizontally: $T\sin\theta = \dfrac{mv^2}{r}$

where r is the radius of the curve and v is the speed of the car.

By division $\tan\theta = \dfrac{v^2}{rg}$. Then

$$a_c = \frac{v^2}{r} = g\tan\theta$$

$$a_c = (9.8\ \text{m/s}^2)\tan 15°$$

$$\boxed{a_c = 2.63\ \text{m/s}^2}$$

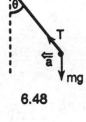

6.48

(b) $r = \dfrac{v^2\cot\theta}{g} = (23\ \text{m/s})^2\dfrac{(\cot 15°)}{(9.80\ \text{m/s}^2)}$

or $r = \dfrac{v^2}{a_c} = \dfrac{(23\ \text{m/s})^2}{2.63\ \text{m/s}^2} = \boxed{201\ \text{m}}$

(c) $v^2 = rg\tan\theta = (201\ \text{m})(9.80\ \text{m/s}^2)\tan 9.0°$

$v = \boxed{17.7\ \text{m/s}}$

6.49 (a) $N = \dfrac{mv^2}{R}$ $f - mg = 0$

$f = \mu_s N$ $v = \dfrac{2\pi R}{T}$

$$\boxed{T = \sqrt{\frac{4\pi^2 R\mu_s}{g}}}$$

6.49

(b) $T = \boxed{2.54\ \text{s}}$

$\#\dfrac{\text{rev}}{\text{min}} = \dfrac{1\ \text{rev}}{2.54\ \text{s}}\left(\dfrac{60\ \text{s}}{\text{min}}\right) = \boxed{23.6\ \dfrac{\text{rev}}{\text{min}}}$

6.50 $\Sigma F_y = 0$ for the block

$N - m_p g - m_B g = 0$

$N = (m_p + m_B)g$

The friction force of the penny on block must equal $m_p \dfrac{v^2}{r}$ if the penny doesn't slip:

$f = \mu N = \mu_{s1}(m_p + m_B)g$

$f - f_p = m_B \dfrac{v^2}{r}$

$m_B \dfrac{v^2}{r} = \mu_{s1}(m_p + m_B)g - m_p \dfrac{v^2}{r}$

$v = \sqrt{\dfrac{r\mu_{s1}(m_p + m_B)g}{(m_B + m_p)}} = \sqrt{(0.12 \text{ m})(0.75)}$

$v = (0.939 \text{ m/s})(\dfrac{1 \text{ rev}}{2\pi(0.12 \text{ m})})(\dfrac{60 \text{ s}}{1 \text{ min}}) = 74.7 \text{ rpm}$

For the penny:

greatest $f_p = \mu_s N = (0.52)(0.0031 \times 9.8) = 0.0158 \text{ N}$

greatest v : $\dfrac{mv^2}{r} = f_p$: $v = \sqrt{\dfrac{r f_p}{m}}$

$v_{\max} = \sqrt{\dfrac{(0.12)(0.0158)}{0.0031}} = \boxed{0.782 \text{ m/s}}$

This is less than the maximum speed for the block,

so the penny slips at 62.2 rpm, but the block stays put.

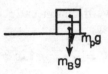

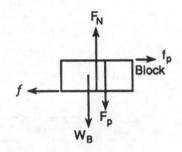

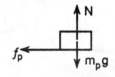

6.50

* 6.51 $v = \dfrac{2\pi r}{T} = \dfrac{2\pi(9 \text{ m})}{(15 \text{ s})} = 3.77 \text{ m/s}$

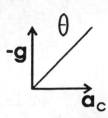

(a) $a_c = \dfrac{v^2}{r} = \boxed{1.58 \text{ m/s}^2}$

(b) $F_{\text{low}} = m(g + a_c) = \boxed{455 \text{ N}}$

(c) $F_{\text{hi}} = m(g - a_c) = \boxed{329 \text{ N}}$

6-51

(d) $F_{\text{med}} = m\sqrt{g^2 + a_c^2} = \boxed{397 \text{ N}}$ at $\theta = \tan^{-1}\dfrac{a_c}{g} = \dfrac{1.58}{9.8} = \boxed{9.15° \text{ inward}}$

6.52 (a) The mass at the end of the chain is in vertical equilibrium. Thus $T \cos \theta = mg$

Horizontally $T \sin \theta = ma_r = \dfrac{mv^2}{r}$

$r = (2.5 \sin \theta + 4)$ m

$r = (2.5 \sin 28° + 4)$ m $= 5.17$ m. Then $a_r = \dfrac{v^2}{5.17 \text{ m}}$.

6.52

By division $\tan \theta = \dfrac{a_r}{g} = \dfrac{v^2}{5.17g}$

$v^2 = 5.17g \tan \theta = (5.17)(9.8)(\tan 28°)$ m^2/s^2

$v = \boxed{5.19 \text{ m/s}}$

(b) $T \cos \theta = mg$; $T = \dfrac{mg}{\cos \theta} = \dfrac{(50 \text{ kg})(9.8 \text{ m/s}^2)}{\cos 28°} = \boxed{555 \text{ N}}$

* 6.53 At terminal velocity, the accelerating force of gravity is balanced by frictional drag:

$mg = arv + br^2v^2$

(a) $mg = 3.1 \times 10^{-9}v + 0.87 \times 10^{-10}v^2$

For water, $m = \rho V = (1000 \text{ kg/m}^3) \left(\dfrac{4}{3}\pi\right)(10^{-5})^3$

$4.1 \times 10^{-11} = (3.1 \times 10^{-9})v + (0.87 \times 10^{-10})v^2$

Assuming v is small, ignore the second term: $\boxed{v = 0.013 \text{ m/s}}$

(b) $mg = 3.1 \times 10^{-8}v + 0.97 \times 10^{-8}v^2$

Here we cannot ignore the second term because the coefficients are of nearly equal magnitude.

$4.1 \times 10^{-8} = (3.1 \times 10^{-8})v + (0.87 \times 10^{-8})v^2$

$v = \dfrac{-3.1 \pm \sqrt{(3.1)^2 + 4(0.87)(4.1)}}{2(0.87)} = \boxed{1.03 \text{ m/s}}$

(c) $mg = 3.1 \times 10^{-7}v + 0.87 \times 10^{-8}v^2$

Assuming $v > 1$ m/s, ignore the first term:

$4.1 \times 10^{-5} = 0.87 \times 10^{-8}v^2$

$v = \boxed{6.87 \text{ m/s}}$

6.54 $m = 4.8 \times 10^{-4}$ kg $r = 5 \times 10^{-3}$ m

$$\Sigma F = m\frac{dv}{dt} = mg - kv^2$$

$$k = \frac{1}{2} C\rho A, \quad \rho = 1.29 \text{ kg/m}^3, \quad C = 0.5, \quad A = \pi r^2$$

(a) Assuming the hailstone starts from rest,

its velocity increases under the acceleration

of gravity until $kv^2 = mg$. $(k = 2.53 \times 10^{-5})$

Then $\dfrac{dv}{dt} = 0$, and $v = \sqrt{\dfrac{mg}{k}} = \boxed{13.6 \text{ m/s}}$

(b) The time–dependence of velocity and position

can be found by numerical integration:

	$a = \dfrac{g - kv^2}{m}$	Δv	v(m/s)	$\Delta x = \bar{v}\Delta t$	x(m)
$t = 0.0$	9.8	0.00	0.00	0.00	0.00
$t = 0.2$	9.8	1.96	1.96	0.196	0.196
$t = 0.4$	9.6	1.92	3.88	0.584	0.780
$t = 0.6$	9.0	1.80	5.68	0.956	1.736
$t = 0.8$	8.1	1.62	7.30	1.298	3.034
$t = 1.0$	7.0	1.40	8.70	1.600	4.634
$t = 1.2$	5.8	1.16	9.86	1.856	6.490
$t = 1.4$	5.1	1.02	10.88	2.074	8.564
$t = 1.6$	3.56	0.71	11.59	2.248	10.812
$t = 1.8$	2.7	0.54	12.13	2.372	13.184
$t = 0.20$	2.0	0.4	12.53	2.466	15.650

6.55 $\Sigma F = mg \sin \theta - \mu \, mg \cos \theta$

$m\dfrac{dv}{dt} = mg \sin \theta - (0.3 + 1.2\sqrt{v}) \, mg \cos \theta$

$a = [4.9 - (0.3 + 1.2\sqrt{v})(8.487)] \ \text{m/s.}$

(a) Using numerical methods (as in preceding problem),

and assuming $v_0 = 1$ m/s

$a = (4.9 - 2.55(1 + 4\sqrt{v}))$

	$a(\text{ m/s}^2)$	Δv	$v(\text{ m/s})$	$\Delta x = \bar{v}\Delta t$	$x(\text{m})$
$t = 0.00$	$- - -$	$- - -$	1.000	0.000	0.000
$t = 0.02$	-7.85	-0.157	0.843	0.0184	0.0184
$t = 0.04$	-7.02	-0.140	0.703	0.0155	0.0339
$t = 0.06$	-6.20	-0.124	0.579	0.0128	0.0467
$t = 0.08$	-5.40	-0.108	0.471	0.0105	0.0572
$t = 0.10$	-4.65	-0.093	0.378	0.0085	0.0657
$t = 0.12$	-3.92	-0.078	0.300	0.0068	0.0725
$t = 0.14$	-3.23	-0.065	0.235	0.0054	0.0779
$t = 0.16$	-2.6	-0.052	0.183	0.0042	0.0821
$t = 0.18$	-2.0	-0.040	0.143	0.0033	0.0854
$t = 0.20$	-1.5	-0.030	0.113	0.0023	0.0877

(b) The terminal velocity can be found

when $\dfrac{dv}{dt} = 0$. There,

$\dfrac{dv}{dt} = 4.9 - 2.55(1 + 4\sqrt{v}) = 0$

$4.9 = 2.55(1 + 4\sqrt{v})$

$2.35 = 10.2\sqrt{v}$

$m = 0.5 \text{ kg}$

$\theta = 30°$

6.55

$\boxed{v = 0.053 \ \text{m/s}}$

The student should verify that regardless of the
initial velocity of the block, that its terminal
velocity will be $v_t = 0.053$ m/s.

CHAPTER 7

7.1   Work $= W = mgh$

$$h = \frac{W}{mg} = \frac{6 \times 10^3 \text{ J}}{(20 \text{ kg})(9.8 \text{ m/s}^2)} = \boxed{30.6 \text{ m}}$$

7.2 $W = Fy \cdot \Delta y = mg \cdot \Delta y = (65 \text{ kg})(9.8 \text{ m/s}^2)(20 \times 0.23 \text{ m}) = \boxed{2.93 \text{ kJ}}$

7.3 $W = Fx = (5000 \text{ N})(3 \text{ km}) = \boxed{15.0 \text{ MJ}}$

7.4   (a) $1 \text{ J} = (1 \text{ kg} \cdot \text{m}^2/\text{s}^2)(10^3 \text{ g/kg})(10^4 \text{ cm}^2/\text{m}^2) = 10^7 \text{ g} \cdot \text{cm}^2/\text{s} = 10^7 \text{ ergs}$

   (b) $1 \text{ J} = (1 \text{ kg} \cdot \text{m}^2/\text{s}^2)[\frac{0.2248 \text{ lb}}{\text{kg} \cdot \text{m/s}^2}](3.281 \text{ ft}/1 \text{ m}) = \boxed{0.737 \text{ ft·lb}}$

7.5 $W = nmgy = (20)(50 \text{ kg})(\frac{9.8 \text{ N}}{\text{kg}})(0.6 \text{ m}) = \boxed{5.88 \text{ kJ}}$

7.6   (a) $W = F_d s = -fs = -(-\mu mg)s = 0.15(100)(9.80)(2 \times 10^3) = \boxed{294 \text{ kJ}}$

   (b) $W_f = fs = (-\mu mg)\text{s} = \boxed{-294 \text{ kJ}}$

7.7   (a) $W = (150 \text{ N})(6 \text{ m}) = \boxed{900 \text{ J}}$

   (b) At constant speed $W_{\text{net}} = 0$ or $W_f = W_{\text{app}} = \boxed{-900 \text{ J}}$

   (c) $W_f = fs \cos\theta = \mu mg \, s \cos 180°$

$$\mu = \frac{W_f}{mg \, s \cos 180°} = -\frac{900 \text{ J}}{(40 \text{ kg})(9.80 \text{ m/s}^2)(6 \text{ m})(-1)} = \boxed{0.383}$$

7.8   (a) $W_F = \mathbf{F} \cdot \mathbf{x} = Fx \cos \theta = (70)(5) \cos 20° = \boxed{329 \ \text{J}}$

(b) $W_f = f \cdot x = fx \cos 180° = -\mu(mg - F \sin \theta)x$

$$= -0.3(147 \ \text{N} - 23.94 \ \text{N})(5 \ \text{m}) = \boxed{-185 \ \text{J}}$$

(c) $W_n = \mathbf{N} \cdot \mathbf{x} = \boxed{0}$

(d) $W_g = \boxed{0}$

(e) $W_{\text{net}} = W_F - W_f = 329 \ \text{J} - 185 \ \text{J} = \boxed{144 \ \text{J}}$

*7.9   <u>Assume</u> you push horizontally

$f = (0.25)(40)(9.8) = 98 \ \text{N}$

(a) $P = fv = (98 \ \text{N})(1.4 \ \text{m/s}) = \boxed{137 \ \text{W}}$

(b) $\boxed{-137 \ \text{W}}$

7.10 $W = mg(\Delta y) = mg(l - l \cos \theta)$

$$= (80 \ \text{kg})(9.8 \ \text{m/s}^2)(12 \ \text{m})(1 - \cos 60°) = \boxed{4.70 \ \text{kJ}}$$

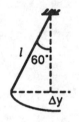

7.10

7.11   (a) $\Sigma F_y = F \sin \theta + N - mg = 0$

$N = mg - F \sin \theta$

$\Sigma F_x = F \cos 20° - \mu_k N = 0$

$N = \dfrac{F \cos \theta}{\mu}$

$mg - F \sin \theta = \dfrac{F \cos \theta}{\mu}$

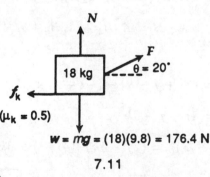

$w = mg = (18)(9.8) = 176.4 \ \text{N}$

7.11

$F(\dfrac{\cos \theta}{\mu} + \sin \theta) = mg$

$F = \dfrac{176.4 \ \text{N}}{\frac{\cos 20°}{0.5} + \sin 20°} = \boxed{79.4 \ \text{N}}$

(b) $W_F = Fd \cos \theta = (79.4 \ \text{N})(20 \ \text{m}) \cos 20° = \boxed{1.49 \ \text{kJ}}$

(c) $f_k = F \cos \theta = 74.6 \ \text{N}$

$W_f = f_k d \cos \theta = (74.6 \ \text{N})(20 \ \text{m}) \cos 180° = \boxed{-1.49 \ \text{kJ}}$

7.12 $A = 4i + 3j, \quad B = -i + 3j$

(a) $A \cdot B = A_x B_x + A_y B_y = 4(-1) + 3(3) = \boxed{5.00}$

(b) $\cos\theta = \dfrac{A \cdot B}{AB} = \dfrac{5}{\sqrt{25}\sqrt{10}} = \dfrac{\sqrt{10}}{10} = 0.316$

$\boxed{\theta = 71.6°}$

7.13 $A = -2i + 3j \quad B = j$

(a) $|A| = \sqrt{(-2)^2 + (3)^2} = \boxed{3.61}$

(b) $A \cdot B = AB\cos\theta = A_x B_x + A_y B_y + A_z B_z$

so $\theta = \cos^{-1}\dfrac{(A_x B_x + A_y B_y + A_z B_z)}{(AB)} = \cos^{-1}(\dfrac{3}{3.61}) = \boxed{33.8°}$

7.14 $A = 5; \ B = 9; \ \theta = 50°. \quad A \cdot B = AB\cos\theta = (5)(9)\cos 50° = \boxed{28.9}$

7.15 $A \cdot B = (A_x i + A_y j + A_z k) \cdot (B_x i + B_y j + B_z k)$

$\begin{aligned} A \cdot B = \ & A_x B_x(i \cdot i) + A_x B_y(i \cdot j) + A_x B_z(i \cdot k) + \\ & A_y B_x(j \cdot i) + A_y B_y(j \cdot j) + A_y B_z(j \cdot k) + \\ & A_z B_x(k \cdot i) + A_z B_y(k \cdot j) + A_z B_z(k \cdot k) \end{aligned}$

$A \cdot B = A_x B_x + A_y B_y + A_z B_z$

7.16 $A - B = (3i + j - k) - (-i + 2j + 5k)$

$A - B = 4i - j - 6k$

$C \cdot (A - B) = (2j - 3k) \cdot (4i - j - 6k)$

$= 0 + (-2) + (+18) = \boxed{16.0}$

7.17 (a) $W = F \cdot s = F_x x + F_y y = (6)(3)\,\text{N}\cdot\text{m} + (-2)(1)\,\text{N}\cdot\text{m} = \boxed{16.0\ \text{J}}$

(b) $\theta = \cos^{-1}\dfrac{F \cdot s}{Fs} = \cos^{-1}\dfrac{16}{\sqrt{[6^2 + (-2)^2][3^2 + 1^2]}} = \boxed{36.9°}$

7.18 $A = 2j$, $B = -5i + 3j$, $\quad A \cdot B = 6.00 \quad A \cdot B = AB \cos\theta$

so $\theta = \cos^{-1}(\dfrac{A \cdot B}{AB}) = \cos^{-1}(\dfrac{6}{\sqrt{(5^2 + 3^2)2}}) = \boxed{59.0°}$

*7.19 $\quad \mathbf{W} = (4i - 5j) \cdot (3i - 4j)$

$\qquad\qquad = 12 + 20 = \boxed{32 \text{ J}}$

7.20 $\quad \mathbf{A} \cdot \mathbf{B} = A_x B_x + A_y B_y + A_z B_z = AB \cos\theta$

$\qquad\qquad = (-5)(0) + (-3)(-2) + (+2)(-2) = 2$

$\qquad A = \sqrt{A_x^2 + A_y^2 + A_z^2} = \sqrt{25 + 9 + 4} = 6.16$

$\qquad B = \sqrt{B_x^2 + B_y^2 + B_z^2} = \sqrt{0 + 4 + 4} = 2.83$

$\qquad 2 = (6.16)(2.83)\cos\theta$

$\qquad \theta = \text{arc}\cos(0.1147) = \boxed{83.4°}$

7.21 (a) $A = 3i - 2j$, $\quad B = 4i - 4j$

$\qquad \theta = \cos^{-1}\dfrac{A \cdot B}{AB} = \cos^{-1}\dfrac{12 + 8}{\sqrt{(13)(32)}} = \boxed{11.3°}$

(b) $B = 3i - 4j + 2k$, $\quad A = -2i + 4j$

$\qquad \cos\theta = \dfrac{A \cdot B}{AB} = \dfrac{-6 - 16}{\sqrt{(29)(20)}} \quad \theta = \boxed{156°}$

(c) $A = i - 2j + 2k$; $\quad B = 3j + 4k$

$\qquad \theta = \cos^{-1}(\dfrac{A \cdot B}{AB}) = \cos^{-1}(\dfrac{-6 + 8}{\sqrt{9} \cdot \sqrt{25}}) = \boxed{82.3°}$

7.22 $\quad W_{\text{net}} = W_1 + W_2 = 2\text{ N}(2\text{ m}) + (-1\text{ N})(1\text{ m}) = \boxed{3.00 \text{ J}}$

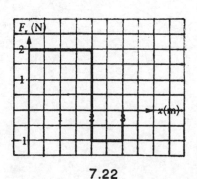

7.22

7.23 $W = \int F_x dx$ and W equals the area under the Force-Displacement Curve

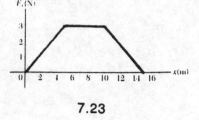

   (a) For the region $0 \le x \le 5$ m, $W = \dfrac{(3 \text{ m})(5 \text{ N})}{2} = \boxed{7.50 \text{ J}}$

   (b) For the region $5 \le x \le 10$, $W = (3 \text{ N})(5 \text{ m}) = \boxed{15.0 \text{ J}}$

   (c) For the region $10 \le x \le 15$, $W = \dfrac{(3 \text{ N})(5 \text{ m})}{2} = \boxed{7.50 \text{ J}}$

   (d) For the region $0 \le x \le 15$, $W = (7.5 + 7.5 + 15) \text{ J} = \boxed{30.0 \text{ J}}$

7.23

7.24 $W = \int\limits_{i}^{f} F\,dx = $ area under curve from x_i to x_f

   (a) $x_i = 0$, $x_f = 8$ m, $W = $ area of triangle $ABC = (1/2)AC \times$ altitude,

   $W_{0 \to 8} = (1/2) \times 8 \text{ m} \times 6 \text{ N} = \boxed{24.0 \text{ J}}$

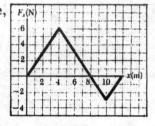

   (b) $x_i = 8$ m, $x_f = 10$ m, $W = $ area of $\triangle CDE = (1/2)\,CE \times$ altitude,

   $W_{8 \to 10} = (1/2)(2 \text{ m}) \times (-3 \text{ N}) = \boxed{-3.00 \text{ J}}$

   (c) $W_{0 \to 10} = W_{0 \to 10} + W_{8 \to 10} = 24 + (-3) = \boxed{21.0 \text{ J}}$

7.24

7.25   (a) Spring constant is given by $F = kx$

   $k = \dfrac{F}{x} = \dfrac{(230 \text{ N})}{(0.4 \text{ m})} = \boxed{575 \text{ N/m}}$

   (b) Work $= F_{\text{avg}} x = (\dfrac{1}{2})(230 \text{ N})(0.4 \text{ m}) = \boxed{46.0 \text{ J}}$

7.26 $F_x = (8x - 16)$ N

(a)

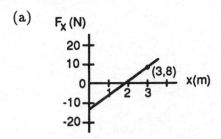

7.26

(b) $W_{net} = \dfrac{-(2 \text{ m})(16 \text{ N})}{2} + \dfrac{(1 \text{ m})(8 \text{ N})}{2} = \boxed{-12.0 \text{ J}}$

7.27 $k = \dfrac{F}{y} = \dfrac{Mg}{y} = \dfrac{(4)(9.8) \text{ N}}{2.5 \times 10^{-2} \text{ m}} = 1.57 \times 10^3 \text{ N/m}$

(a) For 1 kg mass $y = y_1 = \dfrac{mg}{k} = \dfrac{(4)(9.8)}{1.57 \times 10^3} = \boxed{0.938 \text{ cm}}$

(b) Work $= \dfrac{1}{2} ky^2$ where $y = \dfrac{mg}{k} = 4$ cm

Work $= \dfrac{1}{2}(1.57 \times 10^3 \text{ N} \cdot \text{m})(0.04 \text{ m})^2 = \boxed{1.25 \text{ J}}$

7.28 (a)

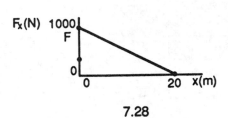

7.28

(b) $F_{av} = \dfrac{F_{max} + F_{min}}{2} = \dfrac{1000 \text{ N} + (1000 - 50x) \text{ N}}{2} = \boxed{(1000 - 25x) \text{ N}}$

(c) Work $= (F_{av})x = 1000x - 25x^2 = (1000)(20 \text{ m}) - (25)(20 \text{ m})^2 = \boxed{10.0 \text{ kJ}}$

7.29 $W = \int F dx = \int\limits_{4}^{7}(3x^3 - 5)dx$

$W = [\frac{3x^4}{4} - 5x]_4^7 = [\frac{3(2401)}{4} - 35] - [\frac{3(256)}{4} - 20] = \boxed{1.59 \ \text{kJ}}$

*7.30 $F = kx$

(a) $k = \frac{F}{x} = \frac{50 \ \text{N}}{0.12 \ \text{m}} = \boxed{417 \ \text{N/m}}$

(b) $W = \frac{1}{2} kx^2 = \frac{1}{2}(417 \ \text{N/m})(0.12 \ \text{m})^2 = \boxed{3 \ \text{J}}$

*7.31 $4 \ \text{J} = \frac{1}{2} k(0.1 \ \text{m})^2$

$\therefore k = 800 \ \text{N/m}$

and to stretch the spring to 0.2 m requires

$\Delta W = \frac{1}{2}(800)(0.2)^2 - 4 \ \text{J} = \boxed{12 \ \text{J}}$

7.32 (a) $K_A = \frac{1}{2}(0.6)(2 \ \text{m/s})^2 = \boxed{1.20 \ \text{J}}$

(b) $\frac{1}{2}mv_B^2 = K_B$

$v_B = \sqrt{\frac{2K_B}{m}} = \sqrt{\frac{(2)(7.5)}{0.6}} = \boxed{5.00 \ \text{m/s}}$

(c) $W = \Delta K = K_B - K_A = \frac{1}{2}m(v_B^2 - v_A^2) = K_B - K_A$

$= 7.5 \ \text{J} - 1.2 \ \text{J} = \boxed{6.30 \ \text{J}}$

7.33 (a) $K = \frac{1}{2}mv^2 = \frac{1}{2}(0.3 \ \text{kg})(15 \ \text{m/s})^2 = \boxed{33.8 \ \text{J}}$

(b) $K = \frac{1}{2}(0.3)(30)^2 = \frac{1}{2}(0.3)(15)^2(4) = 4(33.7) = \boxed{135 \ \text{J}}$

7.34 $K = \frac{mv^2}{2} = \frac{1000(7 \times 10^3)^2}{2} = \boxed{2.45 \times 10^{10} \ \text{J}}$

7.35 (a) $\Delta K = W$

$$\frac{1}{2}\,mv^2 = W$$

$$\frac{1}{2}(2500 \text{ kg})v^2 = 5000 \text{ J}$$

$$v = \boxed{2.00 \text{ m/s}}$$

(b) $W = \mathbf{F} \cdot \mathbf{x}$

$$5000 \text{ J} = F(25 \text{ m})$$

$$F = \boxed{200 \text{ N}}$$

7.36 $\mathbf{v}_0 = (6\mathbf{i} - 2\mathbf{j}) \text{ m/s}$

(a) $v_0 = \sqrt{v_{0x}^2 + v_{0y}^2} = \sqrt{40} \text{ m/s}$

$$K_0 = \frac{1}{2}\,mv_0^2 = \frac{1}{2}(3 \text{ kg})(40 \text{ m}^2/\text{s}^2) = \boxed{60.0 \text{ J}}$$

(b) $\mathbf{v} = 8\mathbf{i} + 4\mathbf{j}$

$$v^2 = \mathbf{v} \cdot \mathbf{v} = 64 + 16 = 80 \text{ m}^2/\text{s}^2$$

$$\Delta K = K - K_0 = \frac{1}{2}m(v^2 - v_0^2) = \frac{3}{2}(80) - 60 = \boxed{60.0 \text{ J}}$$

7.37 (a) $W_F = \mathbf{F} \cdot \mathbf{s} = (130 \text{ N})(5 \text{ m}) = \boxed{650 \text{ J}}$

(b) $W_f = \mathbf{f} \cdot \mathbf{s} = -\mu mgs = -0.3(40)(9.80)5 = \boxed{-588 \text{ J}}$

(c) $W_{\text{net}} = W_F + W_f = 650 - 588 = \boxed{62.0 \text{ J}}$

(d) $\Delta K = 62 \text{ J} = \dfrac{mv_f^2}{2} - \dfrac{mv_i^2}{2}$ or $v_f = \sqrt{\dfrac{2(62)}{40}} = \boxed{1.76 \text{ m/s}}$

7.38 (a) $W = \Delta K = 7.5$ J (for $x = 0$ to $x = 5$ m);

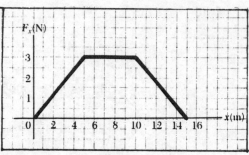

7.38

$$\frac{1}{2}mv_f^2 = 7.5$$

$$v_f^2 = \frac{15}{4}$$

$$v_f = \boxed{1.94 \ \text{m/s}}$$

(b) $W = \Delta K = 22.5$ J (for $x = 0$ to $x = 10$ m);

$$\frac{1}{2}mv_f^2 = 22.5$$

$$v_f^2 = \frac{45}{4}$$

$$v_f = \boxed{3.35 \ \text{m/s}}$$

(c) $W = \Delta K = 30$ J (for $x = 0$ to $x = 15$ m);

$$\frac{1}{2}mv_f^2 = 30$$

$$v_f^2 = \frac{60}{4}$$

$$v_f = \boxed{3.87 \ \text{m/s}}$$

*7.39

$$\mathbf{F} \cdot \mathbf{s} = \frac{1}{2} mv^2$$

$$F(0.72\text{m}) = \frac{1}{2} (0.15 \ \text{kg})(780 \ \text{m/s})^2$$

$$F = \boxed{6340 \ \text{N}}$$

*7.40 $\frac{1}{2}mv^2 = \mathbf{f} \cdot \mathbf{s}$

(a) $\frac{1}{2}(0.005 \ \text{kg})(600 \ \text{m/s})^2 = f(0.04 \ \text{m})$

$f = \boxed{22,500\text{N}}$

(b) $t = \dfrac{s}{\bar{v}} = \dfrac{0.04 \ \text{m}}{300 \ \text{m/s}} = \boxed{1.33 \times 10^{-4} \ \text{s}}$

*7.41 $mgh = \frac{1}{2}mv^2$

$v = \sqrt{2gh} = \sqrt{2(9.8 \text{ m/s}^2)(6 \text{ m})} = \boxed{10.8 \text{ m/s}}$ downward.

7.42   Assume frictionless track

$$W_{\text{net}} = \Delta K = \frac{1}{2}mv^2 - \frac{1}{2}mv_0^2$$

$$mgh = \frac{1}{2}mv^2 - \frac{1}{2}mv_0^2$$

$$mgh + \frac{1}{2}mv_0^2 = \frac{1}{2}mv^2$$

$$v = \sqrt{2gh + v_0^2} = \sqrt{(2)(9.8)(40) + (13 \text{ m/s})^2} = \boxed{30.9 \text{ m/s}}$$

7.43 $W_{net} = \Delta K$

$$m_1 gh - m_2 gh = \frac{1}{2}(m_1 + m_2)v^2$$

$$v^2 = \frac{2(m_1 - m_2)gh}{m_1 + m_2} = 2\frac{(0.3 - 0.2)}{(0.3 + 0.2)}(9.8)(0.4)$$

$$v = \sqrt{1.568} = \boxed{1.25 \text{ m/s}}$$

7.44   (a) $W_s = \frac{1}{2}kx_i^2 - \frac{1}{2}kx_f^2 = \frac{1}{2}(500)(0.5)^2$

$W_{\text{net}} = \frac{mv_f^2}{2} - \frac{mv_i^2}{2}$ so

$v_f = \sqrt{(0.625)2/2} = \boxed{0.791 \text{ m/s to the left}}$

(b) $W_{\text{net}} = W_s + W_f = 0.625 - \mu mgs = 0.625 - 0.35(2)9.8(0.5) = 0.282 \text{ J}$

$W_{\text{net}} = \Delta K$ so $v_F = \sqrt{(0.282)2/2} = \boxed{0.531 \text{ m/s to the left}}$

7.45 $v_0 = 2.0$ m/s; $\mu_k = 0.1$

$$W = \Delta K$$

$$-f_k x = 0 - \frac{1}{2}mv_0^2$$

$$-\mu_k mgx = -\frac{1}{2}mv_0^2$$

$$x = \frac{v_0^2}{2\mu_k g} = \frac{(2.0 \text{ m/s})^2}{2(0.1)(9.8)} = \boxed{2.04 \text{ m}}$$

7.46 $W_{\text{net}} = \Delta K = 0$

$$\int_0^L mg\sin 35° dl - \int_0^d kx\,dx = 0$$

$$mg\sin 35°(L) = \frac{1}{2}kd^2$$

$$d = \sqrt{\frac{2mg\sin 35°(L)}{k}} = \sqrt{\frac{2(12 \text{ kg})(9.8 \text{ m/s}^2)\sin 35°(3 \text{ m})}{3 \times 10^4 \text{ N/m}}} = 0.116 \text{ m} = \boxed{116 \text{ mm}}$$

7.47   (a) $W_g = mgl\sin\theta = (10 \text{ kg})(9.8 \text{ m/s}^2)(5 \text{ m})\sin 20° = \boxed{168 \text{ J}}$

(b) $f_k = \mu_k N = \mu_k\,mg\cos\theta$

   $W_f = lf_k = l\mu_k\,mg\cos\theta$

   $W_f = (5 \text{ m})(0.4)(10)(9.8)\cos 20° = \boxed{184 \text{ J}}$

(c) $W_F = Fl = (100)(5) = \boxed{500 \text{ J}}$

(d) $\Delta K = W_{\text{net}} = W_F - W_f - W_g = \boxed{148 \text{ J}}$

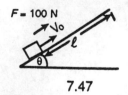

7.47

(e) $\Delta K = \frac{1}{2}mv^2 - \frac{1}{2}mv_0^2$

   $v = \sqrt{\frac{2(\Delta K)}{m} + v_0^2} = \sqrt{\frac{2(148)}{10} + (1.5)^2} = \boxed{5.64 \text{ m/s}}$

7.48

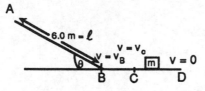

7.48

(a) Work done from $A \longrightarrow B = \Delta K$

$$(l \sin \theta)mg = \frac{1}{2}mv_B^2$$

$$v_B^2 = 2lg \sin \theta = (2)(6.0 \text{ m})(9.8 \text{ m/s}^2) \sin 20°$$

$$v_B^2 = 40.2 \text{ m}^2/\text{s}^2$$

$$v_B = \sqrt{40.2} = \boxed{6.34 \text{ m/s}}$$

(b) From $B \longrightarrow C$:

$$W_{BC} = \Delta K = \frac{m}{2}v_C^2 - \frac{m}{2}v_B^2$$

$$-(BC)f_k = \frac{1}{2}mv_C^2 - \frac{1}{2}mv_B^2 \quad \text{where } f_k = \mu_k mg$$

$$v_C^2 = v_B^2 - 2\mu_k g(BC) = 40.2 \text{ m}^2/\text{s}^2 - (2)(0.5)(9.8)(1 \text{ m}) = 30.4 \text{ m}^2/\text{s}^2$$

$$v_C = \sqrt{30.4} = \boxed{5.52 \text{ m/s}}$$

(c) From $B \rightarrow D : W = \Delta K$

$$-\mu mgd = -\frac{1}{2}mv_B^2$$

$$d = \frac{v_B^2}{2\mu g} = \boxed{4.10 \text{ m}}$$

7.49   (a) $W = \Delta K + \Delta U$

$$fs \cos \theta = \frac{m(v^2 - v_0^2)}{2} + mg(h_f - h_i)$$

$$fs(-1) = \frac{m(-v_0^2)}{2} + mgs \sin 20°$$

$f = 15$ N, $\theta = 180°, v = 0, h_i = 0,$ and $h_f = s \sin 20°$

$$s = \frac{mv_0^2}{(2)(f + mg \sin 20°)} = \frac{(4 \text{ kg})(8 \text{ m/s})^2}{(2)[15 \text{ N} + (4 \text{ kg})(9.80 \text{ m/s}^2) \sin 20°]} = \boxed{4.51 \text{ m}}$$

(b) On the incline the forces acting on the block along the surface are

$mg \sin 20°$ and f; and since $mg \sin 20° = 13.4$ N < 15 N $= f$,

the block will *NOT* slide back down the incline.

7.50 $W_{\text{net}} = \Delta K$

$$(mg \sin \theta - f)l = \frac{1}{2}mv^2 - 0$$

$$f = mg \sin \theta - \frac{mv^2}{2l}$$

$$f = 70(9.8)(\sin 2.87°) - \frac{70(5^2)}{2(30)} = \boxed{5.18 \text{ N}}$$

7.51 $\quad \Sigma F_y = -F_0 \sin 37° + N - mg \cos 37° = 0$

Thus $\quad N = F_0 \sin 37° + mg \cos 37° = 40(0.6) + 3(9.8)(0.8) = 47.5$ N

Thus $\quad f_k = \mu_k N = 0.1(47.5 \text{ N}) = \boxed{4.75 \text{ N}}$

(a) $W_{F_0} = F_0 s \cos 37° = (40 \text{ N})(2 \text{ m})(0.8) = \boxed{63.9 \text{ J}}$

(b) $W_g = (mg)(s)\cos(90° + 37°) = -mgs \sin 37° = -3(9.8)(2)(0.6) = \boxed{-35.3 \text{ J}}$

(c) $W_f = -f_k s = -(4.75 \text{ N})(2 \text{ m}) = \boxed{-9.5 \text{ J}}$

(d) $\Delta K = \Sigma W = W_{F_0} + W_g + W_f = 63.9 - 35.3 - 9.5 = \boxed{19.1 \text{ J}}$

7.52 $\quad$ (a) The forces are all perpendicular to motion thus the work done

by each force is zero.

(b) $f = \mu mg = 0.25(4)(9.80) = 9.8$ N, $\quad s = 2\pi r = 2\pi(2) = 12.57$ m

$\quad W_f = -fs = -(9.80)(12.57) = \boxed{-123 \text{ J}}$

7.53 $\quad$ Power $= \dfrac{W}{t} = \dfrac{mgh}{t} = \dfrac{(700 \text{ N})(10 \text{ m})}{8 \text{ s}} = \boxed{875 \text{ W}}$

*7.54 $\quad$ Power $= 60n = (1.2 \times 10^6 \text{ kg/s})(9.8 \text{ m/s}^2)(50 \text{ m})$

$\quad n = \boxed{9.8 \times 10^6}$

7.55 $\quad$ Assume constant velocity.

$\quad P = \dfrac{mgh}{t} = \dfrac{(200 \text{ kg})(9.8 \text{ m/s}^2)(2 \text{ m})}{1.5 \text{ s}} = \boxed{3.27 \text{ kW}}$

7.56 $\mu = 0.4$ and $v = 5$ m/s

(a) To move at constant speed $F = f = \mu m g$

so $P = Fv = \mu mgv = (0.4)200(9.80)5 = \boxed{3920 \ \text{W}}$

(b) $W = Pt = 3920(3 \ \text{min} \times 60 \ \text{s/min}) = \boxed{706 \ \text{kJ}}$

7.57   (a) $W = \Delta K = \frac{1}{2}(1500 \ \text{kg})(10 \ \text{m/s})^2 = \boxed{75.0 \ \text{kJ}}$

(b) $P = \dfrac{W}{t} = \dfrac{7.5 \times 10^4}{3} = \boxed{25.0 \ \text{kW}}$

(c) $P = Fv = mav = ma^2t$;   in this case $a = \dfrac{10 \ \text{m/s}}{3 \ \text{s}} = \boxed{\dfrac{10}{3} \ \text{m/s}^2}$

Therefore at $t = 2$ s

$P = (1500 \ \text{kg}) \, (\dfrac{10}{3} \dfrac{\text{m}}{\text{s}^2})^2(2 \ \text{s}) = \boxed{33.3 \ \text{kW}}$

7.58 $P_a = f_a v \implies f_a = \dfrac{P_a}{v} = \dfrac{2.24 \times 10^4}{27} = \boxed{830 \ \text{N}}$

*7.59   Power $= \mathbf{F} \cdot \mathbf{v} = (15 \ \text{lb}) \left(10 \ \dfrac{\text{mi}}{\text{hr}}\right) \left(\dfrac{5280 \ \text{ft/mi}}{3600 \ \text{s/hr}}\right)$

$P \ = \ 220 \ \dfrac{\text{ft} \cdot \text{lb}}{\text{s}} = \boxed{0.4 \ \text{hp}}$

7.60   (a) If f is the resisting force then

$$\text{Power} = fv \text{ and } f = \frac{\text{Power}}{v} = \frac{1.3 \times 10^5 \text{ W}}{31 \text{ m/s}} = 4194 \text{ N}$$

On the incline resisting force $= F = f + mg \sin \theta$.

So

$$Fv = \text{ Power}$$

$$v = \frac{1.3 \times 10^5}{\frac{1.3 \times 10^5}{31} + \frac{2.5 \times 10^3}{20}} = \boxed{30.1 \text{ m/s}}$$

(b) $Fv = \text{ Power } = (f + mg \sin \theta)v$

$$= (\frac{1.3 \times 10^5}{31} + \frac{2.5 \times 10^3}{10})(10) = \boxed{44.4 \text{ kW}}$$

7.61   (a) Assume that he runs at constant speed. Then $\Delta K = 0$, so

$$\Delta W_{\text{net}} = \Delta W_A + \Delta W_g = 0.$$

$$\Delta W_g = mg \Delta s \cos(90° + \theta) = 65 \text{ kg} \times 9.8 \text{ m/s}^2 \times 600 \text{ m} \times \cos(110°)$$

$$= 1.31 \times 10^5 \text{ J}$$

Then the athlete does work $\Delta W_A = \Delta W_g = \boxed{131 \text{ kJ}}$

(b) $P = \dfrac{\Delta W_A}{\Delta t} = \dfrac{1.31 \times 10^5 \text{ J}}{80 \text{ s}} = \boxed{1.64 \text{ kW}}$

7.62   (a) $P = Fv$, $v = at$, $v_0 = 0$, $a = \dfrac{F}{m}$; so $P = Fat = \dfrac{F^2 t}{m}$

(b) $P = \dfrac{(20)^2(3)}{5} = \boxed{240 \text{ W}}$

7.63   (a) $P_a = f_a v = (830 \text{ N}) \left(\dfrac{129 \text{ km}}{\text{m}}\right)\left(\dfrac{1000 \text{ m}}{1 \text{ km}}\right)\left(\dfrac{1 \text{ h}}{3600 \text{ s}}\right) = \boxed{29.7 \text{ kW}}$

(b) $P_T = f_T v = (1041 \text{ N})\left(\dfrac{129 \text{ km}}{\text{m}}\right)\left(\dfrac{1000 \text{ m}}{1 \text{ km}}\right)\left(\dfrac{1 \text{ h}}{3600 \text{ s}}\right) = \boxed{37.3 \text{ kW}}$

7.64 $\left(\dfrac{3000 \text{ mi}}{25 \text{ mi/gal}}\right)/2$ people $= 60.0$ gal/person   by car

$\left(\dfrac{3000 \text{ mi}}{1 \text{ mi/gal}}\right)/150$ people $= 20.0$ gal/person   by jet

*7.65   (a) $\dfrac{\frac{1}{2}(900 \text{ kg})(24.6 \text{ m/s})^2}{0.15(1.34 \times 10^8 \text{ J/gal})} = \boxed{1.35 \times 10^{-2} \text{ gal}}$

(b) $\boxed{73.8}$

(c) $\dfrac{1 \text{ gal}}{38 \text{ mi}}\left(\dfrac{55 \text{ mi}}{\text{h}}\right)\left(\dfrac{1.34 \times 10^8 \text{ J}}{\text{gal}}\right)\left(\dfrac{\text{h}}{3600 \text{ s}}\right)(0.15) = \boxed{8.08 \text{ kW} = 1.08 \text{ hp}}$

7.66   We must derive the same *total* energy per gallon for each case.

Using 60 mi/h $= 26.8$ m/s, we have

$$\dfrac{\text{Eff}_1(\text{Power})_1}{(\text{velocity})_1}(\text{fuel economy})_1 = \dfrac{\text{Eff}_2(\text{Power})_2(\text{fuel economy})_2}{\text{velocity}_2}$$

$\text{Eff}_1 = \text{Eff}_2 = 0.14$

$P_1 \;=\;$ available fuel power $= 136 \text{ kW}$

$P_2 \;=\;$ available fuel power $+$ power needed to move 350 kg

$\quad = \; 136 \text{ kW} + \mu W v = 136 \text{ kW} + 0.016(350)(9.8)(26.8)$

$\quad = \; 136 \text{ kW} + 1.47 \text{ kW}$

$\quad = \; 137.47 \text{ kW}$

$(\text{fuel economy})_2 = \dfrac{(136 \text{ kW})(6.4 \text{ km/L})}{137.47 \text{ kW}} = \boxed{6.33 \text{ km/L}}$

7.67 $\dfrac{\mathrm{Eff}_1(\mathrm{Power})_1(f.E.)_1}{v_1} = \dfrac{\mathrm{Eff}_1(\mathrm{Power})_2(f.E.)_2}{v_2}$

$(\mathrm{Power})_2 = (\mathrm{Power})_1 + 11 \ \mathrm{kW} = 136 \ \mathrm{kW} + 11 \ \mathrm{kW} = 147 \ \mathrm{kW}$

$(f.E.)_2 = \dfrac{136 \ \mathrm{kW}(6.4 \ \mathrm{km/L})}{147 \ \mathrm{kW}} = \boxed{5.92 \ \mathrm{km/L}}$

7.68 (a) $K = \gamma mc^2 - mc^2 = (\gamma - 1)mc^2$

$\gamma = \dfrac{1}{\sqrt{1 - v^2/c^2}} = \dfrac{1}{\sqrt{1 - (0.995)^2}} = 10.0$

$mc^2 = (9.11 \times 10^{-31} \ \mathrm{kg})(2.998 \times 10^2 \ \mathrm{m/s})^2 = 8.19 \times 10^{-14} \ \mathrm{kg \cdot m^2/s^2}$

$K = (10.0 - 1)(8.19 \times 10^{-14} \ \mathrm{kg \cdot m^2/s^2}) = \boxed{7.37 \times 10^{-13} \ \mathrm{J}}$

(b) $K_c = \dfrac{1}{2}mv^2 = \dfrac{1}{2}(9.11 \times 10^{-31} \ \mathrm{kg})(0.995c)^2 = 4.05 \times 10^{-14} \ \mathrm{J}$

$\% \ \mathrm{error} = \dfrac{(7.37 \times 10^{-13} \ \mathrm{J} - 4.05 \times 10^{-14} \ \mathrm{J})}{7.37 \times 10^{-13} \ \mathrm{J}} \times 100 = \boxed{94.5\%}$

7.69 (a) $W = \Delta K = (\gamma_2 mc^2 - mc^2) - (\gamma_1 mc^2 - mc^2)$

$= \dfrac{mc^2}{\sqrt{1 - v_2^2/c^2}} - \dfrac{mc^2}{\sqrt{1 - v_1^2/c^2}} = mc^2\left(\dfrac{1}{\sqrt{1 - (\frac{3}{4})^2}} - \dfrac{1}{\sqrt{1 - (\frac{1}{2})^2}}\right)$

$= (1.673 \times 10^{-27} \ \mathrm{kg})(2.998 \times 10^8 \ \mathrm{m/s})^2[1.512 - 1.155] = \boxed{5.37 \times 10^{-11} \ \mathrm{J}}$

(b) $W = \Delta K = 1.503 \times 10^{-10} \ \mathrm{J}\left(\dfrac{1}{\sqrt{1 - (0.995)^2}} - 1.155\right) = \boxed{1.33 \times 10^{-9} \ \mathrm{J}}$

7.70 $\Sigma F_x = 0$

$F - mg \sin 15° - f = 0$

$\Sigma F_y = 0$

$N - mg \cos 15° = 0$

$N = mg \cos 15° = 142 \text{ N}$

$f = \mu N = 56.8 \text{ N}$

$F = mg \sin 15° + 56.8 = 94.8 \text{ N}$

(a) $W_F = Fd = (94.8 \text{ N})(8 \text{ m}) = \boxed{758 \text{ J}}$

(b) $W_f = -fd = (56.8 \text{ N})(8 \text{ m}) = \boxed{454 \text{ J}}$

(c) $W_N = Nd(\cos 90°) = \boxed{0 \text{ J}}$

(d) $W_g = -mgd \sin 15° = \boxed{-304 \text{ J}}$

(Note that $W_{\text{total}} = 0$!)

7.71 $W_{\text{net}} = \Delta K$

$-\mu \, mgl = -\frac{1}{2}mv^2$

$v = \sqrt{2\mu gl} = \sqrt{2(0.1)(9.8)(7)} = \boxed{3.70 \text{ m/s}}$

7.72   (a) $W_w = \boldsymbol{F} \cdot \boldsymbol{d} = mgd = (10 \text{ kg})(9.80 \text{ m/s}^2)(10 \text{ m}) = \boxed{980 \text{ J}}$

(b) $W_g = \boldsymbol{F} \cdot \boldsymbol{d} = (-mg)d = -(10 \text{ kg})(9.80 \text{ m/s}^2)(10 \text{ m}) = \boxed{-980 \text{ J}}$

(c) $P = \boldsymbol{F} \cdot \boldsymbol{v} = mgv = (10)(9.80)(0.25) = \boxed{24.5 \text{ J/s}}$ or $\boxed{24.5 \text{ W}}$

*7.73 If we approximate the force curve as a parabola of equation $F(x) = 240 - 15(x - 4)^2$, then

x	$F(x)$
0	0
2	180
4	240
6	180
8	0

$$W = \int_{x=0}^{8} F(x)\,dx$$

$$= \int_{x=0}^{8} (120x - 15x^2)\,dx$$

$$= 60x^2 - 5x^3 \Big|_0^8 = \boxed{1280 \text{ J}}$$

7.74 (a) $\boxed{\cos \alpha = \dfrac{A_x}{A}}$

Similarly, $\cos \beta = \dfrac{A_y}{A}$ and $\cos \gamma = \dfrac{A_z}{A}$ where $A = \sqrt{A_x^2 + A_y^2 + A_z^2}$

(b) $\cos^2 \alpha + \cos^2 \beta + \cos^2 \gamma = (\dfrac{A_x}{A})^2 + (\dfrac{A_y}{A})^2 + (\dfrac{A_z}{A})^2 = \dfrac{A^2}{A^2} = 1$

7.75 (a) $x = t + 2t^3$, therefore $v = \dfrac{dx}{dt} = 1 + 6t^2$

$$K = \frac{1}{2}mv^2 = \frac{1}{2}(4)(1 + 6t^2)^2 = \boxed{(2 + 24t^2 + 72t^4) \text{ J}}$$

(b) $a = \dfrac{dv}{dt} = \boxed{(12\,t) \text{ m/s}^2}$, $F = ma = 4(12t) = \boxed{(48t) \text{ N}}$

(c) $P = Fv = (48t)(1 + 6t^2) = \boxed{(48t + 288t^3) \text{ W}}$

(d) $W = \int_0^2 P\,dt = \int_0^2 (48\,t + 288\,t^3)\,dt = \boxed{1250 \text{ J}}$

7.76   (a) $W_{\text{net}} = \Delta K$

$$m_1 g h - m_2 g h = \frac{1}{2} m_1 v^2 + \frac{1}{2} m_2 v^2$$

$$v^2 = 2\left(\frac{m_1 - m_2}{m_1 + m_2}\right) g h = 2\left(\frac{3 \text{ kg} - 2 \text{ kg}}{3 \text{ kg} + 2 \text{ kg}}\right)(9.8 \text{ m/s}^2)(2 \text{ m}) = 7.84 \text{ m}^2/\text{s}^2$$

$$v = \sqrt{7.84} \text{ m/s} = \boxed{2.80 \text{ m/s}}$$

(b) $W_{\text{net}} = \Delta K$

$$(m_1 - m_2) g h - f h = \frac{1}{2}(m_1 + m_2) v^2 - 0$$

$$v^2 = \frac{(m_1 - m_2) g h - f h}{\frac{1}{2}(m_1 + m_2)} = \frac{[(3-2)(9.8)(2) - (5)(2)] \text{ N} \cdot \text{m}}{\frac{1}{2}(3+2) \text{ kg}}$$

$$v = \boxed{1.96 \text{ m/s}}$$

*7.77 $mgh = \mathbf{F} \cdot \mathbf{s}$

$$(2100 \text{ kg})(9.8 \text{ m/s}^2)(5.12 \text{ m}) = F(0.12 \text{ m})$$

$$F = \boxed{8.78 \times 10^5 \text{ N}}$$

*7.78 $P = \mathbf{F} \cdot \mathbf{v}$

$$= 120(80 \text{ kg})(9.8 \text{ m/s}^2)(\sin 30°)(3 \text{ m/s})$$

$$= \boxed{141 \text{ kW}}$$

7.79   (a) $W_{\text{net}} = \Delta K$

$$W_s + W_g = 0$$

$$\frac{1}{2}(1.4 \times 10^3 \text{ N/m}) \times (0.1 \text{ m})^2 - (0.2 \text{ kg})(9.8)(\sin 60°)l = 0$$

$$l = \boxed{4.12 \text{ m}}$$

(b) $W_{\text{net}} = \Delta K$

$$W_s + W_g + W_f = 0$$

$$\frac{1}{2}(1.4 \times 10^3 \text{ N/m})(0.1)^2 - [(0.2)(9.8)(\sin 60°) + (0.2)(9.8)(0.4)(\cos 60°)]l = 0$$

$$l = \boxed{3.35 \text{ m}}$$

7.80 (a) The work done in stretching the spring must equal the work later done against friction. In this case, $x = d$ and therefore

$$\frac{1}{2}kd^2 = \mu mgd; \quad \boxed{\mu = \frac{kd}{2mg}}$$

(b) In this case, $x = d/2$ and $\boxed{\mu = \dfrac{kd}{4mg}}$

7.81 (a) $W = \Delta K = \dfrac{m(v_f^2 - v_i^2)}{2} = \dfrac{(0.4)(6^2 - 8^2)}{2} = \boxed{-5.60 \text{ J}}$

(b) $W = -5.6 = F\Delta s = -\mu mg(2\pi r)$

therefore $\mu = \dfrac{5.6}{(0.4)(9.80)(2\pi)(1.5)} = \boxed{0.152}$

(c) After N revolutions, $v = 0$ and all the initial kinetic energy is lost to friction, therefore $K_i = \dfrac{(0.4)(8^2)}{2}$;

$W = (0.152)(0.4)(9.80)(2\pi)(1.5) \text{ N}$ and $K_i = W$, so $N = \boxed{2.28 \text{ rev}}$

7.82   (a) $$W_{\text{net}} = \Delta K$$

$$m_1 gh - \mu m_2 gh = \frac{1}{2}(m_1 + m_2)(v^2 - v_0^2)$$

$$v = \sqrt{\frac{2gh(m_1 - \mu m_2)}{(m_1 + m_2)}}$$

$$= \sqrt{\frac{2(9.8)(20)[0.4 - (0.2)(0.25)]}{(0.4 + 0.25)}} = \boxed{14.5 \ \text{m/s}}$$

(b) $W_f + W_g = \Delta K = 0$

$-\mu(\Delta m_2 + m_2)gh + m_1 gh = 0$

$\mu(\Delta m_2 + m_2) = m_1$

$\Delta m_2 = \dfrac{m_1}{\mu} - m_2 = \dfrac{0.4 \ \text{kg}}{0.2} - 0.25 \ \text{kg} = \boxed{1.75 \ \text{kg}}$

(c) $W_f + W_g = \Delta K = 0$

$-\mu m_2 gh + (m_1 - \Delta m_1)gh = 0$

$\Delta m_1 = m_1 - \mu m_2 = 0.4 \ \text{kg} - (0.2)(0.25 \ \text{kg}) = \boxed{0.350 \ \text{kg}}$

7.83   (a) $dW = \mathbf{F}_s \cdot d\mathbf{s}$

$F_s = -mg\cos\theta; \quad ds = \dfrac{dy}{\cos\theta};$

$W = \displaystyle\int_h^0 (-mg\cos\theta)\dfrac{dy}{\cos\theta} = mgh$

or $W = \displaystyle\int F \, ds; \quad W = \int_h^0 (-mg) \, dy = \boxed{mgh}$

(b) $W = \Delta K = \boxed{mgh}$

(c) $K_f - K_i = \Delta K = W; \quad K_i = \dfrac{1}{2}mv_0^2;$

$K_f = W + K_i = \boxed{\dfrac{1}{2}mv_0^2 + mgh}$

7.84 (a) $P = \dfrac{dW}{dt} = \boldsymbol{F} \cdot \boldsymbol{v}$ and $F = -mg$; $v = v_{y0} - gt$;

substitute $P = (-mg)(-gt) = \boxed{mg^2 t}$

(b) $(0 - y) = v_{y0}t - \dfrac{1}{2}gt^2$ $t^2 = \dfrac{2y}{g}$;

$t = \sqrt{\dfrac{2(40)}{9.80}} = 2.86$ s until projectile hits ground

$P_{(1)} = mg^2 t = (10)(9.80)^2(1) = \boxed{960 \ \text{W}}$

$P_{(2)} = mg^2 t = (10)(9.80)^2(2) = \boxed{1.92\,\text{kW}}$

$P_{(3)} = \boxed{0}$ *because the projectile has already hit the ground.*

7.85 $W_f = \dfrac{20\ \text{N}}{\text{Pulley}}(2\ \text{pulleys})(6\ \text{m}) = -240\ \text{J}$

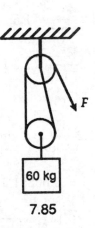

7.85

While 6 m of rope slides across the upper (fixed) pulley,

only 3 m of rope slides across the lower pulley!

$W_f = -(20\ \text{N})(6\ \text{m}) - (20\ \text{N})(3\ \text{m}) = -180\ \text{J}$

Then

$W_{\text{net}} = W_{\text{grav}} + W_{\text{frict}} = mgh + W_f$

$W_{\text{net}} = 1764\ \text{J} + 180\ \text{J} = \boxed{1.94 \ \text{kJ}}$

7.86 (a) Since the particle moves slowly $a = 0$ and $\Sigma F_x = 0$; therefore

$F - T\sin\theta = 0$ and since $\Sigma F_y = 0$, $T\cos\theta - mg = 0$

Solving these equations for F gives $F = mg\tan\theta$

(b) $W = \displaystyle\int \boldsymbol{F} \cdot d\boldsymbol{s}$: From the sketch, we see that $\boldsymbol{F} \cdot d\boldsymbol{s} = F\,ds\cos\theta$

therefore $W = \displaystyle\int_0^\theta (mg\,\tan\theta)(L\,d\theta)\cos\theta = mgL(1 - \cos\theta)$

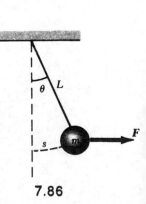

7.86

*7.87   (a) $P = \dfrac{\Delta E}{\Delta t} = \dfrac{\Delta(mgh)}{\Delta t} = \dfrac{\Delta mgh}{\Delta t}$

(b) $\dfrac{\Delta m}{\Delta t}(9.8 \text{ m/s}^2)(87 \text{ m}) = 7.24 \times 10^8 \text{ W}$

Flow rate $= \dfrac{\Delta m}{\Delta t} = \boxed{8.49 \times 10^5 \text{ kg/s}}$

(c) $v = \left(8.49 \times 10^5 \dfrac{\text{kg}}{\text{s}}\right)\left(\dfrac{86400 \text{ s}}{\text{day}}\right)\left(\dfrac{1 \text{ m}^3}{1000 \text{ kg}}\right)$

$= \boxed{7.34 \times 10^7 \text{ m}^3}$

(d) $7.34 \times 10^7 \text{ m}^3 = \pi r^2(10 \text{ m})$

$r = \boxed{1.53 \text{ km}}$

*7.88   (a) $2\dfrac{W \cdot s^3}{m^5}(1.5 \text{ m})^2(8 \text{ m/s})^3 = \boxed{2.3 \text{ kW}}$

(b) $2\dfrac{W \cdot s^3}{m^5}(1.5 \text{ m})^2(24 \text{ m/s})^3 = \boxed{62.2 \text{ kW}}$

*7.89 $\dfrac{1}{2}\left(1.2 \dfrac{N}{cm}\right)(5 \text{ cm})(0.05 \text{ m}) = 0.1 \text{ kg}(9.8 \text{ m/s}^2)(0.05 \text{ m}) \sin 10° + \dfrac{1}{2}(0.1 \text{ kg})v^2$

$0.15 \text{ J} = 0.00851 \text{ J} + 0.05 \text{ kg } v^2$

$v = \sqrt{\dfrac{0.141}{0.05}} = \boxed{1.68 \text{ m/s}}$

7.89

7.90 $P\Delta t = W = \Delta K = \dfrac{(\Delta m)v^2}{2}$

The density is $\rho = \dfrac{\Delta m}{\text{vol}} = \dfrac{\Delta m}{A\Delta x}$

Substituting this into the first equation and solving for

P, since $\dfrac{\Delta x}{\Delta t} = v$ for a constant speed, we get

$P = \dfrac{\rho A v^3}{2}$. Also, since $P = Fv$, $F = \dfrac{\rho A v^2}{2}$.

7.91 $m = 5\,\text{kg}, \quad W = \displaystyle\sum_i F_i \Delta x_i$

Assuming the force is averaged over each 1 m distance

interval, the total work done is the area under the F versus x curve.

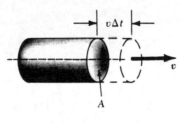

7.91

$\therefore W = \displaystyle\sum_i F_i(1) = \boxed{536.8 \ \text{J}}$

(A small calculator will produce the answer quickly.)

7.92 $m = 0.178$ kg

Moves from $x_1 = 12.8$ m to $x_2 = 23.7$ m.

$$F = \frac{375}{x^3 + 3.75x}$$

The total work done is

$$W = \int_{x_2}^{x_2} F(x)dx = \int_{x=12.8}^{23.7} \frac{375}{x^3 + 3.75x}dx.$$

This numerical integration may be done by Simpson's method.

A BASIC program is given below:

```
10   REM PROGRAM SIMPSON
20   A = 375
30   B = 3.75
40   DEF F(X) = A/(X * *3 + B * X)
50   X0 = 12.80
60   X1 = 23.70
70   N = 100
80   X = X0
90   W = 0
100  S = (X1 − X0)/N
110  K = 0
120  W1 = (S/6) * [F(X) + 4 * F(X + S/2) + F(X + S)]
130  W = W + W1
140  X = X + S
150  K = K + 1
160  IF K = 101 THEN 180
170  GO TO 120
180   WRITE "WORK IS"; W
190  END
```

(Accuracy of Simpson's Method with N = 100 is within 10^{-4}%.)

CHAPTER 8

8.1   (a) $W = W_{OA} + W_{AC} = 0 - mg(y) = \boxed{196 \text{ J}}$

(b) $W = W_{OB} + W_{BC} = -mgy + 0 = \boxed{196 \text{ J}}$

(c) $W = \int F \cdot ds = -mg \cos 45° \sqrt{x^2 + y^2}$

$W = -mg(\cos 45°)\sqrt{2}(5 \text{ m}) = \boxed{196 \text{ J}}$

8.1 – 8.5

Since F_g is conservative, the work done by the force is path independent

8.2   (a) $W = \int_i^f F \cdot ds = F(s_f - s_i)$ depends only on end points and *not* on path

(b) $W = \int F \cdot ds = \int (3i + 4j)\text{N} \cdot (dxi + dyj) = 3x|_0^5 + 4y|_0^5 = 15 + 20 = \boxed{35.0 \text{ J}}$

8.3 $f = 3 \text{ N}$

(a) Path: $O \rightarrow A \rightarrow O$; $W_f = -(5 \text{ m} + 5 \text{ m})(3 \text{ N}) = \boxed{-30.0 \text{ J}}$

(b) Path: $O \rightarrow A \rightarrow C \rightarrow O$; $W_f = -[5 \text{ m} + 5 \text{ m} + 5\sqrt{2} \text{ m}](3 \text{ N}) = \boxed{-51.2 \text{ J}}$

(c) Path: $O \rightarrow C \rightarrow O$; $W_f = -[5\sqrt{2} \text{ m} + 5\sqrt{2} \text{ m}](3 \text{ N}) = \boxed{-42.4 \text{ J}}$

(d) friction is a *nonconservative* force

8.4   (a) $U = -\int_0^x (-Ax + Bx^2)dx = \boxed{\dfrac{Ax^2}{2} - \dfrac{Bx^3}{3}}$

(b) $\Delta U = -\int_2^3 F \, dx = \dfrac{A(3^2 - 2^2)}{2} - \dfrac{B(3^3 - 2^3)}{3} = \boxed{\dfrac{5}{2}A - \dfrac{19}{3}B}$

$\Delta K = \boxed{(-\dfrac{5}{2}A + \dfrac{19}{3}B)}$

8.5   (a) $W_{OA} = \int_0^5 dx\,i \cdot (2yi + x^2 j) = \int_0^5 2y\,dx$ and since along this path, $y = 0$.

$W_{OA} = 0$.

$W_{AC} = \int_0^2 dy\,j \cdot (2yi + x^2 j) = \int_0^2 x^2\,dy$: For $x = 5, W_{AC} = \boxed{125\text{ J}}$

and $W_{OAC} = 0 + 125 = \boxed{125\text{ J}}$

(b)$W_{OB} = \int_0^5 dy\,j \cdot (2yi + x^2 j) = \int_0^5 x^2\,dy$ since along this path $x = 0$,

$W_{OB} = 0$.

$W_{BC} = \int_0^5 dx\,j \cdot (2yi + x^2 j) = \int_0^5 2y\,dx$ since $y = 5$, $W_{BC} = \boxed{50.0\text{ J}}$

and $W_{OBC} = 0 + 50 = \boxed{50\text{ J}}$

(c) $W_{OC} = \int (dxi + dyj) \cdot (2yi + x^2 j) = \int (2y\,dx + x^2\,dy)$

Since $x = y$ along OC $W_{OC} = \int_0^5 dx\,(2x + x^2) = \boxed{66.7\text{ J}}$

(d) F is non-conservative since the work done is path dependent

8.6   (a) $W_C = \Delta K = 80.0$ J;

(b) $\Delta K + \Delta U = 0$, $\Delta U = -80.0$ J

(c)$\Delta K = \dfrac{m(v_s^2 - v_2^2)}{2}$, $v_s = \sqrt{\dfrac{2\Delta K}{m}} = 6.32$ m/s

8.7   (a) $W = \int F_x\,dx = \int_1^5 (2x + 4)\,dx = (\dfrac{2x^2}{2} + 4x)_1^5 = 25 + 20 - 1 - 4 = \boxed{40.0\text{ J}}$

(b) $\Delta K + \Delta U = 0$, $\Delta U = \Delta K = -W = \boxed{-40.0\text{ J}}$

(c) $\Delta K = K_f - \dfrac{mv_1^2}{2}$, $K_f = \Delta K + \dfrac{mv_1^2}{2} = \boxed{62.5\text{ J}}$

8.8   (a) $U_f = K_i - K_f + U_i, \quad U_f = 30 - 18 + 10 = \boxed{22.0 \text{ J}} \quad \boxed{E = 40.0 \text{ J}}$

          (b) Yes, $W_{nc} = \Delta K + \Delta U$; for conservative forces $\Delta K + \Delta U = 0$.

8.9   (a) $F = (3i + 5j) \text{ N} \quad m = 4 \text{ kg}$

          $r = (2i - 3j) \text{ m}$

          $W = 3(2) + 5(-3) = \boxed{-9.00 \text{ J}}$ The result does not depend

          on the path since the force is conservative.

          (b) $W = \Delta K; \quad -9 = \dfrac{4v^2}{2} - 4(\dfrac{4^2}{2})$ so $v = \sqrt{\dfrac{32 - 9}{2}} = \boxed{3.39 \text{ m/s}}$

          (c) $\Delta U = -W = \boxed{9.00 \text{ J}}$

8.10 $U_i + K_i = U_f + K_f$

        $0 + m_1 g h = m_2 g h + \dfrac{1}{2} m_1 v^2 + \dfrac{1}{2} m_2 v^2$

        $(m_1 - m_2) g h = \dfrac{1}{2}(m_1 + m_2) v^2$

        $v^2 = \dfrac{2(m_1 - m_2)}{m_1 + m_2} g h$

        $v = \sqrt{\dfrac{2(1.5 \text{ kg})(9.8 \text{ m/s}^2)(2.5 \text{ m})}{8.5 \text{ kg}}}$

        $v = \boxed{2.94 \text{ m/s}}$

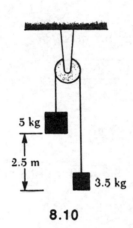

8.10

8.11 $U_i + K_i = U_f + K_f$

$mgh + 0 = mg(2R) + \frac{1}{2}mv^2$

$g(3.5R) = 2g(R) + \frac{1}{2}v^2$

$\boxed{v = \sqrt{3.0gR}}$

$\Sigma F = m\dfrac{v^2}{R}$

$N + mg = m\dfrac{v^2}{R}$

$N = m[\dfrac{v^2}{R} - g] = m[\dfrac{3.0gR}{R} - g]$

$N = 2.0\ mg$

$N = 2.0(0.005\ \text{kg})(9.8\ \text{m/s}^2)$

$= \boxed{0.0980\ \text{N} \quad \text{downward}}$

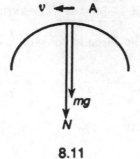

8.11

8.12   (a) $\frac{1}{2}mv_{0y}^2 = mg(20)$

$v_{0y} = \sqrt{2 \times 9.8 \times 20} = \boxed{19.8\ \text{m/s}}$

(b) $\Delta K|_{P \to B} = W_g = mg(60\ \text{m}) = (0.5\ \text{kg})(9.8\ \text{m/s}^2)(60\ \text{m}) = \boxed{294\ \text{J}}$

(c) $v_{0x} = v_{fx} = 30\ \text{m/s}$

$\Delta K|_{P \to B} = \frac{1}{2}mv_{fy}^2 - \frac{1}{2}mv_{0y}^2 = 294\ \text{J}$

$v_{fy}^2 = \dfrac{2}{m}(294) + v_{0y}^2 = 1176 + 392$

$v_{fy} = -39.6\ \text{m/s}$

$\boxed{v_B = (30.0\ \text{m/s})\ \boldsymbol{i} - (39.6\ \text{m/s})\ \boldsymbol{j}}$

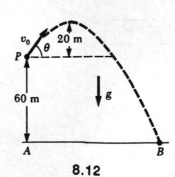

8.12

8.13 (a) $v_{x0} = v_0 \cos 53°$; $v_{y0} = v_0 \sin 53°$;

Since energy is conserved, $E(\text{at } y = h) = E(\text{at } y = \frac{h}{2})$ or

$$mgh + \frac{1}{2}mv_0^2 = mg(\frac{h}{2}) + \frac{1}{2}mv^2 \text{ or}$$

$$\boxed{v = \sqrt{gh + v_0^2}}$$

(b) $v_x = v_{x0} = v_0 \cos 53° = 0.60\, v_0$

$$v^2 = v_{x0}^2 + v_y^2$$

$$v_y = \sqrt{v^2 - v_{x0}^2}, = \sqrt{v_0^2 + gh - v_0^2 \cos^2 53°} = \sqrt{0.64v_0^2 + gh}$$

$$\boxed{v = 0.60v_0\, i - \sqrt{0.64v_0^2 + gh}\, j}$$

8.14 $h = 2(1 - \cos 37°) = 0.4$ m

(a) $mgh = (5\text{ kg})(9.8\text{ m/s}^2)(0.4\text{ m}) = \boxed{19.6\text{ J}}$

(b) $\frac{1}{2}mv_0^2 = mgh + \frac{1}{2}mv^2$ or $v = \sqrt{v_0^2 - 2gh} = \boxed{2.86\text{ m/s}}$

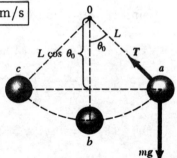

(c) $\Sigma F_r = T - mg \cos\theta = \dfrac{mv^2}{l}$

or $T = m(\dfrac{v^2}{l} + g \cos\theta) = \boxed{59.6\text{ N}}$

(d) $\dfrac{mv_0^2}{2} = mgh$ or $h = \dfrac{v_0^2}{2g} = \boxed{0.816\text{ m}}$

8.14

*8.15   (a) $U = mgy = (0.2)(9.8)y = \boxed{(1.96y) \text{ J}}$

(b) $E = \frac{1}{2}mv_0^2 = \frac{1}{2}(0.2)(20)^2 = \boxed{40 \text{ J}}$

(c) $K = E - U = \boxed{(40 - 1.96y) \text{ J}}$

(d) At maximum height, $mgy = 40$ J.

$$y_{max} = \frac{40}{(0.2)(9.8)} = \boxed{20.4 \ \text{m}}$$

8.16   (a) $K_i + U_i = K_f + U_f$

$$v = \sqrt{2gh} = \boxed{19.8 \text{ m/s}}$$

(b) $E = mgh = \boxed{78.4 \ \text{J}}$

(c) $K_{10} + U_{10} = 78.4$ J

$$K_{10} = 39.2 \text{ J}; \quad U_{10} = 39.2 \text{ J}; \quad \frac{K_{10}}{U_{10}} = \boxed{1.00}$$

8.17   Using conservation of energy

(a) $(5 \text{ kg})g(4 \text{ m}) = (3 \text{ kg})g(4 \text{ m}) + \frac{1}{2}(5 + 3)v^2$

$$v = \sqrt{19.6} = \boxed{4.43 \text{ m/s}}$$

(b) $\frac{1}{2}(3)v^2 = mg\Delta y = 3g\Delta y$

$\Delta y = 1.00$ m

$y_{max} = 4 + \Delta y = \boxed{5.00 \ \text{m}}$

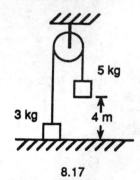

8.17

8.18   Find the velocity at the point where the child leaves the slide, height h

$$(U + K)_i = (U + K)_f$$

$$mgH + 0 = mgh + \frac{1}{2}mv^2$$

$$v = \sqrt{2g(H - h)}$$

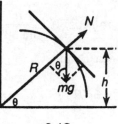

8.18

Use Newton's laws to compare h and H
(Recall the normal force will be zero);

$$\Sigma F_c = ma_c = \frac{mv^2}{R}$$

$$mg \sin \theta - N = \frac{mv^2}{R}$$

$$mg \sin \theta = \frac{m(2g)(H - h)}{R}$$

Put θ in terms of R : $\sin \theta = \dfrac{h}{R}$

$$mg\left(\frac{h}{R}\right) = \frac{2mg(H - h)}{R} \qquad \boxed{h = \frac{2}{3}H}$$

Notice if $H \geq \dfrac{3}{2}R$, the assumption that the child will leave the slide at a height $\dfrac{2}{3}H$ is no longer valid. Then the velocity will be too large for the centripetal force to keep the child on the slide. Thus if $H \geq \dfrac{3}{2}R$, the child will leave the track at $h = R$.

8.19   (a) $\Delta K = \dfrac{1}{2}m(v^2 - v_0^2) = -\dfrac{1}{2}mv_0^2 = \boxed{-160 \text{ J}}$

(b) $\Delta U = mg(3 \text{ m}) \sin 30° = \boxed{73.5 \text{ J}}$

(c) The energy lost to friction is 86.5 J. $\quad f = \dfrac{86.5 \text{ J}}{3 \text{ m}} = \boxed{28.8 \text{ N}}$

(d) $\quad f = \mu_k N = \mu_k mg \cos 30° = 28.8 \text{ N}$

$$\mu = \frac{28.8 \text{ N}}{(5 \text{ kg})(9.8 \text{ m/s}^2) \cos 30°} = \boxed{0.679}$$

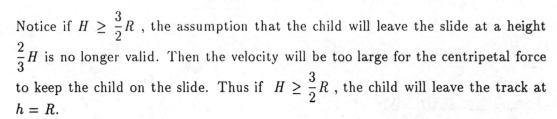

8.19

8.20 $U(x_B) + \frac{1}{2}mv_B^2 = \frac{1}{2}mv_B^2 + U(x_A) + \frac{1}{2}mv_B^2 + \int_0^{h/\sin 30°} -f\,dx$

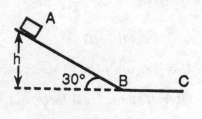

$\frac{1}{2}mv_B^2 = mgh - \mu_k mg \cos 30° \left(\frac{h}{\sin 30°}\right)$

In the region between B and C,

$U(x_C) + \frac{1}{2}mv_C^2 = 0 = U(x_B) + \frac{1}{2}mv_B^2 + \int_0^x -f\,dx$

$0 = mgh - \mu_k mgh \cot 30° - \mu_k mgx$

$x = \dfrac{h - \mu_k h \cot 30°}{\mu_k} = \boxed{1.96 \text{ m}}$

8.20

*8.21 $\Delta E = mgh - \frac{1}{2}mv^2$

$= (50)(9.8)(1000) - \frac{1}{2}(50)(5)^2$

$= \boxed{489 \text{ kJ}}$

8.22 (a) $mgh_1 = \dfrac{mv_1^2}{2}$; $v_1 = \sqrt{2(9.80 \text{ m/s}^2)(5 \text{ m})} = \boxed{9.90 \text{ m/s}}$

(b) $W_f = \Delta U = mg(2 - 5) = \boxed{-14.7 \text{ J}}$

(c) $W_{nc} = \Delta K + \Delta U = \Delta U = \boxed{-14.7 \text{ J}}$

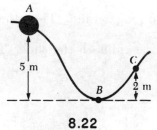

8.22

8.23 (a) $0 = \Delta U + \Delta K = -mgh + \dfrac{mv^2}{2}$

so $v = \sqrt{2gh} = \sqrt{2(9.80)(2 - 2\cos 30°)} = \boxed{2.29 \text{ m/s}}$

(b) $W_{nc} = -mgh + \dfrac{mv^2}{2} = 2.5\left[\dfrac{2^2}{2} - (9.80)(2 - 2\cos 30°)\right] = \boxed{-15.6 \text{ J}}$

8.24 $\frac{1}{2}mv^2 = \int_0^x F_x dx =$ area under the F_x vs x curve.

for $x = 2$ m $\quad \int_1^2 F_x dx = 10$ N-m

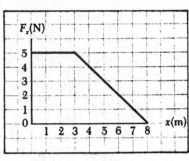

8.24

$\therefore \ v|_{x=2 \text{ m}} = \sqrt{\frac{2}{5}(10)} = \boxed{2.00 \text{ m/s}}$

Similarly

$v|_{x=4 \text{ m}} = \sqrt{\frac{2}{5}(19.5)} = \boxed{2.79 \text{ m/s}}$

$v|_{x=6 \text{ m}} = \sqrt{\frac{2}{5}(25.5)} = \boxed{3.19 \text{ m/s}}$

8.25 $U_i + K_i = U_f + K_f$

$m_2 gh - fh = \frac{1}{2}m_1 v^2 + \frac{1}{2}m_2 v^2$

$f = \mu N = \mu mg$

$m_2 gh - \mu m_1 gh = \frac{1}{2}(m_1 + m_2)v^2$

$v^2 = \dfrac{2(m_2 - \mu m_1)(hg)}{m_1 + m_2}$

$v = \sqrt{\dfrac{2(9.8 \text{ m/s}^2)(1.5 \text{ m})[5 \text{ kg} - 0.4(3 \text{ kg})]}{8.0 \text{ kg}}} = \boxed{3.74 \text{ m/s}}$

8.25

8.26 $U_i + K_i = U_f + K_f$

$\frac{1}{2}kx^2 + 0 - f(d) = \frac{1}{2}mv^2$

$\frac{1}{2}(8.0 \text{ N/m})(0.0050 \text{ m})^2 - (0.032 \text{ N})(0.15 \text{ m}) = \frac{1}{2}(0.0053 \text{ kg})v^2$

$v_2 = \dfrac{2(0.0052 \text{ N} \cdot \text{m})}{0.0053 \text{ kg}} = 1.96 \text{ m}^2/\text{s}^2$

$v = \boxed{1.40 \text{ m/s}}$

8.27 $U_i + K_i = U_f + K_f$

$U_i = K_i$

$2U_i = U_f + K_f$

$2[\frac{1}{2}kx^2] = \frac{1}{2}mv^2 + 0$

$v_{\max}^2 = \dfrac{2kx^2}{m} = \dfrac{2(65\text{ N/m})(0.1\text{ m})^2}{2.5\text{ kg}}$

$v_{\max} = \sqrt{0.52\text{ m}^2/\text{s}^2} = \boxed{0.721\text{ m/s}}$

8.28 (a) $W = \dfrac{kx^2}{2} = \frac{1}{2}(300\text{ N/m})(0.04\text{ m})^2 = \boxed{0.240\ \text{ J}}$

(b) $W = \frac{1}{2}(300\text{ N/m})[(0.04\text{ m})^2 - (0.02\text{ m})^2] = \boxed{0.180\text{ J}}$

8.29 (a) $U_s = \dfrac{kx^2}{2} = \dfrac{(500\text{ N/m})(0.04\text{ m})^2}{2} = \boxed{0.400\ \text{ J}}$

(b) $U_s = \dfrac{(500\text{ N/m})(0.03\text{ m})^2}{2} = \boxed{0.225\ \text{ J}}$

(c) $U_s = \boxed{0\ \text{ J}}$

*8.30 $mgh = \frac{1}{2}mv^2$

$(3\text{ kg})(9.8\text{ m/s}^2)(d + 0.2\text{ m})\sin 30 = \frac{1}{2}400(0.2\text{ m})^2$

$14.7d + 2.94 = 8$

$d = \boxed{0.344\text{ m}}$

8.30

8.31   (a) The spring force is conservative, so the spring does a total of zero

work between pictures (1) and (3) . Therefore

$$W_f = K_f - K_i = \frac{1}{2}(mv_f^2 - mv_i^2) = \frac{1}{2}[8(3^2) - 8(4)^2] = (36 - 64)\,\text{J} = \boxed{-28.0\ \text{J}}$$

(b) $W_f = -f(2x_m) = -2\mu mgx_m$ where x_m = maximum compression of spring

$$-28 = -2(0.4)(8)(9.8)x_m = -62.72x_m \;\rightarrow\; x_m = \boxed{0.446\ \text{m}}$$

*8.32 $k = 2.5 \times 10^4$ N/m, $x_1 = -0.1$ m, $m = 25$ kg

(a) $E = \frac{1}{2}kx_1^2 = \frac{1}{2}(2.5 \times 10^4)(0.1)^2 + 25\ \text{kg}(9.8\ \text{m/s}^2)(-0.1\ \text{m}) = \boxed{100.5\ \text{J}}$

(b) $mg(x_2 - x_1) = 125;$ $\boxed{x_2 = 0.41\ \text{m}}$

(c) At $x = 0,$ $\frac{1}{2}mv_0^2 + mg(0 - x_1) = 125;$ $\boxed{v_0 = 2.84\ \text{m/s}}$

(d) KE and v are at a maximum when $a = 0$, $\Sigma F = 0$ when spring force up = weight down.

$$\left(2.5 \times 10^4 \frac{N}{m}\right) x_d \;=\; (25\ \text{kg})(9.8\ \text{m/s}^2)$$

$$x_d \;=\; \boxed{-9.80\ \text{mm}}$$

(e)

$$100.5\ \text{J} \;=\; \frac{1}{2}\left(2.5 \times 10^4 \frac{N}{m}\right)(-9.8 \times 10^{-3})^2 + (25)(9.8)(-9.8 \times 10^{-3}\ \text{m}) + \frac{1}{2}25v_e^2$$

$$100.5\ \text{J} \;=\; 1.2005\ \text{J} - 2.401\ \text{J} + \frac{1}{2}25v_e^2$$

$$101.7\ \text{J} \;=\; \frac{1}{2}25v_e^2$$

$$v_{max} \;=\; \boxed{2.85\ \text{m/s}}$$

8.33 $\Delta K = 0 - \frac{1}{2}mv^2 = -\frac{1}{2}kx^2 = -mgh_{max}$

$$h_{max} = \frac{\frac{1}{2}kx^2}{mg} = \frac{\frac{1}{2}(5000)(10^{-2})}{(25 \times 10^{-2})(9.8)} = \boxed{10.2\ \text{m}}$$

8.34 $\Delta K = W_{\text{net}} = W_f = \mu_k mgx$

$$W_f = 0 - \frac{1}{2}mv^2 = -\frac{1}{2}kx^2 = -\frac{1}{2}(100)(10^{-2})$$

$$= -\mu_k(2)(9.8)(0.25)$$

$$\mu_k = \boxed{0.102}$$

8.35 $\Delta E = W_f$

$E_f - E_i = -f \cdot d_{BC}$

$\frac{1}{2}k\Delta x^2 - mgh = -\mu mgd$

$\mu = \dfrac{mgh - \frac{1}{2}k \cdot \Delta x^2}{mgd} = \boxed{0.327}$

8.35

*8.36 $1.176 \text{ N} = \left(40\,\dfrac{\text{N}}{\text{m}}\right) x_0$

$x_0 = 0.0294 \text{ m}$

$\frac{1}{2}\left(40\dfrac{\text{N}}{\text{m}}\right)(0.0294 \text{ m})^2 = \frac{1}{2}(0.12)v^2$

$v = \boxed{0.537 \text{ m/s}}$

(b) $\boxed{0.0588 \text{ m}}$

8.36

8.37 $U(r) = \dfrac{A}{r}$; $F_r = -\dfrac{\partial U}{\partial r} = -\dfrac{d}{dr}\left(\dfrac{A}{r}\right) = \boxed{\dfrac{A}{r^2}}$

8.38   (a) $F_x = -\dfrac{\partial U}{\partial x} = \boxed{-2ax + b}$

(b) $F = 0$ when $-2ax + b = 0$ or when $x = \boxed{\dfrac{b}{2a}}$

8.39 $\quad F_x = -\dfrac{\partial U}{\partial x} = -\dfrac{\partial}{\partial x}[3x^3y - 7x]$

$\quad F_x = -(9x^2y - 7) = 7 - 9x^2y$

$\quad F_y = -\dfrac{\partial U}{\partial y} = -\dfrac{\partial}{\partial y}[3x^3y - 7x] \;= -3x^3$

$\quad \boxed{\boldsymbol{F} = (7 - 9x^2y)\boldsymbol{i} + (-3x^3)\boldsymbol{j}}$

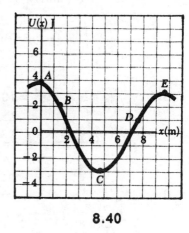

8.40

8.40 (a) F_x is zero at points A, C and E; F_x is positive at point D and

negative at point B.

(b) A, B, D and E are unstable, and C is stable.

8.41

Stable   **Unstable**   **Neutral**

8.41

8.42 (a) as the pipe is rotated, the CM rises, so this is *stable* equilibrium

(b) as the pipe is rotated, the CM moves horizontally, so this is *neutral* equilibrium

(c) as the pipe is rotated, the CM falls, so this is *unstable* equilibrium.

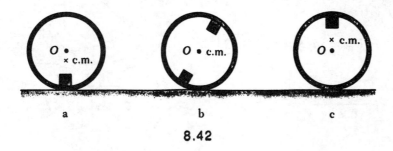

8.42

8.43 (a) $(\Delta K)_{A \to B} = W_{net} = W_g = mg\Delta h = mg(5 - 3.2)$

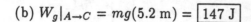

$\frac{1}{2}mv_B^2 - \frac{1}{2}mv_A^2 = m\,9.8(1.8)$

$v_B = \boxed{5.94 \text{ m/s}}$

Similarly $v_c = \sqrt{v_A^2 + 2g(5 - 2)} = \boxed{7.67 \text{ m/s}}$

(b) $W_g|_{A \to C} = mg(5.2 \text{ m}) = \boxed{147 \text{ J}}$

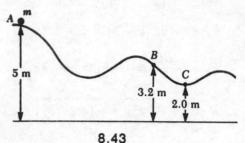

8.43

8.44 (a) $E = mc^2 = (9.11 \times 10^{-31} \text{ kg})(2.997 \times 10^8 \text{ m/s})^2 = \boxed{8.18 \times 10^{-14} \text{ J}}$

(b) $\boxed{3.59 \times 10^{-8} \text{ J}}$ (c) $\boxed{1.80 \times 10^{14} \text{ J}}$ (d) $\boxed{5.38 \times 10^{41} \text{ J}}$

8.45 (a) Rest energy $= mc^2 = (1.673 \times 10^{-27} \text{ kg})(2.997 \times 10^8 \text{ m/s})^2 = \boxed{1.50 \times 10^{-10} \text{ J}}$

(b) $\gamma = \dfrac{1}{\sqrt{1 - (v/c)^2}} = \dfrac{1}{\sqrt{1 - (0.99)^2}} = 7.09$

Total energy $= \gamma mc^2 = 7.09(1.50 \times 10^{-10} \text{ J}) = \boxed{1.06 \times 10^{-9} \text{ J}}$

(c) $K = \gamma mc^2 - mc^2 = 1.06 \times 10^{-9} \text{ J} - 1.50 \times 10^{-10} \text{ J} = \boxed{9.1 \times 10^{-10} \text{ J}}$

8.46 (a) $U_A = mgh_A = (0.2 \text{ kg})(9.8 \text{ m/s}^2)(0.30 \text{ m}) = \boxed{0.588 \text{ J}}$

(b) $K_A + U_A = K_B + U_B$

$K_B = K_B + U_A - U_B = mgh = \boxed{0.588 \text{ J}}$

(c) $v_B = \sqrt{\dfrac{2K_B}{m}} = \sqrt{\dfrac{2(0.588 \text{ J})}{0.2 \text{ kg}}} = \boxed{2.42 \text{ m/s}}$

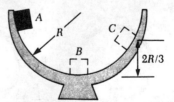

8.46 and 8.47

(d) $U_C = mgh_C = (0.2 \text{ kg})(9.8 \text{ m/s}^2)(0.1 \text{ m}) = \boxed{0.196 \text{ J}}$

$K_C = K_A + U_A - U_C = mg(h_A - h_C)$

$= (0.2 \text{ kg})(9.8 \text{ m/s}^2)(0.3 - 0.1) \text{ m} = \boxed{0.392 \text{ J}}$

8.47 (a) $K_B = \frac{1}{2}mv_B^2 = \frac{1}{2}(0.2 \text{ kg})(1.5 \text{ m/s})^2 = \boxed{0.225 \text{ J}}$

(b) $W_{nc} = \Delta K + \Delta U = K_B - K_A + U_B - U_A$

$= K_B + mg(h_B - h_A)$

$= 0.225 \text{ J} + (0.2 \text{ kg})(9.8 \text{ m/s}^2)(0 - 0.3 \text{ m})$

$= 0.225 \text{ J} - 0.588 \text{ J} = \boxed{-0.363 \text{ J}}$

(c) It's possible to find an effective coefficient of friction, but not the actual value of μ since N and f vary with position.

8.48 $(U + K)_A = (U + K)_f$

$\frac{1}{2}kx^2 = mgh$

$k = \frac{2mgh}{x^2} = \frac{2(0.1 \text{ kg})(9.8 \text{ m/s}^2)(0.6 \text{ m})}{(0.02 \text{ m})^2} = \boxed{2940 \text{ N/m}}$

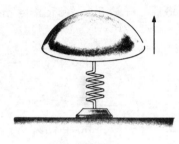

8.48

*8.49 Launch speed is found from

$mg\left(\frac{4}{5}h\right) = \frac{1}{2}mv^2$

$v = \sqrt{2y\left(\frac{4}{5}\right)h}$

$v_y = v\sin\theta$

The height y above the water is (by conservation of energy)

$mgy = \frac{1}{2}mv_y^2 + mg\frac{h}{5}$

$y = \frac{1}{2g}v_y^2 + \frac{h}{5} = \frac{1}{2g}v^2\sin^2\theta + \frac{h}{5}$

$y = \frac{1}{2g}\left[2g\left(\frac{4}{5}h\right)\right]\sin^2\theta + \frac{h}{5} = \boxed{\frac{4}{5}h\sin^2\theta + \frac{h}{5}}$

*8.50 To carry 1 m, the launch velocity must be such that $v_x t = 1$ m and $1.25 = \frac{1}{2}gt^2$. Thus $t = 0.5$ s and $v_x = 2$ m/s.

By conservation of energy,

$$mgy = \frac{1}{2}mv^2$$

$$y = \frac{v^2}{2g} = \frac{4 \text{ m/s}}{2(9.8 \text{ m/s}^2)} = 0.2 \text{ m}$$

and $h = y + 1.25 \text{ m} = \boxed{1.45 \text{ m}}$

8.51 (a) For projectile motion, $R = \dfrac{v_0^2 \sin(2\theta_0)}{g}$ and $\dfrac{R_{max}}{2} = \dfrac{v_0^2}{g}$.

Also, $K_i = \dfrac{mv_0^2}{2}$, so that $K_i = \dfrac{mg\,R_{max}}{2}$

For $(m, R_{max}) = (0.8, 89)$, $(2, 69)$, and $(7.2, 21)$ we find using the above that $K_i = \boxed{349 \text{ J}}$, $\boxed{676 \text{ J}}$ and $\boxed{741 \text{ J}}$ respectively.

(b) $W = F_{av}\Delta x = \Delta K$. Since $\Delta x = 2$ m, $F_{av} = \boxed{175 \text{ N}}$ $\boxed{338 \text{ N}}$ and $\boxed{370 \text{ N}}$, respectively.

(c) A comparison of the discus and shot-put results suggests that it may not be a significant factor. However, the javelin results differ by a factor of about 2(for F_{av}), suggesting that air resistance is important. $\boxed{\text{Yes}}$

8.52 Assume his center of gravity is in the middle of his body, i.e. at a height of 1 m. If no nonconservative forces act, then

$\Delta E = \Delta K = 0$; $mg\Delta h + [0 - \frac{1}{2}mv^2] = 0$ where we assume that his speed while going over the bar is negligible. Then

$m(9.80)(2.3 - 1) - \frac{1}{2}mv^2 = 0$; Solving for v we find $v = \boxed{5.05 \text{ m/s}}$

8.53 (a) The quantity $\nabla_x F(x)i$ must vanish if $F(x)i$ is conservative. Indeed

$$\nabla_x F(x)i = j\left(\frac{\partial F}{\partial z}\right) - k\left(\frac{\partial F}{\partial y}\right) \text{ and } \frac{\partial F}{\partial z} = \frac{\partial F}{\partial y} = 0$$

$$\Delta U = -\int_0^x (ax + bx^2)\,dx = \boxed{-\frac{ax^2}{2} - \frac{bx^3}{3}}$$

(b) $\Delta U = -\int_0^x A e^{\alpha x}\,dx = \boxed{\dfrac{A(1 - e^{\alpha x})}{\alpha}}$

*8.54 $mgh = \dfrac{1}{2}mv^2$

$v = \sqrt{2gh} = \sqrt{2(9.8 \text{ m/s}^2)(150 \text{ m})} = \boxed{54.2 \text{ m/s}}$

8.55 The nonconservative work (due to friction) must equal the change in the kinetic energy plus the change in the potential energy. Therefore;

$$-\mu mgx \cos\theta = \Delta k + \frac{1}{2}kx^2 - mgx \sin\theta \text{ and since } \Delta K = 0, \ v_i = v_f = 0.$$

Thus, $-\mu(2)(9.80)(\cos 37)(0.2) = \dfrac{(100)(0.2)^2}{2} - 2(9.80)(\sin 37)(0.2)$

and we find $\mu = \boxed{0.115}$. Note that in the above we had a *gain* in elastic potential energy for the spring and a *loss* in gravitational potential energy. The net loss in mechanical energy is equal to the energy lost due to friction.

8.56   (a) Since no nonconservative work is done, $\Delta E = 0$; Also $\Delta K = 0$,

therefore, $U_i = U_f$, where $U_i = (mg \sin \theta)x$ and $U_f = \frac{1}{2}kx^2$.

Substituting values yields $2(9.80) \sin 37° = (100)\frac{x}{2}$ and solving

we find $x = \boxed{0.236 \text{ m}}$

(b) $\Sigma F = ma$. Only gravity and the spring force act on the block, so

$-kx + mg \sin \theta = ma$. For $x = 0.23$ m, $a = -5.9$ m/s^2, up the incline.

It depends on its position.

(c) U(gravity) decreases monotonically as the height decreases,

U(spring) increases monotonically as the spring is stretched.

K initially increases, but then goes back to zero.

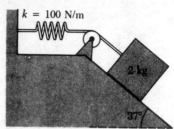

8.56

8.57   Applying Newton's second law at the bottom (b) and top (t) of the

circle gives $T_b - mg = \dfrac{mv_b^2}{R}$ and $-T_t - mg = -\dfrac{mv_t^2}{R}$. Adding

these gives $T_b = T_t + 2mg + \dfrac{m(v_b^2 - v_t^2)}{R}$. Also, energy must be

conserved and $\Delta U + \Delta K = 0$. So, $\dfrac{m(v_b^2 - v_t^2)}{2} + (0 - 2mgR) = 0$

and $\dfrac{m(v_b^2 - v_t^2)}{R} = 4mg$.

Substituting into the above equation gives $\boxed{T_b = T_t + 6mg}$

8.58 (a) If the pendulum is released at a distance x below the point of suspension (where $x < d$) then after it hits the peg the velocity will increase due to the change in the effective length of the supporting string. However, after returning to the bottom of the arc, conservation of energy will ensure that the velocity will be equal to that before hitting the peg and will rise to its initial height.

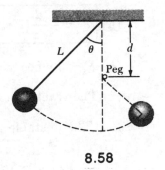

8.58

(b) Relative to the point of suspension,

$$U_i = 0, \quad U_f = -mg[d - (L - d)].$$

From this we find that

$$-mg(2d - L) + \frac{1}{2}mv^2 = 0.$$

Also for centripetal motion

$$mg = \frac{mv^2}{R} \quad \text{where } R = L - d.$$

Upon solving we get $d = \boxed{\dfrac{3L}{5}}$

8.59 $(K + U)_i = (K + U)_f$

$$0 \ + \ 30 \text{ kg} (9.8 \text{ m/s}^2)(0.2 \text{ m}) + \frac{1}{2}(250 \text{ N/m})(0.2 \text{ m})^2$$

$$= \ \frac{1}{2}(50 \text{ kg})v^2 + (20 \text{ kg})(9.8 \text{ m/s}^2)(0.2 \text{ m}) \sin 40°$$

$$58.5 \text{ J} + 5 \text{ J} = (25 \text{ kg})v^2 + 25 \text{ J}$$

$$\boxed{v = 1.25 \text{ m/s}}$$

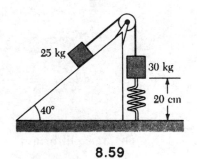

8.59

8.60 (a) $\boxed{F = -\dfrac{d}{dx}(-x^3 + 2x^2 + 3x)i = (3x^2 - 4x - 3)i}$

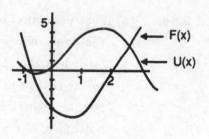

8.60

(b) $F = 0$ when $x = \boxed{1.87 \text{ and } -0.535}$

(c) The stable points are points of minimum $U(x)$,

The unstable points are maxima in $U(x)$.

8.61 Electric Power $= \dfrac{P}{0.35} = \dfrac{mgh/t}{0.35} = \dfrac{(2000 \text{ kg})(9.8 \text{ m/s}^2)(150 \text{ m})}{0.35(605) \text{ s}} = \boxed{140 \text{ kW}}$

It is reasonable to neglect kinetic energy since if we assume the

velocity is approximately 1 m/s , K = 1 kJ, or a power of 0.02 kW,

or about 0.01% of the total power.

*8.62 $E = mgh + \dfrac{1}{2}mv^2$

$= (80,000)(9.8)(10^4) + \dfrac{1}{2}(80,000)\left(\dfrac{900 \times 10^3}{3600}\right)^2$

$= \boxed{10.3 \text{ GJ}}$

*8.63 (a) $mg = kd$

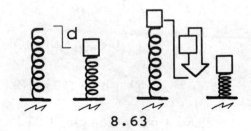

8.63

$mgd_{max} = \dfrac{1}{2}kd_{max}^2$

$dd_{max} = \dfrac{2\,mg}{k} = \dfrac{2kd}{k} = \underline{2d}$

(b) at equilibrium

$mgd = \dfrac{1}{2}kd^2 + \dfrac{1}{2}mv^2$

$mgd = \dfrac{1}{2}mgd + \dfrac{1}{2}mv^2$

$v = \sqrt{gd}$

8.64   Case–I: Surface is frictionless

$$\frac{1}{2}mv^2 = \frac{1}{2}kx^2$$

$$k = \frac{mv^2}{x^2} = \frac{(5 \text{ kg})(1.2 \text{ m/s})^2}{10^{-2} \text{ m}^2} = 7.2 \times 10^2 \text{ N/m}$$

Case–II: Surface is rough, $\mu_k = 0.3$

$$\frac{1}{2}mv^2 = \frac{1}{2}kx^2 - \mu_k mgx$$

$$\frac{5 \text{ kg}}{2}v^2 = \frac{1}{2}(7.2 \times 10^2 \text{ N/m})(10^{-1} \text{ m})^2 - (0.3)(5 \text{ kg})(9.8 \text{ m/s}^2)(10^{-1} \text{ m})$$

$$\boxed{v = 0.923 \text{ m/s}}$$

8.65   (a) Initial compression of spring: $\frac{1}{2}kx^2 = \frac{1}{2}mv^2$

$$\frac{1}{2}(450 \text{ N/m})(\Delta x)^2 = \frac{1}{2}(0.5 \text{ kg})(12 \text{ m/s})^2 \quad \therefore \ \Delta x = \boxed{0.400 \text{ m}}$$

(b) Speed of block at top of track:

$$\Delta E = W_f$$

$$(mgh_T + \frac{1}{2}mv_T^2) - (mgh_B + \frac{1}{2}mv_B^2) = -f(\pi R)$$

$$(0.5 \text{ kg})(9.8 \text{ m/s}^2)(2 \text{ m}) + \frac{1}{2}(0.5 \text{ kg})v_T^2 - \frac{1}{2}(0.5 \text{ kg})(12 \text{ m/s})^2 = -(7 \text{ N})(\pi)(1 \text{ m})$$

$$0.25v_T^2 = 4.21 \quad \therefore \ v_T = \boxed{4.10 \text{ m/s}}$$

(c) Does block fall off at or before top of track?

Block falls if $a_c < g$

$$a_c = \frac{v_T^2}{R} = \frac{(4.1)^2}{2} = 16.8 \text{ m/s}^2$$

therefore $a_c > g$ and the block stays on the track.

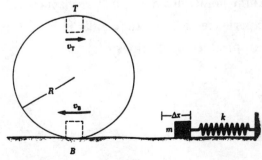

8.65

8.66 $U = Ax^2 - Bx^3$

(a) $-F_x = \dfrac{\partial U}{\partial x} = 2Ax - 3Bx^2$ (1)

$F_x = \boxed{-2Ax + 3Bx^2}$

(b) Eq. (1) has two roots (points where $F = 0$)

$\boxed{x = 0}$ and $\boxed{x = \dfrac{2A}{3B}}$

(c) At a point of stable equilibrium, the potential energy is a minimum,

and $\dfrac{d^2U}{dx^2} \geq 0$. At a point of unstable equilibrium, the potential energy

is a maximum and $\dfrac{d^2U}{dx^2} \leq 0$. For neutral equilibrium, $\dfrac{d^2U}{dx^2} = 0$.

At $x = 0$: $\dfrac{d^2U}{dx^2} = \dfrac{d}{dx}(+2Ax - 3Bx^2)|_{x=0} = +2A - 6Bx|_{x=0}$

$\dfrac{d^2U}{dx^2} = 2A > 0$

$\therefore \boxed{x = 0 \text{ is a point of } stable \text{ equilibrium}}$

At $x = \dfrac{2A}{3B}$, $\dfrac{d^2U}{dx^2} = [+2A - 6Bx]_{\frac{2A}{3B}} = +2A - 6B(\dfrac{2A}{3B})$

$\dfrac{d^2U}{dx^2} = +2A - 4A = -2A < 0$

$\therefore \boxed{x = \dfrac{2A}{3B} \text{ is a point of } unstable \text{ equilibrium}}$

(d) If a particle is displaced from a point of unstable equilibrium, it accelerates away
from the equilibrium point. However, if it is displaced from a point of *stable*
equilibrium, it experiences a force that pulls it back toward the equilibrium
point, and this can produce oscillations.

8.67 $\Sigma F_y = N - mg\cos 37° = 0, \; \therefore \; N = mg\cos 37° = 400$ N

$f = \mu N = (0.25)(400) = 100$ N

$W_f = \Delta E$

$(-100)(20) = \Delta U_A + \Delta U_B + \Delta K_A + \Delta K_B$

$\Delta U_A = m_A g(h_f - h_i) = (50)(9.8)(20\sin 37°) = 5898$ J

$\Delta U_B = m_B g(h_f - h_i) = (100)(9.8)(-20) = -19600$ J

$\Delta K_A = \dfrac{1}{2}m_A(v_f^2 - v_i^2)$

$\Delta K_B = \dfrac{1}{2}m_B(v_f^2 - v_i^2) = \dfrac{m_B}{m_A}\Delta K_A = 2\Delta K_A$

Adding and solving, $\Delta K_A = \boxed{3.92 \text{ kJ}}$

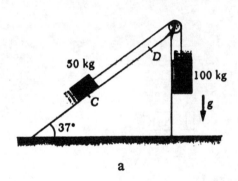

a

b

8.67

*8.68 $\dfrac{1}{2}kx^2 = mgh + \dfrac{1}{2}mv^2$

$\dfrac{1}{2}k(0.5)^2 = (0.1)(9.8)(0.5)\sin 8° + \dfrac{1}{2}(0.1)(0.8)^2$

$k = \boxed{31.1 \text{ N/m}}$

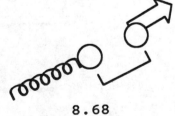

8.68

8.69   (a) $W_{nc} = \Delta K + \Delta U$

$$-\mu mgd = -\frac{1}{2}mv_0^2 + \frac{1}{2}kd^2$$

$$\frac{1}{2}(50 \text{ N/m})d^2 + 0.25(1 \text{ kg})(9.8 \text{ m/s}^2)d - \frac{1}{2}(1 \text{ kg})(3 \text{ m/s}^2) = 0$$

$$d = \frac{[-2.45 \pm 21.35] \text{ N}}{50 \text{ N/m}} = \boxed{0.378 \text{ m}}$$

(b) $W_{nc} = \Delta K + \Delta U$

$$-f(2d) = \frac{1}{2}mv^2 - \frac{1}{2}mv_0^2$$

$$v = \sqrt{(3 \text{ m/s})^2 - \frac{2}{1 \text{ kg}}(2.45 \text{ N})(2)(0.378 \text{ m})} = \boxed{2.30 \text{ m/s}}$$

(c) $W_{nc} = \Delta K + \Delta U$

$$-f(D + 2d) = -\frac{1}{2}(1 \text{ kg})(3 \text{ m/s})^2$$

$$D = \frac{9 \text{ J}}{2(0.20)(1 \text{ kg})(9.8 \text{ m/s}^2)} - 2(0.378 \text{ m}) = \boxed{1.08 \text{ m}}$$

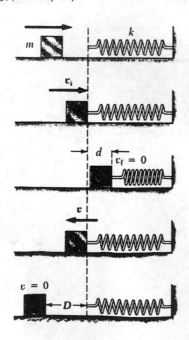

8.69

CHAPTER 9

9.1 $m = 3$ kg , $\boldsymbol{v} = (3\boldsymbol{i} - 4\boldsymbol{j})$ m/s, so $\boldsymbol{p} = m\boldsymbol{v} = (9\boldsymbol{i} - 12\boldsymbol{j})$ kg · m/s

That is, $p_x = 9$ kg · m/s and $p_y = -12$ kg· m/s

$$p = \sqrt{9^2 + (-12)^2} = \boxed{15.0 \text{ kg·m/s}}$$

9.2 $p_{\text{truck}} = mv = (5000 \text{ kg})(10 \text{ m/s}) = 5 \times 10^4$ kg · m/s

Since $p_{\text{car}} = p_{\text{truck}}$, $p_{\text{car}} = 1250 v_{\text{car}} = 5 \times 10^4$ kg · m/s or $v_{\text{car}} = \boxed{40.0 \text{ m/s}}$

* 9.3 $F = \dfrac{I}{\Delta t} = \dfrac{2 \text{ N} \cdot \text{s}}{(1/800)\text{s}} = \boxed{1600 \text{ N}}$

* 9.4 $\Delta p = (0.06)\sqrt{2(9.8)(2)} + 0.06\sqrt{2(9.8)(1.8)} = \boxed{0.732 \text{ kg} \cdot \text{m/s}}$

9.5   (a) $I = \displaystyle\int F dt = \int_{t=0}^{5} F dt =$ area under graph

$$I = \frac{1}{2}(4 \times 2) + (4 \times 1) + \frac{1}{2}(4 \times 2) = \boxed{12.0 \text{ N·s}}$$

(b) $I = p_f - p_i = mv_f - mv_i$

$$v_i = 0, \ v_f = \frac{I}{m} = \frac{12}{2} = \boxed{6.00 \text{ m/s}}$$

(c) $v_i = -2$ m/s

$$v_f = v_i + \frac{I}{m} = -2 \text{ m/s} + \frac{12 \text{ N} \cdot \text{s}}{2 \text{ kg}} = \boxed{4.00 \text{ m/s}}$$

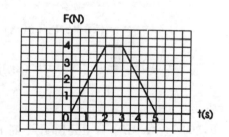

9.5 and 9.6

9.6 $F_{av} = \dfrac{\text{area under } F \text{ vs } t \text{ curve}}{\Delta t} = \dfrac{12 \text{ kg} \cdot \text{m/s}}{5 \text{ s}} = 2.40 \text{ N}$

* 9.7 (a) $I = \int F\, dt$ = area under curve

$$= \frac{1}{2}(1.5 \times 10^{-3}\ \text{s})(18000\ \text{N}) = \boxed{13.5\ \text{N·s}}$$

(b) $F = \dfrac{13.5\ \text{N} \cdot \text{s}}{1.5 \times 10^{-3}\ \text{s}} = \boxed{9.00\ \text{kN}}$

(c) From the graph, we see that $F_{\text{max}} = \boxed{18.0\ \text{kN}}$

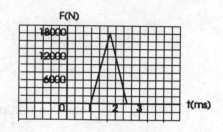

9.7

9.8 $F = m\dfrac{d\mathbf{v}}{dt} + \mathbf{v}\dfrac{dm}{dt} = 0 + (25\ \text{m/s})(-0.60\ \frac{\text{kg}}{\text{s}})\mathbf{i} = \boxed{-15.0\ \mathbf{i}\ \text{N}}$

In each increment dt of time, an increment dm of mass leaves the nozzle.
To balance this force of the nozzle backward, a force must be exerted by the
gardener equal in magnitude but opposite in direction (and thus in the same
direction as $\boldsymbol{v}$).

9.9 (a) $p = mv = (1.67 \times 10^{-27}\ \text{kg})(5 \times 10^{6}\ \text{m/s}) = \boxed{8.35 \times 10^{-21}\ \text{kg} \cdot \text{m/s}}$

(b) $p = (15 \times 10^{-3}\ \text{kg})(500\ \text{m/s}) = \boxed{7.50\ \text{kg} \cdot \text{m/s}}$

(c) $p = (75\ \text{kg})(12\ \text{m/s}) = \boxed{900\ \text{kg} \cdot \text{m/s}}$

(d) $p = (5.98 \times 10^{24}\ \text{kg})(2.98 \times 10^{4}\text{m/s}) = \boxed{1.78 \times 10^{29}\ \text{kg} \cdot \text{m/s}}$

9.10 (a) If p is doubled, v is doubled, so $\boxed{K \text{ is quadrupled}}$ (since K is $\propto$ to v^2).

(b) $p = \sqrt{2\,m\,K}$, so if K is tripled. $\boxed{p \text{ increases by a factor of } \sqrt{3}}$

9.11 (a) Taking $v_i = 0$, Impulse $= mv_f = (0.5\ \text{kg})(10\ \text{m/s}) = \boxed{7.50\ \text{kg} \cdot \text{m/s}}$

(b) $F_{av} = \dfrac{\text{Impulse}}{\Delta t} = \dfrac{7.50\ \text{kg} \cdot \text{m/s}}{0.02\ \text{s}} = \boxed{375\ \text{N}}$

* 9.12 $I = \Delta p = m\Delta v = (70 \text{ kg})(5.2 \text{ m/s}) = \boxed{364 \text{ kg} \cdot \text{m/s}}$

$$F = \frac{\Delta p}{\Delta t} = \frac{364}{.832} = \boxed{438 \text{ N}}$$

9.13   (a) Impulse $= m(v_f - v_i) = (0.15 \text{ kg})[50 \text{ m/s} - (-40 \text{ m/s})] = \boxed{13.5 \text{ kg m/s}}$

(b) $F_{av} = \dfrac{\text{Impulse}}{\Delta t} = \dfrac{13.5 \text{ kg} \cdot \text{m/s}}{2 \times 10^{-3} \text{ s}} = \boxed{6.75 \text{ kN}}$

This is compared to $W = mg = 1.5 \text{ N}$, which is small compared to

F_{av}, so the impulse approximation is valid.

9.14   Assume the initial direction of the ball in the $-x$ direction

Impulse, $\mathbf{I} = \Delta \mathbf{p} = \mathbf{p}_f - \mathbf{p}_i = (0.06)40\,\mathbf{i} - (0.06)(50)(-\mathbf{i}) = \boxed{5.40\,\mathbf{i} \ \text{N} \cdot \text{s}}$

9.15 $\Delta p = F\Delta t$

$\Delta p_y = m(v_{fy} - v_{iy}) = m(v \cos 60°) - mv \cos 60° = 0$

$\Delta p_x = m(-v \sin 60° - v \sin 60°) = -2mv \sin 60° = -2(3.0 \text{ kg})(10 \text{ m/s})(0.866)$

$= -51.96 \text{ kg} \cdot \text{m/s}$

$F_{\text{ave}} = \dfrac{\Delta p_x}{\Delta t} = \dfrac{-51.96 \text{ kg} \cdot \text{m/s}}{0.20 \text{ s}} = \boxed{-260\,i \ \text{N}}$

9.16 $F_N = m_B g + m_W g + \dfrac{\Delta p}{\Delta t}$

$\dfrac{\Delta p}{\Delta t} = \dfrac{\Delta m}{\Delta t}v = \dfrac{0.25\,L}{\text{s}}\left(\dfrac{1 \text{ kg}}{L}\right)v = (0.25 \ \text{kg/s})v$

$v = \sqrt{2gh} = 34.3 \text{ m/s}$

$F_N = (0.75 \text{ kg})(9.8 \text{ m/s}^2) + \dfrac{0.25\,L}{\text{s}}(3 \text{ s})\left(\dfrac{1 \text{ kg}}{L}\right)(9.8 \ \tfrac{\text{m}}{\text{s}^2}) + (0.25 \ \text{kg/s})(34.3\text{m/s})$

$= 7.35 + 7.35 + 8.58 = \boxed{23.3 \text{ N}}$

9.17 $p_i = 0$ for the system (child + stone)

$p_f = (mv)_{\text{stone}} + (mv)_{\text{child}} = 0$ (since p is conserved).

$(mv)_{\text{child}} = -(2\text{ kg})(8\text{ m/s}) = -16\text{ kg} \cdot \text{m/s}$

$v_{\text{child}} = \dfrac{-16\text{ kg} \cdot \text{m/s}}{40\text{ kg}} = \boxed{-0.400\text{ m/s (to the west)}}$

9.18   For the system of two blocks $\Delta p = 0$,

or $p_i = p_f$;therefore,

$0 = M v_m + (3M)(2\text{ m/s})$; solving gives

$v_m = \boxed{-6.00\text{ m/s}}$ (motion toward the left)

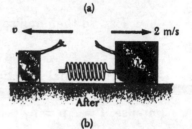

9.18

9.19 $m_B = 60$ kg. $m_G = 40$ kg. $v_g = 4$ m/s to the east

Momentum is conserved: $p_i = 0$ so $p_f = 0$

$0 = m_B v_B + m_G v_G$

$v_B = -\dfrac{m_G v_G}{m_B} = -\dfrac{40 \times 4}{60} = \boxed{-2.67\text{ m/s, west}}$

* 9.20   Each spring absorbs the energy of one car,

$$\frac{1}{2}(0.2\text{ kg})(3\text{ m/s})^2 = \frac{1}{2}\left(3000\ \frac{\text{N}}{\text{m}}\right) x^2$$

$$x = 0.0245\text{ m} = \boxed{2.45\text{ cm}}$$

9.21 Let v_g and v_p be the velocities of the girl and the plank, respectively, relative to the ice. Since there is no net external force acting on the girl–plank system, conservation of momentum can be used.

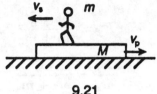

9.21

$p_{\text{initial}} = 0 = p_{\text{final}} = Mv_p - mv_g$

The velocity of the girl relative to the plank is

$v_{g\,rel} = 1.5 \text{ m/s} = v_g + v_p$

(a) To find v_g ,

$$v_g = \frac{M}{m}v_p = \frac{M}{m}(v_{g\,rel} - v_g)$$

$$v_g = \frac{v_{g\,rel}}{1 + \frac{M}{m}} = \frac{1.5 \text{ m/s}}{1 + \frac{3}{10}} = \boxed{1.15 \text{ m/s}}$$

(b) $v_p = -\dfrac{m}{M}v_g = -\dfrac{3}{10}(1.15 \text{ m/s}) = \boxed{-0.345 \text{ m/s}}$

9.22 (a) $\Delta p = 0$; $p_i = p_f$. Since the collision is inelastic, $v_{1f} = v_{2f} = v_f$.

Thus $M_1 v_{1i} + M_2 v_{2i} = (M_1 + M_2)v_f$, solving for v_f gives

$$v_f = \frac{2.5(10) + 5(0)}{2.5 + 5} = \boxed{3.33 \text{ m/s}}$$

(b) $\Delta K = K_f - K_i = \dfrac{1}{2}(M_1 + M_2)v_f^2 - \dfrac{1}{2}M_i v_{1i}^2$

$$\Delta K = \frac{1}{2}(7.5)(3.33)^2 - \frac{1}{2}(2.5)(10)^2 = \boxed{-83.4 \text{ J \ Energy lost}}$$

9.23 $(mv)_{\text{meteorite}} = (m + M)v_{\text{recoil}}$ where M is the earth's mass.

$$v_{\text{recoil}} \approx \frac{(2000 \text{ kg })(120 \text{ m/s})}{(5.98 \times 10^{24} \text{ kg})} = \boxed{4.01 \times 10^{-20} \text{ m/s}}$$

9.24   Ballistic Pendulum

(a) $K_f = \frac{1}{2}(m_1 + m_2)v_f^2$

But $v_f = \dfrac{m_1 v_i}{m_1 + m_2}$ (momentum conservation)

$K_f = \dfrac{m_1^2 v_0^2}{m_1 + m_2}$, $K_i = \dfrac{1}{2}m_1 v_0^2$,

$\dfrac{K_f}{K_i} = \dfrac{m_1}{m_1 + m_2}$

(b) $m_1 = 8\,\text{g}$, $m_2 = 2$ kg ,

Fraction lost $= \dfrac{m_1}{m_1 + m_2} = \dfrac{(8 \times 10^{-3}\,\text{kg})}{(2.008\,\text{kg})} = \boxed{0.398\ \%}$

The rest of the energy is converted to heating block + bullet

* 9.25   Momentum is conserved

$(0.01\,\text{kg})v \;=\; (5.01\,\text{kg})(0.6\,\text{m/s})$

$v \;=\; \boxed{301\,\text{m/s}}$

9.26 $m_H = 90$ kg, $v_{Hi} = 9$ m/s , $m_0 = 120$ kg, $v_{0i} = -3$ m/s

(a) Momentum is conserved

$m_H v_{Hi} + m_0 v_{0i} = (m_H + m_0)v_f$

$90(10) + 120(-4) = (90 + 120)v_f$

$v_f = \boxed{2\ \text{m/s North}}$

(b) $E_i = \dfrac{1}{2}m_H v_{Hi}^2 + \dfrac{1}{2}m_0 v_{0i}^2 = 4500 + 960 = 5460$ J

$E_f = \dfrac{1}{2}(m_H + m_0)v_f^2 = 420$ J

Energy lost $= E_i - E_f = \boxed{5.04\ \text{kJ}}$

The energy is accounted for in terms of the (negative) work which the players do on each other (bruises and fractures).

9.27 $p_i = p_f$

(a) $m_c v_{ic} + m_T v_{iT} = m_c v_{fc} + m_T v_{fT}$

$$v_{fT} = (\frac{1}{m_T})[m_c v_{ic} + m_T v_{iT} - m_c v_{fc}]$$

$$v_{fT} = (\frac{1}{9000 \text{ kg}})[(1200 \text{ kg})(25 \text{ m/s}) + (9000 \text{ kg})(20 \text{ m/s}) - (1200 \text{ kg})(18 \text{ m/s})]$$

$$= \boxed{20.9 \text{ m/s}}$$

(b) $K_{\text{lost}} = K_i - K_f$

$$= \frac{1}{2}m_c v_{ic}^2 + \frac{1}{2}m_T v_{iT}^2 - \frac{1}{2}m_c v_{fc}^2 - \frac{1}{2}m_T v_{fT}^2$$

$$= \frac{1}{2}[m_c(v_{ic}^2 - v_{fc}^2) + m_T(v_{iT}^2 - v_{fT}^2)]$$

$$= \frac{1}{2}[(1200 \text{ kg})(625 - 324)(\text{m}^2/\text{s}^2) + (9000 \text{ kg})(400 - 438.2)\text{m}^2/\text{s}^2]$$

$$K_{\text{lost}} = \boxed{8.74 \text{ kJ}}$$

(Notice if 20.9 m/s were used to determine the energy lost instead of 20.93, the answer would almost *double* (15 kJ). One should keep an extra significant figure until the problem is complete!)

9.28 (a) $mv_{1i} + 3mv_{2i} = 4mv_f$ where $m = 2.5 \times 10^4$ kg

$$v_f = \frac{4 + 3(2)}{4} = \boxed{2.50 \text{ m/s}}$$

(b) $K_f - K_i = \frac{1}{2}(4m)v_f^2 - \left[\frac{1}{2}mv_{1i}^2 + \frac{1}{2}(3m)v_{2i}^2\right]$

$$= 2.5 \times 10^4[12.5 - 8 - 6] = \boxed{-3.75 \times 10^4 \text{ J}}$$

9.29 (a) The fraction of total kinetic energy transferred to the moderator is

$$f_2 = \frac{4m_1 m_2}{(m_1 + m_2)^2}$$ where m_2 is the moderator nucleus and in this case,

$$m_2 = 12m_1 \quad f_2 = \frac{4m_1(12m_1)}{(13m_1)^2} = \frac{48}{169} = \boxed{0.284 \text{ or } 28.4\%} \text{ of the neutron}$$

energy is transferred to the carbon nucleus.

(b) $K_C = (0.284)(1.6 \times 10^{-13} \text{ J}) = \boxed{4.54 \times 10^{-14} \text{ J}}$

$$K_n = (0.716)(1.6 \times 10^{-13} \text{ J}) = \boxed{1.15 \times 10^{-13} \text{ J}}$$

* 9.30 $F = \dfrac{\Delta p}{\Delta t} = \dfrac{(0.01 \text{ kg})(200 \text{ m/s} - 300 \text{ m/s})}{\left(\dfrac{0.02 \text{ m}}{250 \text{ m/s}}\right)} = \boxed{12.5 \text{ kN}}$

* 9.31 For each skater,

$$F = \dfrac{m\Delta v}{\Delta t} = \dfrac{(75 \text{ kg})(5 \text{ m/s})}{(0.1 \text{ s})} = \boxed{3750 \text{ N}}$$

Since F < 4500 N, there are no broken bones.

9.32 $v_{1f} = \dfrac{(m_1 - m_2)}{(m_1 + m_2)}v_{1i} + \dfrac{2m_2}{(m_1 + m_2)}v_{2i}$

$v_{2f} = \dfrac{2m_1}{(m_1 + m_2)}v_{1i} + \dfrac{(m_2 - m_1)}{(m_1 + m_2)}v_{2i}$

In this case $m_1 = m_2$ and we take

$v_{1i} = 2 \text{ m/s}$ and $v_{2i} = -0.5 \text{ m/s}$. Then $v_{1f} = v_{2f} = \boxed{-0.500 \text{ m/s}}$

and $v_{2f} = v_{1f} = \boxed{2.00 \text{ m/s}}$

We see that when the masses are equal in a one dimensional elastic

collision, the two particles *exchange velocities*.

* 9.33 $(200 \text{ g})(55 \text{ m/s}) = (46 \text{ g})v + (200 \text{ g})(40 \text{ m/s})$

$v = \boxed{65.2 \text{ m/s}}$

9.34   (a) We can find the ball's speed before impact

by using energy conservation.

$\frac{1}{2}mv^2 = mgy$ and

$v = \sqrt{2gh} = \sqrt{2(9.80 \text{ m/s}^2)(1.5 \text{ m})} = 5.42 \text{ m/s}$

In an elastic collision we have conservation

of both kinetic energy and momentum.

$(0.2 \text{ kg})(5.42 \text{ m/s}) = (0.2 \text{ kg})v_1 + (0.3 \text{ kg})v_2$

$\frac{1}{2}(0.2 \text{ kg})(5.42 \text{ m/s})^2 = \frac{1}{2}(0.2 \text{ kg})v_1^2 + \frac{1}{2}(0.3 \text{ kg})v_2^2.$

Solving for v_1 and v_2 the

speeds of the ball and block after collision we find:

$v_1 = \boxed{-1.08 \text{ m/s}}$

and $v_2 = \boxed{4.34 \text{ m/s}}$

(b) Again requiring conservation of momentum

when v is the speed of the ball–block combined

after collision we have

$(0.2 \text{ kg} + 0.3 \text{kg})(5.42 \text{ m/s}) = (0.2 \text{ kg} + 0.3 \text{kg})(9.8 \text{ m/s}^2)h$

$\boxed{h = 0.240 \text{ m}}$

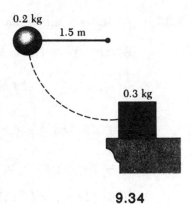

9.34

9.35   At impact momentum is conserved, so: $m_1 v_1 = (m_1 + m_2)v_2$

After impact the change in kinetic energy is equal to the work done by friction:

$$\frac{1}{2}(m_1 + m_2)v_2^2 = f_f d = \mu(m_1 + m_2)dg$$

$$\frac{1}{2}(0.012 \text{ kg})v_2^2 = 0.65(0.112 \text{ kg})(9.8 \text{ m/s}^2)(7.5 \text{ m})$$

$$v_2^2 = 95.6 \text{ m}^2/\text{s}^2 \quad v_2 = 9.8 \text{ m/s}$$

$$(0.012 \text{ kg})v_1 = (0.112 \text{ kg })(9.8 \text{ m/s})$$

$$v_1 = \boxed{91.2 \text{ m/s}}$$

9.36   After n head–on collisions the initial, E_i and the final energy E_f are related by

$$E_f = E_i(\frac{11}{13})^{2n}$$

(a) For $E_f = 1 \text{ eV}$, $E_i = 1 \text{ MeV}$

$$10^{-6} = (\frac{11}{13})^{2n}$$

$$2n \log \frac{11}{13} = -6$$

$$\boxed{n \approx 42 \text{ collisions}}$$

(b) $10^{-6} = (\dfrac{4 - 1}{4 + 1})^{2n} = (\dfrac{3}{5})^{2n}$

$$n \log \frac{3}{5} = -3$$

$$\boxed{n \approx 14 \text{ , about one third as many}}$$

9.37 v_1, speed of m_1 at B before collision.

$$\frac{1}{2}m_1 v_1^2 = m_1 gh \; ; \; v_1 = \sqrt{2 \times 9.8 \times 5} = 9.90 \text{ m/s}$$

v_{1f}, speed of m_1 at B just after collision

$$v_{1f} = \frac{m_1 - m_2}{m_1 + m_2}v_1 = -\frac{1}{3}(9.90) \text{ m/s} = -3.30 \text{ m/s}$$

At the highest point (after collision)

$$m_1 gh_{\text{max}} = \frac{1}{2}m_1(-3.30)^2$$

$$h_{\text{max}} = \frac{(-3.30 \text{ m/s})^2}{2(9.80 \text{ m/s}^2)} = \boxed{0.556 \text{ m}}$$

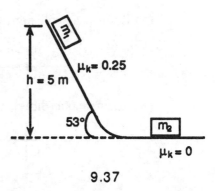

9.37

9.38

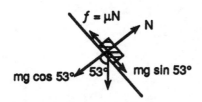

Free-body diagram for m_1

9.38

(a) $N - mg\cos 53° = 0$

$N = mg\cos 53°$

$$\Delta K = \frac{1}{2}mv^2 = W_{\text{net}} = (mg\sin 53° - \mu N)\frac{h}{\sin 53}$$

$$h = \frac{v^2}{2g(1 - \mu \cot 53°)} = \frac{64}{2 \times 9.8(1 - \frac{1}{4}(0.75))} = \boxed{4.02 \text{ m}}$$

(b) $(2 + 6)v_f = 2 \times 8$

$$v_f = \frac{2 \times 8}{8} = \boxed{2.00 \text{ m/s to the right}}$$

* 9.39 Before the collision, the mass $3m$ has a velocity $+v_0$ and mass m has velocity $-v_o$. After the collision, mass $3m$ has velocity v_A and mass m has velocity v_B (see diagram).

(a) Before the collision, the particles approach along the $\pm x$ axis with equal speeds.

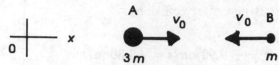

(b) After a one-dimensional "head- on" collision, the particles move along the x axis.

By conservation of momentum,   9.39

$$3mv_0 + m(-v_0) = 3m(v_A) + m(v_B) \quad \text{or} \quad 2v_0 = 3v_A + v_B$$

Because the collision is elastic, kinetic energy is conserved,

$$\frac{1}{2}(3m)v_0^2 + \frac{1}{2}(m)v_0^2 = \frac{1}{2}(3m)v_A^2 + \frac{1}{2}(m)v_B^2$$

Since $v_B = 2v_0 - 3v_A$,

$$4v_0^2 = 3v_A^2 + (2v_0 - 3v_A)^2 \quad \text{and} \quad 12v_A^2 = 12v_Av_0$$

which leads to two possible answers: $v_A = v_0$ or $v_A = 0$. To choose between them, we reason as follows. If $v_A = v_0$, then

$$2v_0 = 3v_0 + v_B \quad \text{or} \quad v_B = -v_0$$

This result says that the two masses have the same velocities after the collision as before. While this does satisfy the conservation of energy and momentum, it implies that the particles pass through each other without interacting—essentially "no collision." So we accept the alternative answer:

$$\boxed{v_A = 0}$$

$$\boxed{v_B = 2v_0}$$

Thus the $3m$ mass comes to rest and the mass m reverses its direction and acquires a speed twice its original value.

9.40   (a) Let v_{1i}, v_{2i} be the speeds of m_1 and m_2 just before collision:

$$\frac{1}{2}m_1 v_{1i}^2 = m_1 g h$$

$$v_{1i} = \sqrt{2gh} = \sqrt{2 \times 9.8 \times 5} = \boxed{9.90 \ \text{m/s} = v_{2i}}$$

$\boldsymbol{v_{1i}}$ points to the right $\boldsymbol{v_{2i}}$ points to the left

(b) From Eqs. 9.20 and 9.21

$$v_{1f} = (\frac{2-4}{6})9.9 + (\frac{2 \times 4}{6})(-9.9) = \boxed{-16.5 \ \text{m/s}}$$

where v_{1f} is the speed of m_1 just after the collision. The minus sign means the velocity vector points to the left. Similarly

$$v_{2f} = (\frac{4}{4+2})9.90 + (\frac{2}{6})(-9.9) = \boxed{+3.30 \ \text{m/s}}$$

(c) At the highest point for m_1 $m_1 g h_1 = \frac{1}{2}m_1 v_{1f}^2$

$$\therefore h_1 = \frac{v_{1f}^2}{2g} = \frac{1}{2g}(-16.5)^2 = \boxed{13.9 \ \text{m}}$$

$$\text{Similarly } h_2 = \frac{1}{19.6}(3.30)^2 = \boxed{0.556 \ \text{m}}$$

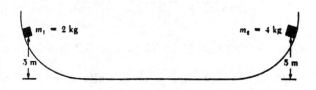

9.40

9.41 $m_1 v_{1i} + m_2 v_{2i} = (m_1 + m_2)v_f$

$3(5)\boldsymbol{i} - 6\boldsymbol{j} = 5\boldsymbol{v}$

$\boldsymbol{v} = \boxed{(3.00\,\boldsymbol{i} - 1.20\,\boldsymbol{j}) \ \text{m/s}}$

9.42   (a) $p_i = p_f$ so $p_{xi} = p_{xf}$ and $p_{yi} = p_{yf}$

$$mv_0 = mv \cos \theta + mv \cos \phi \qquad (1)$$

$$0 = mv \sin \theta - mv \cos \phi \qquad (2)$$

From (2), $\sin \theta = \cos \phi$ or $|\theta| = |\phi| = 45°$

Hence, (1) gives $v = \boxed{\dfrac{v_0}{\sqrt{2}}}$

(b) $\theta = \boxed{45°}$ $\phi = \boxed{-45°}$

9.43 $m_0 = 17 \times 10^{-27}$ kg ; $v_0 = 0$ (The parent nucleus)

$m_1 = 5.0 \times 10^{-27}$ kg ; $v_1 = 6 \times 10^6 j$ m/s

$m_2 = 8.4 \times 10^{-27}$ kg ; $v_2 = 4 \times 10^6 i$ m/s

(a) $m_1 v_1 + m_2 v_2 + m_3 v_3 = 0$ where $m_3 = m_0 = m_1 = m_2 = 3.6 \times 10^{-27}$ kg.

$(5 \times 10^{-27})(6 \times 10^6 j) + (8.4 \times 10^{-27})(4 \times 10^6 i) + (3.6 \times 10^{-27}) v_3 = 0$

$v_3 = (-8.3 \times 10^6 j - 9.3 \times 10^6 i)$ m/s

so $\boxed{v_x = -9.33 \times 10^6 \text{ m/s}}$ and $\boxed{v_y = -8.33 \times 10^6 \text{ m/s}}$

(b) $E = \frac{1}{2} m_1 v_1^2 + \frac{1}{2} m_2 v_2^2 + \frac{1}{2} m_3 v_3^2$

$= \frac{1}{2}[(5 \times 10^{-27})(6 \times 10^6)^2 + (8.4 \times 10^{-27})(4 \times 10^6)^2$

$+ (3.6 \times 10^{-27})(12.5 \times 10^6)^2]$

$\boxed{E = 4.39 \times 10^{-13} \text{ J}}$

9.44 (a) Use Eqs. 9.24a and 9.24b and refer to Figure 9.44 shown below.

Let the puck initially at rest be m_2 .

$m_1 v_{1i} = m_1 v_{1f} \cos\theta + m_2 v_{2f} \cos\phi$

$0 = m_1 v_{1f} \sin\theta - m_2 v_{2f} \sin\phi$

$(0.2 \text{ kg})(2 \text{ m/s}) = (0.2 \text{ kg})(1 \text{ m/s}) \cos 53° + (0.3 \text{ kg}) v_{2f} \cos\phi$

$0 = (0.2 \text{ kg})(1 \text{ m/s}) \sin 53° - (0.3 \text{ kg})(v_{2f} \sin\phi)$

From these equations we find

$\tan\phi = \dfrac{\sin\phi}{\cos\phi} = \dfrac{0.1597}{0.2796} = 0.571, \quad \phi = 29.7°$

Then $v_{2f} = \dfrac{(0.1597 \text{ kg} \cdot \text{m/s})}{(0.3 \text{ kg})(\sin 29.7°)} = \boxed{1.07 \text{ m/s}}$

(b) $f_{\text{lost}} = \dfrac{\Delta K}{K_i} = \dfrac{K_f - K_i}{K_i} = \boxed{-0.318}$

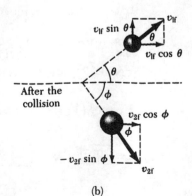

Before the collision

After the collision

(a)   (b)

9.44

9.45 Conservation of momentum: $p_{xi} = p_{xf}$ and $p_{yi} = p_{yf}$, so

$$v_y(0.8) + v_0(0.6) = 5 \quad \text{and} \quad v_y(0.6) = v_0(0.8)$$

$$\boxed{v_0 = 3.01 \, \text{m/s} \; ; \; v_y = 3.99 \, \text{m/s}}$$

* 9.46 (a) By conservation of momentum,

$$(4.5)(20 \, \mathbf{j}) + (2)(60 \, \mathbf{i}) + 3.5 \, \mathbf{v} = 0$$

$$\boxed{\mathbf{v} = -(34.3 \, \text{m/s})\mathbf{i} - (25.7 \, \text{m/s})\mathbf{j}}$$

(b) $E = \dfrac{1}{2}(4.5)(20)^2 + \dfrac{1}{2}(2)(60)^2 + \dfrac{1}{2}(3.5)(34.3^2 + 25.7^2)$

$E = \boxed{7.71 \, \text{kJ}}$

* 9.47 By conservation of momentum (with all masses equal),

$$5 \, \text{m/s} + 0 = (4.33 \, \text{m/s}) \cos 30° + v_{2fx}$$

$$v_{2fx} = 1.25 \, \text{m/s}$$

$$0 = 4.33 \sin 30° + v_{2fy}$$

$$v_{2fy} = -2.16 \, \text{m/s}$$

$$|v| = \boxed{2.50 \, \text{m/s} \quad \text{at} \; -60.0°}$$

9.48 (a) $p_{xi} = m_2 v_i = (200 \, \text{g})(25 \, \text{cm/s}) = 5000 \, \text{g} \cdot \text{cm/s}$

$p_{xf} = (m_1 + m_2)v_f = (200 \, \text{g} + 50 \, \text{g})v_f = p_{xi}$

Therefore, $v_f = \dfrac{5000 \, \text{g} \cdot \text{cm/s}}{250 \, \text{g}} = \boxed{20.0 \, \text{cm/s}}$

(b) No. The earth recoils, but only by a very small amount because of its enormous mass.

9.49   From momentum conservation,

$$p_1 = p_{1f} + p_{2f} \qquad (1)$$

Conservation of kinetic energy gives $\dfrac{p_1^2}{2m} = \dfrac{p_{1f}^2}{2m} + \dfrac{p_{2f}^2}{2m}$ or

$$p_1^2 = p_{1f}^2 + p_{2f}^2 \qquad (2)$$

Squaring Eq. (1)

$$p_1^2 = p_{1f}^2 + p_{2f}^2 + 2p_{1f}p_{2f}\cos\theta \qquad (3)$$

Eqs. (2) and (3) can be simultaneously true if $p_{1f}p_{2f}\cos\theta = 0$

This is possible if $p_{1f} = 0$ or $p_{2f} = 0$. (But this is ruled out by the condition of an "oblique collision.") Therefore $\theta = \pm 90°$ (The two particles get scattered at 90° to each other.)

9.50   Using momentum conservation in the x-direction gives

$$m_1 v_1 = m_1 v_1' \cos\theta_1 + m_2 v_2' \cos\theta_2 \qquad (1)$$

using momentum conservation in the y-direction gives

$$m_2 v_2' \sin\theta_2 = m_1 v_1' \sin\theta_1 \qquad (2) \quad \text{or} \quad v_2' \sin\theta_2 = \frac{m_1}{m_2} v_1' \sin\theta_1 \qquad (3)$$

From Eq. (1) $v_2' \cos\theta_2 = \dfrac{m_1 v_1}{m_2} - \dfrac{m_1}{m_2} v_1' \cos\theta_1$ (4)

From Eqs. (3) and (4)

$$\boxed{\tan\theta_2 = \frac{v_1' \sin\theta_1}{v_1 - v_1' \cos\theta_1}} \qquad (5)$$

No inference can be made about the collision being elastic from Eq. (5); since conservation of KE was not required. to derive this equation. Thus the collision can be elastic or inelastic for Eq. (5) to hold.

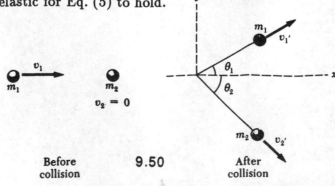

Before collision   9.50   After collision

9.51 $x_c = \dfrac{\Sigma m_i x_i}{\Sigma m_1} = \dfrac{m_1 x_1 + m_2 x_2}{m_1 + m_2}$

$x_c = \dfrac{3(-5) + 3(4)}{7} = \boxed{-0.429 \text{ m}}$

9.52 $\underline{3 \text{ kg}}$ $x = 3$ m, $y = -2$ m

$\underline{4 \text{ kg}}$ $x = -2$ m, $y = 4$ m

$\underline{1 \text{ kg}}$ $x = 2$ m, $y = 2$ m

$x_c = \dfrac{\Sigma m_i x_i}{\Sigma m_i} = \dfrac{3(3) + 4(-2) + 1(2)}{8} = \boxed{0.375 \text{ m}}$

$y_c = \dfrac{\Sigma m_i y_i}{\Sigma m_i} = \dfrac{2(-2) + 3(4) + 1(2)}{8} = \boxed{1.50 \text{ m}}$

9.53 $C.M. = \dfrac{(329{,}390 M_E)(0) + M_E(1.496 \times 10^8 \text{ km})}{329{,}390 M_E + M_E} = \boxed{454 \text{ km}}$

The center of mass of the sun-earth system is well inside the sun.

9.54 $d = 1.30 \times 10^{-10}$ m, $m_{cl} = 35 m_H$

$x_{cm} = \dfrac{m_H x_H + m_{cl} x_{cl}}{m_H + m_{cl}} = \dfrac{m_H(0) + 35 m_H d}{m_H + 35 m_H} = \left(\dfrac{35}{36}\right)d$

$x_{cm} = \left(\dfrac{35}{36}\right) \times 1.30 \times 10^{-10} \text{ m} = \boxed{1.26 \times 10^{-10} \text{ m}}$

9.55 The center of mass will be at R for the two fragments. Therefore the second fragment
will fall at $\boxed{\dfrac{3}{2}R}$

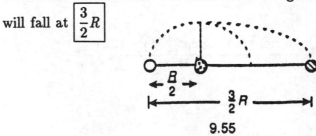

9.55

9.56 $x_c = \dfrac{1}{M} \displaystyle\int x\,dm$

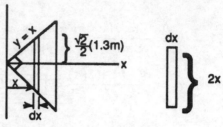

9.56

$dm = \dfrac{M}{A}dA$

$dA = 2x\,dx$

$$x_c = \dfrac{1}{M} \int\limits_{0}^{x=\frac{\sqrt{2}}{2}(1.3\,\text{m})} \dfrac{M}{A}(2x\,dx)(x) = \dfrac{2}{A}\int\limits_{0}^{0.919} x^2\,dx$$

$$= \dfrac{2}{3}\Big[\dfrac{x^3}{A}\Big]_0^{0.919} = \dfrac{2}{3}\,frac{x^3}{x^2}\,\Big|_0^{0.919} = \dfrac{2}{3}x\,\Big|_0^{0.919} = \boxed{0.613\ \text{m}}$$

$\boxed{y_c = 0\ \text{(by symmetry)}}$

9.57 $A = A_1 + A_2 + A_3$

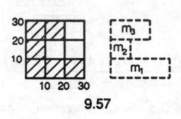

9.57

$M = M_1 + M_2 + M_3$

$\dfrac{M_1}{A_1} = \dfrac{M}{A}$

$A_1 = 300\ \text{cm}^2,\ A_2 = 100\ \text{cm}^2,\ A_3 = 200\ \text{cm}^2$

$A = 600\ \text{cm}^2$

$M_1 = M\Big(\dfrac{A_1}{A}\Big) = \dfrac{300\ \text{cm}^2}{600\ \text{cm}^2}M = \dfrac{M}{2}$

$M_2 = M\Big(\dfrac{A_2}{A}\Big) = \dfrac{100\ \text{cm}^2}{600\ \text{cm}^2}M = \dfrac{M}{6}$

$M_3 = M\Big(\dfrac{A_3}{A}\Big) = \dfrac{200\ \text{cm}^2}{600\ \text{cm}^2}M = \dfrac{M}{3}$

$x_c = \dfrac{x_1 M_1 + x_2 M_2 + x_3 M_3}{M} = \dfrac{15\ \text{cm}(\frac{1}{2}M) + 5\ \text{cm}(\frac{1}{6}M) + 10\ \text{cm}(\frac{1}{3})}{M}$

$\boxed{x_c = 11.7\ \text{cm}}$

$y_c = \dfrac{\frac{1}{2}M(5\ \text{cm}) + \frac{1}{6}M(15\ \text{cm}) + (\frac{1}{3}M)(25\ \text{cm})}{M} = \boxed{13.3\ \text{cm}}$

9.58 (a)
$$Mv_c = m_1v_1 + m_2v_2$$
$$(5+2)v_c = 5(3) + 2(-2.5)$$
$$v_c = \boxed{1.43 \text{ m/s to the right}}$$

(b) $p = Mv_c = 7(1.43) = \boxed{10 \text{ kg·m/s to the right}}$

9.59 (a) $v_c = \dfrac{\Sigma m_i v_i}{M} = \dfrac{(m_1v_1 + m_2v_2)}{M}$

$$v_c = \frac{[2(2i-3j) + 3(i+6j)]}{5} = \boxed{(1.40i + 2.40j) \text{ m/s}}$$

(b) $p = mv_c = 5v_c = \boxed{(7.00i + 12.0j) \text{ kg·m/s}}$

9.60 (a) $v_{cm} = \dfrac{m_1v_1 + m_2v_2}{m_1 + m_2} = \dfrac{(2 \text{ kg})(2i - 10tj) \text{ m/s} + (3 \text{ kg})(4i) \text{ m/s}}{(2+3) \text{ kg}} = (3.2i - 4tj) \text{ m/s}$

At $t = 0.5$ s, $v_{cm} = \boxed{(3.20i - 2.00j) \text{ m/s}}$

(b) $a_{cm} = \dfrac{dv_{cm}}{dt} = \boxed{(-4.00j) \text{ m/s}^2}$

(c) $p = m_1v_1 + m_2v_2 = \boxed{(16i - 20tj) \text{ kg·m/s}}$

9.61 (a) $v_c = \dfrac{m_1v_1 + m_2v_2}{m_1 + m_2} = \dfrac{(3.0 \text{ g})(3.0 \text{ m/s}) + 0}{10 \text{ g}} = 0.90 \text{ m/s to the right}$

For the 3.0 g particle

$v_{(approach)} = 3 \text{ m/s} - 0.90 \text{ m/s} = \boxed{2.10 \text{ m/s}}$

For the 7.0 g particle

$v_{(approach)} = v_c = \boxed{0.900 \text{ m/s}}$

(b) $(p_3)_{cm} = (0.003 \text{ kg})(2.1 \text{ m/s}) = \boxed{6.30 \times 10^{-3} \text{ kg·m/s}}$

$(p_7)_{cm} = (0.007 \text{ kg})(-0.90 \text{ m/s}) = \boxed{-6.30 \times 10^{-3} \text{ kg·m/s}}$

9.62 Let x = distance from shore to center of boat; l = length of boat;

x' = distance boat moves as Juliet moves toward Romeo.

Before: $x_{cm} = \dfrac{[M_B x + M_J(x - \frac{l}{2}) + M_R(x + \frac{l}{2})]}{(M_B + M_J + M_R)}$

After: $x_{cm} = \dfrac{[M_B(x - x') + M_J(x + \frac{l}{2} - x') + M_R(x + \frac{l}{2} - x')]}{(M_B + M_J + M_R)}$

$l(-\dfrac{55}{2} + \dfrac{77}{2}) = x'(-80 - 55 - 77) + \dfrac{l}{2}(55 + 77)$

$x' = \dfrac{55\,l}{212} = \dfrac{55(2.7)}{212} = \boxed{0.700 \text{ m}}$

9.63 Thrust $= |v_e \dfrac{dM}{dt}| = (2.5 \times 10^3 \text{ m/s})(80 \text{ kg/s}) = \boxed{200 \text{ kN}}$

9.64 (a) Thrust $= |v_e \dfrac{dM}{dt}| = (2.6 \times 10^3 \text{ m/s})(1.5 \times 10^4 \text{ kg/s}) = \boxed{3.9 \times 10^7 \text{ N}}$

(b) $\Sigma F_y = \text{Thrust} - Mg = Ma$

$3.9 \times 10^7 - (3 \times 10^6)(9.8) = (3 \times 10^6)\text{a}$

$a = \boxed{3.2 \text{ m/s}^2}$

* 9.65 (a) From Eq 9.42, the thrust

$T = 2.4 \times 10^7 \text{ N} = v_e \dfrac{dM}{dt}$

If $v_e = 3000$ m/s, then

$\dfrac{dM}{dt} = \boxed{8000 \text{ kg/s}}$

(b) From Eq 9.41,

$$v_f - v_i = v_e \ln\left(\dfrac{M_i}{M_f}\right)$$

$$v_f - 0 = (3000 \text{ m/s}) \ln\left(\dfrac{M_i}{0.1\,M_i}\right)$$

$$v_f = \boxed{6.91 \text{ km/s}}$$

9.66 $v = -v_r \ln \dfrac{M_i}{M_f} - gt_b$

In deep space the effect of gravity is not felt, so $v = -v_r \ln \dfrac{M_i}{M_f}$

(a) $M_i = e^{-v/v_r} M_f = e^5 (3.0 \times 10^3 \text{ kg}) = 4.45 \times 10^5 \text{ kg}$

The mass of fuel and oxidizer is

$\Delta M = M_i - M_f = (445 - 3) \times 10^3 \text{ kg} = \boxed{442 \text{ metric tons}}$

(b) $\Delta M = e^2 (3 \text{ metric tons}) - 3 \text{ metric tons} = \boxed{19.2 \text{ metric tons}}$

Because of the exponential, a relatively small increase in fuel
and/or engine efficiency causes a large change in the amount of fuel
and oxidizer required.

9.67 $T = v_2 \dfrac{dm}{dt}$

$\dfrac{dm}{dt} = \dfrac{2.5 \times 10^6 \text{ N}}{3.0 \times 10^3 \text{ m/s}} = 8.33 \times 10^2 \text{ kg/s}$

$\dfrac{dv}{dt} = \dfrac{1}{\rho} \left(\dfrac{dm}{dt} \right) = \dfrac{8.33 \times 10^2 \text{ kg/s}}{1.4 \times 10^3 \text{ kg/m}^3} = \boxed{0.595 \text{ m}^3/\text{s}}$

9.68 $M \dfrac{dv}{dt} = -Mg + v_r \dfrac{dM}{dt}$

$dv = -g \, dt + v_r \dfrac{dM}{M}$

Integrating,

$v \;=\; -gt_b + v_r \displaystyle\int_{M_i}^{M_f} \dfrac{dM}{M} = -gt_b + v_r [\ln M_f - \ln M_i] = -v_r \ln \dfrac{M_i}{M_f} - gt_b$

Since the rate of fuel consumption is constant, the time to burn the fuel is

$t_b = \dfrac{M_i - M_f}{dm/dt}$

9.69 $v_0 = \sqrt{Rg} = 44.3 \text{ m/s}$

$F = \dfrac{mv_0}{\Delta t} = \dfrac{(0.046 \text{ kg})(44.3 \text{ m/s})}{7 \times 10^{-3} \text{ s}} = \boxed{291 \text{ N}}$

9.70 $x_c = \dfrac{(\frac{4}{3}\pi R^3 \rho)R - \frac{4}{3}\pi(\frac{R}{2})^3\rho(\frac{3}{2}R)}{\frac{4}{3}\pi R^3\rho(1-\frac{1}{8})}$

$x_c = \dfrac{13R}{14}$ or *C.M.* is $\boxed{R/14 \text{ from center of sphere}}$

opposite center of void.

9.71   (a) $0 = \Delta p_b + \Delta p_R$; $0 = (0.012)(600) + 4v$;

$v = -\dfrac{(0.012)(600)}{4} = -1.8$ m/s or $\boxed{1.80 \text{ m/s to the left}}$

(b) $F_{av} = \dfrac{\Delta p_r}{\Delta t}$ $\Delta s = \dfrac{1}{2}(v_0 + v)t$;

$t = \dfrac{2\Delta s}{v_0 + v} = \dfrac{2(0.025)}{1.8} = 2.8 \times 10^{-2}$ s

$F_{av} = \dfrac{4(1.8)}{2.8 \times 10^{-2}} = \boxed{257 \text{ N to the left}}$

(c) $\boxed{\text{Larger than part (b)}}$ $\Delta t \propto \Delta s$ and $F \propto \dfrac{1}{\Delta t}$ therefore $F \propto \dfrac{1}{\Delta s}$

9.72   Since no other force acts along the horizontal direction on the

bullet-block system before and after impact, $\Delta P = 0$ or

$(0.008)v_1 = (2.508)v_f$

We can find v_f using the kinematic equations:

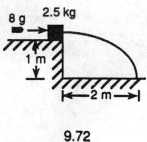

9.72

$\Delta x = v_{0x}t$ or $2 = v_f t$ and $\Delta y = \dfrac{1}{2}a_y t^2$ or

$-1 \text{ m} = \dfrac{1}{2}(-9.8 \text{ m/s}^2)(\dfrac{2}{v_f})^2$

$v_f = 4.43$ m/s

$v_1 = \dfrac{2.508(4.43)}{0.008} = \boxed{1390 \text{ m/s}}$

9.73 $\dfrac{\Delta m}{\Delta t} = (\dfrac{160}{4\text{ s}})(0.130\text{ kg}) = 5.2\text{ kg/s}$

$F = \dfrac{v\Delta m}{\Delta t} = (800\text{ m/s})(5.2\text{ kg/s}) = \boxed{4160\text{ N}}$

Note that, since the velocity of the shells is much greater than the velocity of the helicopter, it is not necessary to use a relative velocity for this calculation. To find the amount its forward speed is reduced, use $M\Delta v = mv$ or

$\Delta v = \dfrac{m}{M}v = \dfrac{(160)(0.130\text{ kg})}{4000\text{ kg}}(800\text{ m/s}) = \boxed{4.16\text{ m/s}}$

9.74 (a) Applying conservation of momentum in the x-direction,

$$MV = m(v_r \cos 60° - V) - (M - m)V$$

$$V = \dfrac{mv_r \cos 60°}{2M} = \dfrac{(50\text{ kg})(300\text{ m/s})(\frac{1}{2})}{40,000\text{ kg}} = \boxed{0.188\ \text{m/s}}$$

(b) $(v_r \sin 60°)^2 = 2gh \qquad h = \dfrac{(300\text{ m/s})^2(\frac{3}{4})}{2(9.8\text{ m/s}^2)} = \boxed{3.44\text{ km}}$

9.75 $T = M\dfrac{dv}{dt} = -v_r\dfrac{dm}{dt} - u\dfrac{d\mu}{dt}$

$T = -(-600\text{ m/s})(3\text{ kg/s}) - (-600\text{ m/s} + 223\text{ m/s})(80\text{ kg/s})$

$= 1800\text{ N} + 30,160\text{ N} = \boxed{32,000\ \text{N}}$

The delivered power is the force (or thrust) multiplied by the velocity;

$P = Tv = (31,960\text{ N})(223\text{ m/s}) = \boxed{7.13 \times 10^6\ \text{W}}$

218

Chapter 9

9.76 We take the direction of motion of the spacecraft to be positive.

Then, the thrust is

$$T = -v_r \frac{dm}{dt} = -(-3000 \text{ m/s})(150 \text{ kg/s}) = \boxed{450,000 \text{ N}}$$

The initial acceleration is

$$a = \frac{dv}{dt} = -\frac{v_r}{M}\frac{dm}{dt} = \frac{T}{M} = \frac{450,000 \text{ N}}{25,000 \text{ kg}} \cdot \frac{g}{9.80 \text{ m/s}^2} = \boxed{1.84g}$$

$$M\frac{dv}{dt} = v_r \frac{dM}{dt}$$

or

$$\frac{dM}{M} = \frac{dv}{v_r}$$

Direct integration gives

$$\int_{M_i}^{M_f} \frac{dM}{M} = \frac{1}{v_r}\int_{0}^{v} dv$$

or

$$v = -v_r \ln(\frac{M_i}{M_f})$$

Substituting numerical values for the 100-s burn,

$M_i = 25,000 \text{ kg}, \quad M_f = M_i - (150 \text{ kg/s})(100 \text{ s}) = 10,000 \text{ kg},$

and $v_r = -3,000 \text{ m/s}$, we find

$$v = -(-3000 \text{ m/s})\ln\frac{25,000}{10,000} = \boxed{2750 \text{ m/s} = 6150 \text{ mi/h}}$$

9.77 Consider the motion of the firefighter during the three intervals:

(1) before, (2) during, and (3) after collision with the platform.

(a) While falling a height of 4 m, his speed changes

from $v_0 = 0$ to v_1 as found from Eq. 8.13

$W_{nc} = (K_f + U_f) - (K_i + U_i)$, or

$K_f = W_{nc} - U_f + K_i + U_i$.

When the initial position of the platform is taken as the

zero level of gravitational potential we have

$\frac{1}{2}mv_1^2 = fh\cos(180°) - 0 + 0 + mgh$; Solving for v_1 gives

$$v_1 = \sqrt{\frac{2(-fh + mgh)}{m}} = \sqrt{\frac{2(-300)(4) + 75(9.8)(4))}{75}} = \boxed{6.81 \ \text{m/s}}$$

(b) During the inelastic collision momentum is conserved and

if v_2 is the speed of the firefighter and platform just

after collision we have $mv_1 = (m + M)v_2$ or

$$v_2 = \frac{m_1v_1}{m + M} = \frac{75(6.81)}{75 + 20} = 5.38 \ \text{m/s}$$

Following the collision and again substituting into Eq. 8.13 and

using the distances as labeled in the figure we have (maintaining

the zero level of gravitational potential at the initial position

of the platform):

$W_{nc} = K_f + U_{fg} + U_{fs} - K_i - U_{ig} - U_{is}$, or

$-fs = 0 + (m + M)g(-s) + \frac{1}{2}ks^2 - \frac{1}{2}(m + M)v^2 - 0 - 0$

This results in a quadratic equation in s:

$2000\,s^2 - (931)\,s + 300\,s - 1375 = 0$ or $\boxed{s = 1.00 \ \text{m}}$

9.78 $p_f = p_1 i + p_2 j$

$p_f = \sqrt{[0.160 \text{ kg } (35 \text{ m/s})]^2 + [70 \text{ kg } (0.20 \text{ m/s})]^2}$

$= \sqrt{(5.6)^2 + (14)^2} = 15.1 \text{ kg} \cdot \text{m/s}$

$|v_f| = \dfrac{15.1 \text{ kg} \cdot \text{m/s}}{70.16 \text{ kg}} = \boxed{0.215 \text{ m/s}}$

$\theta = \arctan\left(\dfrac{14}{5.6}\right) = \boxed{68.2°}$

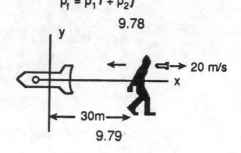

$P_1 = m_1 v_1$

$v = 35$ m/s
$m = 0.160$ kg

$P_2 = m_2 v_2$

70 kg
$v = 0.20$ m/s

$P_f = p_1 i + p_2 j$

9.78

9.79   The ref. frame will be fixed to the space station.

Recoil velocity of the astronaut, v_R

$80 v_R + (0.5)(20) i = 0 \quad \text{or} \quad v_R = -(0.125 \text{ m/s}) i$

$t = \dfrac{30 \text{ m}}{0.125 \text{ m/s}} = \boxed{240 \text{ s}}$

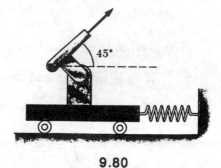

20 m/s

30m

9.79

9.80   (a) $200(125 \cos 45°) + 5000 v_{\text{recoil}} = 0$

$v_{\text{recoil}} = -\dfrac{125 \times 200}{5000} \cos 45° = \boxed{-3.54 \text{ m/s}}$

(b) $\dfrac{1}{2} 5000\, v_{\text{recoil}}^2 = \dfrac{1}{2} k x^2 = \dfrac{1}{2}(2000) x^2$

$x = \boxed{1.77 \text{ m}}$

45°

9.80

(c) $(\Delta P)_{\text{overall}} = 0$. The *vertical* momentum of the "system" changes as the projectiles vertical velocity increases inside the cannon. This results in increased normal force. The horizontal momentum of the system is balanced by the increasing tension in the spring.

9.81   Since the mass per length is uniform, we can express an element of mass dm over an increment of length dx as $dm = (\frac{M}{L})dx$. The magnitude of the force due to the falling chain will be

$$F_1 = \frac{dp}{dt} = v(\frac{dm}{dt}) = v(\frac{M}{L})(\frac{dx}{dt}) = (\frac{M}{L})v^2$$

(Note $\frac{dx}{dt} = v$). After falling a distance x, the velocity of each link is $v^2 = 2gx$, and $F_1 = (\frac{M}{L})(2gx)$. The links already on the table exert a force equal to their weight given by $F_2 = (\frac{Mx}{L})g$, so that

$$F_{\text{total}} = F_1 + F_2 = (\frac{M}{L})(2gx) + (\frac{M}{L})(gx) = \boxed{\frac{3Mgx}{L}}$$

or three times the weight of the chain on the table at that instant.

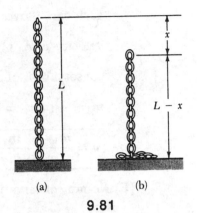

(a)   (b)

9.81

9.82   (a) When the spring is fully compressed each cart moves with same velocity v. Apply conservation of momentum $p_i = p_f$

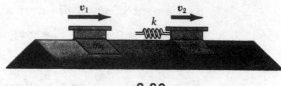

9.82

$$m_1 v_1 + m_2 v_2 = (m_1 + m_2)v$$

$$\boxed{v = \frac{m_1 v_1 + m_2 v_2}{m_1 + m_2}}$$

(b) No nonconservative forces acting therefore $\Delta E = 0$

$$\frac{1}{2}m_1 v_1^2 + \frac{1}{2}m_2 v_2^2 = \frac{1}{2}(m_1 + m_2)v^2 + \frac{1}{2}kx_m^2$$

Substitute for v from (a) and solve for x_m.

$$x_m^2 = \frac{(m_1 + m_2)m_1 v_1^2 + (m_1 + m_2)m_2 v_2^2 - (m_1 v_1)^2 - (m_2 v_2)^2 - 2m_1 m_2 v_1 v_2}{k(m_1 + m_2)}$$

$$x_m = \sqrt{\frac{m_1 m_2(v_1^2 + v_2^2 - 2v_1 v_2)}{k(m_1 + m_2)}} = \boxed{(v_1 - v_2)\sqrt{\frac{m_1 m_2}{k(m_1 + m_2)}}}$$

(c) $m_1 v_1 + m_2 v_2 = m_1 v_{1f} + m_2 v_{2f}$

Conservation of momentum: $v_{1f} = \dfrac{(m_1 v_1 + m_2 v_2 - m_2 v_{2f})}{m_1}$

Conservation of energy: $\dfrac{1}{2}m_1 v_1^2 + \dfrac{1}{2}m_2 v_{2f}^2 = \dfrac{1}{2}m_1 v_{1f}^2 + \dfrac{1}{2}m_2 v_{2f}^2$

$$m_1 v_1^2 + m_2 v_2^2 = m_1 \frac{(m_1 v_1 + m_2 v_2 - m_1 v_{2f})^2}{m_1^2} + m_2 v_{2f}^2$$

$$m_1 v_1^2 + m_2 v_2^2 = \frac{1}{m_1}[(m_1 v_1 + m_2 v_2)^2 + (m_1 v_{2f})^2 - 2(m_1 v_1 + m_2 v_2)(m_1 v_{2f})] + m_2 v_{2f}^2$$

$$m_1 v_1^2 + m_2 v_2^2 = \frac{1}{m_1}(m_1 v_1 + m_2 v_2)^2 + m_1 v_{2f}^2 - 2(m_1 v_1 + m_2 v_2)v_{2f} + m_2 v_{2f}^2$$

$$(m_1 + m_2)v_{2f}^2 - 2(m_1 v_1 + m_2 v_2)v_{2f} + \left(\frac{m_2^2}{m_1}v_2^2 + 2m_2 v_1 v_2 - m_2 v_2^2\right) = 0$$

$$v_{2f} = \frac{2(m_1 v_1 + m_2 v_2) \pm \sqrt{4(m_1 v_1 + m_2 v_2)^2 - 4(m_1 + m_2)(\frac{m_2^2 v_2^2}{m_1} + 2m_2 v_1 v_2 - m_2 v_2^2)}}{2(m_1 + m_2)}$$

$$v_{1f} = \frac{(m_1 - m_2)}{(m_1 + m_2)}v_1 + \frac{2m_2}{(m_1 + m_2)}v_2$$

$$v_{2f} = \left(\frac{2m_1}{m_1 + m_2}\right)v_1 + \left(\frac{m_2 - m_1}{m_1 + m_2}\right)v_2$$

9.83   (a) The center of mass of the system doesn't move.

(b) Before: $x_{cm} = \dfrac{x m_B + (x-2) m_C}{m_B + m_C} = \dfrac{5(70) + 3(40)}{110}$

After: $x_{cm} = \dfrac{(x - x') m_B + (x + 2 + 4 - x') m_C}{m_B + m_C} = \dfrac{(5 - x')70 + (7 - x')40}{110}$

$$5(70) + 3(40) = (5 - x')70 + (7 - x')40$$

$$470 = 350 - 70x' + 280 - 40x'$$

$$110x' = 160$$

$$x' = 1.45 \text{ m}$$

Relative to the pier $x'' = 3 + 4 - 1.45 = \boxed{5.55 \text{ m}}$

(c) No, the child missed the turtle by 0.45 m   (The dotted line in the figure corresponds to the position of the center of mass, which doesn't change.)

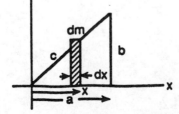

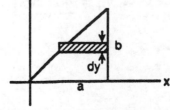

9.83

9.84 $x_{cm} = \dfrac{\int x\,dm}{M} = \dfrac{\sigma \int x \cdot dA}{M} = \dfrac{\sigma \int xy\,dx}{M} = \dfrac{\sigma \frac{b}{a}}{M} \int_0^a x^2\,dx = \dfrac{\sigma b}{Ma} \dfrac{x^3}{3}\Big]_0^a = \dfrac{M}{\frac{1}{2}abM} \dfrac{b}{a} \dfrac{a^3}{3}$

$\boxed{x_{cm} = \dfrac{2}{3}a}$

$y_{cm} = \int \dfrac{y\,dm}{M} = \dfrac{\sigma}{M} \int y(dA) = \dfrac{M}{\frac{1}{2}abM} \int y(a-x)\,dy = \dfrac{2}{ab} \int_0^b ay\,dy - \dfrac{2}{ab} \int_0^b \dfrac{a}{b}y^2\,dy$

$= \dfrac{2a}{ab}\left(\dfrac{b^2}{2}\right) - \dfrac{2a}{ab^2}\left(\dfrac{b^3}{3}\right) = b - \dfrac{2}{3}b = \boxed{\dfrac{1}{3}b}$

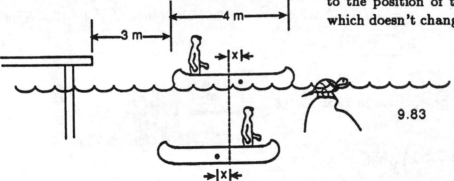

$y = \frac{b}{a}x$
$dA = y\,dx$

$x = \frac{a}{b}y$
$dA = (b - x)dy$

9.84

9.85   (a) Find the speed when the bullet emerges from the block

Momentum conservation: $mv_0 = MV_0 + mv$

The block moves a distance of 5 cm. Assume for an approximation that the block was given an initial velocity, v_0, and the bullet kept going with a constant velocity, v. The block then compresses the spring and stops.

$$\frac{1}{2}MV_0^2 = \frac{1}{2}kx^2$$

$$V_0 = \sqrt{\frac{(900 \text{ N/m})(0.05 \text{ m})^2}{1 \text{ kg}}} = 1.5 \text{ m/s}$$

$$v = \frac{mv_0 - MV_0}{m} = \frac{(0.005 \text{ kg})(400 \text{ m/s}) - (1 \text{ kg})(1.5 \text{ m/s})}{0.005 \text{ kg}} = \boxed{100 \ \text{ m/s}}$$

(b)

Energy lost $= \Delta K - \Delta U$

$$= \frac{1}{2}(0.005 \text{ kg})(100 \text{ m/s})^2 - \frac{1}{2}(0.005 \text{ kg})(400 \text{ m/s})^2 + \frac{1}{2}(900 \text{ N/m})(0.05 \text{ m})^2$$

$$= \boxed{-\ 374 \text{ J}}$$

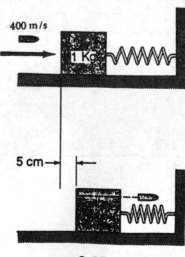

9.85

* 9.86   (a) Utilizing the equation in Example 9.6,

$$v = \left(\frac{m_1 + m_2}{m_1}\right)\sqrt{2gh}$$

$$v_{1_i} \cong \boxed{6.30 \text{ m/s}}$$

(b) Utilizing the two equations,

$$\frac{1}{2}gt^2 = Y \text{ and } X = v_{1_i}t$$

we combine them to find

$$v_{1_i} = \frac{X}{\sqrt{2Y/g}}$$

From the data, $v_{1_i} = \boxed{6.17 \text{ m/s}}$

CHAPTER 10

10.1   (a) $\alpha = \dfrac{\omega - \omega_0}{t} = \dfrac{12 \text{ rad/s}}{3 \text{ s}} = \boxed{4.00 \text{ rad/s}^2}$

(b) $\theta = \omega_0 t - \dfrac{1}{2}\alpha t^2 = \dfrac{1}{2}(4 \text{ rad/s}^2)(3 \text{ s})^2 = \boxed{18.0 \text{ rad}}$

10.2 $\omega_0 = (33\dfrac{1}{3} \dfrac{\text{rev}}{\text{min}})(\dfrac{2\pi \text{ rad}}{\text{rev}})(\dfrac{\text{min}}{60 \text{ s}}) = 3.49 \text{ rad/s}$

$\omega = \omega_0 + \alpha t$

$0 = 3.49 \text{ rad/s} + \alpha(60 \text{ s})$

$\alpha = \dfrac{-3.49 \text{ rad/s}}{60 \text{ s}} = -0.0582 \text{ rad/s}^2$

$\theta = \theta_0 + \omega_0 t + \dfrac{1}{2}\alpha t^2$

$\theta = 0 + (349 \text{ rad/s})(60 \text{ s}) - \dfrac{1}{2}(0.0582 \text{ rad/s})(60 \text{ s})^2$

$= 209.4 - 104.76 = (104.64 \text{ rad})(\dfrac{\text{rev}}{2\pi \text{ rad}}) = \boxed{16.7 \text{ rev}}$

10.3   (a) $\omega = \dfrac{2\pi \text{ rad}}{365 \text{ days}} \dfrac{1 \text{ day}}{24 \text{ h}} \dfrac{1 \text{ h}}{3600 \text{ s}} = \boxed{1.99 \times 10^{-7} \text{ rad/s}}$

(b) $\omega = \dfrac{2\pi \text{ rad}}{27.3 \text{ days}} \dfrac{1 \text{ day}}{24 \text{ h}} \dfrac{1 \text{ h}}{3600 \text{ s}} = \boxed{2.65 \times 10^{-6} \text{ rad/s}}$

10.4   (a) $\omega = \dfrac{d\theta}{dt} = \boxed{2at + 3bt^2}$

(b) $\alpha = \dfrac{d\omega}{dt} = \boxed{2a + 6bt}$

10.5 (a) $\omega_i = \dfrac{100 \times 2\pi}{60}$ rad/s $= 10.47$; $\omega_f = 0$

$$t = \dfrac{100 \times 2\pi}{60 \times 2} = \boxed{5.24 \text{ s}}$$

(b) $\theta = \omega_i t + \dfrac{1}{2}\alpha t^2 = (\dfrac{10}{3}\pi)(\dfrac{10}{6}\pi) - (\dfrac{10}{6})^2\pi^2 = \boxed{27.4 \text{ rad}}$

10.6 $\theta \big|_{t=0} = \boxed{5.00 \text{ rad}}$; $\theta \big|_{t=3s} = 5 + 30 + 18 = \boxed{53.0 \text{ rad}}$

$\omega\big|_{t=0} = \dfrac{d\theta}{dt}\big|_{t=0} = 10 + 4t\big|_{t=0} = \boxed{10.0 \text{ rad/s}}$

$\omega\big|_{t=3s} = \dfrac{d\theta}{dt}\big|_{t=3s} = 10 + 4t\big|_{t=3s} = \boxed{22.0 \text{ rad/s}}$

$\alpha\big|_{t=0} = \dfrac{d\omega}{dt}\big|_{t=0} = \boxed{4.00 \text{ rad/s}^2}$

$\alpha\big|_{t=3s} = \dfrac{d\omega}{dt}\big|_{t=3} = \boxed{4.00 \text{ rad/s}^2}$

10.7 $\omega = \alpha t = 5 \times 8 = 40$ rad/s

$\omega_f^2 = 0 = \omega^2 + 2\alpha'\theta$

$\alpha' = -\dfrac{\omega^2}{2\theta} = -\dfrac{(40)^2}{2 \times 2\pi \times 10} = -\dfrac{40}{\pi}$ rad/s^2 = $\boxed{-12.7 \text{ rad/s}^2}$

$\omega_f = 0 = \omega + \alpha' t$

$t = \dfrac{\omega}{-\alpha'} = \pi$ s $= \boxed{3.14 \text{ s}}$

*10.8 (a) $s = \bar{v}t = (11 \text{ m/s})(9 \text{ s}) = 99$ m

$\theta = \dfrac{s}{r} = \dfrac{99 \text{ m}}{0.29 \text{ m}} = 341$ rads $= \boxed{54.3 \text{ rev}}$

(b) $\omega = \dfrac{v}{r} = \dfrac{22 \text{ m/s}}{0.29 \text{ m}} = 75.9$ rad/s $= \boxed{12.1 \text{ rev/s}}$

10.9 (a) $v = r\omega$; $\omega = \dfrac{v}{r} = \dfrac{45 \text{ m/s}}{250 \text{ m}} = \boxed{0.180 \text{ rad/s}}$

(b) $a_r = \dfrac{v^2}{r} = \dfrac{45 \text{ m/s}^2}{0.250 \text{ m}} = \boxed{8.10 \text{ m/s}^2 \text{ toward the center of track}}$

*10.10 $a = \dfrac{\Delta v}{\Delta t} = \dfrac{30 \text{ m/s}}{6 \text{ s}} = 5 \text{ m/s}^2$

$\alpha = \dfrac{a}{r} = \dfrac{5 \text{ m/s}^2}{0.2 \text{ m}} = \boxed{25 \text{ rad/s}^2}$

10.11 $\alpha = 4 \text{ rad/s}^2, \ \omega_0 = 0, \ \theta = 1 \text{ rad}, \ \omega = \omega_0 + \alpha t = 4t,$

$\theta = \theta_0 + \omega_0 t + \dfrac{1}{2}\alpha t^2 = 1 + 2t^2$

(a) At $t = 2 \text{ s}, \omega = 4t = \boxed{8.00 \text{ rad/s}}$

(b) $v = r\omega = (1 \text{ m})(8 \text{ rad/s}) = \boxed{8.00 \text{ m/s, tangent to circle}}$

$a_r = \omega^2 r = (8^2)(1) = \boxed{64.0 \text{ m/s}^2 \text{ toward center}}$

$a_t = \alpha = (4)(1) = \boxed{4.00 \text{ m/s}^2}$

(c) $\theta = 1 + 2t^2 = 1 + 8 = \boxed{9.00 \text{ rad}}$

*10.12 (a) $\omega = \dfrac{v}{r} = \dfrac{25 \text{ m/s}}{1 \text{ m}} = \boxed{25 \text{ rad/s}}$

(b) $\alpha = \dfrac{\Delta\omega}{\Delta t}; \quad \Delta\theta = \overline{\omega}\Delta t; \quad \Delta t = \dfrac{\Delta\theta}{\overline{\omega}} = \dfrac{(1.25)(2\pi)}{12.5}$

$\alpha = \dfrac{25 \text{ rad/s}}{0.2\pi \text{ s}} = \boxed{39.8 \text{ rad/s}^2}$

(c) $\Delta t = \dfrac{\Delta\omega}{\alpha} = \dfrac{25 \text{ rad/s}}{39.8 \text{ rad/s}^2} = \boxed{0.628 \text{ s}}$

10.13 (a) $\omega = 2\pi f = \dfrac{2\pi \text{ rad}}{\text{rev}} \dfrac{1200}{60} \text{ rev/s} = \boxed{126 \text{ rad/s}}$

(b) $v = \omega R = (126 \text{ rad/s})(0.03 \text{ m}) = \boxed{3.78 \text{ m/s}}$

(c) $a_t = \omega^2 R = (126)^2(0.08) = \boxed{1.27 \text{ km/s}^2}$

(d) $s = \theta R = \omega t R = (126 \text{ rad/s})(2 \text{ s})(0.08 \text{ m}) = \boxed{20.2 \text{ m}}$

10.14 $v = \dfrac{36 \times 10^3}{60 \times 60} = 10 \text{ m/s}$

$\omega = \dfrac{v}{r} = \dfrac{10}{0.25} = \boxed{40.0 \text{ rad/s}}$

10.15 $K_A + U_A = K_p + U_p$

$6 \times 9.8 \times 5 = \dfrac{1}{2}(6)v_p^2 + 6 \times 9.8 \times 2$

$v_P^2 = 58.8 \text{ m}^2/\text{s}^2$

10.15

Radial acceleration at P, $a_r = \dfrac{v_P^2}{R} = \boxed{29.4 \text{ m/s}^2}$

Tangential acceleration at P, $a_t = g = \boxed{9.80 \text{ m/s}^2}$

10.16 $K = \dfrac{1}{2}I\omega^2 = \dfrac{1}{2}(80 \text{ kg} \cdot \text{m}^2)(600 \,\dfrac{\text{rev}}{\text{min}})^2(\dfrac{2\pi \text{ rad}}{\text{rev}})^2(\dfrac{\text{min}}{60 \text{ s}})^2 = \boxed{158 \text{ kJ}}$

10.17 (a) $I = \sum_j m_j r_j^2$; in this case $r_1 = r_2 = r_3 = r_4$

$I = \sqrt{(3 \text{ m})^2 + (2 \text{ m})^2} = \sqrt{13} \text{ m}$

$I = [\sqrt{13} \text{ m}]^2[3 + 2 + 2 + 4] \text{ kg} = \boxed{143 \text{ kg} \cdot \text{m}^2}$

(b) $K = \dfrac{1}{2}I\omega^2 = \dfrac{1}{2}(143 \text{ kg} \cdot \text{m}^2)(6 \text{ rad/s})^2 = \boxed{2.57 \times 10^3 \text{ J}}$

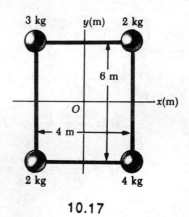

10.17

*10.18 $v = 38 \text{ m/s}$ $\omega = 125 \text{ rad/s}$

$\text{RATIO} = \dfrac{\frac{1}{2}I\omega^2}{\frac{1}{2}mv^2} = \dfrac{\frac{1}{2}\left(\frac{2}{5}mr^2\right)\omega^2}{\frac{1}{2}mv^2}$

$\text{RATIO} = \dfrac{\frac{2}{5}(0.38)^2(125^2)}{(38)^2} = \boxed{\dfrac{1}{160}}$

10.18

10.19 $m_1 = 4$ kg, $r_1 = y_1 = 3$ m; $m_2 = 2$ kg, $r_2 = |y_2| = 2$ m;

$m_3 = 3$ kg, $r_3 = |y_3| = 4$ m; $\omega = 2$ rad/s about the x axis

(a) $I_x = m_1 r_1^2 + m_2 r_2^2 + m_1 r_2^2 = (4)(3^2) + (2)(2^2) + (3)(4^2)$

$\quad = \boxed{92.0 \text{ kg·m}^2}$

$K = \frac{1}{2} I_x \omega^2 = \frac{1}{2}(92)(2^2) = \boxed{184 \text{ J}}$

(b) $v_1 = r_1 \omega = (3)(2) = \boxed{6.00 \text{ m/s}}$

$v_2 = r_2 \omega = (2)(2) = \boxed{4.00 \text{ m/s}}$

$v_3 = r_3 \omega = (4)(2) = \boxed{8.00 \text{ m/s}}$

$K_1 = \frac{1}{2} m_1 v_1^2 = \frac{1}{2}(4)(6^2) = 72 \text{ J}$

$K_2 = \frac{1}{2} m_2 v_2^2 = \frac{1}{2}(2)(4^2) = 16 \text{ J}$

$K_3 = \frac{1}{2} m_3 v_3^2 = \frac{1}{2}(3)(8^2) = 96 \text{ J}$

$K = K_1 + K_2 + K_3 = 72 + 16 + 96 = \boxed{184 \text{ J}} = \frac{1}{2} I_x \omega^2$

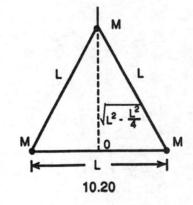

10.19

10.20 $I(x) = M\left(L^2 - \dfrac{L^2}{4}\right) = \boxed{\dfrac{3}{4} M L^2}$

$I(y) = M\left(\dfrac{L^2}{4} + \dfrac{L^2}{4}\right) = \boxed{\dfrac{M L^2}{2}}$

$I(z) = I(x) + I(y) = \boxed{\dfrac{5}{4} M L^2}$

10.20

10.21 $I = Mx^2 + m(L-x)^2$

$\dfrac{dI}{dx} = 2Mx - 2m(L-x) = 0$ (for an extremum)

$\therefore x = \dfrac{mL}{m+m}$

$\dfrac{d^2I}{dx^2} = 2m + 2M$; therefore I is minimum when

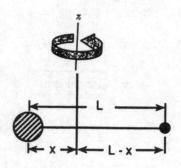

10.21

the axis of rotation passes through $x = \dfrac{mL}{M+m}$, which is also the center of mass of the system. The moment of inertia about an axis passing through x is

$I_{CM} = M(\dfrac{mL}{M+m})^2 + m(1 - \dfrac{m}{M+m})^2 L^2$

$= \dfrac{Mm}{M+m}L^2 = (\dfrac{1}{\frac{1}{m}+\frac{1}{M}})L^2 = \mu L^2$

where $\dfrac{1}{\mu} = \dfrac{1}{m} + \dfrac{1}{M}$

10.22 See Fig. 10.9 in text and Example 10.6. The shaded element of width dx has a mass dm equal to the mass per unit length multiplied by the element of length, dx. That is $dm = (\dfrac{M}{L})dx$. Substituting into Equation 10.6, with $r = x$,

$$I = \int r^2 dm = \int_0^L x^2 \dfrac{M}{L}dx = \dfrac{1}{3}\dfrac{M}{L}(x^3)_0^L = \dfrac{1}{3}\dfrac{M}{L}L^3 = \dfrac{1}{3}ML^2$$

10.23   (a) $I = I_c + MR^2 = \dfrac{1}{2}MR^2 + MR^2 = \boxed{\dfrac{3}{2}MR^2}$

(b) $I = I_c + MR^2 = \dfrac{2}{5}MR^2 + MR^2 = \boxed{\dfrac{7}{5}MR^2}$

10.24 (a) $\tau_0 = (25\ \text{N})(2\ \text{m})(\cos 30°) - (10\ \text{N})(4\ \text{m})(\sin 20°) = \boxed{29.6\ \text{N·m}}$

(b) $\tau_c = (30\ \text{N})(2\ \text{m})(\sin 45°) - (10\ \text{N})(2\ \text{m})(\sin 20°) = \boxed{35.6\ \text{N·m}}$

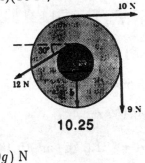

10.24

10.25 $\tau_{\text{net}} = (0.1\ \text{m})(12\ \text{N}) - (0.25\ \text{m})(9\ \text{N}) - (0.25\ \text{m})(10\ \text{N})$

$= \boxed{-3.55\ \text{N·m}}$

10.25

10.26 $\Sigma\tau = 0 = mg(3r) - T(r)$

$2T = Mg\sin 45° = 0$

$T = \dfrac{Mg\sin 45°}{2} = \dfrac{150\ \text{kg}(g)\sin 45°}{2} = (53.0g)\ \text{N}$

$m = \dfrac{T}{3g} = \dfrac{53.0g}{3g} = \boxed{17.7\ \text{kg}}$

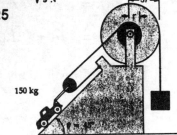

10.26

10.27 During acceleration,

$\alpha = \dfrac{\Delta\omega}{\Delta t} = \dfrac{12\ \text{rad/s}}{0.6\ \text{s}} = 20\ \text{rad/s}^2$

$\tau_{\text{net}} = I\alpha \qquad \tau_M - \tau_F = 20I$

During deceleration, $\quad \omega_f^2 = \omega_0^2 + 2\alpha^1 \cdot \Delta\theta$

$\alpha' = \dfrac{\omega_f^2 - \omega_0^2}{2 \cdot \Delta\theta} = \dfrac{0 - (12)^2}{2(40\pi)} = -0.573\ \text{rad/s}^2$

$\tau_F = I\alpha' = -0.573I$

Let P_F = power dissipated by friction $\quad P_M$ = power delivered by motor :

$\dfrac{P_F}{P_M} = \dfrac{(\tau_F \cdot \Delta\theta)/\Delta t}{(\tau_M \cdot \Delta\theta)/\Delta t} = \dfrac{\tau_F}{\tau_M} = \dfrac{0.573I}{20I + 0.573I} = \dfrac{0.573}{20.573} = \boxed{2.79\%}$

10.28 $\tau = 36 \text{ N} \cdot \text{m} = I\alpha; \quad \omega = \omega_0 + \alpha t;$

$10 \text{ rad/s} = 0 + \alpha(6 \text{ s})$

$\alpha = \dfrac{10}{6} \text{ rad/s}^2 = 1.67 \text{ rad/s}^2$

(a) $I = \dfrac{\tau}{\alpha} = \dfrac{36 \text{ N} \cdot \text{m}}{1.67 \text{ rad/s}^2} = \boxed{21.6 \text{ kg} \cdot \text{m}^2}$

(b) $\omega = \omega_0 + \alpha t$

$\quad 0 = 10 + \alpha(60)$

$\quad \alpha = -0.167 \text{ rad/s}^2$

$\quad \tau = I\alpha = (21.6 \text{ kg} \cdot \text{m}^2)(0.167 \text{ rad/s}^2) = \boxed{3.60 \text{ N} \cdot \text{m}}$

(c) No. of revolutions $\theta = \theta_0 + \omega_0 t + \dfrac{1}{2}\alpha t^2$. During first 6 s:

$\theta = \dfrac{1}{2}(1.67)(6)^2 = 30.06 \text{ rad}$

During next 60 s

$\theta = 10(60) - \dfrac{1}{2}(0.167)(60)^2 = 299.4$

$\theta_{\text{total}} = (329.5 \text{ rad})\dfrac{\text{rev}}{2\pi \text{ rad}} = \boxed{52.4 \text{ rev}}$

10.29 $P = \tau\omega = 2\pi\tau f = (2\pi)(50 \text{ N} \cdot \text{m})(\dfrac{2400}{60} \text{ rev/s}) = 1.26 \times 10^4 \text{ W} = \boxed{12.6 \text{ kW}}$

*10.30 $m = 0.075 \text{ kg} \quad F = 0.8 \text{ N}$

(a) $\tau = rF = (30 \text{ m})(0.8 \text{ N}) = \boxed{24 \text{ N} \cdot \text{m}}$

(b) $\alpha = \dfrac{\tau}{I} = \dfrac{rF}{mr^2} = \dfrac{24}{(0.75)(30)^2} = \boxed{0.0356 \text{ rad/s}^2}$

(c) $a_T = \alpha r = (0.0356)(30) = \boxed{1.07 \text{ m/s}^2}$

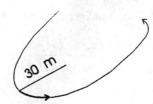

10.30

10.31 $I = 5 \text{ kg} \cdot \text{m}^2$

$T = 20 \text{ N}, \quad R = 0.5 \text{ m}$

(a) $\tau = TR = I\alpha$

$$\alpha = \frac{IR}{I} = \frac{(20 \text{ N})(0.5 \text{ m})}{5 \text{ kg} \cdot \text{m}^2} = \boxed{2.00 \text{ rad/s}^2}$$

(b) $\omega = \omega_0 + \alpha t = (2 \text{ rad/s}^2)(3 \text{ s}) = \boxed{6.00 \text{ rad/s}}$

(c) $K = \frac{1}{2}I\omega^2 = \frac{1}{2}(5 \text{ kg} \cdot \text{m}^2)(6 \text{ rad/s})^2 = \boxed{90.0 \text{ J}}$

(d) $\theta = \frac{1}{2}\alpha t^2 = \frac{1}{2}(2 \text{ rad/}^2)(3 \text{ s})^2 = 9 \text{ rad}$

$s = R\theta = \boxed{4.50 \text{ m}}$

$R = 0.5 \text{ m}$

$T = 20 \text{ N}$

10.31

*10.32 $E = \frac{1}{2}(15 \text{ kg})v^2 + \frac{1}{2}(10 \text{ kg})v^2 + \frac{1}{2}\left(\frac{1}{2}mr^2\omega^2\right) = (15 \text{ kg} - 10 \text{ kg})g(1.5 \text{ m})$

$E = \frac{1}{2}(25 \text{ kg})v^2 + \frac{1}{4}(3 \text{ kg})v^2 = (5)(9.8)(1.5) \text{ J}$

$v = \boxed{2.36 \text{ m/s}}$

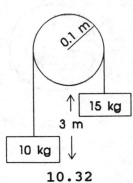

10.32

10.33   (a) Find the velocity of CM

$$(K + U)_i \; = (K + U)_f$$

$$0 + mgR \; = \frac{1}{2}I\omega^2$$

$$\omega \; = \sqrt{\frac{2mgR}{I}} = \sqrt{\frac{2mgR}{\frac{3}{2}mR^2}}$$

$$v_{\text{cm}} \; = R\sqrt{\frac{4g}{3R}} = \boxed{2\,\sqrt{\frac{Rg}{3}}}$$

(b) $v_L = 2v_{\text{cm}} = \boxed{4\,\sqrt{\dfrac{Rg}{3}}}$

(c) $v_{\text{cm}} = \sqrt{\dfrac{2mgR}{2m}} = \boxed{\sqrt{Rg}}$

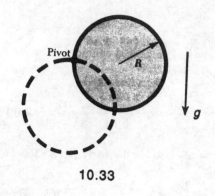

10.33

10.34 $N - 70 = 0$

$N = 70$ N

force of friction, $f = \mu N$

frictional torque, $\tau = rf$

$$\tau \; = \; 0.5f = I\alpha = \frac{1}{2}(100)(0.5)^2\alpha_f$$

$$\therefore \; \alpha_f \; = \; \frac{\mu(0.5)(70)}{12.5} = 2.8\mu$$

$$\omega_f \; = \; \omega_i - \alpha_f t$$

$$\therefore \; \alpha_f \; = \; \frac{\omega_i}{t} = \frac{50 \times 2\pi}{60 \times 6} = 2.8\mu$$

$$\boxed{\mu = 0.312}$$

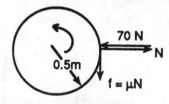

10.34

10.35 (a) $50 - T = 5.102a$

$$TR = I\alpha = I\frac{a}{R}$$

$$I = \frac{1}{2}MR^2 = 0.0938 \text{ kg} \cdot \text{m}^2$$

$$50 - T = 5.102(\frac{TR^3}{I})$$

$$50 - T = 3.4T$$

$$\boxed{T = 11.4 \text{ N}}$$

$$a = \frac{50 - 11.4}{5.102} = \boxed{7.57 \text{ m/s}^2}$$

$$v = \sqrt{2a(y - y_0)} = \boxed{9.53 \text{ m/s}}$$

(b) Use conservation of energy:

$$(K + U)_i = (K + U)_f$$

$$mgh = \frac{1}{2}mv^2 + \frac{1}{2}I\omega^2$$

$$2mgh = mv^2 + I(\frac{v^2}{R^2})$$

$$= v^2(m + \frac{I}{R^2})$$

$$v = \sqrt{\frac{2mgh}{m + \frac{I}{R^2}}} = \sqrt{\frac{2(50 \text{ N})(6 \text{ m})}{5.102 \text{ kg} + \frac{0.0938}{(0.25)^2}}} = \boxed{9.53 \text{ m/s}}$$

*10.36 $E = \frac{1}{2}I\omega^2 = \frac{1}{2}\left(\frac{1}{2}MR^2\right)\left(\frac{3000 \times 2\pi}{60}\right)^2$

$$= 6.17 \times 10^6 \text{ J}$$

$$P = \frac{\Delta E}{\Delta t} = 10^4 \text{ J/s}$$

$$\Delta t = \frac{6.17 \times 10^6 \text{ J}}{10^4 \text{ J/s}} = \boxed{617 \text{ s}} = 10.3 \text{ min}$$

*10.37 (a) $I = \frac{1}{2}MR^2 = \frac{1}{2}(2 \text{ kg})(0.07 \text{ m})^2 = 4.9 \times 10^{-3} \text{ kg} \cdot \text{m}^2$

$$\alpha = \frac{\tau}{I} = \frac{0.6}{4.9 \times 10^{-3}} = 122 \text{ rad/s}$$

$$\alpha = \frac{\Delta\omega}{\Delta t}$$

$$\Delta t = \frac{\Delta\omega}{\alpha} = \frac{1200\left(\frac{2\pi}{60}\right)}{122} = \boxed{1.03 \text{ s}}$$

(b) $\theta = \frac{1}{2}\alpha t^2 = \frac{1}{2}(122 \text{ rad/s})(1.03 \text{ s})^2 = 64.7 \text{ rad} = \boxed{10.3 \text{ rev}}$

10.38 $I_z = \int r^2 dm$

First find the moment of inertia of a disk, radius r,

about the $z-$axis. Using polar coordinates, we have

$$I_{\text{disk}} = \alpha \int r^2 2\pi r \, dr$$

$$= \sigma(2\pi)\frac{r^4}{4} = \frac{\sigma\pi r^4}{2}$$

Next find the sum of disks forming the sphere

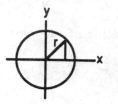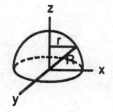

10.38

$$I_{\text{sphere}} = \int_{-R}^{R} \rho\frac{(\pi)r^4}{2}dz \quad r^4 = (R^2 - z^2)^2$$

$$= \int_{-R}^{R} \rho\frac{\pi}{2}(R^2 - z^2)^2 dz$$

$$= \frac{\rho\pi}{2}\int_{-R}^{R}(R^2 - z^2)^2 dz$$

$$= \frac{\rho\pi}{2}\int_{-R}^{R}(R^4 + z^4 - 2R^2z^2)dz$$

$$= \frac{\rho\pi}{2}[R^4 z + \frac{z^5}{5} - 2R^2\frac{z^3}{5} \, |_{-R}^{R}]$$

$$= \frac{\rho\pi}{2}[R^5 - (-R^5) + (\frac{R^5}{5} + \frac{R^5}{5}) - \frac{2}{3}R^2(R^3 + R^3)]$$

$$= \frac{\rho\pi}{2}[2 + \frac{2}{5} - \frac{4}{3}]R^5 = (\frac{m}{\frac{4}{3}\pi R^3})\frac{\pi}{2}R^5[\frac{16}{15}] = \boxed{\frac{2}{5}mR^2}$$

10.39 For the cylinder; $\sum \tau = (2T)R = \frac{1}{2}MR^2\frac{a}{R}$ (1)

where a is the acceleration of the falling masses.

For each of the falling masses, $\sum F = ma = mg - T$ (2)

(a) Combining Equations (1) and (2) we find $\boxed{T = \dfrac{Mmg}{M + 4m}}$

(b) $\boxed{a = \dfrac{4mg}{M + 4m}}$

(c) After the masses have fallen a distance h

10.39

we have $v^2 = 2ah$, also $\omega R = v$ so that $\omega = \sqrt{\dfrac{8mgh}{(M + 4m)R^2}}$

*10.40 for a spherical shell $\frac{2}{3}dm\, r^2 = \frac{2}{3}4\pi r^2 dr\, r^2\rho$

$$
\begin{aligned}
I &= \int dI = \int \frac{2}{3}(4\pi r^2)r^2\rho(r)dr \\[2mm]
&= \int_0^R \frac{2}{3}4\pi r^4 \left(14.2 - 11.6\frac{r}{R}\right)\left(10^3\,\frac{\text{kg}}{\text{m}^3}\right)dr \\[2mm]
&= \frac{2}{3}\,4\pi\,(14.2 \times 10^3)\,\frac{R^5}{5} - \frac{2}{3}\,4\pi\,(11.6 \times 10^3)\frac{R^5}{6} \\[2mm]
I &= \frac{8\pi}{3}10^3 R^5 \left(\frac{14.2}{5} - \frac{11.6}{6}\right) \\[2mm]
M &= \int dm = \int 4\pi r^2 \left(14.2 - 11.6\frac{r}{R}\right)10^3 dr \\[2mm]
&= 4\pi 10^3 \left(\frac{14.2}{3} - \frac{11.6}{4}\right)R^3 \\[2mm]
\frac{I}{MR^2} &= \frac{\frac{8\pi}{3}10^3 R^5 \left(\frac{14.2}{5} - \frac{11.6}{6}\right)}{4\pi 10^3 R^3 R^2 \left(\frac{14.2}{3} - \frac{11.6}{4}\right)} = \frac{2}{3}\left(\frac{.907}{1.83}\right) = \underline{0.3297} \\[2mm]
\therefore\quad I &= 0.33MR^2
\end{aligned}
$$

10.41 (a) $W = \frac{1}{2}I\omega^2 - \frac{1}{2}I\omega_0^2$; $\omega_0 = 0$; $I = \frac{1}{2}mR^2$

$W = \frac{1}{16}(64) = \boxed{4.00 \text{ J}}$

(b) $t = \frac{\omega}{\alpha} = \frac{\omega r}{a} = \frac{(8 \text{ rad/s})(0.5 \text{ m})}{2.5 \text{ m/s}^2} = \boxed{1.60 \text{ s}}$

(c) $\theta = \theta_0 + \omega_0 t + \frac{1}{2}\alpha t^2$; $\theta_0 = 0$; $\omega_0 = 0$

$\theta = \frac{1}{2}\alpha t^2 = \frac{1}{2}(\frac{2.5 \text{ m/s}^2}{0.5 \text{ m}})(1.6 \text{ s})^2 = 6.40 \text{ rad}$

$s = r\theta = (0.5 \text{ m})(6.4 \text{ rad}) = \boxed{3.2 \text{ m} < 4 \text{ m Yes}}$

10.42 (a) $I = \frac{1}{2}mr^2 = \frac{1}{2}(200 \text{ kg})(0.3 \text{ m})^2 = \boxed{9.00 \text{ kg·m}^2}$

(b) $\omega = (100 \text{ rev/min})(1 \text{ min }/60 \text{ s})(2\pi \text{ rad})/1 \text{ rev} = \boxed{10.5 \text{ rad/s}}$

$W = K_f = \frac{1}{2}I\omega^2 = \frac{1}{2}\frac{mr^2}{2}\omega^2 = \frac{1}{2}(9)(104.7)^2 = \boxed{49.3 \text{ kJ}}$

(c) $\omega_f = 500 \text{ rev/min} \times 1 \text{ min }/60 \text{ s} \times (2\pi \text{ rad})/(1 \text{ rev}) = \boxed{52.4 \text{ rad/s}}$

$K = \frac{1}{2}I\omega^2 = 12356 \text{ J}$

$W = \Delta K = 12356 - 49329 = \boxed{-37.0 \text{ kJ}}$

10.43 (a) Since no conservative forces act, $\Delta E = 0$.

$(K_f - K_i) + (U_f - U_i) = 0$

$(\frac{1}{2}I\omega^2 - 0) + (0 - \frac{1}{2}mgL) = 0$

$\boxed{\omega = \sqrt{\frac{3g}{L}}}$

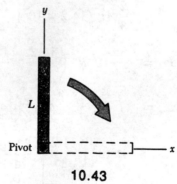

10.43

(b) $\tau = I\alpha$ so that in the horizontal position, $\frac{mg\ell}{2} = \frac{mL^2}{3}\alpha$ $\alpha = \boxed{\frac{3g}{2L}}$

(c) $a_x = a_r = (\frac{\ell}{2})\omega^2 = \boxed{-\frac{3g}{2}}$ $a_y = a_t = \alpha(\frac{\ell}{2}) = \boxed{\frac{3g}{4}}$

(d) Using $F = ma$ we have $R_x = ma_x = \boxed{-\frac{3}{2}mg}$

$R_y - mg = -ma$ or $R_y = \boxed{\frac{1}{4}mg}$

*10.44 $\quad \alpha = \dfrac{\omega_f - \omega_i}{t}$

$$\omega_i = \frac{v_i}{r} = \frac{\sqrt{2gh}}{r} = 8.30 \text{ rad/s}$$

$$\omega_f = \frac{v_f}{r} = \frac{\sqrt{2gh}}{r} = 8.54 \text{ rad/s}$$

$$\alpha = \frac{\omega_f^2 - \omega_i^2}{2\theta} \quad \text{(Eq. 10.8)}$$

$$\alpha = \frac{(8.30)^2 - (8.54)^2}{2(2\pi)} = \boxed{-0.322 \text{ rad/s}^2}$$

10.45 (a) $Mk^2 = \dfrac{MR^2}{2}, \quad k = \boxed{\dfrac{R}{\sqrt{2}}}$

(b) $Mk^2 = \dfrac{ML^2}{12}, \quad k = \boxed{\dfrac{L\sqrt{3}}{6}}$

(c) $Mk^2 = \dfrac{2}{5}MR^2, \quad k = \boxed{R\sqrt{\dfrac{2}{5}}}$

10.46 $v = \dfrac{2h}{t}; \quad \omega = \dfrac{v}{r} = \dfrac{2h}{tr}$

$$Mgh = \frac{1}{2}Mv^2 + \frac{1}{2}\left(I + \frac{1}{2}mr^2\right)\omega^2$$

$$\frac{1}{2}I\left(\frac{4h^2}{t^2r^2}\right) = Mgh - \frac{1}{2}M\left(\frac{4h^2}{t^2}\right) - \frac{1}{4}mr^2\left(\frac{4h^2}{t^2r^2}\right)$$

$$\boxed{I = Mr^2\left(\frac{gt^2}{2h} - 1\right) - \frac{mr^2}{2}}$$

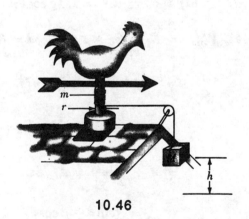

10.46

10.47 τ_f will oppose the torque causing the motion:

$$\sum \tau = I\alpha = TR - \tau_f \Rightarrow \tau_f = TR - I\alpha \quad (1)$$

Now find T, I and α in given or known terms

and substitute into equation(1)

$$\sum F_y = T - mg = -ma \text{ then } T = m(g-a) \quad (2)$$

also $\Delta y = v_0 t + \dfrac{at^2}{2} \Rightarrow a = \dfrac{2y}{t^2} \quad (3)$

and $\alpha = \dfrac{a}{R} = \dfrac{2y}{Rt^2} \quad (4)$

$$I = \frac{1}{2}M\left[R^2 + \left(\frac{R}{2}\right)^2\right] = \frac{5}{8}MR^2 \quad (5)$$

10.47

Substituting (2), (3), (4) and (5) into (1) we find

$$\tau_f = m\left(g - \frac{2y}{t^2}\right)R - \frac{5}{8}\frac{MR^2 2y}{(Rt^2)} = R\left[m\left(g - \frac{2y}{t^2}\right) - \frac{5}{4}\frac{My}{t^2}\right]$$

10.48 $K_f = \dfrac{1}{2}Mv_f^2 + \dfrac{1}{2}I_0\omega_f^2 : \quad U_f = Mgh_f = 0; \quad K_i = \dfrac{1}{2}Mv_i^2 + \dfrac{1}{2}I\omega_i^2 = 0;$

$U_i = Mgh_i : f = \mu N = \mu Mg\cos\theta; \omega = \dfrac{v}{r}; h = d\sin\theta \text{ and } I = \dfrac{1}{2}mr^2$

(a) $W_{nc} = E_f - E_i \quad$ or $\quad -fd = K_f + U_f - K_i - U_i$

$$-fd = \frac{1}{2}Mvf_f^2 + \frac{1}{2}I\omega_f^2 - Mgh$$

$$-\mu Mg\cos\theta = \frac{1}{2}Mv^2 + (mr^2/2)(v^2/r^2)/2 - Mgd\sin\theta$$

$$\frac{1}{2}[M + \frac{m}{2}]v^2 = Mgd\sin\theta - \mu Mg\cos\theta \text{ or}$$

$$v^2 = 2Mgd\frac{(\sin\theta - \mu\cos\theta)}{(m/2) + M}$$

$$v_d = 4gd\frac{M}{(m+2M)}(\sin\theta - \mu\cos\theta)]^{1/2}$$

(b) $v^2 = v_0^2 - 2as, \quad v_d^2 = 2ad$

$$a = \frac{v_d^2}{2d} = \boxed{2g(\frac{M}{m+2M})(\sin\theta - \mu\cos\theta)}$$

*10.49 (a) $E = \frac{1}{2}\left(\frac{2}{5}MR^2\right)(\omega^2)$

$= \frac{1}{2}\frac{2}{5}(6 \times 10^{24})(6.4 \times 10^6)^2 \left(\frac{2\pi}{86400}\right)^2 = \boxed{2.6 \times 10^{29} \text{ J}}$

(b) $\dfrac{dE}{dt} = \dfrac{d}{dt}\left[\dfrac{1}{2}\left(\dfrac{2}{5}MR^2\right)\left(\dfrac{2\pi}{T}\right)^2\right]$

$= \dfrac{1}{5}MR^2(4\pi)^2(-2T^{-3})\dfrac{dT}{dt}$

$= \dfrac{1}{5}MR^2\left(\dfrac{2\pi}{T}\right)^2\left(\dfrac{-2}{T}\right)\dfrac{dT}{dt}$

$= (2.6 \times 10^{29} \text{ J})\left(\dfrac{-2}{86400 \text{ s}}\right)\left(\dfrac{10 \times 10^{-6} \text{ s}}{3.15 \times 10^7 \text{ s}}\right)(86400 \text{ s/day})$

$\dfrac{dE}{dt} = \boxed{-1.65 \times 10^{17} \text{ J/day}}$

*10.50 $\theta = \omega t$

$t = \dfrac{\theta}{\omega} = \dfrac{(31°/360°) \text{ rev}}{900 \text{ rev/60 s}} = 0.00574 \text{ s}$

$v = \dfrac{0.8 \text{ m}}{0.00574 \text{ s}} = \boxed{139 \text{ m/s}}$

10.51 (a) $m_2 g \; - \; T_2 = m_2 a$

$$T_2 \; = \; m_2(g-a) = (20 \text{ kg}) \, (9.8 - 2) \text{ m/s}^2 = \boxed{156 \text{ N}}$$

$$T_1 \; = \; m_1 g \sin 37° = m_1 a$$

$$T_1 \; = \; m_1 g \sin 37° + m_1 a$$

$$= \; (15 \text{ kg}) \, (9.85 \sin 37° + 2) \text{ m/s} = \boxed{118 \text{ N}}$$

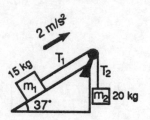

10.51

(b) $(T_2 - T_1)R = I\alpha = I(\dfrac{a}{R})$

$$I = \frac{(T_2 - T_1)R^2}{a} = \frac{(156 - 118) \text{ N}(0.25 \text{ m})^2}{2 \text{ m/s}^2} = \boxed{1.19 \text{ kg·m}^2}$$

10.52 (a)

$$W \; = \; \Delta K + \Delta U$$

$$= \; K_f - K_i + U_f - U_i$$

$$0 \; = \; \frac{1}{2}mv^2 + \frac{1}{2}I\omega^2 - mgd \sin\theta - \frac{1}{2}kd^2$$

$$\frac{1}{2}\omega^2(I + mR^2) \; = \; mg \, d \sin\theta + \frac{1}{2}kd^2$$

$$\boxed{\omega = \sqrt{\frac{2mgd\sin\theta + kd^2}{I + mR^2}}}$$

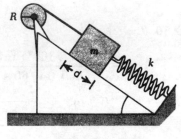

10.52

(b) $\omega \; = \; \sqrt{\dfrac{2(0.5 \text{ kg})(9.8 \text{ m/s}^2)(0.2 \text{ m})(\sin 37°) + (50 \text{ N/m})(0.2 \text{ m})^2}{1 \text{ kg} \cdot \text{m}^2 + (0.5 \text{ kg})(0.3 \text{ m})^2}}$

$$= \; \sqrt{\frac{1.18 + 2}{1.05}} = \sqrt{3.04} = \boxed{1.74 \text{ rad/s}}$$

*10.53 $3.5 = \omega_0 e^0$

$\qquad 2 = 3.5 e^{-\sigma 9.3s}$

$\qquad \omega_0 = \underline{3.5 \text{ rad/s}}$

$\qquad \sigma = \underline{6.02 \times 10^{-2} \text{ s}^{-1}}$

(a) $\alpha = \dfrac{d\omega}{dt} = \dfrac{d}{dt}\omega_0 e^{-\sigma t}$

$\qquad = \omega_0(-\sigma)e^{-\sigma t}$

$\qquad = 3.5\dfrac{\text{rad}}{\text{s}}\left(-6.02 \times 10^{-2}\text{s}^{-1}\right)e^{-3(6.02\times10^{-2})}$

$\qquad \alpha = \boxed{-0.176 \dfrac{\text{rad}}{\text{s}^2}}$

(b) $\theta = \displaystyle\int_0^t \omega_0 e^{-\sigma t}dt = \dfrac{\omega_0}{-\sigma}[e^{-\sigma t} - 1]$

$\qquad = \dfrac{\omega_0}{\sigma}(1 - e^{-\sigma t})$

$\qquad \theta = \dfrac{3.5 \text{ rad/s}}{(6.02 \times 10^{-2})1/\text{s}}(1 - e^{-(6.02\times10^{-2}1/\text{s})2.5\text{s}})$

$\qquad = \boxed{8.12 \text{ rad}}$

$\qquad = \boxed{1.29 \text{ rev}}$

(c) $\theta|_\infty = \dfrac{\omega_0}{\sigma}(1 - e^{-\infty}) = \dfrac{(3.5 \text{ rad/s})}{(6.02 \times 10^{-2}\text{s}^{-1})}$

$\qquad = \boxed{58.2 \text{ rad}}$

$\qquad = \boxed{9.26 \text{ rev}}$

10.54   (a) While decelerating, $\tau_F = I\alpha' = (20000)[\dfrac{2(2\pi/60)}{10}] = 419 \text{ N} \cdot \text{m}$

While accelerating, $\qquad \tau_{\text{net}} = I\alpha$

$\qquad\qquad\qquad \tau_m - \tau_F = I\alpha$

$\qquad\qquad\qquad \tau_m = 419 + (20000)[\dfrac{10(2\pi/60)}{12}] = \boxed{2160 \text{ N} \cdot \text{m}}$

(b) $P = \tau \cdot \omega = \tau_F \omega = (419 \text{ N} \cdot \text{m})(\dfrac{10 \times 2\pi \text{ rad}}{60 \text{ s}}) = \boxed{439 \text{ W}} \ (\approx 0.6 \text{ hp})$

CHAPTER 11

11.1 $v_c = 10$ m/s; $M = 10$ kg

    (a) $K_{\text{trans}} = \frac{1}{2}Mv_c^2 = \frac{1}{2}(10)(10^2) = \boxed{500 \text{ J}}$

    (b) $K_{\text{rot}} = \frac{1}{2}I\omega^2$; Now $I = \frac{1}{2}MR^2$ so

        $K_{\text{rot}} = \frac{1}{4}MR^2\omega^2$; But $R\omega = v_c$ (no slipping) so

        $K_{\text{rot}} = \frac{1}{4}Mv_c^2 = \frac{1}{4}(10)(10^2) = \boxed{250 \text{ J}}$

    (c) $K_{\text{rot}} = K_{\text{trans}} + K_{\text{rot}} = 500 + 250 = \boxed{750 \text{ J}}$

11.2 $W = \Delta K = \Delta K_{\text{rot}} + \Delta K_{\text{trans}} = \frac{1}{2}I\omega^2 + \frac{1}{2}Mv^2$

Use $I = \frac{2}{5}MR^2$ and $v = R\omega$ so that

$W = \frac{1}{5}MR^2\omega^2 + \frac{1}{2}M(R\omega)^2 = \frac{1}{2}MR^2\omega^2[\frac{2}{5} + 1]$

$W = \frac{1}{2}(150 \text{ kg})(0.2 \text{ m})^2 (50 \text{ s}^{-1})^2(1.4) = \boxed{1.05 \times 10^4 \text{ J}}$

11.3   (a) $\tau = I\alpha$

        $mgR\sin\theta = (I_{\text{cm}} + mR^2)\alpha$

        $a = \dfrac{mgR^2\sin\theta}{I_{\text{cm}} + mR^2}$

        $a_{\text{hoop}} = \dfrac{mgR^2\sin\theta}{2mR^2} = \boxed{\dfrac{1}{2}g\sin\theta}$

        $a_{\text{disk}} = \dfrac{mgR^2\sin\theta}{\frac{3}{2}mR^2} = \boxed{\dfrac{2}{3}g\sin\theta}$

11.3

The disk moves with $\dfrac{4}{3}$ the acceleration of the hoop.

    (b) $Rf = I\alpha$

        $f = \mu N = \mu mg\cos\theta$

        $\mu = \dfrac{f}{mg\cos\theta} = \dfrac{I\alpha/R}{R^2mg\cos\theta}$

        $= \dfrac{(\frac{2}{3}g\sin\theta)(\frac{1}{2}mR^2)}{R^2mg\cos\theta} = \boxed{\dfrac{1}{3}\tan\theta}$

11.4 $K = \frac{1}{2}mv^2 + \frac{1}{2}I\omega^2 = \frac{1}{2}[m + \frac{I}{R^2}]$, where $\omega = v/R$ since no slipping. Also

$U_0 = mgh, U_f = 0$, and $v_0 = 0$;   Because energy is conserved, $K + U = K_0 + U_0$ or

$$\frac{1}{2}[m + \frac{I}{R^2}]v^2 = mgh; \text{ thus, } v^2 = \frac{2gh}{[1 + (I/mR^2)]}$$

For a disk, $I = \frac{1}{2}mR^2$, so

$$v^2 = \frac{2gh}{[1 + (1/2)]} \text{ or } v_{\text{disk}} = \sqrt{\frac{4gh}{3}}$$

For a ring, $I = mR^2$ so $v^2 = \frac{2gh}{2}$ or $v_{\text{ring}} = \sqrt{gh}$

Since $v_{\text{disk}} > v_{\text{ring}}$ the disk reaches the bottom first.

*11.5 $K = \frac{1}{2}I\omega^2 + \frac{1}{2}mv^2$

$K = \frac{1}{2}(1.6 \times 10^{-2} \text{ kg} \cdot \text{m}^2)\left(\frac{4 \text{ m/s}}{0.1 \text{ m}}\right)^2 + \frac{1}{2}(4 \text{ kg})(4 \text{ m/s})^2$

$= 12.8 + 32 = \boxed{44.8 \text{ J}}$

11.6   Method 1: $\dfrac{K)_{\text{total}}^{\text{cylin.}}}{K)_{\text{total}}^{\text{sph.}}} = \dfrac{\frac{1}{2}Mv^2 + \frac{1}{2}(\frac{1}{2}MR^2)\frac{v^2}{R^2}}{\frac{1}{2}Mv^2 + \frac{1}{2}(\frac{2}{5}MR^2)\frac{v^2}{R^2}} = \boxed{\dfrac{15}{14}}$

Method 2: $\dfrac{K_c}{K_s} = \dfrac{\frac{1}{2}I_c\omega^2}{\frac{1}{2}I_s\omega^2} = \dfrac{\frac{1}{2}MR^2 + MR^2}{\frac{2}{5}MR^2 + MR^2} = \boxed{\dfrac{15}{14}}$

11.7   (a) $\mathbf{A} \times \mathbf{B} = \begin{vmatrix} i & j & k \\ -3 & 4 & 0 \\ 2 & 3 & 0 \end{vmatrix} = \boxed{-17k}$

(b) $|\mathbf{A} \times \mathbf{B}| = |\mathbf{A}||\mathbf{B}|\sin\theta$

$17 = 5\sqrt{13}\sin\theta \qquad \theta = \text{arc sin}\left(\frac{17}{5\sqrt{13}}\right) = \boxed{70.5°}$

*11.8 $M \times N = \begin{vmatrix} i & j & k \\ 6 & 2 & -1 \\ 2 & -1 & -3 \end{vmatrix} = \boxed{(-7)i + (16)j + (-10)k}$

11.9   (a) in the negative z direction given by the right-hand rule

        (b) in the positive z direction given by the right-hand rule

11.10   (a) $\tau = r \times F = \begin{vmatrix} i & j & k \\ 1 & 3 & 0 \\ 3 & 2 & 0 \end{vmatrix} = i(0 - 0) - j(0 - 0) + k(2 - 9) = \boxed{-7k \text{ N·m}}$

        (b) $\tau = \begin{vmatrix} i & j & k \\ 1 & -3 & 0 \\ 3 & 2 & 0 \end{vmatrix} = \boxed{11k \text{N} \cdot \text{m}}$

11.11 $| A \times B | = A \cdot B \Rightarrow AB \sin\theta = AB \cos\theta \Rightarrow \tan\theta = 1 \text{ or } \theta = \boxed{45.0°}$

11.12 $A \times B = A_x B_x(i \times j) + A_x B_y(i \times j) + A_x B_z(i \times k)+$

$A_y B_x(j \times i) + A_y B_y(j \times j) + A_y B_z(j \times k)+$

$A_z B_y(k \times i) + A_z B_y(k \times j) + A_z B_z(k \times k)$

$= 0 + A_x B_y k + A_x B_z(-j) + A_y B_x(-k) + 0+$

$A_y B_z i + A_z B_x j + A_z B_y(-i) + 0$

$= (A_y B_z - A_z B_y)i + (A_z B_x - A_x B_2)j + (A_x B_y - A_y B_x)k$

This is also equal to the determinant in question.

11.13 $\boxed{| F_3 | = | F_1 | + | F_2 |}$

The torque produced by F_3 depends on the perpendicular distance OD, therefore translating the point of application of F_3 to any other point along BC will not change the net torque.

*11.14 $\mathbf{r} \times \mathbf{F}$ = $(4\mathbf{i} + 5\mathbf{j}) \times (2\mathbf{i} + 3\mathbf{j})$

$\qquad\qquad$ = $12\mathbf{k} - 10\mathbf{k} = \boxed{(2\text{ N}\cdot\text{m})\mathbf{k}}$

11.15 $L = \sum m_1 v_i r_i = (4 + 3)(5)(0.5)$ = $\boxed{17.5\text{ kg}\cdot\text{m}^2/\text{s}}$

*11.16 $\mathbf{L} = \mathbf{r} \times \mathbf{p} = (1.7\mathbf{i}) \times (12\mathbf{j}) = \boxed{(20.4\mathbf{k})\text{ kg}\cdot\text{m}^2/\text{s}}$

11.17 r = $6i + 5tj$

$\qquad \dfrac{dr}{dt}$ = $5j$, so

$\qquad p$ = $mv = m\dfrac{dr}{dt} = 10j\text{ kg}\cdot\text{m/s}$

$$L = mr \times \frac{dr}{dt} = m(6i + 5tj) \times 5j = 2\begin{vmatrix} i & j & k \\ 6 & 5t & 0 \\ 0 & 5 & 0 \end{vmatrix} = \boxed{60k}$$

11.18 $L = r \times p = r \times mv$ and $|\,L\,| = rmv\sin\theta = (r\sin\theta)mv$

$\qquad$ (a) $L = 2dmv(-k) + 2d(3m)vk = \boxed{4dmvk}$

$\qquad$ (b) $L = 0 + 0 = \boxed{0}$

$\qquad$ (c) $L = dmvk + d3mv(-k) = \boxed{-2dmvk}$

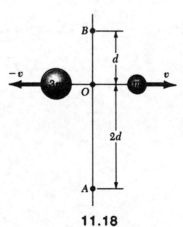

11.18

*11.19 $\mathbf{L}$ = $(1.5\mathbf{i} + 2.2\mathbf{j})\text{ m} \times (1.5\text{ kg})(4.2\mathbf{i} - 3.6\mathbf{j})\text{ m/s}$

$\qquad\qquad$ = $(-8.1\mathbf{k} - 13.86\mathbf{k})\text{ kg}\cdot\text{m}^2/\text{s}$

$\qquad \mathbf{L}$ = $\boxed{-22.0\mathbf{k}\text{ kg m}^2/\text{s}}$

11.20 (a) $L = rmv \sin\theta = (10,000 \text{ m})(12,000 \text{ kg})(175 \text{ m/s}) \sin 90°$

$\qquad\qquad = \boxed{2.10 \times 10^{10} \text{ kg·m}^2/\text{s}}$

(b) $r \sin\theta$ = perpendicular distance from the line of flight to earth's surface.

Therefore $L = constant$ as plane moves in level flight.

11.21 (a) $L = I\omega = \frac{2}{5}MR^2\omega = \frac{2}{5}(5.99 \times 10^{24} \text{ kg})(6.37 \times 10^6 \text{ m})^2(\frac{2\pi \text{ rad}}{24(3600) \text{ s}})$

$\qquad\qquad = \boxed{7.07 \times 10^{33} \text{ kg} \cdot \text{m}^2/\text{s}}$

(b) $L = I\omega = MR^2\omega = (5.99 \times 10^{24} \text{ kg})(1.49 \times 10^{11} \text{ m})^2(\frac{2\pi}{366(24)(3600)\text{s}})$

$\qquad\qquad = \boxed{2.65 \times 10^{40} \text{ kg} \cdot \text{m}^2/\text{s}}$

11.22 (a) The initial torque is

$\qquad |\tau| = |\mathbf{r} \times \mathbf{F}| = (0.08 \text{ m})(4 \text{ kg})(9.8 \text{ m/s}^2) = \boxed{3.14 \text{ N·m}}$

(b) $|\mathbf{L}| = |\mathbf{r} \times m\mathbf{v} + I\omega| = Rmv + \frac{1}{2}MR^2(\frac{v}{R}) = R(m + \frac{M}{2})v = \boxed{0.40v}$

(c) $\tau = \frac{dL}{dt} = (0.40a)\text{kg} \cdot \text{m/s}^2; \quad a = \frac{3.14\text{N} \cdot \text{m}}{0.4 \text{ kg} \cdot \text{m/s}^2} = \boxed{7.85 \text{ m/s}^2}$

11.23 (a) $\boxed{\text{zero}}$

(b) At the highest point of the trajectory,

$$L_1 \;=\; r_1 \times mv_1$$

$$=\; \left(\frac{v_0^2 \sin 2\theta}{2g}\,i + \frac{(v_0 \sin \theta)^2}{2g}\,j\right) \times mv_0 x i$$

$$=\; \boxed{\dfrac{-m(v_0 \sin \theta)^2 v_0 \cos \theta}{2g}\,k}$$

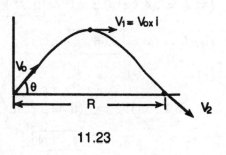

11.23

(c) $L_2 \;=\; Ri \times mv_2,$ where $R = \dfrac{v_0^2 \sin^2 \theta}{g}$

$$=\; mRi \times (v_0 \cos \theta i - v_0 \sin \theta j)$$

$$=\; -mRv_0 \sin \theta k = \boxed{\dfrac{-mv_0^3 \sin 2\theta \sin \theta}{g}\,k}$$

$$x = \frac{1}{2}R = \frac{v_0^2 \sin 2\theta}{2g} \;\text{ and }\; y = h_{\max} = \frac{(v_0 \sin \theta)^2}{2g}$$

(d) The downward force of gravity exerts a torque in the $-z$ direction.

11.24 (a) $L = I\omega = (\frac{1}{2}MR^2)\omega = \frac{1}{2}(3 \text{ kg})(0.2 \text{ m})^2(6 \text{ rad/s}) = \boxed{0.36 \text{ kg·m}^2/\text{s}}$

(b) $L = I\omega = [\frac{1}{2}MR^2 + M(\frac{R}{2})^2] = \frac{3}{4}(3 \text{ kg})(0.2 \text{ m})^2(6 \text{ rad/s}) = \boxed{0.54 \text{ kg·m}^2\text{s}}$

11.25 (a) $I = \dfrac{1}{12}m_1 L^2 + m_2(0.5)^2 = \dfrac{1}{12}(0.1)(1)^2 + (0.4)(\frac{1}{2})^2 = 0.1083 \text{ kg · m}^2$

$$L = I\omega = 0.1083(4) = \boxed{0.433 \text{ kg·m}^2/\text{s}}$$

(b) $I = \dfrac{1}{3}m_1 L^2 + M_2 R^2 = \dfrac{1}{3}(0.1)(1)^2 + 0.4(1)^2 = 0.433$

$$L = I\omega = 0.433(4) = \boxed{1.73 \text{ kg·m}^2/\text{s}}$$

*11.26   (a) $I = 2(4 \text{ kg})(0.2 \text{ m})^2 = \boxed{0.32 \text{ kg} \cdot \text{m}^2}$

   (b) $L = I\omega = \boxed{0.96 \text{ kg} \cdot \text{m}^2/\text{s}}$

   (c)
$$2rF = I\alpha$$
$$2(0.2 \text{ m})F = (0.32 \text{ kg} \cdot \text{m}^2)\left(6\frac{1}{\text{s}^2}\right)$$
$$F = \boxed{4.80 \text{ N}}$$

11.27   (a) $I_1\omega_0 = (I_1 + I_2)\omega$

$$\boxed{\omega = \frac{I_1\omega_0}{I_1 + I_2}}$$

   (b) $\dfrac{K_f}{K_i} = \dfrac{\frac{1}{2}(I_1 + I_2)(\frac{I_1\omega_0}{I_1+I_2})^2}{\frac{1}{2}I_1\omega_0^2} = \boxed{\dfrac{I_1}{I_1 + I_2} < 1}$

   Energy is lost since $K_f < K_i$

*11.28
$$I_1\omega_1 = I_2\omega_2$$
$$(250 \text{ kg m}^2)\left(10 \frac{\text{rev}}{\text{min}}\right) = (250 \text{ kg} \cdot \text{m}^2 + 25 \text{ kg}(2 \text{ m})^2)\omega_2$$
$$\omega_2 = \boxed{7.14 \text{ rev/min}}$$

11.29   (a) L is conserved: $L_i = 0; L_f = mvr + I\omega = 0$

   Therefore $\omega = \dfrac{60(2)(1.5)}{500} = \boxed{0.360 \text{ rad/s, counterclockwise}}$

   where the negative sign indicates that ω is counterclockwise

   (b) $W = K_f - K_i = \dfrac{1}{2}mv^2 + \dfrac{1}{2}I\omega^2 - 0$

   $W = \dfrac{1}{2}(60)(1.5)^2 + \dfrac{1}{2}(500)(0.36)^2 = \boxed{99.9 \text{ J}}$

11.30 (a) Angular momentum is conserved. Let M = mass of rod and m = mass of each bead. From $I_1\omega_1 = I_2\omega_2$ we have

$$\left[\frac{1}{12}M\ell^2 + 2mr_1^2\right]\omega_1 = \left[\frac{1}{12}M\ell^2 + 2mr_2^2\right]\omega_2$$

When $\ell = 0.5$ m, $r_1 = 0.1$ m, $r_2 = 0.25$ m and with other values as stated in the problem, we find $\omega_2 = \boxed{9.2\ s^{-1}}$

(b) Since this action does not result in an external torque on the rod, L = constant and ω is unchanged.

11.31 (a) $I = I_s + 2mR^2 = 8 + 20R^2$

$I_i = 8 + 20(1^2) = 28$ kg·m^2; $I_f = 8 + 20(0.25)^2 = 9.25$ kg·m^2

Angular momentum is conserved.

$$I_i\omega_i = I_f\omega_f; \quad \omega_f = \frac{I_i\omega_i}{I_f} = \frac{28}{9.25}(2) = \boxed{6.05\ \text{rad/s}}$$

(b) $E_i = K_i = \dfrac{1}{2}I_i\omega_i = \dfrac{1}{2}28(2)^2 = 56.0$ J

$E_f = K_f = \dfrac{1}{2}I_f\omega_f^2 = \dfrac{1}{2}9.25(6.05)^2 = 169$ J

$\Delta E = E_f - E_1 = \boxed{113\ \text{J}}$

11.32 $m = 10^{-2}$ kg; $v_0 = 5$ m/s; $M = 1$ kg; $R = 0.2$ m

(a) Angular momentum is conserved.

$$L_i = mv_0 R; L_f = I\omega \text{ where } I = I_s + mR^2 = \frac{2}{5}MR^2 + mR^2$$

so $\left[\dfrac{2}{5}MR^2 + mR^2\right]\omega = mv_0 R$

Substituting in the given values we find

$\omega = \boxed{0.61\ \text{rad/s}}$

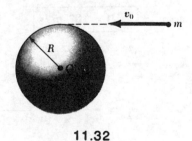

11.32

(b) $K_i = \dfrac{mv_0^2}{2} = \dfrac{10^{-2} \times 5^2}{2} = 0.125$ J

$K_f = \dfrac{I\omega^2}{2} = \dfrac{[\frac{2}{5}MR^2 + mR^2]\omega^2}{2}$

$= \dfrac{1}{2}[\dfrac{2}{5}(1)(0.2)^2 + (0.1)(0.2)^2](0.61)^2 = 3.05 \times 10^{-3}$ J

$E_{\text{lost}} = K_i - K_f = 0.125 - 0.00305 = \boxed{0.122\ \text{J}}$

11.33 (a) $\boxed{L_i = mv\ell}$ $\Sigma\tau_{\text{ext}} = 0$, so $L_i = L_f$

$$v_f = \left(\frac{m}{m + M}\right)v_i$$

$$L_f = (m + M)v_f\ell$$

11.33 and 11.34

(b) $K_i = \frac{1}{2}mv^2$;

$$K_f = \frac{1}{2}(M + m)v_f^2;$$

$$v_f = \left(\frac{m}{M + m}\right)v \Rightarrow \text{ velocity of the bullet and block}$$

$$\text{Fraction of } K \text{ lost} = \frac{\frac{1}{2}mv^2 - \frac{1}{2}\frac{m^2}{M+m}v^2}{\frac{1}{2}mV^2} = \boxed{\frac{M}{M + m}}$$

11.34 (a) Total angular momentum $= 2(200)10^{-2} = L_{\text{bullet}} + L_{\text{block}}$

$$L_{\text{block}} = 4 - 2(10^{-2})25 = \boxed{3.50 \text{ kg·m}^2/\text{s}}$$

(b) $K_{\text{loss}} = K_i - K_f$

$$= \frac{1}{2}(10^{-2})(200)^2 - \left\{\frac{1}{2}(2) + \frac{1}{2}(10^{-2})(25)^2\right\} = \boxed{196 \text{ J}}$$

11.35 (a) $L = \hbar = mvr$ $v = \dfrac{\hbar}{mr}$

$$= \frac{1.054 \times 10^{-34}}{0.529 \times 10^{-10} \times 9.11 \times 10^{-31}}$$

so $v = \boxed{2.19 \times 10^6 \text{ m/s}}$

(b) $K = \dfrac{mv^2}{2} = \boxed{2.18 \times 10^{-18} \text{ J}}$

(c) $\omega = \dfrac{L}{I} = \dfrac{(1.054 \times 10^{-34})}{9.11 \times 10^{-31} \times (0.529 \times 10^{-10})^2} = \boxed{4.13 \times 10^{16} \text{ rad/s}}$

11.36 Energy is conserved so $\Delta U + \Delta K(\text{rot}) + \Delta K(\text{trans}) = 0$

$$mg(R-r)(\cos\theta - 1) + [\tfrac{1}{2}mv^2 - 0] + \tfrac{1}{2}[\tfrac{2}{5}mr^2]\omega^2 = 0$$

Since $r\omega = v$, this gives

$$\omega = \sqrt{\frac{10}{7}\frac{(R-r)(1-\cos\theta)g}{r^2}}$$

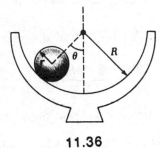

11.36

11.37 (a) $K_{\text{orbital}} = \tfrac{1}{2}MR_{se}^2\omega_{\text{orb}}^2$

$$= \tfrac{1}{2}6\times10^{24}(1.5)^2\times10^{22}\left(\frac{2\pi}{365\times24\times60\times60}\right)^2 = \boxed{2.63\times10^{33}\text{ J}}$$

(b) $K_{\text{rot}} = \tfrac{1}{2}I\omega_{\text{rot}}^2 = \tfrac{1}{2}(\tfrac{2}{5}MR^2)\omega_{\text{rot}}^2$

$$= \tfrac{1}{5}6\times10^{24}(6.4)^2\times10^{12}\left(\frac{2\pi}{24\times60\times60}\right)^2 = \boxed{2.57\times10^{29}\text{ J}}$$

(c) $\dfrac{K_{\text{orb}}}{K_{\text{rot}}} \cong \boxed{1.03\times10^4}$

11.38 (a) $L_i = L_f$

$$(\tfrac{1}{2}MR^2)\omega_0 = (\tfrac{1}{2}MR^2 + mr^2)\omega_f$$

$$\omega_f = \frac{\tfrac{1}{2}MR^2\omega_0}{\tfrac{1}{2}MR^2 + mr^2} = \frac{\tfrac{1}{2}(30\text{ kg})(2\text{ m})^2(4\pi\text{ rad/s})}{\tfrac{1}{2}(30\text{ kg})(2\text{ m})^2 + (0.25\text{ kg})(1.8\text{ m})^2} = \boxed{12.4\text{ rad/s}}$$

(b) No;

$$K_f - K_i = \tfrac{1}{2}(60.81\text{ kg}\cdot\text{m}^2)(12.4\text{ rad/s})^2 - \tfrac{1}{2}(60\text{ kg}\cdot\text{m}^2)(4\pi\text{ rad/s})^2$$

$$= \boxed{-63.1\text{ J, lost to thermal energy}}$$

11.39 $\Sigma F = T - Mg = -Ma : \Sigma\tau = TR = I\alpha = \frac{1}{2}MR^2(\frac{a}{R})$

11.39

(a) Combining the above two equations we find

$$T = M(g-a) \text{ and } a = \frac{2T}{M}, \text{ thus } T = \frac{Mg}{3}$$

(b) $a = \frac{2T}{M} = \frac{2}{M}(\frac{Mg}{3}) = \frac{2}{3}g$

(c) Requiring conservation of mechanical energy we have

$$\Delta U + \Delta K_{\text{rot}} + \Delta K_{\text{trans}} = 0$$

$$(0 - mgh) + \frac{1}{2}[\frac{1}{2}MR^2]\omega^2 - 0 + [\frac{1}{2}Mv^2 - 0] = 0$$

When there is no slipping $\omega = \frac{v}{R}$, and $v = \sqrt{\frac{4gh}{3}}$

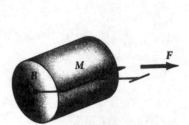

11.40

11.40 (a) $\Sigma F = F - f = Ma; \quad \Sigma\tau = fR = I\alpha$

Using $I = \frac{1}{2}MR^2$ and $\alpha = \frac{a}{R}$ we find $a = \frac{2F}{3M}$

(b) When there is no slipping $f = \mu Mg$. Substituting this into the torque

equation of part (a) we have $\mu MgR = \frac{1}{2}MRa$ and $\mu = \frac{F}{3Mg}$.

11.41 (a) $\Sigma\tau = MgR - MgR = \boxed{0}$

(b) $\Sigma\tau = \frac{dL}{dt}$, and since $\Sigma\tau = 0$, $\boxed{L = \text{constant}}$

Since the total angular momentum of the system is zero, the monkey and bananas move upward with the same speed at any instant, and he will not reach the bananas (until they get tangled in the pulley). Also, since the tension in the rope is the same on both sides, Newton's second law applied to the monkey and bananas give the same acceleration upwards.

11.41

11.42   (a) $\Delta K_{\text{rot}} + \Delta K_{\text{trans}} + \Delta U = 0$

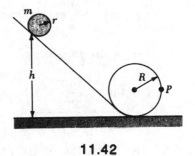

11.42

Note that initially the center of mass of the sphere is a distance $h + r$ above the bottom of the loop and as the mass reaches the top of the loop, this distance above the reference level is $2R - r$. The conservation of energy requirement gives

$$mg(h + r) = mg(2R - r) + \frac{1}{2}mv^2 + \frac{1}{2}I\omega^2$$

For the sphere $I = \frac{2}{5}mr^2$ and $v = r\omega$ so that the expression becomes

$$gh + 2gr = 2gR + \frac{7}{10}v^2 \qquad (1)$$

Note that $h = h_{\min}$ when the speed of the sphere at the top of the loop satisfies the condition

$$\Sigma F = mg = \frac{mv^2}{(R - r)} \text{ or}$$

$v^2 = g(R - r)$. Substituting into this Eq. (1) gives

$$h_{\min} = 2(R - r) + 0.7(R - r) \text{ or } \boxed{h_{\min} = 2.7(R - r)}$$

(b) When the sphere is initially at $h = 3R$ and finally at point P, the conservation of energy equation gives

$$mg(3R + r) = mgR + \frac{1}{2}mv^2 + \frac{1}{5}mv^2 \text{ or}$$

$$v^2 = \frac{10}{7}(2R + r)g.$$

Therefore at point P

$$\Sigma F_y = -mg$$

$$\Sigma F_x = -N = -\frac{mv^2}{R - r} = -\frac{(\frac{10}{7})(2R + r)}{R - r}mg$$

*11.43 From conservation of energy,

$$\frac{1}{2}I\left(\frac{v}{r}\right)^2 + \frac{1}{2}mv^2 = mgh$$

$$I\frac{v^2}{r^2} = 2mgh - mv^2$$

$$\underline{I = mr^2\left(\frac{2gh}{v^2} - 1\right)}$$

11.44 (a) With the origin at the point of contact $\Sigma\tau = MgR\sin\theta = I\alpha$, and using the parallel axis theorem, $I = \frac{2}{5}MR^2 + MR^2 = \frac{7}{5}MR^2$. If the sphere rolls without slipping $\alpha = a/R$. Substituting for I and x in the torque equation we have $a = \frac{5}{7}g\sin\theta$.

(b) The net force along the direction of the incline is

$$\Sigma F = mg\sin\theta - f = m\frac{5}{7}g\sin\theta \quad \text{where } f = \mu N = \mu mg\cos\theta.$$

Therefore $\mu = \frac{2}{7}\tan\theta$.

11.45 $\mathbf{r} = 2t^2 i + 3j; \quad p = mv = m\frac{d\mathbf{r}}{dt} = (5)(4t)i = 20ti$

$$\mathbf{L} = r \times p = (-60tk) \text{ kg} \cdot \text{m}^2/\text{s}$$

$$\tau = \frac{d\mathbf{L}}{dt} = (-60k) \text{ N} \cdot \text{m}$$

11.46 (a) $\mathbf{L} = r \times p = \begin{vmatrix} i & j & k \\ x & y & z \\ p_x & p_y & p_z \end{vmatrix}$

or $\mathbf{L} = i(yp_z - zp_y) + j(zp_x - xp_z) + k(xp_y - yp_x)$

(b) In the xy plane, $z = 0$ and $p_z = \frac{mdz}{dt} = 0$; so $L = (xp_y - yp_x)k = L_z k$

*11.47 $\tau \cdot \theta = \frac{1}{2}I\omega^2$

$$(25 \text{ N} \cdot \text{m})(15 \cdot 2\pi) = \frac{1}{2}(0.13 \text{ kg} \cdot \text{m}^2)\omega^2$$

$$\omega = 190 \text{ rad/s} = \boxed{30.3 \text{ rev/s}}$$

11.48 $I = \frac{1}{2}MR^2 = \frac{1}{2}(1200)(0.9)^2 = 486 \text{ kg} \cdot \text{m}^2$

(a) $K = \frac{1}{2}I\omega^2 = \frac{1}{2}(486)(\frac{2\pi}{60} \times 3500)^2 = 3.26 \times 10^7 \text{ J}$

(b) $30 \text{ hp} = 2.24 \times 10^4 \text{ W}$

$$t = \frac{3.26 \times 10^7 \text{ J}}{2.24 \times 10^4 \text{ W}} = 24.3 \text{ min}$$

11.49 (a) $\tau = |r \times F| = |r||F| \sin 0 = 0$

Angular momentum is conserved.

$$L_f = L_i$$

$$mrv = mr_0v_0$$

$$\boxed{v = \frac{r_0v_0}{r}}$$

(b) $T = \dfrac{mv^2}{r} = \dfrac{m(r_0v_0)^2}{r^3}$

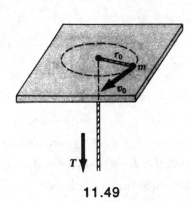

11.49

(c) The work is done by the centripetal force in the *negative* direction.
Method 1:

$$W = \int \mathbf{F} \cdot d\ell = -\int T\,dr' = -\int_{r_0}^{r} \frac{m(r_0v_0)^2}{(r')^3}dr' = \frac{m(r_0v_0)^2}{2(r')^2}\Big|_{r_0}^{r}$$

$$= \frac{m(r_0v_0)^2}{2}\left(\frac{1}{r^2} - \frac{1}{r_0^2}\right)$$

$$= \frac{1}{2}mv_0^2\left(\frac{r_0^2}{r^2} - 1\right)$$

Method 2:

$$W = \Delta K = \frac{1}{2}mv^2 - \frac{1}{2}mv_0^2 = \frac{1}{2}mv_0^2\left(\frac{r_0^2}{r^2} - 1\right)$$

(d) Using the data given, we find $v = 4.50 \text{ m/s}$; $T = 10.1 \text{ N}$; $W = 0.450 \text{ J}$.

11.50 The frictional force $F = \mu M g$ acts to slow the ball

$$v = v_0 - (F/M)t.$$

It also exerts a torque RF and starts the ball rolling

$$I\omega = RFt.$$

(a) The ball starts rolling without slipping at time $t = \tau$, when $\omega = v/R$:

$$\omega = v/R = [v_0 - (F/M)\tau]/R = (RF/I)\tau.$$

Solve for τ with $I = (\frac{2}{5})MR^2$ and $F = \mu M g$:

$$\tau = (v_0/R)[(RF/I) + (F/MR)] = \frac{2}{7}\frac{v_0}{\mu g}g$$

$$v(\tau) = v_0 - \left(\frac{\mu M g}{M}\right)\tau = \left(\frac{5}{7}\right)v_0$$

(b) The distance x traveled by the ball from $t = 0$ to $t = \tau$ is

$$x = \int_{t=0}^{t} v \, dt = \int_{t=0}^{t} (v_0 - \mu g t) \, dt = \frac{12}{49}\frac{v_0^2}{\mu g}$$

11.51 (a) If the acceleration is a, we have $F_x = ma$ and $F_y - W + N = 0$. Taking the origin at the center of gravity, the torque equation gives $F_y(L-d) + F_x h - Nd = 0$. Solving these equations, we have

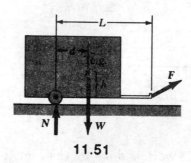

11.51

$$\boxed{F_y = \frac{W}{L}\left(d - \frac{ah}{g}\right)}$$

(b) If $F_y = 0$, then

$$d = \frac{ah}{g} = \frac{2(1.5)}{9.80} = \boxed{0.306 \text{ m}}$$

(c) Using the given data

$$\boxed{F_x = -306 \text{ N} \quad \text{and} \quad F_y = 553 \text{ N}}$$

11.52 (a) There are no horizontal forces acting on the rod, so its cm will not move horizontally. From conservation of energy

$$\frac{1}{2}MgL = \frac{1}{2}Mv^2_{cm} + \frac{1}{2}I\omega^2$$

$$= \frac{1}{2}Mv^2_{cm} + \frac{1}{2}(\frac{1}{12}ML^2)\omega^2$$

using $v^2_{cm} = (\frac{L}{2}\omega)^2$

$$\frac{1}{2}MgL = \frac{1}{2}Mv^2_{cm} + \frac{1}{2}(\frac{Mv^2_{cm}}{3})$$

$$\boxed{v_{cm} = \sqrt{\frac{3}{4}g\ell}, \text{ vertically downward}}$$

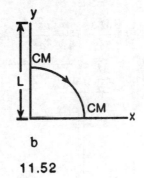

Just before hitting the surface. The CM will fall straight down

a

(b) From conservation of energy $\frac{1}{2}Mg\ell = \frac{1}{2}I\omega^2$

$$= \frac{1}{2}(\frac{1}{3}M\ell^2)\omega^2$$

$$= \frac{1}{2}(\frac{4M}{3}v^2_{cm})$$

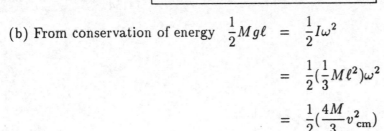

b

11.52

$$\boxed{v_{cm} = \sqrt{\frac{3}{4}g\ell}, \text{ vertically downward.}}$$

*11.53 (a) $L = 2(5\text{ m})(75\text{ kg})(5\text{ m/s}) = \boxed{3750\text{ kg m}^2/\text{s}}$

(b) $K_1 = 2(\frac{1}{2})(75\text{ kg})(5\text{ m/s})^2 = \boxed{1875\text{ J}}$

(c) Angular momentum is conserved

$$L = \boxed{3750\text{ kg m}^2/\text{s}}$$

(d) By conservation of L,

$$3750 = 2(2.5)(75)(v)$$

$$\therefore v = \boxed{10.0\text{ m/s}}$$

(e) $K_2 = 2\frac{1}{2}(75\text{kg})(10\text{ m/s})^2 = \boxed{7500\text{ J}}$

(f) $W = K_2 - K_1 = \boxed{5.62\text{ kJ}}$

11.54 For the cube to tip over the center of mass (CM) must rise so that its over the axis of rotation AB. To do this the CM must be raised a distance of $a(\sqrt{2} - 1)$

$$\therefore Mga(\sqrt{2} - 1) = \underbrace{\frac{1}{2}I_{\text{cube}}\omega^2}_{K_{\text{rot}} \text{ of cube}}$$

from conservation of angular momentum.

$$\frac{4a}{3}mv = \left(\frac{8Ma^2}{3}\right)\omega$$

$$\omega = \frac{mv}{2Ma}$$

$$\frac{1}{2}\left(\frac{8Ma^2}{3}\right)\frac{m^2v^2}{4M^2a^2} = Mga(\sqrt{2} - 1)$$

$$v = \frac{M}{m}\sqrt{3ga(\sqrt{2} - 1)}$$

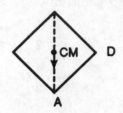

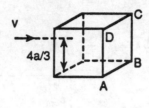

11.54

*11.55

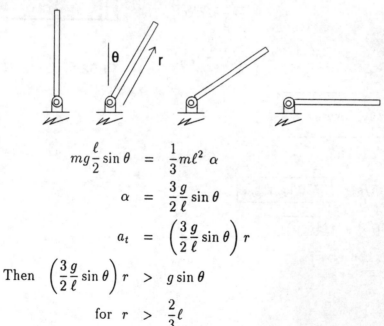

$$mg\frac{\ell}{2}\sin\theta = \frac{1}{3}m\ell^2\,\alpha$$

$$\alpha = \frac{3}{2}\frac{g}{\ell}\sin\theta$$

$$a_t = \left(\frac{3}{2}\frac{g}{\ell}\sin\theta\right)r$$

Then $\left(\frac{3}{2}\frac{g}{\ell}\sin\theta\right)r > g\sin\theta$

for $r > \frac{2}{3}\ell$

$\therefore$ About 1/3 the length of the chimney will have a tangential acceleration greater than $g\sin\theta$.

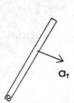

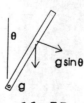

11.55

11.56 (a) from conservation of energy

$$Mgh = \frac{1}{2}Mv_1^2 + \frac{1}{2}I\omega^2 \qquad (1)$$

$$= \frac{1}{2}Mv_1^2 + \frac{1}{2}(\frac{2}{5}MR^2)\frac{v_1^2}{R^2} = 0.7Mv_1^2$$

$$v_1 = \boxed{\sqrt{\frac{10}{7}gh}}$$

Case (b)

$$Mgh = \frac{1}{2}Mv_2^2 \quad (2)$$

$$v_2 = \boxed{\sqrt{2gh}}$$

In case (1), acceleration along the incline is a_1

$$v_1^2 = v_0^2 + 2aL$$

$$v_1^2 = 2a_1\frac{h}{\sin\theta}$$

$$a_1 = \frac{v_1^2 \sin\theta}{2h} = \frac{5}{7}g\sin\theta$$

$$\therefore \quad t_1 = \frac{v_1}{a_1} = \sqrt{\frac{14h}{5g\sin^2\theta}}$$

Similarly

$$t_2 = \sqrt{\frac{2h}{g\sin\theta}} \quad , \text{ so } \frac{t_1}{t_2} = \sqrt{\frac{7}{5}} = 1.18$$

11.57 (a) $\Sigma F = F + f = Ma_{cm}$

$$\Sigma\tau = FR - fR = I\alpha$$

$$FR - (Ma_{cm} - F)R = \frac{Ia_{cm}}{R}$$

$$a_{cm} = \frac{4F}{3M}$$

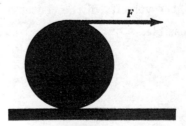

11.57

(b) $f = Ma_{cm} - F = M(\frac{4F}{3M}) - F = \frac{1}{3}F$

(c) $v^2 = v_0^2 + 2a(x - x_0)$

$$v = \sqrt{\frac{8Fd}{3M}}$$

11.58 (a) The net torque is zero at the point of contact, so the angular momentum before and after the collision must be equal.

$$(\tfrac{1}{2}MR^2)\omega_0 = (\tfrac{1}{2}MR^2)\omega + MR(R\omega) \qquad \omega = \frac{\omega_0}{3}$$

(b) $$\frac{\Delta E}{E} = \frac{\tfrac{1}{2}(\tfrac{1}{2}MR^2)(\frac{\omega_0}{3})^2 + \tfrac{1}{2}M(\frac{R\omega_0}{3})^2 - \tfrac{1}{2}(\tfrac{1}{2}MR^2)\omega_0^2}{\tfrac{1}{2}(\tfrac{1}{2}MR^2)\omega_0^2} = \frac{\tfrac{1}{6}MR^2\omega_0^2}{\tfrac{1}{4}MR^2\omega_0^2} = \frac{2}{3}$$

11.59 (a) $$\Delta t = \frac{\Delta P}{f} = \frac{Mv}{\mu Mg} = \frac{MR\omega}{\mu Mg} = \boxed{\frac{R\omega_0}{3\mu g}}$$

(b) $W = \Delta K = \tfrac{1}{2}I\omega^2 = \dfrac{1}{18}MR^2\omega_0^2$ (See Problem 11.58)

$$\mu Mgx = \frac{1}{18}MR^2\omega_0^2 \qquad \boxed{x = \frac{R^2\omega_0^2}{18\mu g}}$$

11.60 (a) The mass of the roll decreases as it unrolls. We have $m = \dfrac{Mr^2}{R^2}$ where M is the initial mass of the roll. Since $\Delta E = 0$, we then have $\Delta U(\text{gravity}) + \Delta K(\text{trans}) + \Delta K(\text{rot}) = 0$. Thus, when

$$I = \frac{mr^2}{2}, \quad (mgr - MgR) + \frac{mv^2}{2-0} + [\frac{mr^2}{2}\frac{\omega^2}{2-0}] = 0$$

Since $\omega r = v$, this becomes $v = \sqrt{\dfrac{4g(R^3 - r^3)}{3r^2}}$

(b) Using the given data we find $v = 5.31 \times 10^4$ m/s

(c) We have assumed that $\Delta E = 0$. When the roll gets to the end, we will have an inelastic collision with the surface. The energy goes into heat. With the assumption we made, there are problems with this question. It would take an infinite time to unwrap the tissue since $dr \to 0$. Also, as r approaches zero, the velocity of the center of mass approaches infinity, which is physically impossible.

11.61   Angular momentum is conserved during the inelastic collision.

$$mv_0a = I\omega$$

$$\omega = \frac{mv_0a}{I} = \frac{3v_0}{8a}$$

The condition that the box falls off the table is that the center of mass must reach its maximum height as the box rotates, $h = a\sqrt{2}$. Using conservation of energy:

$$\frac{1}{2}I\omega^2 = Mg(a\sqrt{2} - a)$$

$$\frac{1}{2}\left(\frac{8Ma^2}{3}\right)\left(\frac{3v_0}{8a}\right)^2 = Mg(a\sqrt{2} - a)$$

$$\boxed{v_0^2 = \frac{16}{3}ga(\sqrt{2} - 1)}$$

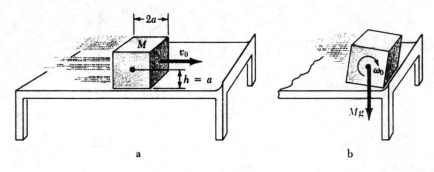

a   b

11.61

CHAPTER 12

*12.1 $F = W = \boxed{10 \text{ N}}$

$T = rF = (0.6)(10) = \boxed{6.0 \text{ N} \cdot \text{m}}$

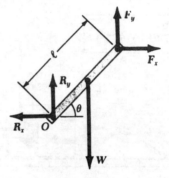

12.1

12.2 Use distances, angles, and forces as shown in Figure 12.15 of the text. The conditions of equilibrium are:

$$\boxed{\begin{array}{l} F_y + R_y - W = 0 \\[2mm] -R_x + F_x = 0 \\[2mm] F_y \ell \cos \theta - W \dfrac{\ell}{2} \cos \theta - F_x \ell \sin \theta = 0 \end{array}}$$

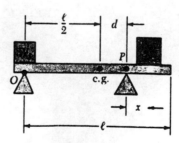

12.2

12.3 Take torques about P.

$$\Sigma \tau_p = N_0 [\frac{\ell}{2} + d] - W_1 [\frac{\ell}{2} + d] - Wd + W_2 x = 0$$

We want to find x for which $N_0 = 0$.

$$\boxed{x = \frac{(W_1 + W)d + W_1 \ell/2}{W_2}}$$

12.3 and 12.4

12.4 $N_0 = \frac{1}{2}N_p$ $\Sigma F_y = N_0 + N_p - (W_1 + W_2 - W) = 0$

If $W = 0$, $\Sigma F_y = N_0 + N_p - (W_1 + W_2) = 0$

Take torques around P

$\Sigma \tau_p = N_0[\frac{\ell}{2} + d] - W_1(\frac{\ell}{2} + d) - Wd + W_2 x = 0$

If $W = 0$, $N_0[\frac{\ell}{2} + d] = W_1(\frac{\ell}{2} + d) - W_2 x$

Thus, $N_0 = W_1 - \dfrac{W_2 x}{\frac{\ell}{2} + d}$

Also $N_p = W_1 + W_2 - N_0 = W_2(1 + \dfrac{x}{\ell/2 + d})$

and since $N_0 = \frac{1}{2}N_p$

then $W_1 - [\dfrac{W_2 x}{\ell/2 + d}] = \frac{1}{2}W_2(1 + \dfrac{x}{\ell/2 + d})$

Now solve above equation for x :

$$\boxed{x = (\frac{\ell}{2} + d)(\frac{2}{3}\frac{W_1}{W_2} - \frac{1}{3})}$$

12.5 $F_v - 1200 = 0$

$\boxed{F_v = 1200 \text{ N}}$ is the normal force exerted by the floor

$\Sigma \tau_A = (800)2 \cos 37° + (400)5 \cos 37° - 6F_w = 0$

$\boxed{F_w = 480 \text{ N}}$ reaction force exerted by the wall on the ladder.

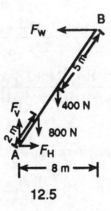

12.5

12.6 $\tan \alpha = \dfrac{0.5}{6}$

$\alpha = 4.76°$

$F = 2T \sin \alpha$

$T = \dfrac{F}{2 \sin \alpha} = \boxed{3.01 \text{ kN}}$

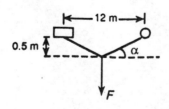

12.6

12.7 Refer to Figure 12.23 of the text and note that the center of gravity is located on the lateral line of symmetry of the T. Let m_1 = the mass of the vertical section and m_2 = the mass of the horizontal section of the T. Then

$$y_{cm} = \frac{m_2 y_1 + m_2 y_2}{m_1 + m_2} = \frac{A_2 y_2 + A_2 y_2}{A_1 + A_2}$$

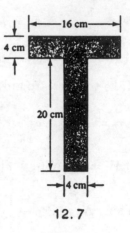

12.7

Measuring from an origin at the bottom of the T,

$y_1 = 10$ cm, $y_2 = 22$ cm, $A_1 = 80$ cm^2, $A_2 = 64$ cm^2 and

$$y_{cm} = \frac{(80)(10)\text{cm}^3 + (64)(22)\text{cm}^3}{144 \text{ cm}^2} = \boxed{15.3 \text{ cm}}$$

$x_{cm} = \boxed{8.00 \text{ cm}}$

12.8 Take the origin to be at the outside corner of the L. The mass will be proportional to the area. The (x, y) coordinates of the C.M. of the top (4×14) rectangle is $(2 \text{ cm}, 11 \text{ cm})$.

The (x, y) coordinates of the C.M. of the bottom (4×12) rectangle is $(6 \text{ cm}, 2 \text{ cm})$.

$$x_c = \frac{\sigma[(A_{top})2 + (A_{bottom})6]}{\sigma(A_{top} + A_{bottom})}$$

$$= \frac{(4 \times 14)2 + (4 \times 12)6}{(4 \times 14) + (4 \times 12)} = \boxed{3.85 \text{ cm}}$$

$$y_c = \frac{\sigma[(A_{top})11 + (A_{bot})2]}{\sigma(A_{top} + A_{bot})} = \boxed{6.85 \text{ cm}}$$

12.9 Let the fourth mass (8 kg) be placed at (x, y), then

$$x_{cg} = 0 = \frac{(3)(4) + m_4(x)}{12 + m_4}$$

$$x = -\frac{12}{8} = \boxed{-1.50 \text{ m}}$$

Similarly,

$$y_{cg} = 0 = \frac{(3)(4) + 8y}{12 + 8}$$

$$y = \boxed{-1.50 \text{ m}}$$

12.10 $\quad x_{cg} \quad = \dfrac{\int_0^L x\, dm}{\int_0^L dm} = \dfrac{\int_0^L x\lambda(x)\, dx}{\int_0^L \lambda(x)\, dx} = \dfrac{A\int_0^L x^2\, dx}{A\int_0^L x\, dx} = \dfrac{L^3/3}{L_2/2} = \boxed{\dfrac{2}{3}L}$

12.11 If balanced then $\Sigma\tau = 0 = 0.4(0.3) - 0.1(0.2) - x(0.4)$

so $x = \dfrac{[0.4(0.3) - 0.1(0.2)]}{0.4} = \boxed{0.25 \text{ m}}$ to the right of the point of support,
or 0.75 m from the left.

12.12 $W \rightarrow$ standard weight

$W' \rightarrow$ weight of goods sold.

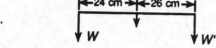

$W(0.24) = W'(0.26)$

$W = W'(\dfrac{13}{12})$

12.12

$(\dfrac{W - W'}{W'})100 = (\dfrac{13}{12} - 1) \times 100 = \boxed{8.33\%}$

12.13 $\quad N = (M + m)\text{g}$

$H = f$

$H_{\max} = f_{\max} = \mu_s(m + M)\text{g}$

$\Sigma\tau_A \quad = 0 = \dfrac{mgL}{2}\cos 60° + Mg\cos 60° - HL\sin 60°$

$\dfrac{x}{L} \quad = \dfrac{H\tan 60°}{Mg} - \dfrac{m}{2M} = \dfrac{\mu_s(m + M)\tan 60°}{M} - \dfrac{m}{2M}$

$\quad = \dfrac{3}{2}\mu_s\tan 60° - \dfrac{1}{4} = \boxed{0.789}$

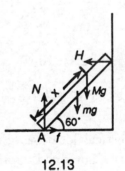

12.13

12.14 Consider the edge of the scaffold to be the pivot point and note in the figure that
$d = 1.5$ m

$\Sigma\tau_0 = (30\text{g N})(1.5 \text{ m}) - (70\text{g N})x = 0; \quad x = \dfrac{3}{7}(1.5 \text{ m}) = \boxed{0.643 \text{ m}}$

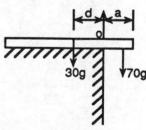

12.14

12.15 The torque about the front wheel is zero.

$$0 = (1.2 \text{ m})(mg) - 3 \text{ m} (2F_r)$$

Thus, the force at each rear wheel is

$$F_r = 0.2mg = \boxed{2.94 \text{ kN}}$$

The force at each front wheel is then

$$F_f = \frac{mg - 2F_r}{2} = \boxed{4.41 \text{ kN}}$$

12.16 $\tau = |\, r \times \boldsymbol{F} \,| = (1.5)(48)(9.80)(1) = \boxed{706 \text{ N·m}}$

12.17 (1) $ph = I_c \omega_0$

(2) $p = M v_0$

If the ball rolls without slipping.

$R\omega_0 = v_0$

So,

$$h = \frac{I_c \omega_0}{p} = \frac{I_c \omega_0}{M v_0} = \frac{I_c}{MR} = \boxed{\frac{2}{5} R}$$

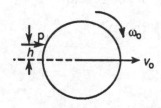

12.17

*12.18 (a) $T_e \sin 42° = 20 \text{ N}$ $T_e = \boxed{29.9 \text{ N}}$

(b) $T_e \cos 42° = T_m$ $T_m = \boxed{22.2 \text{ N}}$

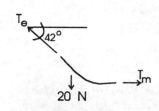

12.18

12.19 The vertical location of the c.g. (or cm) is not necessary. Only the horizontal position of cm is pertinent, which is halfway between the two ends of the sign.

$$T_1 + T_2 = W$$

$$\Sigma\tau_A = T_2(0.75) - W(0.5) = 0 \qquad T_2 = \boxed{\frac{2}{3}W}$$

$$T_1 = \boxed{\frac{1}{3}W}$$

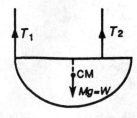

12.19

12.20 Let the string tied at B be the weaker one.

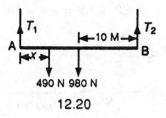

12.20

$$T_1 + T_2 = 1470 \text{ N}$$

$$T_1 = 1470 - T_2 = 870 \text{ N}$$

$$\Sigma \tau_A = 490x + (980)(5) - 600 \times 10 = 0$$

$$x = \boxed{2.24 \text{ m}}$$

*12.21 $\boxed{x = \dfrac{3L}{4}}$

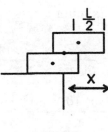

12.21

If the CM of the two bricks does not lie over the edge, then the bricks balance.

If the lower brick is placed $\frac{L}{4}$ over the edge, then the second brick may be placed so that its end protrudes $\frac{3L}{4}$ over the edge.

*12.22 To find U, measure distances and forces from point A. Then, balancing torques,

$$(0.75)U = 29.4(2.25)$$

$$U = \boxed{88.2 \text{ N}}$$

To find D, measure distances and forces from point B. Then, balancing torques,

$$(0.75)D = (1.5)(29.4)$$

$$D = \boxed{58.8 \text{ N}}$$

Also, notice that $U = D + W$, so $\sum F_y = 0$.

*12.23 $\dfrac{F}{A} = Y\dfrac{\Delta\ell}{\ell}$

$$\Delta\ell = \frac{F}{A}\frac{\ell}{Y} = \frac{(200)(9.8)(4)}{(0.2 \times 10^{-4})(8 \times 10^{10})} = \boxed{4.9 \text{ mm}}$$

*12.24 $\Delta\ell = \dfrac{F}{A}\dfrac{\ell}{Y} = \dfrac{(115)(1.12)}{(6 \times 10^{-7})(20 \times 10^{10})} = \boxed{1.07 \text{ mm}}$

12.25 $L = 4$ cm. $F = 3000$ N. $S = 8.4 \times 10^{10}$ N/m²

$$S = \frac{\text{Stress}}{\text{Strain}} = \frac{F/A}{\text{Strain}}$$

Shearing Strain $= \dfrac{F/A}{S} = \dfrac{3000}{(0.04)^2(8.4 \times 10^{10})} = \boxed{2.23 \times 10^{-5}}$

12.26 In this problem, $F = mg = 10(9.80) = 9.80$ N, $A = \pi d^2/4$,

and the maximum stress $= \dfrac{F}{A} = 1.5 \times 10^8$ N/m²

$$A = \frac{\pi d^2}{4} = \frac{F}{\text{Stress}} = \frac{98.0 \text{ N}}{1.5 \times 10^8 \text{ N/m}^2} = 6.53 \times 10^{-7} \text{m}^2$$

$$d^2 = \frac{4(6.53 \times 10^{-7} \text{ m}^2)}{\pi}$$

$$d = \boxed{9.12 \times 10^{-4} \text{ m}}$$

12.27 $B = 2.8 \times 10^{10}$ N/m² for Hg

$$\Delta V = (-5 \times 10^{-4})V_0 \text{ therefore } \frac{\Delta V}{V_0} = -5 \times 10^{-4}$$

$$B = -\frac{\Delta P}{\Delta V/V_0}$$

$$\Delta P = -B\frac{\Delta V}{V_0} = (2.8 \times 10^{10} \text{ N/m}^2)(\frac{0.1}{100}) = \boxed{2.8 \times 10^7 \text{ N/m}^2}$$

*12.28 $B = \dfrac{\Delta P}{\Delta V/V}$

$$\Delta V = \frac{\Delta P V}{B} = \frac{(1.36 \times 10^{10} \text{ Pa})(1 \text{ cm}^3)}{14 \times 10^{10} \text{ Pa}}$$

$$= 9.71 \times 10^{-2} \text{ cm}^3$$

$$V_{new} = \boxed{1.097 \text{ cm}^3}$$

12.29 (a) Stress $= F/A$ and $F = A$ (Stress) $= (\pi)(0.005 \text{ m})^2(4 \times 10^3 \text{ N/m}^2)$

$$= \boxed{3.14 \times 10^4 \text{ N}}$$

(b) $S = \dfrac{F_t}{A}$

$F_t = S(2\pi r)t$

$= (4 \times 10^8 \text{ N})(2\pi)(0.005 \text{ m})^2 = \boxed{62.8 \text{ kN}}$

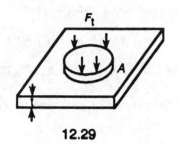

12.29

*12.30 $\dfrac{F}{A} = Y\dfrac{\Delta \ell}{\ell}$

(a) $\dfrac{380(9.8)}{\pi \left(\dfrac{d^2}{4}\right)} = 20 \times 10^{10} \dfrac{9 \times 10^{-3}}{18}$

$$\sqrt{\dfrac{380(9.8)(4)18}{\pi(20 \times 10^{10})(9 \times 10^{-3})}} = d = \boxed{6.89 \text{ mm}}$$

(b) $A = 3.72 \times 10^{-5} \text{ m}^2$

$\dfrac{F}{A} = 1 \times 10^8 \text{ Pa} \quad \boxed{\text{No}}$

*12.31 $\Delta P = B\dfrac{\Delta V}{V} = \left(2 \times 10^9 \dfrac{\text{N}}{\text{m}^2}\right)(0.09) = \boxed{180 \text{ MPa}} = 1800 \text{ atm}$

*12.32 $\dfrac{F}{A} = Y\dfrac{\Delta \ell}{\ell}$

$\dfrac{90(9.8)}{\pi(5 \times 10^{-3} \text{ m})^2} = Y\left(\dfrac{1.6}{50}\right)$

$Y = \boxed{3.51 \times 10^8 \text{ Pa}}$

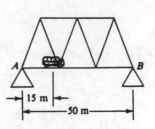

12.33 Let N_A and N_B be the normal forces at the points of support.

Choosing the origin at point A and using $\Sigma F_y = \Sigma \tau = 0$, we find:

$N_A + N_B - (8 \times 10^4 g) - (3 \times 10^4 g) = 0$, and

$-(3 \times 10^4 g)15 - (5 \times 10^4 g)25 + N_g(50) = 0$

12.33

The equations combine to give $N_A = \boxed{5.98 \times 10^5 \text{ N}}$ and $N_B = \boxed{4.80 \times 10^5 \text{ N}}$

12.34 $Mg = F_B \sin 60°$

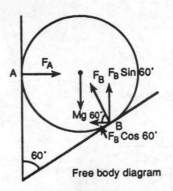

$F_B \cos 60° = F_A$

$F_B = \dfrac{Mg}{\sin 60°} = \boxed{1.155 Mg}$

$F_A = F_B \cos 60° = \dfrac{Mg}{\tan 60°} = \boxed{0.577 Mg}$

Free body diagram

12.34

12.35 (a) See figure

(b) Using $\Sigma F_x = \Sigma \tau = 0$, we have (with A the bottom of the ladder):

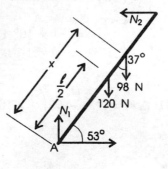

$\Sigma F_x = T - N_2 = 0$

$\Sigma F_y = N_1 - 218 \text{ N} = 0$

$\Sigma \tau_A = 98x \cos 53° + 120(\frac{\ell}{2}) \cos 53° - N_2 \ell \sin 53° = 0$

12.35

where x is the distance of the monkey from the bottom of the ladder. When $x = \ell/3$, the above equation gives

$T = \dfrac{(18.66 + 36.11)}{0.7986} = \boxed{69.8 \text{ N}}$

(c) The rope breaks when $T = 110 \text{ N} = N_2$

$\Sigma \tau_A = 10(9.8)x \cos 53° + 120(\ell/2) \cos 53° - 110\ell \sin 53° = 0$

$x = \dfrac{110\ell \sin 53° - 60\ell(\cos 53°)}{10(9.8) \cos 53°} = \boxed{0.877\ \ell}$

12.36 (a) See sketch

(b) Since $\Sigma F_x = \Sigma F_y = \Sigma \tau = 0$, we have

$\Sigma F_x = R_x - T \cos 60° = 0$

$\Sigma F_y = R_y + T \sin 60° - 700 - 200 - 80 = 0$

Choosing the origin at the pivot point

$\Sigma \tau_0 = -700x - 200(3) - 80(6) + (T \sin 60°)6 = 0$

If $x = 1$, we can solve the above to get

$\boxed{T = 343 \text{ N}; R_x = 171 \text{ N}; R_y = 683 \text{ N}}$

(c) If $T = 900$ N, then solve the torque equation to get $x = \boxed{5.14 \text{ m}}$

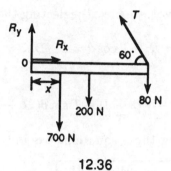

12.36

12.37 Choosing the origin at the pivot point and applying equations 12.2 and 12.3 we have

$\Sigma F_x = R_x - T \cos 30° = 0$

$\Sigma F_y = R_y + T \sin 30° - (10 + 20)g = 0$

$\Sigma \tau = \ell T \sin 67° - (\frac{\ell}{2})(10)g \sin 53° - \ell(20)g \sin 53° = 0$

Solving the above equations gives

$R_x = \boxed{184 \text{ N}}$; $R_y = \boxed{187 \text{ N}}$ and $T = \boxed{213 \text{ N}}$

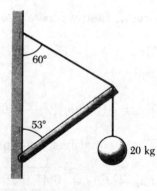

12.37

12.38 Using $\Sigma F_x = \Sigma F_y = \Sigma \tau = 0$, we have $\Sigma F_x = R_x - T \cos 25° = 0$. $\Sigma F_y = R_y + T \sin 15° - 3200 = 0$ and choosing origin at the pivot

$\Sigma \tau = 1200(\frac{\ell}{2}) \cos 65° + 2000(\ell) \cos 65° - T(\frac{3}{4}\ell) = 0$

$T = 2600(\frac{4}{3}) \cos 65° = \boxed{1.47 \text{ kN}}$

$R_x = T \cos 25° = \boxed{1.33 \text{ kN}}$

$R_y = 3200 - 1470 \sin 25° = \boxed{2.58 \text{ kN}}$

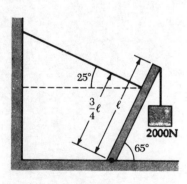

12.38

12.39 Using $\Sigma F_x = \Sigma F_y = \Sigma \tau = 0$, choosing the origin at the pivot, we have (neglecting the weight of the beam)

$$\Sigma F_x = R_x - T\cos\theta = 0, \quad \Sigma F_y = R_y + T\sin\theta - W = 0,$$
and

$$\Sigma \tau = -W(\ell + d) + T\sin\theta(2\ell + d) = 0.$$

Solving these equations we find:

(a) $\boxed{T = \dfrac{W(\ell + d)}{\sin\theta(2\ell + d)}}$ and

(b) $\boxed{R_x = \dfrac{W(\ell + d)\cot\theta}{2\ell + d}; \quad R_y = \dfrac{W\ell}{2\ell + d}}$

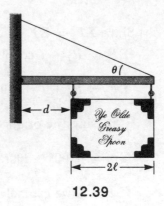

12.39

12.40 At point B since the support is *smooth* the reaction force is in the x direction. If we choose point A as the origin, then we have (assuming the crane is uniform):

$$\Sigma F_x = F_{Bx} - F_{Ax} = 0, \quad \Sigma F_{Ay} - (3000 + 10000)g = 0,$$
and

$$\Sigma \tau = -(3000g)(2) - (10000g)(6) + F_{Bx}(1) = 0$$

These equations combine to give

$$F_{Ax} = F_{Bx} = \boxed{6.47 \times 10^5 \text{ N}}$$

$$F_{Ay} = \boxed{1.27 \times 10^4 \text{ N}} \text{ and } F_{By} = \boxed{0}$$

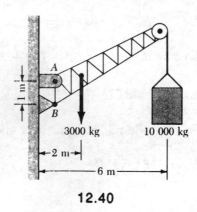

12.40

12.41   (a) $\Sigma F_x = 0 = f - N_x$; $\Sigma F_y = 0 = N_y - 800 - 500$ and

$\Sigma \tau = 0 = 4(800) \sin 30° + 7.5(500) \sin 30° - 15 N_x \sin 60°$

Solve the torque equation to find the force exerted by the wall

$$N_x = \frac{[4(800) + 7.5(500)] \tan 30°}{15} = 268 \text{ N}$$

Next substitute this value into the F_x equation to find

$f = N_x = \boxed{268 \text{ N}}$ in the position x-direction. Solve the ΣF_y equation to find

$N_y = \boxed{1300 \text{ N}}$ in the positive y-direction.

(b) $f = \mu N_y$;

$\Sigma F_x = f - N_x = 0$

$\Sigma F_y = N_y - 500 - 800 = 0$

$\Sigma \tau = 500(7.5 \cos 60°) + 800(9 \cos 60°) - \mu N_y(15) \sin 60° = 0$

$$\mu = \frac{500(7.5 \cos 60°) + 800(9 \cos 60°)}{15 \sin 60°} \cdot [\frac{1}{1300}] = \boxed{0.324}$$

12.42   We can use $\Sigma F_x = \Sigma F_y = \Sigma \tau = 0$ and by choosing the origin at the floor we find (with N_1 the normal force on the horizontal and N_2 the normal force on the vertical wall).

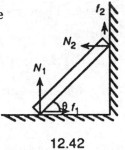

$\Sigma F_x = f_1 - N_2 = 0$ or, $\mu N_1 = N_2$

$\Sigma F_y = f_2 + N_1 - 200 = 0$ or, $\mu N_2 + N_1 = 200$

$\Sigma \tau = 200(\frac{\ell}{2}) \cos 60° - N_2(\ell) \sin 60° - f_2(\ell) \cos 60°$

Solving these equations gives $\boxed{\mu = 0.268}$

12.42

12.43 $\Sigma F_x = -T\cos 20° + R_x = 0$ **(1)**

$\Sigma F_y = T\sin 20° + R_y - 10,000 = 0$ **(2)**

$\Sigma \tau = 10,000(4)\cos 60° - T(4)\sin 80° = 0$ **(3)**

From (3) $T = \dfrac{10,000(0.5)}{0.9848} = 5077\ \text{N} = \boxed{5.08\ \text{kN}}$

From (1) $R_x = T\cos 20° = (5.08\ \text{kN})(\cos 20°) = \boxed{4.77\ \text{kN}}$

From (2) $R_y = 10,000 - T\sin 20° = \boxed{8.26\ \text{kN}}$

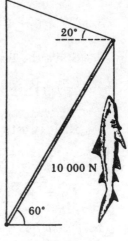

12.43

12.44 Choose the origin at the point where R is applied to the foot. Then we have

$\Sigma F_x = R\sin(15°) - T\sin\theta = 0$
$\Sigma F_y = 700 - R\cos(15°) + T\cos\theta = 0$

$\Sigma \tau = -700(\cos\theta)(0.18) + T(0.07) = 0$

We first solve the above equations to find θ.

This gives
$\cos^4\theta[324(1+\cot^2(15°))]+$

$\cos^2\theta[252 - 324\cot^2(15°)] + 49 = 0.$

Let $u = \cos^2\theta$. Then we can solve for u using the quadratic formula:

$u = \cos^2\theta = 0.01165$ or 0.8693

If we assume θ is closer in value to $0°$ than $90°$, then

$\theta = \cos^{-1}\sqrt{0.8693} = \boxed{21.2°}$

Substituting for θ we then have

$T = \boxed{1.68\times 10^3\ \text{N}}$ and $R = \boxed{2.34\times 10^3\ \text{N}}$

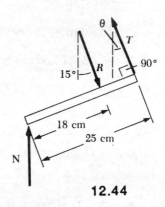

12.44

12.45 Choosing the origin at the contact of R, we have

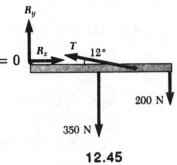

$$\Sigma F_x = -R_x + T\cos(12°) = 0; \quad \Sigma F_y = R_y + T\sin(12°) - 200 - 350 = 0$$

$$\Sigma \tau = 200d + 350(\frac{d}{2}) - T\sin(12°)(\frac{2d}{3}) = 0$$

Solving these equations we find:

$$T = \frac{(3(175 + 200)\text{ N}}{2\sin(12°)} = \boxed{2710\text{ N}}$$

$$R_x = T\cos(12°) = \boxed{2650\text{ N}} \text{ and } R_y = 550\text{ N} - T(\sin 12°) = -12\text{ N}$$

12.45

*12.46 $T_1 \sin 8° = 200$ N

$\quad\quad\quad T_1 = \boxed{1.44\text{ kN}}$

$\quad\quad\quad T_m = T_1 \cos 8° = 1.42$ kN

$\quad\quad\quad T_2 = \boxed{1.44\text{ kN}}$

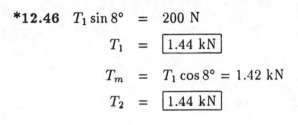

12.46

12.47 (a) Locate the origin at the bottom left corner of the block and let x = distance between the *resultant normal force* and the *front of the block*. Then we have
$$\Sigma F_x = 200\cos(37°) - \mu N = 0. \quad (1)$$

$$\Sigma F_y = 200\sin(37°) + N - 400 = 0, \quad (2) \text{ and}$$
$$\Sigma \tau = N(0.6 - x) - 400(0.3) + 200\sin 37°(0.6) \quad (3)$$
$$\quad\quad -200\cos 37°(0.4) = 0$$

From (2) $N = 400 - 200\sin 37° = 280$ N

From (3) $x = [72.2 - 120 + 260(0.6) - 64]/280 =$

$\boxed{20.1\text{ cm}}$ to the left of the front edge. From (1)

$$\mu = \frac{200\cos 37°}{280} = \boxed{0.571}$$

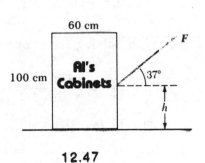

12.47

(b) In this case, locate the origin $x = 0$ at the bottom right corner of the block. Since the block is about to tip, we can use $\Sigma \tau = 0$ to find h :

$$\Sigma \tau = 400(0.3) - 300\cos 37°(h) = 0$$

$$h = \frac{120}{300\cos 37°} = \boxed{0.501\text{ m}}$$

12.48 (a) $\Sigma \tau_A = 1.0F - 0.3(400) = 0$

$$F = \frac{120}{1.0} = \boxed{120 \text{ N}}$$

(b) $\Sigma F_y = F_A - 400 = 0$

$$\mu = \frac{f}{F_A} = \frac{F}{400} = \frac{120}{400} = \boxed{0.30}$$

(c) $\Sigma \tau = F' \sqrt{(1.9)^2 + (0.6)^2} - 400(0.3) = 0$

$$F' = \frac{120}{1.17} = \boxed{103 \text{ N}}$$

$$\tan \theta = \frac{1.0}{0.6} \quad \theta = 59°$$

$$\phi = 90 - 59° = \boxed{31°}$$

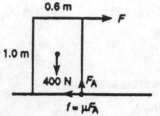

12.48

a   b

12.49 (a) We can use $\Sigma F_x = \Sigma F_y = \Sigma \tau = 0$ with origin at the point of contact on the floor. Then $\Sigma F_x = T - \mu N = 0$,

$$\Sigma F_y = N - W - w = 0 \text{ and}$$
$$\Sigma \tau = W(\cos \theta)\ell + \frac{w(\cos \theta)\ell}{2} - T(\sin \theta)\ell = 0$$

Solving the above equations gives

$$W = \frac{w}{2} \frac{(2\mu \sin \theta - \cos \theta)}{(\cos \theta - \mu \sin \theta)}$$

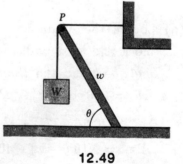

12.49

(b) At the floor, we have the normal force in the y-direction and frictional force in the x-direction. The reaction force then is

$$R = \sqrt{N^2 + (\mu N)^2} = (W + w)\sqrt{1 + \mu^2}$$

At point P, the force of the beam on the rope is

$$F = \sqrt{T^2 + W^2} = \boxed{\sqrt{W^2 + \mu^2(W + w)^2}}$$

*12.50 Clearly, the upward and downward forces must balance:

$N_A + N_C = 1000$ N

And the torques must balance. Taking moments about A,

$(1000 \text{ N})(8.66 \text{ m}) = N_C(13.66 \text{ m})$

$\therefore$ $\boxed{N_C = 634 \text{ N}}$ and $\boxed{N_A = 366 \text{ N}}$

12.51 Use forces as labeled in the figure and note that $\sin\theta = (15)^{1/2}/4$ and $\cos\theta = 1/4$. For the left half of the ladder we have

$$\Sigma F_x = T - P_x = 0 \tag{1}$$

$$\Sigma F_y = P_y + N_1 - 70g = 0 \tag{2}$$

$$\Sigma\tau = (70g)(1/4)(1) + [T\sqrt{\frac{15}{4}}]2 - N_1(1/4)(4) = 0 \tag{3}$$

For the right half of the ladder we have

$$\Sigma F_x = P_x - T = 0$$

$$\Sigma F_y = N_2 - P_y = 0 \tag{4}$$

$$\Sigma\tau = N_2(1/4)4 - (T\sqrt{\frac{15}{4}})2 = 0 \tag{5}$$

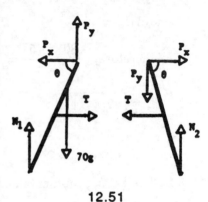

12.51

From Eqs. (3) and (5), $N_2 + (1/4)(70g) - N_1 = 0$.

From Eqs. (2) and (4), $N_2 - 70g + N_1 = 0$.

(a) From Eq. (3), $T = 2[N_1 - (70/4)g]/\sqrt{15} = \boxed{133 \text{ N}}$

(b) From these results we have $N_1 = \boxed{429 \text{ N}}$ and

$N_2 = \boxed{257 \text{ N}}$

(c) From Eq. (4), $P_y = N_2 = \boxed{257 \text{ N}}$ From Eq. (1),

$P_x = T = \boxed{133 \text{ N}}$

*12.52 $\dfrac{F}{A}$ = Stress

$$F = \left(8 \times 10^7 \ \dfrac{N}{m^2}\right) 4\pi \left(\dfrac{7 \times 10^{-3} \ m}{2}\right)^2$$

$$= (8 \times 10^7)\pi(49 \times 10^{-6} \ N)$$

$$F = \boxed{12.3 \ kN}$$

*12.53 The sum of the torques about the point at which the bracket touches the wall at 0 are:

$F_s(3 \ cm) + (80 \ N)(5 \ cm) = N(9 \ cm)$

and $F_s = N$

Therefore, $\dfrac{(80 \ N)(5)}{6} = F_s$

$F_s = \boxed{66.7 \ N}$

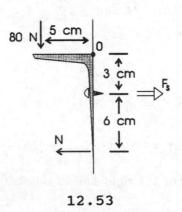

12.53

*12.54 (a) Taking moments above N,

$(R \sin 30°)0 + (R \cos 30°)(5 \ cm) - (150 \ N)(30 \ cm) = 0$

$R = 1039.2 \ N = \boxed{1.04 \ kN}$

(b) $f = R \sin 30° - 150 \ N = 370 \ N$

$N = R \cos 30° = 900 \ N$

$\mathbf{F}_{surface} = (370 \ N)\mathbf{i} + (900 \ N)\mathbf{j}$

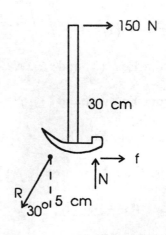

12.54

*12.55 $f_1 = N_2 = \mu N_1$

$f_2 = \mu N_2$

$F + N_1 + f_2 = W$

and $F = f_1 + f_2$

As F grows so do f_1 and f_2.

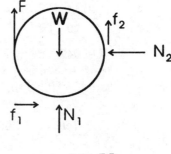

12.55

Therefore, since $\mu = \dfrac{1}{2}$, $f_1 = \dfrac{N_1}{2}$ and $f_2 = \dfrac{N_2}{2} = \dfrac{N_1}{4}$

$F + N_1 + \dfrac{N_1}{4} = \underline{W}$ (1)

and $F = \dfrac{N_1}{2} + \dfrac{N_1}{4} = \dfrac{3}{4}N_1$ (2)

$F + \dfrac{5}{4}N_1 = \underline{W}$

$F + \dfrac{5}{4}\left(\dfrac{4}{3}F\right) = W$

$\dfrac{8}{3}F = W$

$\boxed{F = \dfrac{3}{8}W}$

12.56 (a) $\mid F \mid = k\Delta L$, Young's modulus is $Y = (\dfrac{F}{A})/(\dfrac{\Delta L}{L})$

$Y = \dfrac{kL}{A};\ \boxed{k = \dfrac{YA}{L}}$

(b) $W = -\displaystyle\int_0^{\Delta L} F\,dx = -\int_0^{\Delta L}(-kx)\,dx = \dfrac{YA}{L}\int_0^{\Delta L} x\,dx = \boxed{YA\dfrac{(\Delta L)^2}{2L}}$

12.57 $S = 1.5 \times 10^{10}\ \text{N/m}^2$

Shear Strain $= \dfrac{\Delta x}{h} = \dfrac{5\ \text{m}}{10 \times 10^3\ \text{m}} = 5 \times 10^{-4}$

Shear Stress $=\ S \times$ Shear Strain

$=\ (1.5 \times 10^{10}\ \text{N/m}^2)(5 \times 10^{-4}) = \boxed{7.51 \times 10^6\ \text{N/m}^2}$

12.58 $\overline{F} = \dfrac{\Delta p}{\Delta t} = \dfrac{(30 \text{ kg})(30 \text{m/s})}{0.11 \text{ s}} = 8182 \text{ N}$

$A = \pi r^2 = 0.00042 \text{ m}^2$

$P = \dfrac{F}{A} = 1.969 \times 10^7 \text{ N/m}^2$

$\text{Strain} \;\; = \dfrac{\text{stress}}{Y} = \dfrac{1.969 \times 10^6 \text{ N/m}^2}{20 \times 10^{10} \text{ N/m}^2}$

$\qquad\qquad = \boxed{9.85 \times 10^{-5}}$

12.59   (a) $F = m\dfrac{\Delta v}{\Delta t} = 1\dfrac{(10-1)}{(0.002)} = \boxed{4500 \text{ N}}$

(b) $\dfrac{F}{A} = \dfrac{4500 \text{ N}}{(0.01)(0.1) \text{m}^2} = \boxed{4.50 \times 10^6 \text{ N/m}^2}$

(c) $\boxed{\text{This is more than sufficient to break the board}}$

12.60   The tension in this cable is not uniform, so this becomes a fairly difficult problem.

$$\dfrac{dL}{L} = \dfrac{F}{YA} \qquad\qquad\qquad \underbrace{\dfrac{dL}{L} = \dfrac{\mu g y}{YA}}_{\text{elongation per unit length}}$$

$$\Delta y = \int_0^{L_0} \left(\dfrac{dL}{L}\right) dy = \dfrac{\mu g}{YA}\int_0^{L_0} y\,dy = \dfrac{1}{2}\dfrac{\mu g L_0^2}{YA}$$

$F = $ weight of cable below $= \mu g y$

$$\Delta y = \dfrac{1}{2}\dfrac{(2.4)(9.8)(500)^2}{(2\times 10^{11})(3\times 10^{-4})} = 0.049 \text{ m} = 4.9 \text{ cm}$$

* Note that the uniform increase of F with y allows us to treat this as a weightless-cable problem with a load equal to half its own weight.

$$\Delta L = \dfrac{F_{av}/A}{Y/L_0} = \dfrac{\frac{1}{2}(2.4 \times 500 \times 9.8)/(3\times 10^{-4})}{(2\times 10^{11})/(500)}$$

$\Delta L = \boxed{4.90 \text{ cm}}$

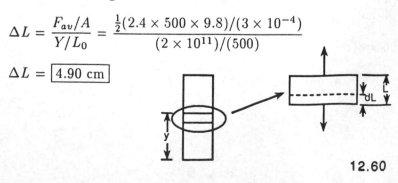

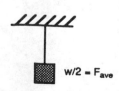

12.60

CHAPTER 13

13.1 $x = 4\cos(3\pi t + \pi)$. Compare this with $x = A\cos(\omega t + \phi)$ to find

(a) $\omega = 2\pi f = 3\pi$ or $\boxed{f = 1.50 \text{ Hz}}$ $T = \dfrac{1}{f} = \boxed{0.667 \text{ s}}$

(b) $A = \boxed{4.00 \text{ m}}$

(c) $\phi = \boxed{\pi \text{ rad}}$

(d) $x(t = 0.25 \text{ s}) = 4\cos(1.75\pi) = \boxed{2.83 \text{ m}}$

13.2   (a) $v = \dfrac{dx}{dt} = 4\dfrac{d}{dt}[\cos(3\pi t + \pi)] = \boxed{-12\pi \sin(3\pi t + \pi) \text{ m/s}}$

(b) $a = \dfrac{dv}{dt} = (-12\pi)\dfrac{d}{dt}[\sin(3\pi t + \pi)] = \boxed{-36\pi^2 \cos(3\pi t + \pi) \text{ m/s}^2}$

(c) By inspection of the results of (a) and (b), $v_{\text{max}} = \boxed{12\pi \text{ m/s}}$ and

$a_{\text{max}} = \boxed{36\pi^2 \text{ m/s}^2}$

(d) From part (a), $v(at\ t = 0) = -12\pi \sin(\pi) = \boxed{0}$

From part (b), $a(at\ t = 0) = \boxed{-36\pi^2 \cos(\pi) = 36\pi^2 \text{ m/s}^2}$

13.3   (a) $x = 5\cos\dfrac{2t + \pi}{6}$;   At $t = 0, x = 5\cos(\dfrac{\pi}{6}) = \boxed{4.33 \text{ cm}}$

(b) $v = \dfrac{dx}{dt} = -10\sin\dfrac{2t + \pi}{6}$;   At $t = 0, v = \boxed{-5.00 \text{ cm/s}}$

(c) $a = \dfrac{dv}{dt} = -20\cos\dfrac{2t + \pi}{6}$;   At $t = 0, a = \boxed{-17.3 \text{ cm/s}^2}$

(d) $A = \boxed{5.00 \text{ cm}}$ and $T = \dfrac{2\pi}{\omega} = \dfrac{2\pi}{2} = \boxed{3.14 \text{ s}}$

13.4 Since it travels 20 cm in *each circle*, $4A = 20$ cm, $A = 5$ cm $= 5 \times 10^{-2}$ m,

(a) $|\,a_{max}\,| = A\omega^2 = 50$ m/s^2, so $\omega^2 = \dfrac{50}{5 \times 10^{-2}} = 10^{-3} \Rightarrow \omega = \boxed{31.6 \text{ rad/s}}$

(b) $|\,v_{max}\,| = A\omega = (5 \times 10^{-2} \text{ m})(3.16 \text{ rad/s}) = \boxed{1.58 \text{ m/s}}$

13.5 $x = (8.0 \text{ cm}) \cos(2t + \pi/3)$

(a) $v = -(16.0 \text{ cm/s}) \sin\left(2t + \dfrac{\pi}{3}\right)$; At $t = \dfrac{\pi}{2}$ s, $v = \boxed{13.9 \text{ cm/s}}$

$a = -(32.0 \text{ cm/s}^2) \cos\left(2t + \dfrac{\pi}{3}\right)$; At $t = \dfrac{\pi}{2}$ s, $a = \boxed{16.0 \text{ cm/s}^2}$

(b) $v_{max} = \boxed{16.0 \text{ cm/s}}$; this occurs when $t = \dfrac{1}{2}[\sin^{-1}(1) - \dfrac{\pi}{3}] = \boxed{0.262 \text{ s}}$

(c) $a_{max} = \boxed{32.0 \text{ cm/s}^2}$; this occurs when $t = \dfrac{1}{2}[\cos^{-1}(-1) - \dfrac{\pi}{3}] = \boxed{1.05 \text{ s}}$

*13.6 (a) $\boxed{20 \text{ cm}}$

(b) $v_{max} = \omega A = 2\pi f A = \boxed{94.2 \text{ cm/s}}$
This occurs as the particle passes through equilibrium.

(c) $a_{max} = \omega^2 A = (2\pi f)^2 A = \boxed{17.8 \text{ m/s}^2}$
This occurs at maximum excursion from equilibrium.

13.7 (a) At $t = 0, x = 0$ and v is positive (to the right). Therefore, this situation corresponds to Special Case II on page 331, where $x = A\sin\omega t$ and $v = v_0\cos\omega t$. Since $f = 1.5$ Hz, $\omega = 2\pi f = 3\pi$; also, $A = 2$ cm, so that $\boxed{x - 2\sin 3\pi t \text{ cm}}$

(b) $v_{max} = v_0 = A\omega = 2(3\pi) = \boxed{6\pi \text{ cm/s}}$ The particle has this speed at $t = 0$ and next at $t = \dfrac{T}{2} = \boxed{\dfrac{1}{3}}$ s

(c) $a_{max} = A\omega^2 = 2(3\pi)^2 = \boxed{18\pi^2 \text{ cm/s}^2}$ The acceleration has this value for the first time at $t = \dfrac{3T}{4} = \boxed{0.500 \text{ s}}$

(d) Since $T = \dfrac{2}{3}$ s and $A = 2$ cm, the particle will travel 8 cm in this time. Hence, in 1 s ($= \dfrac{3T}{2}$) the particle will travel 8 cm + 4 cm = $\boxed{12.0 \text{ cm}}$

13.8 $x = A\cos\omega t, \qquad A = 0.05$ m

$v = -A\omega\sin\omega t \qquad a = -A\omega^2\cos\omega t$

If $f = 3600$ rpm $= 60$ Hz, then $\omega = 120\pi$ s^{-1}

$v_{max} = (0.05)(120\pi)$ m/s $= \boxed{18.8 \text{ m/s}}$

$a_{max} = (0.05)(120\pi)^2$ m/s$^2 = \boxed{7.11 \text{ km/s}^2}$

13.9 $k = 6$ N/m

$W = mg = 0.2$ N

For a force balance, $W = kx$. Therefore, $x = \dfrac{mg}{k} = \dfrac{0.2 \text{ N}}{6 \text{ N/m}} = \boxed{3.33 \text{ cm}}$

13.10 $T = 2\pi\sqrt{\dfrac{m}{k}}$ and $k = \dfrac{F}{x} = \dfrac{(0.01)(9.80)}{0.039} = 2.51$ N/m so that

$T = 2\pi\sqrt{\dfrac{0.025}{2.51}} = \boxed{0.627 \text{ s}}$

*13.11 $f = \dfrac{\omega}{2\pi} = \dfrac{1}{2\pi}\sqrt{\dfrac{k}{m}}$

$T = \dfrac{1}{f} = 2\pi\sqrt{\dfrac{m}{k}}$

Solving for k,

$k = \dfrac{4\pi^2 m}{T} = \dfrac{(4\pi)^2(7\text{ kg})}{(2.6\text{ s})^2} = \boxed{40.9\text{ N/m}}$

13.12 $m = 1$ kg, $k = 25$ N/m and $A = 3$ cm; At $t = 0, x = -3$ cm

(a) $\omega = \sqrt{\dfrac{k}{m}} = \sqrt{\dfrac{25}{1}} = 5$ rad/s so that

$T = \dfrac{2\pi}{\omega} = \dfrac{2\pi}{5} = \boxed{1.26\text{ s}}$

(b) $v_{max} = A\omega = (3\times 10^{-2}\text{ m})(5\text{ rad/s}) = \boxed{0.150\text{ m/s}}$

(c) $a_{max} = A\omega^2 = (3\times 10^{-2}\text{ m})(5\text{ rad/s})^2 = \boxed{0.750\text{ m/s}^2}$

Because $x = -3$ cm and $v = 0$ at $t = 0$, the required solution is

$x = -A\cos\omega t$, or $\boxed{x = -3.00\cos(5t)\text{ cm}}$ $\boxed{v = \dfrac{dx}{dt} = 15.0\sin(5t)\text{ cm/s}}$

$a = \dfrac{dv}{dt} = \boxed{75.0\cos(5t)\text{ cm/s}^2}$

13.13 (a) $T = \dfrac{12}{5} = \boxed{2.40\text{ s}}$

(b) $f = \dfrac{1}{T} = \dfrac{1}{2.40} = \boxed{0.417\text{ Hz}}$

(c) $\omega = 2\pi f = 2\pi(0.417) = \boxed{2.62\text{ rad/s}}$

13.14 $x = 0.25 \cos(2\pi t)$ m; so when $x = 0.10$ m, $t = 0.185$ s

(a) $v = \dfrac{dx}{dt} = -2\pi(0.25)\sin(2\pi t) = -1.57\sin(2\pi t)$ m/s;

At $t = 0.185$ s, $v = -1.57\sin(2\pi \times 0.185) = \boxed{-1.44 \text{ m/s}}$

$a = \dfrac{dv}{dt} = -4\pi^2(0.25)\cos(2\pi t) = -9.87\cos(2\pi t)$ m/s^2

At $t = 0.185$ s, $a = -9.87\cos(2\pi \times 0.185) = \boxed{-3.92 \text{ m/s}^2}$

(b) $v_{max} = A\omega = (0.25)(2\pi) = \boxed{1.57 \text{ m/s}}$

$a_{max} = A\omega^2 = (0.25)(2\pi)^2 = \boxed{9.87 \text{ m/s}^2}$

13.15 (a) $\omega = \sqrt{\dfrac{k}{m}} = \sqrt{\dfrac{8 \text{ N/m}}{0.5 \text{ kg}}} = 4 \text{ s}^{-1}$, therefore position is given by

$x = 10\sin(4t)$ cm. From this we find that

$v = 40\cos(4t)$ cm/s; $\qquad v_{max} = \boxed{40.0 \text{ cm/s}}$

$a = -160\sin(4t)$ cm/s^2; $\quad a_{max} = \boxed{160 \text{ cm/s}^2}$

(b) $t = (\tfrac{1}{4})\sin^{-1}(\tfrac{x}{10})$ and when $x = 6$ cm, $t = 0.161$ s and we find

$v = 40\cos[4(0.161)] = \boxed{32.0 \text{ cm/s}}$

$a = -160\sin[4(0.161)] = \boxed{-96.0 \text{ cm/s}^2}$

(c) Using $t = (\tfrac{1}{4})\sin^{-1}(\tfrac{x}{10})$; when $x = 0, t = 0$ and when $x = 8$ cm, $t = 0.23$ s.

Therefore $\Delta t = \boxed{0.232 \text{ s}}$

*13.16 $k = \dfrac{\Delta mg}{\Delta x} = \dfrac{(0.04 \text{ kg})(9.8 \text{ m/s}^2)}{(0.05 \text{ m})} = 7.84 \text{ N/m}$

(a) $\omega = \sqrt{\dfrac{k}{m}} = \sqrt{\dfrac{7.84}{0.14}} = 7.48 \text{ rad/s}$

$f = \dfrac{\omega}{2\pi} = \boxed{1.19 \text{ Hz}}$

(b) $\dfrac{T}{4} = \dfrac{1}{4f} = \boxed{0.21 \text{ s}}$

(c) $F_{max} = -kA = (7.84 \text{ N/m})(0.1 \text{ m}) = \boxed{0.784 \text{ N}} \text{ down}$

13.17 (a) $v_{\max} = \omega_0 A$

$A = \dfrac{v_{\max}}{\omega_0} = \dfrac{1.5 \text{ m/s}}{2.0 \text{ rad/s}} = \boxed{0.750 \text{ m}}$

(b) $x = \boxed{-(0.750 \text{ m})\sin 2.0t}$

13.18 $m = 100 \text{ g}, \quad T = 0.25 \text{ s}, \quad E = 2 \text{ J}; \quad \omega = \dfrac{2\pi}{T} = \dfrac{2\pi}{0.25} = 25.1 \text{ rad/s}$

(a) $k = m\omega^2 = (0.2 \text{ kg})(25.1 \text{ rad/s})^2 = \boxed{126 \text{ N/m}}$

(b) $E = \dfrac{kA^2}{2} \Rightarrow A = \sqrt{\dfrac{2E}{k}} = \sqrt{\dfrac{2(2)}{126}} = \boxed{0.178 \text{ m}}$

13.19 (a) $E = \dfrac{kA^2}{2} = \dfrac{(250 \text{ N/m})(0.035 \text{ m})^2}{2} = \boxed{0.153 \text{ J}}$

(b) $v_{\max} = A\omega$ where $\omega = \sqrt{\dfrac{k}{m}} = \sqrt{\dfrac{250}{0.5}} = 22.4 \text{ s}^{-1}$,

$v_{\max} = \boxed{0.784 \text{ m/s}}$

(c) $a_{\max} = A\omega^2 = (0.035 \text{ m})(22.4 \text{ s}^{-1})^2 = \boxed{17.5 \text{ m/s}^2}$

*13.20 $v_{max} = \omega A = 1.6 \text{ m/s}$

$E = \tfrac{1}{2}mv_{max}^2 = \tfrac{1}{2}(0.3 \text{ kg})(1.6 \text{ m/s})^2 = \boxed{0.384 \text{ J}}$

13.21 $A \Rightarrow 2A$

(a) $E = \dfrac{kA^2}{2}$, $\boxed{\text{so doubling } A \text{ *quadruples* } E}$

(b) $v_{\max} = A\omega$, $\boxed{\text{so doubling } A \text{ *doubles* } v_{\max}}$

(c) $a_{\max} = A\omega^2$, $\boxed{\text{so doubling } A \text{ *doubles* } a_{\max}}$

(d) $\boxed{\text{The period undergoes no change}}$ (because T depends only on k and m.)

*13.22 (a) $E = \dfrac{1}{2}kA^2 = \dfrac{1}{2}(35 \text{ N/m})(0.04 \text{ m})^2 = \boxed{0.028 \text{ J}}$

(b) $v = \omega\sqrt{A^2 - x^2} = \sqrt{\dfrac{k}{m}}\sqrt{A^2 - x^2}$

$ = \sqrt{\dfrac{35}{0.05}}\sqrt{(0.04)^2 - (0.01)^2} = \boxed{1.02 \text{ m/s}}$

(c) $\dfrac{1}{2}mv^2 = \dfrac{1}{2}kA^2 - \dfrac{1}{2}kx^2$

$\phantom{(c) \dfrac{1}{2}mv^2} = \dfrac{1}{2}(35)[(0.04)^2 - (0.01)^2] = \boxed{12.2 \text{ mJ}}$

(d) $\dfrac{1}{2}kx^2 = E - \dfrac{1}{2}mv^2 = \boxed{15.8 \text{ mJ}}$

13.23 From energy considerations, $v^2 + \omega^2 x^2 = \omega^2 A^2$

$v_{\max} = \omega A$ and $v = \dfrac{v_{\max}}{2} = \dfrac{\omega A}{2}$ so $\dfrac{1}{2}\omega^2 A^2 + \omega^2 x^2 = \omega^2 A^2$.

From this we find $x^2 = \dfrac{3A^2}{4}$ and

$x = \dfrac{A\sqrt{3}}{2} = \boxed{\pm 2.60 \text{ cm}}$ where $A = 3.0$ cm

*13.24   (a) $k = \dfrac{F}{x} = \dfrac{20 \text{ N}}{0.2 \text{ m}} = \boxed{100 \text{ N/m}}$

(b) $\omega = \sqrt{\dfrac{k}{m}} = \sqrt{50} \text{ rad/s} \quad f = \dfrac{\omega}{2\pi} = \boxed{1.13 \text{ Hz}}$

(c) $v_{max} = \omega A = \sqrt{50}(0.2) = \boxed{1.41 \text{ m/s}}$ at $x = 0$

(d) $a_{max} = \omega^2 A = 50(0.2) = \boxed{10 \text{ m/s}^2}$ at $x = \pm A$

(e) $E = \dfrac{1}{2}kA^2 = \dfrac{1}{2}(100)(0.2)^2 = \boxed{2 \text{ J}}$

(f) $v = \omega\sqrt{A^2 - x^2} = \sqrt{50}\sqrt{\dfrac{8}{9}(0.2)^2} = \boxed{1.33 \text{ m/s}}$

(g) $a = \omega^2 x = (50)\left(\dfrac{0.2}{3}\right) = \boxed{3.33 \text{ m/s}^2}$

13.25   (a) $T = 2\pi\sqrt{\dfrac{\ell}{g}}, \quad \ell = T^2 g = \dfrac{4\pi^2(25 \text{ s})^2(9.80 \text{ m/s}^2)}{4\pi^2} = \boxed{1.55 \text{ m}}$

(b) $T = 2\pi\sqrt{\dfrac{1.55}{1.67}} = \boxed{6.06 \text{ s}}$

13.26 $T = 2\pi\sqrt{\dfrac{L}{g}} = 2\pi\sqrt{\dfrac{10 \text{ m}}{9.80 \text{ m/s}^2}} = \boxed{6.35 \text{ s}}$

$f = \dfrac{1}{T} = \dfrac{1}{6.35 \text{ s}} = \boxed{0.158 \text{ Hz}}$

*13.27 $\omega = \sqrt{\dfrac{g}{L}} = \dfrac{2\pi}{T}$

Solving for L,

$L = \dfrac{gT^2}{4\pi^2} = \dfrac{(9.8)(9.4)^2}{4\pi^2} = \boxed{21.9 \text{ m}}$

*13.28 (a) $T = 1.996$ s, 1.732 s, 1.422 s

(b) $T = 2\pi\sqrt{\dfrac{g}{L}}$

$$g_{exp} = \frac{LT^2}{4\pi^2} \simeq 9.85 \text{ m/s}^2$$

(c) % error $\simeq 0.51\%$

13.29 $\theta_0 = 15° = \dfrac{\pi}{12}$ rads

$$-mg\sin\theta = m\ell\frac{d^2\theta}{dt^2}$$

$$-\frac{g}{\ell}\theta = \frac{d^2\theta}{dt^2}$$

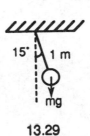

13.29

$$\theta = \theta_0\cos\omega t, \quad \omega = \sqrt{\frac{g}{\ell}}.$$

$$v = \ell\frac{d\theta}{dt} = -\ell\theta_0\omega\sin\omega t$$

(a) $v_{max} = 1(\dfrac{\pi}{12})\sqrt{\dfrac{g}{\ell}} = \boxed{0.820 \text{ m/s}}$

(b) $\dfrac{d^2\theta}{dt^2} = \dfrac{g}{\ell}\theta_0 = (\dfrac{9.8}{1})(\dfrac{\pi}{12}) = \boxed{2.56 \text{ rad/s}^2}$

(c) $F_{max} = mg\theta = (0.25)(9.8)(\dfrac{\pi}{12}) = \boxed{0.641 \text{ N}}$

13.30 For a simple pendulum. $T_0 = 2\pi\sqrt{\dfrac{L}{g}} = 2\pi\sqrt{\dfrac{1}{9.80}} = 2.01$ s

$$T = 2\pi\sqrt{\frac{I}{mgd}}; \quad \text{In this case, } I = \frac{ML^2}{3} \text{ and } d = \frac{L}{2};$$

so $T^2 = 4\pi^2(\dfrac{2L}{3g}) \Rightarrow L = \dfrac{3gT^2}{8\pi^2} = \dfrac{3(9.80)(2.01)^2}{8\pi^2} = \boxed{1.50 \text{ m}}$

13.31 $T = 2\pi\sqrt{\dfrac{\ell}{g}};$ $\Delta T = 2\pi\sqrt{\ell}(\dfrac{1}{\sqrt{g_2}} - \dfrac{1}{\sqrt{g_1}}) = 2\pi\sqrt{3}(\dfrac{1}{\sqrt{9.79}} - \dfrac{1}{\sqrt{9.80}}) = \boxed{1.78 \times 10^{-3} \text{ s}}$

13.32 For the simple pendulum, $T_1 = 2\pi\sqrt{\dfrac{\ell}{g}}$

For the physical pendulum, $T_2 = 2\pi\sqrt{\dfrac{I}{mgd}}$.

A ring with axis on its rim has $I = 2mR^2$ and $d = R$ so that

$$T_2 = 2\pi\sqrt{\frac{2R}{g}} \qquad \text{When } T_1 = T_2, \quad \boxed{\ell = 2R}$$

*13.33 $f = 0.45$ Hz, $d = 0.35\,m$ and $m = 2.2$ kg

$$T = \frac{1}{f}; \quad T = 2\pi\sqrt{\frac{I}{mgd}}; \quad T^2 = 4\pi^2\left(\frac{I}{mgd}\right)$$

$$I = T^2\frac{mgd}{4\pi^2} = \left(\frac{1}{f}\right)^2\frac{mgd}{4\pi^2} = \frac{(2.2)(9.80)(0.35)}{(0.45\ \text{s}^{-1})^2(4\pi^2)}$$

$$I = \boxed{0.944\ \text{kg·m}^2}$$

*13.34 $\omega = \dfrac{2\pi}{T}$, $T = \dfrac{2\pi}{\omega} = \dfrac{2\pi}{4.43} = \boxed{1.42\ \text{s}}$

$$\omega = \sqrt{\frac{g}{L}}, \quad L = \frac{g}{\omega^2} = \frac{9.8}{(4.43)^2} = \boxed{0.5\ \text{m}}$$

13.35 $T = 0.25$ s; $I = mr^2 = (0.02)(0.005)^2$

    (a) $I = \boxed{5.00 \times 10^{-7}\ \text{kg·m}^2}$

    (b) $I\dfrac{d^2\theta}{dt^2} = -\kappa\theta; \qquad \sqrt{\dfrac{\kappa}{I}} = \omega = \dfrac{2\pi}{T}$

13.35

$$\kappa = I\omega^2 = (5 \times 10^{-7})\left(\frac{2\pi}{0.25}\right)^2 = \boxed{3.16 \times 10^{-4}\ \frac{\text{N·m}}{\text{rad}}}$$

13.36 Since bv has units of force and $[v] = \dfrac{L}{T}$, then

$$[bv] = [\text{Force}] = \frac{ML}{T^2}$$

$$[b] = \frac{ML/T^2}{L/T} = \frac{M}{T}$$

13.37 Show that $x = Ae^{-bt/2\,m}\cos(\omega t + \delta)$ is a solution of $-kx - b\dfrac{dx}{dt} = m\dfrac{d^2x}{dt^2}$ (1)

and $\omega = \sqrt{\dfrac{k}{m} - (\dfrac{b}{2m})^2}$ (2)

$$x = Ae^{-bt/2m}\cos(\omega t + \delta) \tag{3}$$

$$\frac{dx}{dt} = Ae^{-bt/2m}(-\frac{b}{2m})\cos(\omega t + \delta) - Ae^{-bt/2m}\omega(\sin(\omega t + \delta)) \tag{4}$$

$$\frac{d^2x}{dt^2} = -\frac{b}{2m}\{Ae^{-bt/2m}(-\frac{b}{2m})\cos(\omega t + \delta) - Ae^{-bt/2m}\omega\sin(\omega t + \delta)\}$$

$$+\{Ae^{-bt/2m}(-\frac{b}{2m})\omega\sin(\omega t + \delta) + Ae^{-bt/2m}\omega^2\cos(\omega t + \delta)\} \tag{5}$$

Substitute (3), (4) into the left side of (1) and (5) into the right side of (1);

$$-kAe^{-bt/2m}\cos(\omega t + \delta) + \frac{b^2}{2\,m}Ae^{-bt/2m}\cos(\omega t + \delta) + b\omega Ae^{-bt/2m}\sin(\omega t + \delta) =$$

$$-\frac{b}{2}\{Ae^{-bt/2m}(-\frac{b}{2m})\cos(\omega t + \delta) - Ae^{-bt/2m}\omega\sin(\omega t\delta)\} + \frac{b}{2}Ae^{-bt/2m}\omega\sin(\omega t + \delta)$$

$$-m\omega^2 Ae^{-bt/2m}\cos(\omega t + \delta)$$

Substitute for (3) and compare the coefficients of $Ae^{-bt/2m}\cos(\omega t + \delta)$ and

$Ae^{-bt/2m}\sin(\omega t + \delta))$:

cos-term: $-k + \dfrac{b^2}{2m} = -\dfrac{b}{2}(-\dfrac{b}{2m}) - m\omega^2 = +\dfrac{b^2}{4m} + (m)(\dfrac{k}{m} - \dfrac{b^2}{4m^2}) = -k + \dfrac{b^2}{4m}$

sin-term: $b\omega = +\dfrac{b}{2}(\omega) + \dfrac{b}{2}\omega = b\omega$

Since the coefficients are equal, $x = Ae^{-bt/2m}\cos(\omega t + \delta)$ is a solution of the equation

13.38 $E = \frac{1}{2}mv^2 + \frac{1}{2}kx^2$

$\frac{dE}{dt} = mv\frac{d^2x}{dt^2} + kxv$

Use Eq. 13.30 $\quad m\frac{d^2x}{dt^2} = -kx - bv$

$\frac{dE}{dt} = v(kx - bv) + kvx$

$\frac{dE}{dt} = -bv^2 < 0$

13.39 $\theta_0 = 15°$ $\qquad \theta(t = 1000) = 5.5°$

$x = Ae^{-bt/2m}$

$\frac{x_{1000}}{x_0} = \frac{Ae^{-bt/2m}}{A} = \frac{5.5}{15} = e^{-b(1000)/2m} \cong e^{-1}$

$\therefore \frac{b}{2m} = \boxed{1.00 \times 10^{-3} \text{ s}^{-1}}$

13.40 $F = 3\cos(2\pi t)$ N and $k = 20$ N/m.

(a) $\omega = \frac{2\pi}{T} = 2\pi$ rad/s so $T = \boxed{1.00 \text{ s}}$

(b) In this case, $\omega_0 = \sqrt{\frac{k}{m}} = \sqrt{\frac{20}{2}} = 3.16$ rad/s.

Taking $b = 0$ in Eq. 13.35 gives

$A = (\frac{F_0}{m})(\omega^2 - \omega_0^2)^{-1} = \frac{3}{2}[4\pi^2 - (3.16)^2]^{-1}$

$= 0.0509 \text{ m} = \boxed{5.09 \text{ cm}}$

13.41 (a) $f = \frac{1}{2\pi}\sqrt{\frac{k}{m}} = \frac{1}{2\pi}\sqrt{\frac{240}{3}} = \boxed{1.42 \text{ Hz}}$

(b) $f = \frac{1}{2\pi}\sqrt{\frac{g}{\ell}} = \frac{1}{2\pi}\sqrt{\frac{9.80 \text{ m/s}^2}{1.5 \text{ m}}} = \boxed{0.407 \text{ Hz}}$

13.42 $\quad F_0\cos(\omega t) - kx = m\dfrac{d^2x}{dt^2} \quad \omega_0 = \sqrt{\dfrac{k}{m}}$ $\hfill (1)$

$x = A\cos(\omega t + \delta)$ $\hfill (2)$

$\dfrac{dx}{dt} = -A\omega\sin(\omega t + \delta)$ $\hfill (3)$

$\dfrac{d^2x}{dt^2} = -A\omega^2\cos(\omega t + \delta)$ $\hfill (4)$

Substitute (2) and (4) into (1):

$F_0\cos(\omega t) - kA\cos(\omega t + \delta) = m(-A\omega^2)\cos(\omega t + \delta)$

Solve for the amplitude: $\quad (kA - mA\omega^2)\cos(\omega t + \delta) = F_0\cos\omega t$

For these to be equal, δ must be zero and $(kA - mA\omega^2) = F_0$

Thus: $A = \dfrac{F_0/m}{\frac{k}{m} - \omega^2}$

13.43 From Eq. 13.35

$A = \dfrac{F_0/M}{\sqrt{(\omega^2 - \omega_0^2)^2}}$

$\omega = 2\pi f = (20\pi\ \text{s}^{-1}) \qquad \omega_0^2 = \dfrac{k}{m} = \dfrac{200}{(40/9.8)} = 49\ \text{s}^{-2}$

$F_0 = mA(\omega^2 - \omega_0^2)$

$F_0 = (\dfrac{40}{9.8})(0.02)(4000 - 49) = \boxed{322\ \text{N}}$

13.44 Assume that each spring supports an equal portion of the car's mass, i.e. $\dfrac{m}{4}$.

Then $T = 2\pi\sqrt{\dfrac{m}{4k}}$ and $k = \dfrac{4\pi^2 m}{4T^2} = \dfrac{1500}{(4)(1.5)^2} = \boxed{6580\ \text{N/m}}$

13.45 $\dfrac{T_1}{T_0} = \dfrac{2\pi/\omega_1}{2\pi/\omega_0} = \dfrac{2\pi/\sqrt{k/m_1}}{2\pi/\sqrt{k/m_0}}$

$\dfrac{T_1}{T_0} = \sqrt{\dfrac{m_1}{m_0}} = \sqrt{1.1}$

$T_1 = \sqrt{1.1} \times 1.55 = \boxed{1.57 \text{ s}}$

13.46 If $a_{\text{max}} > g$, the block will separate from the plate.

$a_{\text{max}} = g = A\omega_0^2 \qquad A = \dfrac{g}{\omega_0^2} = \dfrac{gT^2}{4\pi^2} = \boxed{0.357 \text{ m}}$

13.47 (a) $E = \dfrac{1}{2}I\omega^2 + mgh$ where $I = mL^2$ and $\omega = \dfrac{v}{L}$.

When the pendulum makes an angle θ with the vertical,
the mass is a distance above the lowest point,

$h = L(1 - \cos\theta)$.

$\boxed{E = \dfrac{1}{2}mv^2 + mgL(1 - \cos\theta)}$

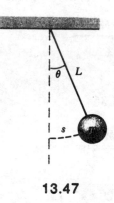

(b) $U = mgL(1 - \cos\theta)$ and for small angles

$U \cong mgL[1 - (1 - \dfrac{\theta^2}{2})] = \dfrac{1}{2}mgL\theta^2$.

Also, since $\theta L = s$ and $\omega^2 = \dfrac{g}{\ell}$, we have

$\boxed{U = \dfrac{m\omega^2 s^2}{2}}$

13.47

13.48 Refer to the free body diagram. At some instant of time we have (for the platform).

$\Sigma F_x = -kx + f_s = ma$

If the block doesn't slide, its acceleration is the same as the platform and

$f_s = \mu mg = ma$ where a is the maximum acceleration $A\omega^2$.

Therefore $\mu = \dfrac{A\omega^2}{g} = \dfrac{A(4\pi^2)}{gT^2} = \dfrac{(0.3 \text{ m})(4\pi^2)}{(9.80 \text{ m/s}^2)(2 \text{ s})^2} = \boxed{0.302}$

13.49 Referring to the sketch we have $F = -mg \sin \theta$ and

$\tan \theta = \dfrac{x}{R}$. For small displacements, $\tan \theta \approx \sin \theta$ and

$$F = -\frac{mg}{R}x = -kx \text{ and } \boxed{\omega = \sqrt{\frac{k}{m}} = \sqrt{\frac{g}{R}}}$$

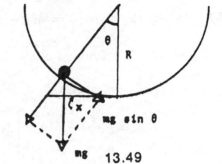

13.49

13.50 Energy is conserved and is given as

$$E = \frac{1}{2}kx^2 + mgx + \frac{1}{2}I\omega^2 \text{ where } I = \frac{1}{3}mL^2.$$

If we add the term $\dfrac{(mg)^2}{k}$ to each side of the

above equation and using $v = \omega L$ we get

$$E + \frac{(mg)^2}{2k} = \frac{1}{2}k(x + \frac{mg}{k})^2 + \frac{1}{2}\frac{m}{3}v^2$$

By defining $E_{\text{eff}} = E + \dfrac{mg}{2k}$ and

$x_{\text{eff}} = x + \dfrac{mg}{k}$ and $m_{\text{eff}} = \dfrac{m}{3}$, we have

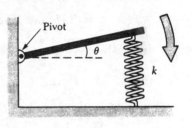

13.50

$E_{\text{eff}} = \dfrac{1}{2}k(x_{\text{eff}})^2 + \dfrac{1}{2}(m_{\text{eff}})v^2$ so the motion is

simple harmonic with $\omega = \sqrt{\dfrac{k}{m_{\text{eff}}}} = \sqrt{\dfrac{3k}{m}}$.

13.51 (a) At the pivot, $T = Mg + Mg = \boxed{2Mg}$

At P, a fraction of the rod's mass $\dfrac{y}{L}$

pulls down as well as does the ball. Here

$$T = Mg\left(\frac{y}{L}\right) + Mg = \boxed{Mg\left(1 + \frac{y}{L}\right)}$$

(b) Relative to the pivot, $I = \dfrac{1}{3}ML^2 + ML^2$.

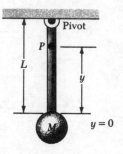

13.51

For a physical pendulum,

$$T = 2\pi\sqrt{\frac{I}{mgd}}$$

where $m = 2M$ and d is the distance

from the pivot to the center of

mass. Therefore,

$$d = \frac{ML/2 + ML}{M + M} = \frac{3L}{4} \text{ and}$$

we have $T = \dfrac{4\pi}{3}\sqrt{\dfrac{2L}{g}}$

For $L = 2$, $T = \dfrac{4\pi}{3}\sqrt{\dfrac{2(2\text{ m})}{9.80\text{ m/s}^2}} = \boxed{2.68\text{ s}}$

13.52 (a) For each segment of the spring $dK = \dfrac{1}{2}dm\ v_x^2$. Also,

$v_x = \dfrac{x}{\ell}v$ and $dm = \dfrac{m}{\ell}dx$.

Therefore the total kinetic energy is

$$K = \frac{1}{2}Mv^2 + \frac{1}{2}\int_0^\ell \left(\frac{x^2v^2}{\ell^2}\right)\frac{m}{\ell}dx = \boxed{\frac{1}{2}\left(M + \frac{m}{3}\right)v^2}$$

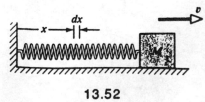

13.52

(b) $\omega = \dfrac{k}{m_{\text{eff}}}$ and $\dfrac{1}{2}m_{\text{eff}}v^2 = \dfrac{1}{2}\left(M + \dfrac{m}{3}\right)v^2$.

Therefore $T = \dfrac{2\pi}{\omega} = 2\pi\sqrt{\dfrac{M + m/3}{k}}$

13.53 (a) $\Delta K + \Delta U = 0$, thus $K_{\text{top}} + U_{\text{top}} = K_{\text{bot}} + U_{\text{bot}}$, where

$K_{\text{top}} = U_{\text{bot}} = 0.$ Therefore $mgh = \frac{1}{2}I\omega^2$, but

$h = R - R\cos\theta = R(1 - \cos\theta),$

$\omega = \dfrac{v}{R}$ and $I = \dfrac{MR^2}{2} + \dfrac{mr^2}{2} + mR^2$. Substituting we find

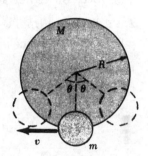

$mgR(1 - \cos\theta) = \dfrac{1}{2}(\dfrac{MR^2}{2} + \dfrac{mr^2}{2} + mR^2)\dfrac{v^2}{R^2}$

$mgR(1 - \cos\theta) = [\dfrac{M}{4} + \dfrac{mr^2}{4R^2} + \dfrac{m}{2}]v^2$

and $v^2 = 4gR\dfrac{(1 - \cos\theta)}{(M/m + r^2/R^2 + 2)}$

13.53

so $v = \sqrt{\dfrac{2Rg(1 - \cos\theta)}{M/m + r^2/R^2 + 2}}$

(b) $T = 2\pi\sqrt{\dfrac{I}{m_T g d_{\text{cm}}}};$ $m_T = m + M;$ $d_{\text{cm}} = \dfrac{mR + M(0)}{m + M}$

$$\boxed{T = 2\pi\sqrt{\dfrac{\frac{1}{2}MR^2 + \frac{1}{2}mr^2 + mR^2}{mgR}}}$$

13.54 (a) When the mass is displaced a distance x from equilibrium spring 1 is stretched a distance x_1 and spring 2 is stretched a distance x_2. By Newton's third law, we expect $k_1 x_1 = k_2 x_2$. When this is combined with the requirement that $x = x_1 + x_2$ we find $x_1 = [k_2/(k_1 + k_2)]x$. The force on either spring is given by $F_1 = k_1 x_1 = [k_1 k_2/(k_1 + k_2)]x = ma$ where a is the acceleration of the mass m. This is in the form $F = k_{\text{eff}} x = ma$ and from Eq. 13.16 we find $T = 2\pi \sqrt{\dfrac{m}{k_{\text{eff}}}}$;

$$T = 2\pi \sqrt{\frac{m(k_1 + k_2)}{k_1 k_2}}$$

(a)

(b)

13.54

(b) In this case each spring is stretched by the distance x which the mass is displaced. Therefore the restoring force is $F = -(k_1 + k_2)x$, and $k_{\text{eff}} = (k_1 + k_2)$ so that $T = 2\pi \sqrt{\dfrac{m}{(k_1 + k_2)}}$.

13.55 For the pendulum (see sketch) we have $\tau = I \dfrac{d^2\theta}{dt^2}$ and $\dfrac{d^2\theta}{dt^2} = -\alpha$;

$r = mgL\sin\theta + kxh\cos\theta = -I\alpha$.

For small amplitude vibrations, use the approximations:

$\sin\theta \approx \theta, \cos\theta \approx 1$,

and $x \approx s = h\theta$. Therefore

$$\frac{d^2\theta}{dt^2} = -\left(\frac{mgL + kh^2}{I}\right)\theta = -\omega^2\theta$$

$$\omega = \sqrt{\frac{mgL + kh^2}{mL^2}}$$

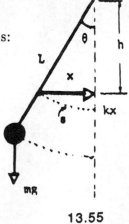

13.55

*13.56 $\omega_0 = \sqrt{\dfrac{k}{m}} = \dfrac{2\pi}{T}$

(a) $k = \dfrac{4\pi^2 m}{T^2} = \boxed{38.6 \text{ N/m}}$

(b) $m = \dfrac{kT^2}{4\pi^2} = \boxed{1.32 \text{ kg}}$

13.57 $\dfrac{d^2 x}{dt} = A\omega^2$ $f_{\max} = \mu_s N = \mu_s mg = mA\omega^2$

$A = \dfrac{\mu_s g}{\omega^2} = \boxed{6.62 \text{ cm}}$

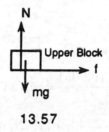

13.57

*13.58 $\Sigma T_{CG} = I_{cm}\alpha$ For θ small,

$-MgR\theta = \dfrac{1}{2}ML^2\dfrac{d^2\theta}{dt^2}$

$-\left(\dfrac{12gR}{L^2}\right)\theta = \dfrac{d^2\theta}{dt^2}$

For harmonic motion,

$-\omega^2\theta = \dfrac{d^2\theta}{dt^2}$ $\therefore\ \omega = \sqrt{\dfrac{12gR}{L^2}} = \dfrac{2\pi}{T}$

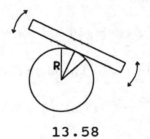

13.58

Then $T = \dfrac{2\pi}{\omega} = 2\pi\sqrt{\dfrac{L^2}{12gR}} = \dfrac{\pi L}{\sqrt{3gR}}$

*13.59 (a) $T = \dfrac{2\pi}{\omega} = 2\pi\sqrt{\dfrac{L}{g}} = \boxed{3.00 \text{ s}}$

(b) $E = \dfrac{1}{2}mv^2 = \dfrac{1}{2}(6.74)(2.06)^2 = \boxed{14.3 \text{ J}}$

(c) At maximum angular displacement,

$mgh = \dfrac{1}{2}mv^2$

$h = L - L\sin\theta = L(1 - \sin\theta)$

$h = \dfrac{v^2}{2g} = 0.217 \text{ m}$

$\sin\theta = 1 - \dfrac{h}{L}$

$\boxed{\theta \simeq 25.5°}$

13.60   (a) For these initial conditions, the solution can be written as

$x = A\cos\omega t$. With $A = 16$ cm, and $T = 4$ s, this becomes

$x = 16\cos\dfrac{2\pi t}{4} = 16\cos\dfrac{\pi t}{2}$. Therefore, at $t = 0.5$ s,

$x = (16\text{ cm})\cos[\dfrac{\pi(0.50)}{2}] = \boxed{11.3\text{ cm}}$

(b) $\omega = \sqrt{\dfrac{k}{m}} = \dfrac{2\pi}{T}$. Therefore

$k = \dfrac{4\pi^2(0.005)}{4} = 0.123$ N/m. The force is then $F = -kx$ and

$F_{(t=0.5)} = -(0.123\text{ N/m})(0.113\text{ m}) = \boxed{-0.014\text{ N}}$ The minus sign indicates that the spring exerts a force on the mass directed toward the equilibrium position.

(c) If $x = 8$ cm $= (16\text{ cm})\cos\dfrac{\pi t}{2}$, then $t = \dfrac{2}{\pi}\cos^{-1}\dfrac{1}{2} = 0.667$ s and for

$x = 16, t = 0$. Therefore $\Delta t = \boxed{0.667\text{ s}}$

(d) $v = \dfrac{dx}{dt} = -8\pi\sin(\dfrac{\pi t}{2})$.   When $x = 8$ cm, $t = 0.667$ s, and

$v = (-8\pi\text{ cm/s})\sin[\dfrac{\pi}{2}(0.667)] = \boxed{\pm\,21.8\text{ cm/s}}$

(e) The total energy of the spring is conserved. Therefore, at any time

$E = \dfrac{1}{2}kA^2 = \dfrac{1}{2}(0.123\text{ N/m})(0.16\text{ m})^2 = \boxed{1.58\times10^{-3}\text{ J}}; \boxed{k = 0.123\text{ N/m}}$

13.61 $M_{D_2} = 2M_{H_2}$

$$\frac{\omega_D}{\omega_H} = \frac{\sqrt{k/M_D}}{\sqrt{k/M_H}} = \sqrt{\frac{M_H}{M_D}} = \sqrt{\frac{1}{2}}$$

$$f_{D_2} = \frac{f_{H_2}}{\sqrt{2}} = \boxed{0.919 \times 10^{14} \text{ Hz}}$$

13.62 $\tau = k\theta \qquad U = \int_0^\theta \tau d\theta = \int_0^\theta \kappa \theta d\theta = \frac{1}{2}\kappa\theta^2$

13.63 (a) $\omega_0 = \sqrt{\dfrac{k}{m}} = \boxed{15.8 \text{ rad/s}}$

(b) $F_s - mg = ma = m(\dfrac{1}{3}g)$

$$F_s = \frac{4}{3}mg = 26.1 \text{ N}$$

$$x_s = \frac{F_s}{k} = \boxed{5.23 \text{ cm}}$$

(c) When the acceleration of the car is zero, the new equilibrium position can be found as follows: $F'_s = mg = 19.6$ N $\qquad x'_s = \dfrac{F'_s}{k} = 3.92$ cm

Thus, $| x_0 | = | x'_s - x_s | = \boxed{1.31 \text{ cm}}$

The phase is $\boxed{\pi \text{ rad}}$

*13.64 At the lowest point, $K = \frac{1}{2}Mv^2 + \frac{1}{2}I\Omega^2$ where Ω is the rotation rate of the sphere. At the highest point of oscillation, the CM of the ball is a height h higher than at the center of the trough. There, all the energy is potential energy,

$$U = Mgh = Mg(4R)(1 - \cos\theta),$$

For small angles, $(1 - \cos\theta) \cong \dfrac{\theta^2}{2}$.   (Appendix B)

$$\therefore \quad U = 2MgR\theta^2$$

also, $v = 4R\dfrac{d\theta}{dt}$ and $\Omega_{ball} = \dfrac{1}{R}\dfrac{ds}{dt} = \dfrac{(5R)d\theta}{Rdt}$

$$\therefore \quad K = \frac{1}{2}M\left(4R\frac{d\theta}{dt}\right)^2 + \frac{1}{2}\left(\frac{2}{5}MR^2\right)\left(5\frac{d\theta}{dt}\right)^2$$

$$K = 8MR^2\left(\frac{d\theta}{dt}\right)^2 + 5MR^2\left(\frac{d\theta}{dt}\right)^2 = 13MR^2\left(\frac{d\theta}{dt}\right)^2 \qquad \textbf{13.64}$$

And, of course, energy is conserved...

$$E = K + U = 13MR^2\left(\frac{d\theta}{dt}\right)^2 + MgR\theta^2$$

Since, $E =$ constant in time, $\dfrac{dE}{dt} = 0 = 13MR^2\, 2\dfrac{d\theta}{dt}\dfrac{d^2\theta}{dt^2} + 2MgR\, 2\theta\dfrac{d\theta}{dt}$

Cancel M, R, $\dfrac{d\theta}{dt}$

$$13R\frac{d^2\theta}{dt^2} = -2g\theta \quad \text{or} \quad \ddot{\theta} = -\frac{2\,g}{13R}\theta$$

The classic form of SHM with $\omega = \sqrt{\dfrac{2\,g}{13R}}$

$$\ddot{\theta} = \omega^2\theta$$

$$\omega = \sqrt{\frac{2\,g}{13R}} \quad \text{and} \quad T = \frac{2\pi}{\omega} = 2\pi\sqrt{\frac{13R}{2g}}$$

13.65   (a) $\Sigma F = -2T\sin\theta \boldsymbol{j}$ where $\theta = \tan^{-1}\dfrac{y}{L}$. Therefore, for a small displacement

$$\sin\theta \approx \tan\theta = \frac{y}{L} \quad \text{and} \quad \boxed{F = \frac{-2Ty}{L}\boldsymbol{j}}$$

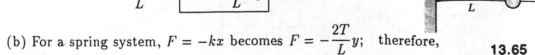

13.65

(b) For a spring system, $F = -kx$ becomes $F = -\dfrac{2T}{L}y$;   therefore,

$$\boxed{\omega = \sqrt{\frac{k}{m}} = \sqrt{\frac{2T}{mL}}}$$

13.66 (a)

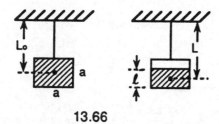

13.66

(b) $T = 2\pi\sqrt{\dfrac{L}{g}}$ $\dfrac{dT}{dt} = \dfrac{\pi}{\sqrt{g}}\dfrac{1}{\sqrt{L}}\dfrac{dL}{dt}$ (1)

We need to find $L(t)$ and $\dfrac{dL}{dt}$. From the diagram in (a),

$$L = L_0 + \frac{a}{2} - \frac{\ell}{2}; \quad \frac{dL}{dt} = -\left(\frac{1}{2}\right)\frac{d\ell}{dt}$$

But $\dfrac{dM}{dt} = \rho\dfrac{dV}{dt} = -\rho A\dfrac{d\ell}{dt}$. Therefore

$$\frac{d\ell}{dt} = -\frac{1}{\rho A}\frac{dM}{dt}; \quad \frac{dL}{dt} = \left(\frac{1}{2\rho A}\right)\frac{dM}{dt} \tag{2}$$

Also, $\displaystyle\int_{L_0}^{L} dL = \left(\frac{1}{2\rho A}\right)\frac{dM}{dt}\int_{0}^{t} dt$

$$L = L_0 + \left(\frac{1}{2\rho A}\right)\left(\frac{dM}{dt}\right)t \tag{3}$$

Substituting Eq. (2) and Eq. (3) into Eq. (1):

$$\boxed{\frac{dT}{dt} = \frac{\pi}{\sqrt{g}}\left(\frac{1}{2\rho a^2}\right)\left(\frac{dM}{dt}\right)\frac{1}{\sqrt{L_0 + \frac{1}{2\rho a^2}\left(\frac{dM}{dt}\right)t}}}$$

(c) Substitute Eq. 3 into the eq. for the period

$$\boxed{T = \frac{2\pi}{\sqrt{g}}\sqrt{L_0 + \frac{1}{2\rho a^2}\left(\frac{dM}{dt}\right)t}} \quad \text{Or one can obtain } T \text{ by integrating (b):}$$

$$\int_{T}^{T_0} dT = \frac{\pi}{\sqrt{g}}\left(\frac{1}{2\rho a^2}\right)\frac{dM}{dt}\int_{0}^{t}\frac{dt}{\sqrt{L_0 + \frac{1}{2\rho a^2}\left(\frac{dM}{dt}\right)t}}$$

$$T - T_0 = \frac{\pi}{\sqrt{g}}\left(\frac{1}{2\rho a^2}\right)\left(\frac{dM}{dt}\right)\left[\frac{2}{\frac{1}{2\rho a^2}\left(\frac{dM}{dt}\right)}\right]\left[\sqrt{L_0 + \frac{1}{2\rho a^2}\left(\frac{dM}{dt}\right)t} - \sqrt{L_0}\right]$$

But $T_0 = 2\pi\sqrt{\dfrac{L_0}{g}}$, so

$$T = \frac{2\pi}{\sqrt{g}}\sqrt{L_0 + \frac{1}{2\rho a^2}\left(\frac{dM}{dt}\right)t}$$

*13.67   (a) Assuming a Hooke's Law type spring,

$$F = Mg = kx,$$

and from the slope of the data, $\boxed{k \cong 1.73 \text{ N/m}}$

(b) Utilizing the measured times of oscillation, $k = \left(\dfrac{2\pi}{T}\right)^2 (M + m/3)$ and from the slope of the data, $\boxed{k \cong 1.77 \text{ N/m}}$

(c) Utilizing the axis-crossing point,

$m_s \cong \boxed{0.0041 \text{ kg}} \cong 4.1$ grams

CHAPTER 14

14.1 $\quad F = \dfrac{Gm_1 m_2}{r^2} = \dfrac{(6.672 \times 10^{-11})(2)(2)}{(0.30)^2} = \boxed{2.97 \times 10^{-9} \text{ N}}$

14.2 (a) At the midpoint between the two masses, the forces exerted by the

200 kg and 500 kg masses are oppositely directed and from

$F = \dfrac{Gm_1 m_2}{d^2}$ we have

$\Sigma F = \dfrac{G(50 \text{ kg})(500 \text{ kg} - 200 \text{ kg})}{(0.2 \text{ m})^2}$

$\Sigma F = \boxed{2.5 \times 10^{-5} \text{ N}}$ directed toward the 500 kg mass.

(b) At a point between the two masses at a distance r

from the 500 kg mass, the net force will be zero when

$\dfrac{G(50)(200)}{(0.4 - r)^2} = \dfrac{G(500)(50)}{r^2}$

or $r = \boxed{0.245 \text{ m}}$

14.3 The magnitude of either force is given by

$F = (6.672 \times 10^{-11})\dfrac{(5)(5)}{(0.25)^2} = 2.67 \times 10^{-8} \text{ N}$

$\Sigma F_x = (2.67 \times 10^{-8}) + (2.67 \times 10^{-8})\cos(60°) = \boxed{4.01 \times 10^{-8} \text{ N}}$

$\Sigma F_y = (2.67 \times 10^{-8})\sin(60°) = \boxed{2.31 \times 10^{-8} \text{ N}}$

$R = (\Sigma F_x^2 + \Sigma F_y^2)^{1/2} = \boxed{4.62 \times 10^{-8} \text{ N}}$

$\theta = \tan^{-1}(\Sigma F_x / \Sigma F_y)^{1/2} = \boxed{30°}$ from the side of the triangle or the force

is directed along the bisector toward the other masses.

14.4 Let the distance from M to the point where A third mass will

experience no force be x. Then

$$\Sigma F = \frac{GM(4M)}{(d-x)^2} - \frac{GM(M)}{x^2} = 0 \text{ or}$$

$$\frac{4}{(d-x)^2} = \frac{1}{x^2} \text{ and } 3x^2 + 2dx - d^2 = 0$$

This can be factored to yield $(3x - d)(x + d) = 0$.

Therefore $x = d/3$ or $x = -d$. Only the positive answer is acceptable,

so $x = \boxed{\dfrac{d}{3}}$

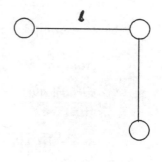

*14.5 $g = \dfrac{Gm}{l^2} \uparrow + \dfrac{Gm}{l^2} \rightarrow + \dfrac{Gm}{2l^2} \nearrow$

$\qquad = \dfrac{2Gm}{l^2}\cos 45 + \dfrac{Gm}{2l^2} \nearrow$

$\quad g = \boxed{\dfrac{Gm}{l^2}\left(\dfrac{2\sqrt{2}+1}{2}\right)}$ toward the opposite corner

14.5

*14.6 $a = \dfrac{MG}{(4R_E)^2} = \dfrac{9.8 \text{ m/s}^2}{16} = \boxed{0.613 \text{ m/s}^2}$ toward the earth

*14.7 The astronaut's weight on the moon is

$$W = mg_{moon} = 140 \text{ N} \qquad g_{moon} = \frac{GM_{moon}}{R_{moon}^2}$$

At a height R_{moon} above the surface,

$$g\prime = \frac{GM_{moon}}{(2R_{moon})^2} = \frac{g_{moon}}{4}$$

Therefore, the orbiting astronaut's weight is $\dfrac{W}{4} = \boxed{35 \text{ N}}$

14.8 $m_1 + m_2 = 5.0 \text{ kg}, \quad m_2 = 5.0 \text{ kg} - m_1$

$$F = G\frac{m_1 m_2}{r^2}$$

$$1 \times 10^{-8} \text{ N} = 6.67 \times 10^{-11} \frac{\text{N} \cdot \text{m}^2}{\text{kg}^2} = \frac{m_1(5.0 - m_1)}{(0.20 \text{ m})^2}$$

$$5.0 \, m_1 - m_1^2 = \frac{1 \times 10^{-8}}{6.67 \times 10^{-11}}(0.04)$$

$$m_1^2 - 5m_1 + 6 = 0$$

$$(m_1 - 3)(m_1 - 2) = 0$$

$$m_1 = 3 \text{ kg or 2 kg} \quad \text{and} \quad m_2 = 2 \text{ kg or 3 kg}$$

*14.9 $\quad g_{\text{Mars}} = \dfrac{GM_{\text{Mars}}}{(R_{\text{Mars}})^2} = \dfrac{G(0.108 \, M_E)}{(0.6R_E)^2}$

$$g_{\text{Mars}} = \frac{GM_E}{R_E}\left(\frac{0.108}{0.36}\right) = 0.3g = \boxed{2.94 \text{ m/s}^2}$$

*14.10 $g = \dfrac{GM}{R^2} = \dfrac{G\rho\frac{4}{3}\pi R^3}{R^2} = \dfrac{4}{3}\pi G\rho R$

If $\dfrac{g_m}{g_E} = \dfrac{1}{6} = \dfrac{\frac{4}{3}\pi G\rho_m R_m}{\frac{4}{3}\pi G\rho_E R_E}$

Then $\dfrac{\rho_m}{\rho_E} = \left(\dfrac{g_m}{g_E}\right)\left(\dfrac{R_E}{R_m}\right) = \left(\dfrac{1}{6}\right)(4) = \boxed{\dfrac{2}{3}}$

14.11 Centripetal force = gravitational force between stars centers

$$\frac{Mv^2}{a} = \frac{MGM}{(2a)^2}$$

For a circular orbit, $v = \dfrac{2\pi a}{T}$ for each star.

Solving, $M = 12.6 \times 10^{31} \text{ kg} = 63$ solar masses for each star.

The two blue-giant stars comprising Plaskett's binary system are the heaviest known.

14.12   (a) $v = \dfrac{2\pi r}{T} = \dfrac{2\pi (384,400) \times 10^3}{27.3 \times (86,400)} = 1024$ m/s

(b) In one second, the moon falls a distance

$$x = \frac{1}{2}at^2 = \frac{1}{2}\frac{v^2}{r}t^2 = \frac{1}{2}\frac{(10^3)^2}{(384 \times 10^6)} \times (1)^2 = 0.00136 \text{ m} = 1.4 \text{ mm}$$

$$x = \frac{1}{2}at^2 = \frac{1}{2}\frac{MG}{r^2}t^2 = \frac{1}{2}\frac{(6 \times 10^{24}) \times (6.67 \times 10^{-11})}{(384 \times 10^6)^2} = 0.00135 \text{ m} = 1.4 \text{ mm}.$$

The moon only moves inward 1 mm for every 1024 meters it moves

along a straight-line path.

14.13 $T^2 = \dfrac{4\pi^2 R^3}{MG}$ or $M = \dfrac{4\pi^2 R^3}{GT^2}$

$$M = \frac{(4\pi^2)(3.84 \times 10^8 \text{ m})^3}{(6.672 \times 10^{-11} \text{ N} \cdot \text{m}^2/\text{kg}^2)(2.36 \times 10^6 \text{ s})^2} = \boxed{6 \times 10^{24} \text{ kg}}$$

For elliptical orbits, R should be replaced by the semi-major axis, a.

*14.14 By conservation of angular momentum,

$r_p v_p = r_a v_a$

$$\frac{v_p}{v_a} = \frac{r_a}{r_p} = \frac{2289 \text{ km} + 6.37 \times 10^3 \text{ km}}{459 \text{ km} + 6.37 \times 10^3 \text{ km}} = \frac{8659 \text{ km}}{6829 \text{ km}} = \boxed{1.27}$$

14.15 $T^2 = \dfrac{4\pi^2 d^3}{GM}$ (Kepler's Third Law with $m \ll M$)

$M = \dfrac{4\pi^2 d^3}{GT^2} = 1.9 \times 10^{27}$ kg (approx 316 Earth masses).

14.16 $r = [\dfrac{M_m G T^2}{4\pi^2}]^{1/3}$

$= [(6.42 \times 10^{23})(6.67 \times 10^{-11})(459 \min \times 60 \text{ s/min})^2/4\pi^2]^{1/3} = \boxed{9.37 \times 10^6 \text{ m}}$

14.17 $\Sigma \tau = 0$ and $L = $ constant; therefore $m v_a r_a = m v_p r_p$ and

$v_p = (\dfrac{r_a}{r_p})v_a = (\dfrac{6.99}{4.60})(3.88 \times 10^4 \text{ m/s}) = \boxed{5.90 \times 10^4 \text{ m/s}}$

*14.18 $F = (6.67 \times 10^{-11})\dfrac{(10^3)(5.98 \times 10^{24})}{(42 \times 10^6)^2} = \boxed{226 \text{ N}}$

*14.19 $\dfrac{GM_y}{(R_J + d)^2} = \dfrac{4\pi^2(R_J + d)}{T^2}$

$GM_J T^2 = 4\pi^2(R_J + d)^3$

$\left(6.67 \times 10^{-11} \dfrac{\text{Nm}^2}{\text{kg}^2}\right)(1.90 \times 10^{27} \text{ kg})(9.9 \times 3600)^2 = 4\pi^2(6.99 \times 10^7 + d)^3$

$d = \boxed{8.98 \times 10^7 \text{ m}} = \boxed{89,800 \text{ km}}$ above the planet

14.20 By Kepler's Third Law $T^2 = ka^3$ (a = semi-major axis)

For any object orbiting the sun, with T in years and a in A.U. , $k = 1$

Therefore $(75.6)^2 = (\dfrac{0.57 + x}{2})^3$

The farthest distance $x = 2(75.6)^{2/3} - 0.57 = \boxed{35.2 \text{ A.U.}}$

(out around the orbit of Pluto)

14.21 $g_1 = g_2 = \dfrac{MG}{r^2 + a^2}$

$g_{1y} = -g_{2y}$

$g_y = g_{1y} + g_{2y} = 0$

$g_{1x} = g_1 \cos\theta$

$\cos\theta = \dfrac{r}{(a^2 + r^2)^{1/2}}$

$a = 2g_{1x} = \dfrac{2MGr}{(r^2 + a^2)^{3/2}}$

14.21

14.22 $\cos \theta = \dfrac{r}{(a^2 + r^2)^{1/2}}$

$dg_x = dg \cos \theta \quad g_y = 0$

$\displaystyle\int dg_x = \int \dfrac{GdM}{a^2 + r^2} \cos \theta$

$g_x = \displaystyle\int \dfrac{GdM}{(a^2 + r^2)} \dfrac{r}{(a^2 + r^2)^{1/2}}$

$g_x = \dfrac{GMr}{(a^2 + r^2)^{3/2}}$ Inward along r.

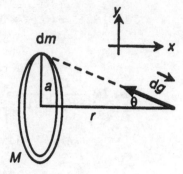

14.22

14.23 $F = 0 = \dfrac{GM_E m}{(L - x)^2} - \dfrac{GM_M m}{x^2}$

$M_M(L - x)^2 = M_E x^2$

Solving for x,

$x = L \dfrac{M_M \pm \sqrt{M_E M_M}}{M_M - M_E}$

For $x > 0$,

14.23

$x \;\; = L \dfrac{M_M - \sqrt{M_E M_M}}{M_M - M_E} = (3.84 \times 10^5 \text{ km}) \dfrac{7.35 - \sqrt{(7.35)(597)}}{7.35 - 597}$

$= \boxed{3.84 \times 10^4 \text{ km from the moon's center}}$

14.24   (a) $U = -\dfrac{GmM}{R}$

$U = -\dfrac{(6.67 \times 10^{-11})(100)(5.98 \times 10^{24})}{[(6.37 \times 10^6) + (2 \times 10^6)]} = \boxed{-4.77 \times 10^9 \text{ J}}$

(b) $F = \dfrac{GmM}{R^2} = \dfrac{|U|}{R} = \dfrac{4.77 \times 10^9}{8.37 \times 10^6} = \boxed{569 \text{ N}}$

14.25 (a) $U_{Tot} = U_{12} + U_{13} = U_{23}$

$$= -3(6.67 \times 10^{-11})(0.005)^2/0.3 = \boxed{-1.67 \times 10^{-14} \text{ J}}$$

(b) At the center of the equilateral triangle.

14.26 $U = -G\dfrac{mM}{R}$, and $g = \dfrac{GM_e}{R_e^2}$ so that

$$\Delta U = GmM(\frac{1}{R_e} - \frac{1}{3R_e}) = \frac{2}{3}mgR_e$$

$$\Delta U = \frac{2}{3}(1000 \text{ kg})(9.80 \text{ m/s}^2)(6.37 \times 10 \text{ m}^6) = \boxed{4.17 \times 10^{10} \text{ J}}$$

*14.27 (a) $\rho = \dfrac{M_s}{\frac{4}{3}\pi r_e^3} = \dfrac{(1.991 \times 10^{30} \text{ kg})}{\frac{4}{3}\pi(6.37 \times 10^6 \text{ m})^3} = \boxed{1.84 \times 10^9 \text{ kg/m}^3}$

(b) $g = \dfrac{GM_s}{r_e^2} = \dfrac{(6.67 \times 10^{-11} \text{ N} \cdot \text{m}^2/\text{kg}^2)(1.991 \times 10^{30} \text{ kg})}{(6.37 \times 10^6 \text{ m})^2}$

$$= \boxed{3.27 \times 10^6 \text{ m/s}^2}$$

(c) $U_J = \dfrac{-GM_s m}{r_e} = \dfrac{-(6.67 \times 10^{-11} \text{ N} \cdot \text{m}^2/\text{kg}^2(1.99 \times 10^{30} \text{ kg})(1\text{kg})}{(6.37 \times 10^6 \text{ m})}$

$$= \boxed{-2.08 \times 10^{13} \text{ J}}$$

*14.28 $\dfrac{1}{2}mv_e^2 = \dfrac{GM_e m}{r_e}$

$$\frac{1}{2}v_m^2 = \frac{GM_m}{r_m}$$

$$\frac{v_m^2}{v_e^2} = \frac{M_m r_e}{M_e r_m} = \left(\frac{1}{81}\right)\left(\frac{4}{1}\right)$$

$$\frac{v_m}{v_e} = 0.222$$

$$v_m = \boxed{2.49 \text{ km/s}}$$

14.29 $\dfrac{mv_1^2}{2} - \dfrac{GM_e m}{R_e} = -\dfrac{GM_e m}{r_{max}} + \dfrac{mv_f^2}{2}$

or $\quad v_f^2 = v_1^2 - \dfrac{2GM_e}{R_e}$

and $v_f = (v_1^2 - \dfrac{2GM_e}{R_e})^{1/2}$

$\qquad = [(2.0 \times 10^4)^2 - 1.25 \times 10^8]^{1/2} = \boxed{1.66 \times 10^4 \text{ m/s}}$

*14.30 $\quad E_{tot} = -\dfrac{GM_m}{2r}$

$\Delta E = \dfrac{GM_m}{2}\left(\dfrac{1}{r_s} - \dfrac{1}{r_b}\right)$

$\qquad = \dfrac{(6.67 \times 10^{-11})(5.98 \times 10^{24})}{2}\dfrac{10^3 \text{ kg}}{10^3 \text{ m}}\left(\dfrac{1}{6370 + 100} - \dfrac{1}{6370 + 200}\right)$

$\qquad = 4.69 \times 10^8 \text{ J} = \boxed{469 \text{ MJ}}$

14.31 (a) $v_{esc} = \sqrt{\dfrac{2GM_e}{R_e}} = 1.12 \times 10^4 \text{ m/s};$

$\qquad K = \dfrac{1}{2}(3000)(1.12 \times 10^4)^2 = \boxed{1.88 \times 10^{11} \text{ J}}$

(b) $P_{av} = \dfrac{K}{\Delta t} = \dfrac{(1.88 \times 10^{11} \text{ J})}{(21 \text{ days} \times 8.64 \times 10^4 \text{ s/day})} = 103 \text{ kW}$

*14.32   engine on : $v_f = 0 + (2)(9.8)(40) = 784$ m/s

$$y_f = \left(\frac{784}{2}\right)(40) = 15,680 \text{ m}$$

engine off : $0 - 784^2 = 2(9.8)\Delta y$

$$\Delta y = 31,360 \text{ m}$$

$$y_{max} = \boxed{47.0 \text{ km}}$$

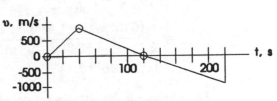

fall : $47040 = \frac{1}{2}9.8\,t^2$

$$178 \text{ s} + 40 \text{ s} = \boxed{218 \text{ s}}$$

14.33 To obtain the orbital velocity we use $\Sigma F = \dfrac{mMG}{R^2} = \dfrac{1}{2}mv_0^2$ or

$$v_0 = \sqrt{\frac{MG}{R}}$$

We can obtain the escape velocity from $\dfrac{1}{2}mv_{esc}^2/2 = \dfrac{mMG}{R}$ or

$$v_{esc} = \sqrt{\frac{2MG}{R}} = \sqrt{2}\,v_0.$$

*14.34 (a) By conservation of angular momentum,

$$mv_p D = mv_a(4D)$$

$$\left(\frac{v_p}{v_a}\right) = \boxed{4.00}$$

(b) Total energy $E = K + U$ is conserved. Therefore,

$$K_a + U_a = K_p + U_p \text{ and}$$

$$\left(\frac{E_p}{E_a}\right) = \boxed{1.00}$$

14.35 $\dfrac{v_i^2}{R_E + h} = \dfrac{GM_E}{(R_E + h)^2}$

$$K_i = \frac{1}{2}mv_i^2 = \frac{1}{2}\frac{GM_E m}{R_E + h}$$

$$= \frac{1}{2}\frac{(6.67 \times 10^{-11} \text{ N} \cdot \text{m}^2/\text{kg}^2)(5.97 \times 10^{24} \text{ kg})(500 \text{ kg})}{(6.38 \times 10^6 \text{ m}) + (0.500 \times 10^6 \text{ m})}$$

$$= 1.45 \times 10^{10} \text{ J}$$

The change in gravitational potential energy is

$$\Delta U = \frac{GM_E m}{R_i} - \frac{GM_E m}{R_f} = GM_E m\left(\frac{1}{R_i} - \frac{1}{R_f}\right)$$

$$= (6.67 \times 10^{-11} \text{ N} \cdot \text{m}^2/\text{kg}^2)(5.97 \times 10^{24} \text{ kg})(500 \text{ kg})(-1.14 \times 10^{-8} \text{ m}^{-1})$$

$$= -2.27 \times 10^9 \text{ J}$$

Also, $K_f = \dfrac{1}{2}mv_f^2 = \dfrac{1}{2}(500 \text{ kg})(2 \times 10^3 \text{ m/s})^2 = 1.00 \times 10^9 \text{ J}$

The energy lost to friction is

$$E_f = K_i - K_f - \Delta U = (14.5 - 1.00 + 2.27) \times 10^9 \text{ J} = \boxed{1.58 \times 10^{10} \text{ J}}$$

14.36 To find the velocity of the satellite in its circular orbit, use

$$\frac{v_0^2}{r} = \frac{GM}{r^2}$$

$$v_0^2 = \frac{GM}{r}$$

To escape from earth's gravitational attraction,

$$\frac{1}{2}m(v^2 + v_0^2) - \frac{GMm}{r} = 0$$

$$v = \sqrt{\frac{2GM}{r} - v_0^2} = \sqrt{\frac{GM}{r}}$$

$$= \sqrt{\frac{GM}{R_E + 10^6 \text{ m}}} = 7.35 \times 10^3 \text{ m/s} = \boxed{7.35 \text{ km/s}}$$

This is about 2/3 the escape velocity necessary at the earth's surface.

14.37 (a) $v_{\text{solar escape}} = \sqrt{\dfrac{2M_{\text{sun}}G}{R_{E\cdot\text{sun}}}} = 42\ \text{km/s}$

(b) $v = \sqrt{\dfrac{2M_{\text{sun}}G}{R_{E-s}\,x}} = \dfrac{42}{\sqrt{x}}$

if $v = \dfrac{125{,}000\ \text{km}}{3{,}600\ \text{s}}$ then $x = 1.47\ \text{A.U.} = 2.2 \times 10^{11}\ \text{m}$

(at or beyond the orbit of Mars, 125,000 km/h is sufficient for escape)

14.38 By symmetry, F is in the y direction.

$dM = \left(\dfrac{M}{\pi R}\right)R\,d\theta = \left(\dfrac{M}{\pi}\right)d\theta$ and $dF = \dfrac{Gm\,dM}{R^2}$

$dF_y = \dfrac{Gm\,dM\,\cos\theta}{R^2} = \dfrac{[Gm(\frac{M}{\pi})d\theta\,\cos\theta]}{R^2}$

$F_y = \displaystyle\int_{-\pi/2}^{\pi/2} \dfrac{GmM}{\pi R^2}\cos\theta\,d\theta = \dfrac{GMm}{\pi R^2}\sin\theta\Big|_{-\pi/2}^{\pi/2}$

$F_y = \dfrac{GMm}{\pi R^2}[1-(-1)] = \dfrac{2GmM}{\pi R^2}$

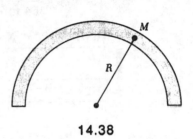

14.38

14.39 The force exerted on the mass by an element of length of the rod is given by $dF = Gm\,dm/x^2$ where x is the distance between the mass m and the increment of length dx.

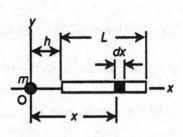

14.39

Using $dm = \lambda\,dx = (\lambda_0 + Ax^2)\,dx$, we have

$F = \displaystyle\int dF = Gm\int_d^{L+d} \dfrac{(\lambda_0 + Ax^2)}{x^2}\,dx$

$= \dfrac{GML\lambda_0}{d(L+d)} + GmAL$

14.40 28. (a) $\boxed{0}$ (b) $F = (6.67 \times 10^{-11})(80)(0.05)/1^2 = \boxed{2.67 \times 10^{-10} \text{ N}}$

toward the center of the sphere.

14.41 (a) $F = \dfrac{GmM}{r^2} = \dfrac{(6.67 \times 10^{-11} \text{ N} \cdot \text{m}^2/\text{kg}^2)(0.05 \text{ kg})(500 \text{ kg})^2}{(1.5 \text{ m})^2} = \boxed{7.41 \times 10^{-10} \text{ N}}$

(b) $F = \dfrac{(6.67 \times 10^{-11} \text{ N} \cdot \text{m}^2/\text{kg}^2)(0.05 \text{ kg})(500 \text{ kg})}{(0.4 \text{ m})^2} = \boxed{1.04 \times 10^{-8} \text{ N}}$

(c) In this case the mass m is a distance r from a sphere of mass,

$$M = (500 \text{ kg})(\frac{0.2 \text{ m}}{0.4 \text{ m}})^3 = 62.5 \text{ kg and}$$

$$F = \frac{(6.67 \times 10^{-11} \text{ N} \cdot \text{m}^2/\text{kg}^2)(0.05 \text{ kg})(62.5 \text{ kg})}{(0.2 \text{ m})^2}$$

$$F = \boxed{5.21 \times 10^{-9} \text{ N}}$$

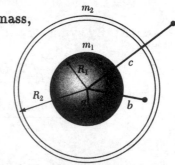

14.41

14.42 (a) $F = -\dfrac{Gmm_1 a}{R_1^3}$ toward the center of the sphere

(b) $F = -\dfrac{Gmm_1}{b^2}$ toward the center of the sphere

(c) $F = -\dfrac{Gm(m_1 + m_2)}{c^2}$ toward the center of the sphere

14.43 The acceleration of an object at the center of the earth due to the

gravitational force of the moon is given by $a = G\dfrac{M_{\text{moon}}}{d^2}$

At the point nearest the moon, $a_+ = G\dfrac{M_m}{(d-r)^2}$.

At the point furthest from the moon, $a_- = G\dfrac{M_m}{(d+r^2)}$

$$\Delta a = a_+ - a = GM_m(\frac{1}{(d-r)^2} - \frac{1}{d^2})$$

For $d \gg r$, $\Delta a = \dfrac{2GM_m r}{d^3} = 1.11 \times 10^{-6} \text{ m/s}^2$

Across the planet, $\dfrac{\Delta g}{g} = \dfrac{2\Delta a}{g} = \dfrac{2.22 \times 10^{-6} \text{ m/s}^2}{9.8 \text{ m/s}^2}$

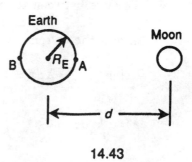

14.43

14.44 $\dfrac{mv^2}{2} = mgh$ $h = 70,000\text{ m}$ $g_{Io} = \dfrac{GM}{r^2} = 1.8\text{ m/s}^2.$

$v = \sqrt{2gh}$

$v = \sqrt{2(1.8)(70,000)} \cong 500\text{ m/s}$ (over 1000 mph).

14.45   For a 6 km diameter cylinder, $r = 3000$ m and to simulate $1\,g = 9.8\text{ m/s}^2$,

$g = \dfrac{v^2}{r} = \omega^2\, r$

$\omega = \sqrt{\dfrac{g}{r}} = 0.057\ \text{rads/s}$

The required rotation rate of the cylinder is 1 rev/110 s

(For a description of proposed cities in space, see Gerard K. O'Neill

in *Physics Today*, Sept. 1974.)

*14.46 $g_e = \dfrac{GM_e}{r_e^2}$

$g_p = \dfrac{GM_p}{r_p^2}$

$\dfrac{g_p\, r_p^2}{g_e\, r_e^2} = \dfrac{M_p}{M_e}$

$2\left(\dfrac{1}{4}\right) = \dfrac{M_p}{M_e} = \boxed{0.500}$

$M_p = \dfrac{1}{2}M_e$

*14.47 $F = \left(6.67 \times 10^{-11}\dfrac{\text{Nm}^2}{\text{kg}^2}\right)\dfrac{(1.5)(15 \times 10^{-3})}{(4.5 \times 10^{-2})^2} = 7.41 \times 10^{-10}\text{ N}$

$= \boxed{741\text{ pN}}$

14.48 $F_{24} = \dfrac{G(2)(4)}{(0.3)^2} j$

$F_{26} = \dfrac{G(2)(6)}{(0.5)^2} i$

$F_{22} = \dfrac{G(2)(2)}{0.34}$ at $\theta = \tan^{-1}(\dfrac{0.3}{0.5}) = 31°$

$\Sigma F_x = G(\dfrac{12}{0.25}) + G(\dfrac{4}{0.34}) \cos 31° = 58.05G$

$\Sigma F_y = G(\dfrac{8}{0.09}) + G(\dfrac{4}{0.34}) \sin 31° = 94.95G$

$F = \sqrt{(\Sigma F_x)^2 + (\Sigma F_y)^2} = 111.3G = \boxed{7.42 \times 10^{-9} \text{ N}}$

$\theta = \tan^{-1}(\dfrac{\Sigma F_y}{\Sigma F_x}) = \tan^{-1}(\dfrac{94.95G}{58.08G}) = \boxed{58.5°}$

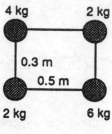

14.48

14.49   (a) From Example 14.9 we have $F = (-\dfrac{GmM_e}{R_e^3})r = -kr$.

Therefore $k = \dfrac{GmM_e}{R_e^3}$ and $A = \dfrac{L}{2}$.

(b) Mechanical energy is conserved during the motion of m. Therefore

$K_i + U_i = K_f + U_f$ where the initial position (i) is at the surface and

the final position (f) is at the midpoint of the path. From this we

have $0 - \dfrac{GMm}{R} = \dfrac{1}{2}mv^2 - (\dfrac{GmML^2}{8R^3} + \dfrac{GmM}{R})$ where

we have found U_f at the midpoint by substituting in

$r = [R^2 - (L/2)]^2$. Solving for v, the speed at the midpoint of the

path, we find $v = \dfrac{L}{2}(\dfrac{GM}{R^3})^{1/2}$.

(c) $v_{max} = \boxed{1550 \text{ m/s}}$

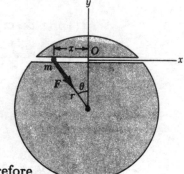

14.49

14.50 (a) $\qquad T^2 \;=\; k\,r^3$

$\qquad\qquad (1\text{ y})^2 \;=\; k(1\text{ AU})^3$

$\qquad\qquad\quad k \;=\; 1\text{ y}^2/\text{AU}^3$

(b) $T^2 = kr^3$

$\qquad T = (5.2)^{3/2} = \boxed{11.9\text{ y}}$

14.51 $\quad a = \dfrac{F}{m} = \dfrac{Gm}{r^2} = \dfrac{(6.67 \times 10^{-11})(4 \times 10^7)}{10^4} = \boxed{2.67 \times 10^{-7}\text{ m/s}^2}$

14.52 For this flight path

$a_c = g$

$\dfrac{v^2}{r} = g$

$r = \dfrac{v^2}{g} = \boxed{1814\text{ m}} = \boxed{1.81\text{ km}}$

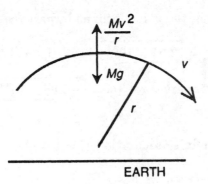

14.52

14.53 From Eq. 10.11,

$a = \omega^2 r = 1000g = 9800\text{ m/s}^2$

$\omega = \sqrt{\dfrac{9800}{0.1}} = \sqrt{98{,}000} = 313\;\text{ rads/s}$

$\dfrac{\omega}{2\pi}(60) \cong \boxed{3000\text{ rpm}}$

14.54 (a) The net torque exerted on the earth is zero. Therefore the angular

momentum is conserved; $mr_1v_1 = mr_2v_2$ and

$$v_a = v_p(\frac{r_p}{r_a}) = (3.027 \times 10^4 \text{ m/s})(\frac{1.471}{1.521}) = \boxed{2.93 \times 10^4 \text{ m/s}}$$

(b) $K_p = \frac{1}{2}mv_p^2 = \frac{1}{2}(5.98 \times 10^{24})(3.027 \times 10^4)^2 = \boxed{2.74 \times 10^{33} \text{ J}}$

$$U_p = -\frac{GmM}{r}$$

$$U_p = -\frac{(6.673 \times 10^{-11})(5.98 \times 10^{24})(1.99 \times 10^{30})}{1.471 \times 10^{11}} = \boxed{-5.4 \times 10^{33} \text{ J}}$$

(c) Using the same form as in part (b), find

$$K_a = \boxed{2.57 \times 10^{33} \text{ J}} \text{ and } U_a = \boxed{-5.22 \times 10^{33} \text{ J}}$$

$$\text{Compare } K_p + U_p = \boxed{-2.66 \times 10^{33} \text{ J}} \text{ and } K_a + U_a = \boxed{-2.65 \times 10^{33} \text{ J}}$$

14.55 (a) At infinite separation $U = 0$ and at rest $K = 0$. Since energy is

conserved we have

$$0 = \frac{1}{2}m_1v_1^2 + \frac{1}{2}m_2v_2^2 - \frac{Gm_1m_2}{d} \qquad (1)$$

The initial momentum is zero and momentum is conserved.

Therefore $0 = m_1v_1 - m_2v_2$ \qquad (2)

Combine Eqs. (1) and (2) to find

$$v_1 = m_2\sqrt{\frac{2G}{d(m_1 + m_2)}} \text{ and } v_2 = m_1\sqrt{\frac{2G}{d(m_1 + m_2)}}$$

Relative velocity $v_r = v_1 - (-v_2) = \sqrt{\frac{2G(m_1 + m_2)}{d}}$

(b) Substitute given numerical values into the equation found for v_1

and v_2 in part (a) to find $v_1 = 1.03 \times 10^4$ m/s and

$v_2 = 2.58 \times 10^3$ m/s. Therefore

$$K_1 = \frac{1}{2}m_1v_1^2 = \boxed{1.07 \times 10^{32} \text{ J}} \text{ and } K_2 = \frac{1}{2}m_2v_2^2 = \boxed{2.67 \times 10^{31} \text{ J}}$$

Physics for Scientists and Engineers

323

*14.56 (a) $g = \dfrac{GM}{r^2} = \dfrac{(6.67 \times 10^{-11})(1.991 \times 10^{30})}{(10^4 \text{ m})^2} = \boxed{1.33 \times 10^{12} \text{ m/s}^2}$

(b) $W = mg = (70 \text{ kg})(1.33 \times 10^{12} \text{ m/s}^2) = \boxed{9.29 \times 10^{13} \text{ N}}$

(c) $\dfrac{GMM_n}{r} = \dfrac{(6.67 \times 10^{-11})(1.99 \times 10^{30})(1.67 \times 10^{-27})}{(10^4 \text{ m})}$

$= \boxed{2.22 \times 10^{-11} \text{ J}}$

14.57 (a) From Kepler's third law, $T^2 = (\dfrac{4\pi^2}{MG})d^3$ where M is the mass

of the moon.

$M = \dfrac{4\pi^2 d^3}{GT^2}$

$M = \dfrac{4\pi^2(1.849 \times 10^6)^3}{(6.673 \times 10^{-11})(119 \times 60)^2} = \boxed{7.34 \times 10^{22} \text{ kg}}$

(b) $T = 2\pi d/v$. Substituting this for T in the equation for Kepler's

third law, we find

$v = \sqrt{\dfrac{GM}{d}} = \sqrt{\dfrac{(6.673 \times 10^{-11})(7.34 \times 10^{22})}{(1.849 \times 10^6)}} = \boxed{1.63 \times 10^3 \text{ m/s}}$

(c) Total energy, $E = K + U = \dfrac{1}{2}mv^2 - \dfrac{GmM}{d}$.

From part (b) we found $v = \sqrt{\dfrac{GM}{d}}$, therefore

$E = \dfrac{1}{2}m(\dfrac{GM}{d}) - \dfrac{mGM}{d} = -\dfrac{GmM}{2d}$

$E = -\dfrac{(6.673 \times 10^{-11})(9.979 \times 10^3)(7.34 \times 10^{22})}{2(1.849 \times 10^6 \text{ m})}$

$E = 1.32 \times 10^{10} \text{ J}$

$E_{\text{min}} = |E| = \boxed{1.32 \times 10^{10} \text{ J}}$

14.58   (a) $T = \dfrac{2\pi r}{v} = \dfrac{2\pi(30{,}000 \times 9.46 \times 10^{15} \text{ m})}{2.50 \times 10^5 \text{ m/s}} = 7.13 \times 10^{15} \text{ s} = \boxed{2.3 \times 10^8 \text{ y}}$

$\cong 0.23$ million years

(b) $M = \dfrac{4\pi^2 a^3}{GT^2} = \dfrac{4\pi^2(30{,}000 \times 9.46 \times 10^{15} \text{ m})^3}{(6.67 \times 10^{-11} \text{ N} \cdot \text{m}^2/\text{kg}^2)(7.13 \times 10^{15} \text{ s})^2} = 2.66 \times 10^{41} \text{ kg}$

$= \boxed{1.34 \times 10^{11} \text{ solar masses}}$

The number of stars is approximately 10^{11}.

*14.59 Centripetal acceleration comes from gravitational acceleration.

$$\frac{v^2}{r} = \frac{M_c G}{r^2} = \frac{4\pi^2 r^2}{T^2 r}$$

$$GM_c T^2 = 4\pi^2 r^3$$

$$(6.67 \times 10^{-11})(20)(1.99 \times 10^{30})(5 \times 10^{-3})^2 = 4\pi^2 r^3$$

$$r_{\text{orbit}} = \boxed{119 \text{ km}}$$

*14.60 By conservation of angular momentum and using conservation of energy,

$$r_p v_p = r_a v_a$$

$$\frac{1}{2}v_p^2 - \frac{GM_e}{r_p} = \frac{1}{2}v_a^2 - \frac{GM_e}{r_a}$$

$$\frac{1}{2}v_p^2 - \frac{GM_e}{r_p} = \frac{1}{2}\frac{r_p^2 v_p^2}{r_a^2} - \frac{GM_e}{r_a}$$

$$v_p^2 r_a^2 r_p - 2GM_e r_a^2 = r_p^3 v_p^2 - 2GM_e r_p r_a$$

$$v_p^2(r_p)(r_a^2 - r_p^2) = 2GM_e r_a(r_a - r_p)$$

$$v_p^2 r_p(r_a + r_p) = 2GM_e r_a$$

$$v_p = \sqrt{\frac{2GM_e r_a}{r_p(r_a + r_p)}} = \sqrt{\frac{2(6.67 \times 10^{-4})(5.98 \times 10^{24})(9370 \times 10^3)}{6770 \times 10^3(16140 \times 10^3)}}$$

$$v_p = 8.27 \text{ km/s}$$

$$v_a = \frac{r_p v_p}{r_a} = \frac{6770}{9370}\,8.27 = 5.98 \text{ km/s}$$

$$v_a, v_p = \boxed{5.98 \text{ km/s}, \ 8.27 \text{ km/s}}$$

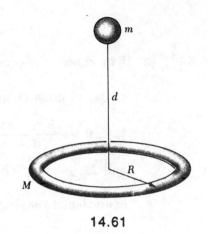

14.61

14.61   (a) $T = \sqrt{\dfrac{4\pi^2}{GM}r^3} = \boxed{5300 \text{ s}}$

       (b) $v = \dfrac{2\pi r}{T} = \boxed{7.79 \text{ km/s}}$

       (c) $E = \dfrac{mv^2}{2} + \dfrac{mGM}{R_E} - \dfrac{mGM}{r} = \boxed{6.46 \times 10^9 \text{ J}}$

*14.62   (a) $\quad a_c \;=\; \dfrac{mv^2}{r} = \dfrac{Gmm}{r^2}$

               $a_c \;=\; \dfrac{(1.25 \times 10^6 \text{ m/s})^2}{1.53 \times 10^{11} \text{ m}} = \boxed{10.2 \text{ m/s}^2}$

       (b) $\quad$ diff $\;=\; 10.2 - 9.9 = 0.312 \text{ m/s}^2 = \dfrac{GM^2}{r}$

               $M \;=\; \dfrac{(0.312 \text{ m/s}^2)(1.53 \times 10^{11})^2}{6.67 \times 10^{-11}}$

               $M \;=\; \boxed{1.10 \times 10^{32} \text{ kg}}$

14.63   (a) If we consider a hollow shell in the sphere with radius r and

        thickness dr then $dM = \rho dV = \rho(4\pi r^2 dr)$. The total mass is then

$$M = \int_0^R (Ar)(4\pi r^2 dr) = \pi A R^4 \text{ and } A = \frac{M}{\pi R^4}.$$

       (b) The total mass of the sphere acts as if it were at the center of the

        sphere and $F = -\dfrac{GmM}{r^2}$ directed toward the center of the sphere.

       (c) Inside the sphere at a distance r from the center, $dF = (\dfrac{Gm}{r^2})dM$

        where dM is just the mass of a shell enclosed within the radius r.

        Therefore $F = -Gm\displaystyle\int \frac{dM}{r^2} = -Gm\int_0^r Ar(4\pi r^2)\frac{dr}{r^2} = -\frac{GmMr^2}{R^4}.$

14.64   (a) If we choose the coordinate of the

center of mass at the origin,

then $0 = \dfrac{(Mr_2 - mr_1)}{M + m}$

and $Mr_2 = mr_1$. (Note: this is

equivalent to saying that the net

torque must be zero and the two

experience no angular acceleration.)

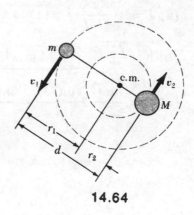

14.64

For each mass $F = ma$ and

$mr_1\omega_1^2 = \dfrac{MGm}{d^2}$ and $Mr_2\omega_2^2 = \dfrac{MGm}{d^2}$. Combining these two

equations and using $d = r_1 + r_2$

gives $\omega_1 = \omega_2 = \omega$ and

$T = \dfrac{2\pi}{\omega}$ or $T = \dfrac{4\pi^2 d^3}{G(M + m)}$.

14.65 $T^2 \;=\; \dfrac{4\pi^2}{G(M + m)}d^3 \qquad d = 1.97 \times 10^7$ m

$M + m \;=\; \dfrac{4\pi^2 d^3}{GT^2}$ where $T = 6.4 \times 86400$ s

$M + m \;=\; \boxed{1.48 \times 10^{22} \text{ kg}}$

This is about $\frac{1}{5}$ the mass of Earth's moon, for both Pluto and its satellite. Pluto is
the smallest planet in our solar system.

14.66   Utilize the result of problem 64

$$T^2 = \frac{4\pi^2}{G(M+m)}d^3$$

$$d = \sqrt[3]{\frac{G(M+m)T^2}{4\pi^2}} = 1.5 \times 10^{16} \text{ m} = \boxed{100{,}000 \text{ A.U.}}$$

(or approximately 1.6 lightyears)

For more information on the possible existence of a solar companion star, see the articles by Whitmire and Jackson and Davis, Hut, and Muller in *Nature* Vol. 308, pp. 713–717 (1984).

14.67   (a) The density is just $\rho = \dfrac{M}{V} = \dfrac{3M}{4\pi R^3}$. From Kepler's 3rd law,

$$T^2 = \left(\frac{4\pi^2}{GM}\right)r^3 \text{ where } r = R + h. \text{ Combining these two}$$

equations, we find $\rho = \dfrac{3\pi}{GT^2}\left(1 + \dfrac{h}{R}\right)^3$.

(b) If the satellite is close to the surface, then $h/R << 1$ and

$$\rho = \frac{3\pi}{GT^2} = \frac{3\pi}{(6.67 \times 10^{11})(1.2 \times 10^4)^2}$$

$$\rho = \boxed{981 \text{ kg/m}^3}$$

*14.68

$$g = \frac{GM_e}{r^2}$$

$$\frac{dg}{dr} = GM_e(-2)r^{-3} = -2\frac{GM_e}{r^2}\frac{1}{r} = \frac{-2g}{r}$$

$$\frac{dg}{g} = -2\frac{dr}{r}$$

$$(10^{-11})\left(\frac{1}{2}\right)(6 \times 10^6 \text{ m}) = dr = \boxed{30 \text{ }\mu\text{m}}$$

14.69 (a) $U = \int F\, dr$. Initially take the particle from ∞ and move it to the

sphere's surface. Then $U \int\limits_{0}^{R} (\dfrac{GmM}{r^2})dr = -\dfrac{GmM}{R}$.

Now move it to a position r from the center of the sphere. The

force in this case is a function of the mass enclosed by r at any

point. Since $\rho = \dfrac{M}{(4/3)\pi R^3}$ we have

$$U = \int\limits_{R}^{r} Gm(4/3)\pi r^3 \rho\, \frac{dr}{r^2} = \frac{GmM}{R^3}(\frac{r^2}{2} - \frac{R^2}{2})$$

and the total gravitational potential energy is

$$U = \frac{GmM}{2R^3}(r^2 - 3R^2) \quad \text{or} \quad U = (\frac{GmM}{2R^3})r^2 - \frac{3GmM}{2R}$$

(b) $U(R) = -\dfrac{GMm}{R}$ and $U(0) = -\dfrac{3GmM}{2R}$ therefore

$$W_g = -[U(0) - U(R)] = \frac{GMm}{2R}$$

14.70 (a) See Eq. 14.20.

(b) $E = \int\limits_{r=0}^{R_0} -\dfrac{GM_r}{r}\rho 4\pi r^2\, dr = \int\limits_{r=0}^{R_0} -\dfrac{G\rho 4\pi r^3}{3r}\rho 4\pi r^2 dr$

Collecting terms,

$$E = -\frac{G\rho^2 16\pi^2}{3} \int\limits_{r=0}^{R_0} r^4 dr = \frac{-16\,G\rho^2\pi^2 R_0^5}{15}$$

Substituting,

$$\boxed{E_{\text{planet}} = -\frac{3}{5}\frac{GM_0^2}{R_0}}$$

(For an interesting application of this problem, see S. VanWyk

"Star Wars" in the December 1985 *American Journal of Physics.*)

CHAPTER 15

15.1 $\quad M = \rho_{iron}V = (7860 \ kg/m^3)(\frac{4}{3}\pi(0.015 \ m)^3)$

$\boxed{M = 0.111 \ kg}$

15.2 $\quad \rho = \dfrac{535 \ g}{25 \ cm^3} = 21.4 \ g/cm^3 \quad \boxed{Platinum}$

15.3 $\quad N =$ sum of number of protons and neutrons in the nucleus, $m = Nm_p$

and $V = N(4\pi r^3/3)$.

$\rho = \dfrac{m}{v} = \dfrac{Nm_p}{N(4\pi r^3/3)} = \dfrac{1.67 \times 10^{-27} \ kg}{4\pi(10^{-15} \ m)^3/3}$

$\approx \boxed{4 \times 10^{17} \ kg/m^3}$

15.4 $\quad \rho = \dfrac{M}{V} = \dfrac{0.5}{185 \times 10^{-6}} = 2.70 \times 10^3 \ kg/m^3$

No. The crown is made of aluminum.

15.5 $\quad \rho = \dfrac{F}{A} = \dfrac{50(9.80)}{n(0.5 \times 10^{-2})^2} = \boxed{6.24 \times 10^6 \ N/m^2}$

*15.6 The atmospheric pressure we feel is actually the weight of the earth's atmosphere, Mg, distributed over the surface area of the earth, $4\pi R^2$.

Then, $p = \dfrac{Mg}{4\pi R^2}$ and

$M = \dfrac{4\pi R^2 P}{g} = \dfrac{4\pi(6.37 \times 10^6 \ m)^2(1.01 \times 10^5 \ N/m^2)}{(9.8 \ m/s^2)}$

$= \boxed{5.26 \times 10^{18} \ kg}$

15.7 $\quad \rho = \dfrac{M}{\frac{4}{3}\pi r^3} = \dfrac{2 \times 10^{30} \ kg}{\frac{4}{3}\pi(10^4 \ m)^3} = \boxed{4.8 \times 10^{17} \ kg/m^3}$

(the density of nuclear matter)

15.8 $P = P_a + \rho g h = 1.01 \times 10^5 \text{ N/m}^2 + (10^3 \text{ kg/m}^3)(9.80 \text{ m/s})(30 \text{ m})$

$= 1.01 \times 10^5 \text{ N/m}^2 + 2.94 \times 10^5 \text{ N/m}^2$

$= \boxed{3.95 \times 10^5 \text{ Pa}}$

15.9   Require, $P = 3P_a = P_a + \rho g h$, thus

$h = \dfrac{2P_a}{\rho g} = \dfrac{2(1.01 \times 10^5 \text{ N/m}^2)}{(10^3 \text{ kg/m}^3 \times 9.80 \text{ m/s}^2)} = \boxed{20.6 \text{ m}}$

15.10   Since the pressure is the same on both sides, $F_1/A_1 = F_2/A_2$. In this case,

$\dfrac{15,000}{200} = \dfrac{F_2}{3}$,   or $F_2 = \boxed{225 \text{ N}}$

15.11 $F_{el} = F_{\text{fluid}}$ or $kx = \rho g h A$; and

$h = \dfrac{kx}{\rho g A}$

$= \dfrac{(1000 \text{ N/m}^2)(0.005 \text{ m})}{(10^3 \text{ kg/m}^3)(9.80 \text{ m/s}^2)\pi(0.01 \text{ m})^2} = \boxed{1.62 \text{ m}}$

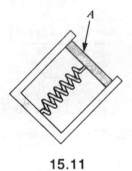

15.11

15.12   The pressure on the bottom due to the water is

$P_b = g\rho z = 1.96 \times 10^4 \text{ Pa}$

So, $F_b = P_b A = 5.87 \times 10^6 \text{ N}$

On each end,

$F = \bar{P}A = (9.8 \times 10^3 \text{ Pa})(20 \text{ m}^2) = 196 \text{ kN}$

On the side

$F = \bar{P}A = (9.8 \times 10^3 \text{ Pa})(60 \text{ m}^2) = 588 \text{ kN}$

15.13 $W = (80 \text{ kg})(9.8 \text{ m/s}^2) = 784 \text{ N}$

$W = F = PA = (1.01 \times 10^5 \text{ Pa})(A)$

$A = \dfrac{W}{P} = \dfrac{784}{1.01 \times 10^5} = \boxed{7.76 \times 10^{-3} \text{ m}^2}$

15.13

15.14 $F = PA(\rho gh)(A)$

$F = (10^3 \text{ kg/m}^3)(9.8 \text{ m/s}^2)(4 \text{ m})(2 \text{ m} \times 0.7 \text{ m})$

$\boxed{F = 5.5 \times 10^4 \text{ N}}$

15.15 The bulk modulus for water is

$B = 2.1 \times 10^9 \text{ N/m}^2$ (Table 12.1)

$\therefore$ Since $-B\dfrac{\Delta V}{V} = \Delta P$

$-\dfrac{\Delta V}{V} = \dfrac{(499 \text{ atm})(1.01 \times 10^5 \text{ Pa/atm})}{2.1 \times 10^9 \text{ N/m}^2} = 0.024$

The fractional decrease in volume of 1 kg of water is therefore 0.024. The density increase of water at 5 km depth is therefore $\dfrac{1}{0.976} = 1.025$ times. (A 2.5% increase).

15.16 At any depth h behind the dam, the hydrostatic pressure $P = \rho gh$ (Eq. 15.11)

For water of density $\rho = 1000 \text{ kg/m}^3$,

$F = \displaystyle\int_{h=0}^{h=150} \rho gh \, w \, dh = \dfrac{1}{2}\rho gh^2 w = \boxed{1.32 \times 10^{11} \text{ N}}$

(or approx. 15 million tons)

15.17 $P = \rho gh = (920 \text{ kg/m}^3)(9.8 \text{ m/s}^2)(10^3 \text{ m}) = \boxed{9 \times 10^6 \text{ Pa}^2}$

(approx. 90 atm)

15.18 $P = P_a + \rho gh = 1.013 \times 10^5 \text{ N/m}^2$

$+ (13.595 \times 10^3)(9.80)(0.2) \text{ N/m}^2$

$= 1.279 \times 10^5 \text{ N/m}^2$ The gauge pressure is

$P - P_a = \boxed{2.66 \times 10^4 \text{ Pa}}$

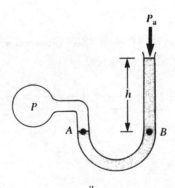

15.18

15.19 Require that $P_a = \rho g h$, thus

$$h = \frac{P_a}{\rho g} = \frac{(1.01 \times 10^5 \text{ N/m}^2)}{(10^3 \text{ kg/m}^3)(9.80 \text{ m/s}^2)} = \boxed{10.3 \text{ m}}$$

15.20 The pressure at the depth h_1 is $P_1 = P_a + \rho g h_1$. Hence, the pressure at the depth $h_1 + h_2$ is $P = P_1 + \rho g h_2 = P_a + \rho g h_1 + \rho g h_2$.

15.21 $P_0 = \rho g h$

$$h = \frac{P_0}{\rho g} = \frac{1.013 \times 10^5 \text{ Pa}}{(0.984 \times 10^3 \text{ kg/m}^3)(9.81 \text{ m/s}^2)} = \boxed{10.5 \text{ m}}$$

15.22 $\Delta P_0 = \rho g \Delta h = -2.67 \times 10^3 \text{ Pa}$

$$P = P_0 + \Delta P_0 = (1.013 - 0.027) \times 10^5 \text{ Pa} = \boxed{0.986 \times 10^5 \text{ Pa}}$$

15.23 $P_a = P_0 + (\ell + \ell' - h)\rho_w g = P_0 + \ell' \rho_k g + \ell \rho_w g$

Solving for h,

$$h = \ell'(1 - \frac{\rho_k}{\rho_w}) = \boxed{1.08 \text{ cm}}$$

15.24 Archimedes principle tells us that B = weight of the displaced water,

or $B = \rho_w V g \approx (10^3 \text{ kg/m}^3)(0.2 \text{ m}^3)(9.80 \text{ m/s}^2) = \boxed{1.96 \times 10^3 \text{ N}}$. The result is the *same* if the object is steel.

15.25 Buoyant force = weight $(\rho_{\text{sea water}})g(1-f)V = \rho_{\text{ice}}gV$ where f is the fraction of the iceberg above water.

$$f = 1 - \frac{\rho_{\text{ice}}}{\rho_{\text{sea water}}} = 1 - \frac{0.92}{1.03} = \boxed{0.107} \text{ or } f = \boxed{10.7\%}$$

*15.26 (a) $\rho_{obj}gV = 15$ N $\quad \dfrac{\rho_{obj}}{\rho_{H_2O}} = 5 \quad \boxed{\rho_{obj} = 5000 \text{ kg/m}^3}$

$\rho_{H_2O}gV = 3$ N

(b) $\rho_{fluid}gV = 2$ N $\quad \dfrac{\rho_{H_2O}}{\rho_{fluid}} = \dfrac{2}{3} \quad \boxed{\rho_{fluid} = 667 \text{ kg/m}^3}$

15.27 (a) According to Archimedes,

$$B = \rho_w V g = (1 \text{ g/cm}^3)[20 \times 20 \times (20 - h)]g$$

But $B =$ Weight of Block $= Mg = \rho_{wood}V_{wood}g = (0.65 \text{ g/cm}^3)(20 \text{ cm})^3 g$

$$(0.65)(20)^3 g = (1)(20)(20)(20 - h)g$$

$$20 - h = 20(0.65)$$

$$h = 20(1 - 0.65) = \boxed{7 \text{ cm}}$$

(b) $B = W + Mg$ where $M =$ mass of lead

$$1(20)^3 g = (0.65)(20)^3 g + Mg$$

$$M = 20^3(1 - 0.65) = (20)^3(0.35) = 2800 g = \boxed{2.8 \text{ kg}}$$

*15.28 $\rho_{air}gV - \rho_{He}gV - W = 0$

$$W = mg = (\rho_{air} - \rho_{He})g(400)$$

$$m = (1.11 \text{ kg/m}^3)(400 \text{ m}^3) = \boxed{444 \text{ kg}}$$

*15.29 $\rho_{H_2O}g\dfrac{1}{2}V - \rho_{pl}gV = 0$

$$\rho_{pl} = \dfrac{1}{2}\rho_{H_2O} = \boxed{500 \text{ kg/m}^3}$$

$$\rho_{oil}g\dfrac{4}{10}V - \rho_{pl}gV = 0$$

$$\rho_{oil} = \dfrac{10}{4}(500 \text{ kg/m}^3) = \boxed{1250 \text{ kg/m}^3}$$

15.30   (a) $P = P_a + \rho g h$;   Taking $P = 1.0130 \times 10^3$ N/m² and $h = 5$ cm,

we find $P_{top} = 1.0179 \times 10^5$ N/m². For $h = 17$ cm, we get

$P_{bot} = 1.0297 \times 10^5$ N/m²

Since the areas of the top and bottom are

$A = (0.1 \text{ m} \times 0.1 \text{ m}) = 10^{-2}$m², we find

$F_{top} = P_{top}A = \boxed{1.0179 \times 10^3 \text{ N}}$ and $F_{bot} = \boxed{1.0297 \times 10^3 \text{ N}}$

(b) As in Example 15.7, $T + B - Mg = 0$, where

$B = \rho_w V g = (10^3 \text{ kg/m}^3)(1.2 \times 10^{-3}\text{m}^3)(9.80 \text{ m/s}^2) = 11.8$ N, and

$Mg = 10(9.80) = 98$ N. Therefore, $T = Mg - B = 98.0 - 11.8 = \boxed{86.2 \text{ N}}$

(c) $F_{bot} - F_{top} = (1.0297 - 1.0179) \times 10^3 \text{ N} = \boxed{11.8 \text{ N}}$

which is equal to B found in part (b).

15.31 $F_b = F_g$

$\rho g V = \rho g (\frac{2}{3} \pi r^3) = mg$

$m = \frac{2}{3} \pi r^3 \rho = \boxed{0.611 \text{ kg}}$

*15.32 $-F + \rho_{\text{H}_2\text{O}} g \frac{4}{3}\pi \left(\frac{d}{2}\right)^3 - \rho_{\text{pp}} g \frac{4}{3}\pi \left(\frac{d}{2}\right)^3 = 0$

$F = (\rho_{\text{H}_2\text{O}} - \rho_{\text{pp}}) g \frac{\pi d^3}{6}$

$F = (1000 - 84)\, 9.8 \frac{\pi (0.038)^3}{6} = \boxed{0.258 \text{ N}}$

15.33 $F_g = (m + \rho_s V)g$

$F_b = \rho_w V g$

Since $F_b = F_g$,

$m + \rho_s V = \rho_w V$

$V = Ah = \dfrac{m}{\rho_w - \rho_s}$

$A = \dfrac{m}{(\rho_w - \rho_s)h} = \boxed{1.07 \text{ m}^2}$

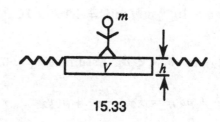

15.33

15.34 $V = (2.0 \text{ m})(0.50 \text{ m})(0.08 \text{ m}) = 0.08 \text{ m}^3$

$F_B = \rho_w g V = (10^3 \text{ kg/m}^3)\,(9.8 \text{ m/s}^2)(0.08 \text{ m}^3) = 784 \text{ N}$

$m = 80 \text{ kg} - 2.3 \text{ kg} = \boxed{77.7 \text{ kg}}$

15.35 The balloon stops rising when

$(\rho_{\text{air}} - \rho_{He})gV = Mg$

or, when

$(\rho_{\text{air}} - \rho_{He})V = M$

Therefore

$V = \dfrac{M}{(\rho_{\text{air}} - \rho_{He})}$

$V = \dfrac{400}{(1.25 \, e^{-1} - 0.18)} = \boxed{1430 \text{ m}^3}$

15.36 (a) $\dfrac{dV}{dt} = vA$ or $v = \dfrac{1}{A}\left(\dfrac{dV}{dt}\right)$

$v = \left(\dfrac{1}{\pi r^2}\right)\dfrac{dV}{dt} = \left(\dfrac{1}{\pi(0.05 \text{ m})^2}\right)\left(\dfrac{2 \text{ m}^3}{60 \text{ s}}\right) = \boxed{4.24 \text{ m/s}}$

(b) $v_2 = \dfrac{A_1 v_1}{A_2} = \dfrac{(A_1)(4.24 \text{ m/s})}{(A_1/4)} = \boxed{17.0 \text{ m/s}}$

15.37 Assuming the top is open to the atmosphere, then $P_1 = P_a$.

Flow rate = 2.5×10^{-3} m^3/ min = 4.167×10^{-5} m^3/s.

(a) $A_1 \gg A_2$, so $v_1 \ll v_2$. Assuming $v_1 \approx 0$, and $P_1 = P_2 = P_a$,

$$P_1 + \frac{\rho v_1^2}{2} + \rho g y_1 = P_2 + \frac{\rho v_2^2}{2} + \rho g y_2$$

$$v_2 = (2gy_1)^{1/2} = [2(9.80)(16)]^{1/2} = \boxed{17.7 \text{ m/s}}$$

(b) Flow rate = $A_2 v_2 = (\frac{\pi d^2}{4})(17.7) = 4.167 \times 10^{-5}$ m^3/s.

$$d = \boxed{1.73 \times 10^{-3} \text{ m}} = 1.73 \text{ mm}$$

*15.38 $P_{\text{in}} - P_{\text{out}} = \frac{1}{2}\rho v^2 = \frac{1}{2}1000(30)^2 = \underline{450 \text{ kPa}}$

$$\Delta P = \boxed{4.44 \text{ atm}}$$

*15.39 By Bernoulli's Law,

$$8 \times 10^4 \frac{\text{N}}{\text{m}^2} + \frac{1}{2}1000v^2 = 6 \times 10^4 \frac{\text{N}}{\text{m}^2} + \frac{1}{2}1000(16v^2)$$

$$2 \times 10^4 \frac{\text{N}}{\text{m}^2} = \frac{1}{2}1000(15v^2)$$

$$v = 1.63 \text{ m/s}$$

$$\frac{dm}{dt} = \rho A v = 1000\pi(0.05)^2(1.63 \text{ m/s}) = \boxed{12.8 \text{ kg/s}}$$

15.39

15.40   (a) Flow rate = 25 liters/30 s

$$A_2 v_2 = 833 \text{ cm}^3/\text{s}$$

$$v_2 = \frac{833 \text{ cm}^3/\text{s}}{\pi(1)^2 \text{ cm}^2} = 265 \text{ cm/s} = \boxed{2.65 \text{ m/s}}$$

(b) $A_1 v_1 = A_2 v_2$

$$v_1 = (\frac{A_2}{A_1})v_2 = (2.6)^2(265) = 29.4 \text{ cm/s} = 0.294 \text{ m/s}.$$

$$P_1 + \frac{\rho v_1^2}{2} + \rho g y_1 = P_2 + \frac{\rho v_2^2}{2} + \rho g y_2$$

Taking $P_2 = P_a$, gives

$$
\begin{aligned}
P_1 - P_a &= \frac{1}{2}\rho(v_2^2 - v_1^2) + \rho g y^2 \\
&= \frac{1}{2}(10^3)[(2.65)^2 - (0.294)^2] + (10^3)(9.80)(2) \\
&= \boxed{2.31 \times 10^4 \text{ Pa}}
\end{aligned}
$$

15.41   Flow rate $Q = 0.012 \text{ m}^3/\text{s} = v_1 A_1 = v_2 A_2$

$$v_2 = \frac{Q}{A_2} = \frac{0.012}{A_2} = \boxed{31.6 \text{ m/s}}$$

15.42   For a constant–density fluid,

$$A_1 v_1 = A_2 v_2, \text{ so } \frac{\pi(3.6 \text{ m})^2}{4}(3 \text{ m/s}) = \frac{\pi(1.2 \text{ m})^2}{4}(v_2)$$

$$v_2 = (3 \text{ m/s})(9) = \boxed{27 \text{ m/s}}$$

15.43   Utilizing Bernoulli's equation: $\Delta P + \frac{\rho v^2}{2} + \rho g y = $ constant,

Pressure is converted entirely into kinetic energy, and this is converted into gravitational potential energy.

$$\Delta P \longrightarrow \frac{1}{2}\rho v^2 \longrightarrow \rho g h \text{ where } \rho = 1000 \text{ kg/m}^3$$

(a) $\rho g y = (10^3)(9.8)(40) = \frac{1}{2}\rho v^2$ $\boxed{v = 28 \text{ m/s}}$

(b) $\Delta P = (10^3)(9.8)(40) = 3.92 \times 10^5 \text{ Pa}$ $\Delta P = \boxed{3.92 \text{ atm}}$

15.44 $Mg = (P_1 - P_2)A$ for a balanced condition

$$\frac{(16000)(9.80)}{A} = 7.0 \times 10^4 - P_2 \text{ where } A = 80 \text{ m}^2,$$

$$P_2 = 7.0 \times 10^4 - 0.196 \times 10^4 = \boxed{6.8 \times 10^4 \text{ Pa}}$$

15.45 $P_1 + \frac{1}{2}\rho v_1^2 = P_2 + \frac{1}{2}\rho_2 v_2^2; \quad \Delta P = P_1 - P_2 = \frac{1}{2}\rho(v_2^2 - v_1^2)$

$W = F_{\text{net}} = \Delta P(A) = \frac{1}{2}\rho(v_2^2 - v_1^2)A.$ Therefore

$$W = \frac{1}{2}(1 \text{ kg/m}^3)[(65 \text{ m/s})^2 - (50 \text{ m/s})^2](50 \text{ m}^2) = \boxed{4.31 \times 10^4 \text{ N}}$$

15.46 $P_1 + \frac{\rho v_1^2}{2} = P_2 + \frac{\rho v_2^2}{2}$ (Bernoulli Equation)

$$v_1 A_1 = v_2 A_2 \quad \text{where} \quad \frac{A_1}{A_2} = 4$$

$$\Delta P = P_1 - P_2 = \frac{\rho}{2}(v_2^2 - v_1^2) = \frac{\rho}{2}v_1^2\left(\frac{A_1^2}{A_2^2} - 1\right)$$

$$\Delta P = \frac{\rho v_1}{2}(15) = 21,000 \text{ Pa.}$$

$$v_1 = 2 \text{ m/s} \quad v_2 = 8 \text{ m/s} \quad \text{and} \quad Q = v_1 A_1 = \boxed{6.28 \times 10^{-4} \text{ m}^3/\text{s}}$$

15.47 $\rho_{\text{Air}}\frac{v^2}{2} = \Delta P = \rho_{Hg}g\Delta h$

$$v = \sqrt{\frac{2\rho_{Hg}g\Delta h}{\rho_{\text{Air}}}} = \boxed{103 \text{ m/s}}$$

15.48   (a) $P_0 + \rho g h_1 + 0 = P_0 + 0 + \frac{1}{2}\rho v_3^2$

$v_3 = \sqrt{2gh_1}$

If $h_1 = 1$ m, $v_3 = \boxed{4.43 \text{ m/s}}$

(b) $P + \rho g h_2 + \frac{1}{2}\rho v_2^2 = P_0 + 0 + \frac{1}{2}\rho v_3^2$

Since $v_2 = v_3$,

$P = P_0 - \rho g h_2$

Since $P \geq 0$,

$h \leq \dfrac{P_0}{\rho g} = \dfrac{(1.013 \times 10^5)}{\text{Pa}}(10^3 \text{ kg/m}^3)(9.81 \text{ m/s}^2) = \boxed{10.3 \text{ m}}$

15.49 $mg(h_0 - h) = \frac{1}{2}mv_x^2$

$v_x^2 = 2g(h_0 - h)$

$v_x = \sqrt{2g(h_0 - h)}$

$x = v_x t$

$y = h = \frac{1}{2}gt^2$

$t = \sqrt{\dfrac{2h}{g}}$

$x = v_x\sqrt{\dfrac{2h}{g}}$

$x = \sqrt{2g(h_0 - h)}\sqrt{\dfrac{2h}{g}}$

$x = 2\sqrt{h(h_0 - h)}$

15.50 $x = v_x t$ $y = \frac{1}{2}gt^2$

$v_x = \sqrt{2g(20 - y)}$ and $t = \sqrt{\frac{2y}{g}}$

$x = \sqrt{2g(20 - y)}\sqrt{\frac{2y}{g}} = \sqrt{4y(20 - y)}$

Maximize x with respect to y :

$\frac{dx}{dy} = 0.$ $\frac{dx}{dy} = \frac{\frac{1}{2}(80 - 8y)}{\sqrt{4y(20 - y)}} = 0$ when $y = 10$ cm.

For $y = 10$ cm, $v_x = \sqrt{20g}$ $t = \sqrt{\frac{20}{g}}$.   Then $x = \boxed{20 \text{ cm}}$

15.50

15.51 $P = (\text{Eff.})\frac{\rho v^3 A}{2} = (0.20)(1.25)(8)^3(\pi)(5)^2 \cong \boxed{5 \text{ kW}}$

15.52   Power consumption $= \frac{8.3 \times 10^{19}}{(356)(24)(60)(60)} = 2.63 \times 10^{12}$ W

Power Output $= 200$ GW $= 2.00 \times 10^{11}$ W

Fraction of Power Supplied $= \frac{2.00 \times 10^{11}}{2.63 \times 10^{12}} = \boxed{0.076}$ or $\boxed{7.6\%}$

15.53   (a) $K = \frac{1}{2}mv^2 = \frac{1}{2}\rho V v^2$. In a time Δt, a column of air of

length Δx and area A passes through the blades.

Therefore $V = A\Delta x = A\frac{\Delta x}{\Delta t}\Delta t = Av\Delta t$

and $K = \frac{1}{2}\rho Av^3 \Delta t$.

(b) The power is $P = \frac{K}{\Delta}t = \frac{1}{2}\rho Av^3$.

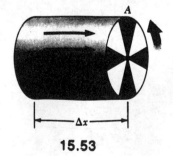

15.53

15.54 $RN = \dfrac{\rho v d}{\eta} = \dfrac{850 \times 3 \times 1.2}{0.3} = 10,200$

$\boxed{\text{Turbulent}}$

15.55 $\eta = \dfrac{\pi R^4 (P_A - P_B)}{8QL} = \dfrac{\pi (0.70 \times 10^{-3} \text{ m})^4 [(1.01 \times 10^5 \text{ Pa})/20]}{8[(292 \times 10^{-6} \text{ m}^3)/600 \text{ s}](1.50 \text{ m})}$

$= \boxed{0.652 \times 10^{-3} \text{ Pa} \cdot \text{s}}$

The liquid is water.

15.56 Buoyancy force $B = W_{\text{girl}} + W_{\text{block}}$. This can be written as

$\rho_{\text{water}} V_{\text{block}} g = W_{\text{girl}} + V_{\text{block}} \rho_{\text{block}} g$. Therefore

$\rho_{\text{block}} = \dfrac{\rho_{\text{water}} V_{\text{block}} g - W_{\text{girl}}}{V_{\text{block}} g}$

$= \dfrac{(10^3)(0.06)(9.80) - 490}{(0.06)(9.80)}$

$\rho_{\text{block}} = \boxed{1.67 \times 10^2 \text{ kg/m}^3}$ or $\rho_{\text{block}} = 0.167 \rho_{\text{water}}$

15.57 $B = -\dfrac{\Delta P}{\Delta V/V} = 14 \times 10^{10} \text{ N/m}^2$ for copper

If $\dfrac{\Delta \rho}{\rho} = 0.001$, then $\dfrac{\Delta V}{V} = -0.001$. Solving for ΔP gives

$\Delta P = -B(\dfrac{\Delta V}{V}) = (-14 \times 10^{10})(-0.001) = \boxed{1.4 \times 10^8 \text{ N/m}^2}$

15.58 The pressure on each side of the interface between the liquids

is equal. Therefore $p = p_a + \rho_1 g h_1 = P_a + \rho_2 g h_2$ and
$\rho_2 = (\dfrac{h_1}{h_2}) \rho_1$

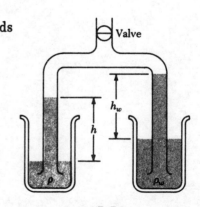

15.58

*15.59 Assume $v_{\text{inside}} \cong 0$

$$P + 0 + 0 \;=\; 1\,\text{atm} + \frac{1}{2}(1000)(30\,\text{m/s})^2 + 1000(9.8)(0.5)$$

$$P_{\text{gauge}} \;=\; P - 1\,\text{atm} = 4.5 \times 10^5 + 4.9 \times 10^3 = \boxed{455\,\text{kPa}}$$

*15.60 $\qquad\qquad P \;=\; \rho g h$

$$1.013 \times 10^5 \;=\; (1.3)(9.8)h$$

$$h \;=\; \boxed{7.95\,\text{km}}$$

For Mt. Everest, 29300 ft = 8.88 km $\boxed{\text{Yes}}$

15.61 The "balanced" condition is one in which the apparent weight of the body equals the apparent weight of the weights. This condition can be written as $W - W_b = W' - W_b'$, where W_b and W_b' are the buoyant forces on the body and weights respectively. The buoyant force experienced by an object of volume V in air equals (Volume of object) $(\rho_a g)$, so we have

$W_b = V\rho_a g$ and $W_b' = \dfrac{W'}{g}(\dfrac{1}{\rho})\rho_a g$. Therefore

$$W = W' + (V - \frac{W'}{\rho g})\rho_a g$$

*15.62 $\dfrac{2.46\ rad}{2\pi}\pi(0.6\ \text{cm})^2$

$$A_{\text{all}} \;=\; \pi(0.6)^2 = 1.13\ \text{cm}^2$$

$$A_{\text{water}}g\,A_{\text{under}} \;=\; \rho_{\text{wood}}A_{\text{all}}g$$

15.62

$$\rho_{\text{wood}} \;=\; \dfrac{1.13 - 0.330}{1.13} = 0.709 \qquad \boxed{709\ \text{kg/m}^3}$$

*15.63 $$\text{RN} = \dfrac{\rho v \text{d}}{\eta} \;=\; 2000$$

$$\dfrac{(1000\ \text{kg/m}^3)v(2.5 \times 10^{-2}\ \text{m})}{(10^{-3}\ \text{Pa}\cdot\text{s})} \;=\; 2000$$

$$25v \;=\; 2 \qquad \boxed{v = 8\ \text{cm/s}}$$

*15.64 $$P \;=\; Fv = \Delta P A\dfrac{d}{t} = \Delta P\dfrac{V}{t} = Q\Delta P$$

$$=\; (1.013 \times 10^5\ \text{N/m}^2)\left(\dfrac{50 \times 10^{-3}\ \text{m}^3}{\text{s}}\right) = \boxed{5.06\ \text{kW}}$$

15.65 $F = PA = (0.2\ \text{atm})(1.01 \times 10^5\ \text{Pa/atm})(99\ \text{m}^2)$

$$\boxed{F = 2 \times 10^6\ \text{N}}$$

*15.66 $v_1 A_1 = v_2 A_2$

$v_2 = \underline{45.6 \text{ m/s}}$

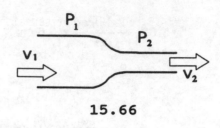

15.66

$10.2(1.013 \times 10^5 \text{ N/m}^2) + 0 + \frac{1}{2}(1000 \text{ kg/m}^3)(11.4 \text{ m/s})^2$

$= P_2 + \frac{1}{2}(1000 \text{ kg/m}^3)(45.6 \text{ m/s})^2$

$10.2(1.013 \times 10^5 \text{ N/m}^2) = P_2 + 9.747 \times 10^5$

$P_2 = 1.0333 \times 10^6 - 9.747 \times 10^5 = \boxed{58.6 \text{ kPa}}$

15.67   The torque is $\tau = \int d\tau = \int r\,dF$.

From Figure 15.67, we have

$$\tau = \int_0^H y[\rho g(H - y)w\,dy] = \frac{1}{6}\rho g w H^3$$

The total force is given as $\frac{1}{2}\rho g w H^2$.

If this were applied at a

height y_{eff} such that the torque

remains unchanged, we have

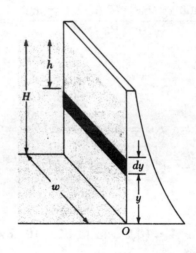

15.67

$\frac{1}{6}\rho g w H^3 = y_{\text{eff}}[\frac{1}{2}\rho g w H^2]$ and $y_{\text{eff}} = \boxed{\frac{1}{3}H}$

15.68   (a) The pressure on the surface of the two hemispheres is constant at

all points and the force on each element of surface area is directed

along the radius of the hemispheres. The applied force along the

axis must balance the force on the "effective" area which is the

projection of the actual surface onto a plane perpendicular to the

x-axis, $A = \pi R^2$. Therefore $F = (P_a - P)\pi R^2$.

(b) For the values given

$$F = (P_a - 0.1P_a)\pi(0.3 \text{ m})^2 - 0.254 P_a$$

$$= (0.254 \text{ m}^2)(1.01 \times 10^5 \text{ N/m}^2) = \boxed{2.57 \times 10^4 \text{ N}}$$

15.68

*15.69

$$\rho_{Cu} V = 3.083 \text{ g}$$

$$\rho_{Zn}(xV) + \rho_{Cu}(1 - x)V = 2.517 \text{ g}$$

$$\rho_{Zn}\left(\frac{3.083}{\rho_{Cu}}\right) x + 3.083(1 - x) = 2.517$$

$$\left(1 - \frac{7.133}{8.960}\right) x = \left(1 - \frac{2.517}{3.083}\right)$$

$$x = 0.9004$$

$$\%Zn = \boxed{90.04\%}$$

*15.70

$$F = \frac{d(mv)}{dt} = \left(\frac{dm}{dt}\right)_{\text{air}} v_{\text{air}} = (mg)_{\text{helo}}$$

$$\left(\frac{dm}{dt}\right)_{\text{air}} = \frac{(mg)_{\text{helo}}}{v_{\text{air}}} = \frac{(800)(9.8)}{40} = \boxed{196 \text{ kg/s}}$$

15.71   Power $= \dfrac{dE}{dt} = \dfrac{d}{dt}(mgh) = \dfrac{dm}{dt}(gh)$

Power $= [3200(1000) \text{ kg/s}](9.8 \text{ m/s}^2)(160 \text{ m})$

$$= 5 \times 10^9 \text{ W} = \boxed{5000 \text{ MW}}$$

(Actual turbine efficiencies are on the order of 90%.)

15.72 (a) Weight of granite = Weight of "fluid" displaced.

$$\rho_g t A g = \rho_p d A g \qquad \rho_g t = \rho_p d$$

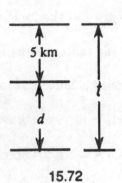

15.72

(b) $\rho_g t = \rho_p d$

$$d = t - 5 \ \text{km}$$

$$\frac{\rho_g}{\rho_p} t = t - 5$$

$$\frac{\rho_g}{\rho_p} = \frac{2800 \ \text{kg/m}^3}{3300 \ \text{kg/m}^3} = 0.848$$

$$0.848t = t - 5$$

$$0.152t = 5 \ \text{km}$$

$$\boxed{t \cong 33 \ \text{km}}$$

15.73 (a) $\rho_{av} = \dfrac{M}{V} = \dfrac{\rho_1 s^2 h_1 + \rho_2 s^2 h_2}{s^2 (h_1 + h_2)} = \dfrac{\rho_1 h_1 + \rho_2 h_2}{h_1 + h_2}$

(b) We need $\rho_w s^2 d = M$ so $d = \dfrac{M}{\rho_w s^2} = \dfrac{\rho_1 h_1 s^2 + \rho_2 h_2 s^2}{\rho_w s^2}$

(c) Same result $d' = d$

(d) Gravitational energy of water is same in both cases; but

gravitational potential energy of the raft differs. The potential

energy is higher when slab #2 is on top.

P.E. Difference = gm_2 (height diff. of C. of M. #2)

$-gm_1$ (height diff. of C. M. of #1)

$= gm_2 [\dfrac{h_1 + h_2}{2} - \dfrac{h}{2}] - gm_1 [\dfrac{h_2 + h_1}{2} - \dfrac{h_1}{2}]$

P.E. Difference = $g(m_2 h_1 - m_1 h_2)$; but $m_2 = \rho_2 s^2 h_2$ and $m_1 = \rho_1 s^2 h_1$

so P.E. Diff. = $gs^2(\rho_2 h_2 h_1 - \rho_1 h_2 h_1) = (\rho_2 - \rho_1)s^2 h_1 h_2 g$

*15.74 (a) $P = \dfrac{\Delta E}{\Delta t} = \dfrac{\Delta mgH}{\Delta t} = \left(\dfrac{\Delta m}{\Delta t}\right)gH$

(b) $P_{EL} = .85(8.5 \times 10^5)(9.8)(87) = \boxed{616\ \text{MW}}$

15.75 (a) The required tension T_ℓ is given by

$$T_\ell = M_b g - \frac{M_b}{\rho_b}\rho_w g = (1 - \frac{\rho_w}{\rho_b})M_b g$$

(b) $T_u = T_\ell + [(1 - \frac{\rho_w}{\rho_c})\rho_c \pi d^2 \frac{h}{4}]g$

(c) $T'_\ell = M_b g; \quad T'_\mu = T'_\ell + \frac{1}{4}\rho_c \pi d^2 hg$

(d) $\quad T_\ell = (1 - \dfrac{1}{2.38})(2 \times 10^3)(9.81) = \boxed{1.14 \times 10^4\ \text{N}}$

$T_u = (1.138 \times 10^4) + [(1 - \dfrac{1}{7.86})(7.86 \times 10^3)\pi(2 \times 10^{-2})^2(100)(9.81)/4]$

$\quad = (1.138 + 0.211) \times 10^4 = \boxed{1.35 \times 10^4\ \text{N}}$

$T'_\ell = M_b g = \boxed{1.96 \times 10^4\ \text{N}}; \quad T_{u'} - T'_\ell = \dfrac{\rho_c \pi d^2 hg}{4} = 2.422 \times 10^3\ \text{N}$

$\Rightarrow T'_u = (1.962 + 0.2422) \times 10^4 = \boxed{2.20 \times 10^4\ \text{N}}$

15.76 From Eq. 15.9, we have $\dfrac{dP}{dy} = -\rho g$. Also at any given height the

density of air is proportional to pressure, or $\dfrac{P}{\rho} = \dfrac{P_0}{\rho_0}$. Combining

these two equations we have $\displaystyle\int_{P_0}^{P}\dfrac{dP}{P} = -g\dfrac{\rho_0}{P_0}\int_{0}^{h}dy$; and integrating gives

$P = P_0 e^{-\alpha h}$

15.77 Let s stand for the edge of the cube, h for the depth of immersion, ρ_c stand for the density of the ice, ρ_w stand for density of water, and ρ_a stand for density of the alcohol.

(a) According to Archimedes' principle, at equilibrium we have

$$\rho_c g s^3 = \rho_w g h s^2 \quad \Longrightarrow \quad h = s \frac{\rho_c}{\rho_w}$$

With $\rho_c = 0.917 \times 10^3 \text{ kg/m}^3$, $\rho_w = 1.00 \times 10^3 \text{ kg/m}^3$, and $s = 20$ mm, we get $h = 20(0.917) = 18.34 \text{ mm} \approx \boxed{18.3 \text{ mm}}$

(b) We assume that the top of the cube is still above the alcohol surface. Letting h_a stand for the thickness of the alcohol layer, we have

$$\rho_a g s^2 h_a + \rho_w g s^2 h_w = \rho_c g s^3 \quad \Longrightarrow \quad h_w = (\rho_c/\rho_w)s - (\rho_a/\rho_w)h_a$$

With $\rho_a = 0.806 \times 10^3 \text{ kg/m}^3$ and $h_a = 5$ mm, we obtain

$$h_w = 18.34 - (0.806)(5) = 14.31 \text{ mm} \approx \boxed{14.3 \text{ mm}}$$

(c) Here $h_w' = s - h_a'$, so Archimedes' principle gives...

$$\rho_a g s^2 h_a' + \rho_w g s^2 (s - h_a') = \rho_c s^3 \Longrightarrow \rho_a h_a' + \rho_w (s - h_a') = \rho_c s$$

$$\Longrightarrow h_a' = \frac{s(\rho_w - \rho_c)}{(\rho_w - \rho_a)} = 20 \frac{(1.000 - 0.917)}{(1.000 - 0.806)}$$

$$= 8.557 \approx \boxed{8.56 \text{ mm}}$$

CHAPTER 16

16.1 Replace x by $x - vt = x - 4.5t$ to get $y = \dfrac{6}{[(x - 4.5t)^2 + 3]}$

16.2

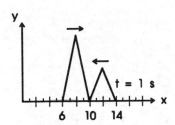

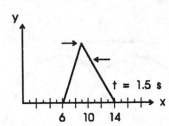

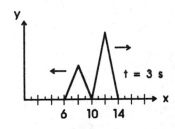

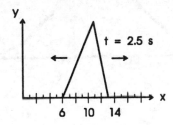

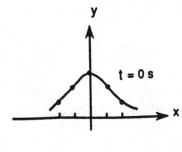

16-2

16.3

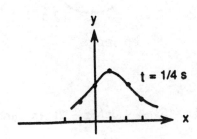

16.3

16.4 Solution:

(a) Since any wave function must be of the form $y = f(x - vt), v = -2$ cm/s.

(b) Plotting the function at $t = 0$ and $t = 1$,

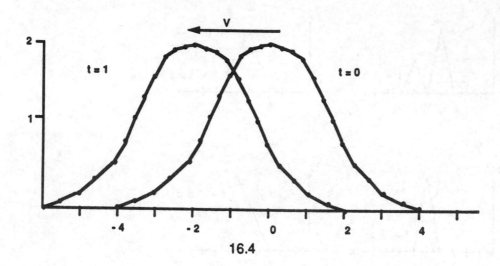

16.4

*16.5 (a)

16.5a

(b)

16.5b

16.6 Solution: $y = 3\cos(4x - 5t) + 4\sin(5x - 2t)$ evaluated at the given x and t values.

(a) $y = 2.19$

(b) $y = -2.81$

(c) $y = 1.15$

16.7 Solution:

(a) $\phi_1 = 20(5) - 30(2) = 40$ rad $\qquad \phi_2 = 25(5) - 40(2) = 45$ rad

$\Delta\phi = 5$ radians $= 286° = \boxed{-74°}$

(b) $\Delta\phi = |20x - 30t - [25x - 40t]| = |-5x + 10t| = |-5x + 20| = \pm\pi$

for $x < 4$, $-5x + 20 = \pm\pi$

$5x = 20 \pm \pi$

$x = 4 \pm \pi = 7.14,\ \boxed{0.858 \text{ cm}}$

16.8 Solution: $y = \dfrac{1}{ax - bt} + \dfrac{1}{ax + bt} = \dfrac{ax + bt + ax - bt}{(ax - bt)(ax + bt)} = \dfrac{2ax}{a^2x^2 - b^2t^2}$

The non-physical points are when $x = \pm bt/a$ since the relation is undefined at these points.

16.9 (a) $y_1 = f(x - vt)$, so wave 1 travels in $+x$ direction.

$y_2 = f(x + vt)$, so wave 2 travels in $-x$ direction.

(b) To cancel, $y_1 + y_2 = 0$:

$$\frac{5}{(3x - 4t)^2 + 2} = \frac{+5}{(3x + 4t - 6)^2 + 2}$$

$(3x - 4t)^2 = (3x + 4t - 6)^2$

$3x - 4t = \pm(3x + 4t - 6)$

$+\text{root} \longrightarrow 8t = 6 \longrightarrow t = 0.75$ s (at $t = 0.75$ s, the waves cancel everywhere)

$-\text{root} \longrightarrow 6x = 6 \longrightarrow x = 1$ (at $x = 1$, the waves cancel always.)

16.10 $v = \sqrt{\dfrac{F}{\mu}}$; $F = v^2\mu = v^2(\dfrac{m}{\ell}) = (50 \text{ m/s})^2(\dfrac{0.06 \text{ kg}}{5 \text{ m}}) = \boxed{30 \text{ N}}$

*16.11 $v = \sqrt{\dfrac{T}{\mu}} = \sqrt{\dfrac{1350 \text{kg} \cdot \text{m/s}^2}{0.005 \text{ kg s}^2}} = \boxed{520 \text{ kg/m}}$

16.12 $\mu = \dfrac{F}{v^2} = \dfrac{20 \text{ N}}{(60 \text{ m/s})^2} = 5.56 \times 10^{-3} \text{ kg/m}$

$M = \mu L = (5.56 \times 10^{-3} \text{ kg/m})(15 \text{ m}) = \boxed{8.33 \times 10^{-2} \text{ kg}}$

16.13 $\mu = \dfrac{F}{v^2} = \dfrac{6 \text{ N}}{(20 \text{ m/s})^2} = 0.015 \text{ kg/m}$

$F' = \mu v'^2 = (0.015 \text{ kg/m})(30 \text{ m/s})^2 = \boxed{13.5 \text{ N}}$

*16.14 $v = \sqrt{\dfrac{F}{\mu}} = \sqrt{\dfrac{430 \text{ kg} \cdot \text{m/s}^2}{0.5 \text{ kg/m}}} = \boxed{82.9 \text{ m/s}}$

16.15 $v = \sqrt{\dfrac{F}{\mu}} = \sqrt{\dfrac{As}{\rho A}} = \sqrt{\dfrac{s}{\rho}}$

$v_{\max} = \sqrt{\dfrac{2.7 \times 10^9 \text{ Pa}}{7.86 \times 10^3 \text{ kg/m}^3}} = \boxed{586 \text{ m/s}}$

16.16 $F = \mu v^2 = (\rho \dfrac{\pi d^2}{4})v^2 = \dfrac{1}{4}(8.93 \times 10^3 \text{ kg/m}^3)(1.5 \times 10^{-3} \text{ m})^2 \pi (200 \text{ m/s})^2 = \boxed{631 \text{ N}}$

16.17 Solution: The total time is the sum of the two times.

In one wire $t = L/v = L\sqrt{\mu/T}$ where $\mu = \rho A = \pi \rho d^2/4$

Thus, $t = L(\pi \rho d^2/4T)^{\frac{1}{2}}$

For copper $t = (20)[(\pi)(8920)(0.001)^2/(4)(150)]^{\frac{1}{2}} = 0.137$ s

For steel $t = (30)[(\pi)(7860)(0.001)^2/(4)(150)]^{\frac{1}{2}} = 0.192$ s

The total time is $0.137 + 0.192 = \boxed{0.329 \text{ s}}$

16.18 From the free–body diagram,

$$mg = 2T \sin \theta$$

$$T = \frac{mg}{2 \sin \theta}$$

The angle θ is found from

$$\cos \theta = \frac{3L/8}{L/2} = \frac{3}{4} \quad \therefore \quad \theta = 41.4°$$

(a) $v = \sqrt{\dfrac{T}{\mu}} = \sqrt{\dfrac{mg}{2\mu \sin 41.4°}} = 30.4\sqrt{m}$

(b) $v = 60 = 30.4\sqrt{m}$ and $\boxed{m = 3.9 \text{ kg}}$

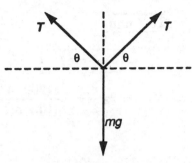

Free Body Diagram

16.18

16.19 $y = 15 \cos(0.157x - 50.3t)$

(a) See Figure at right.

(b) $T = \dfrac{2\pi}{\omega} = \dfrac{2\pi}{50.3} = \boxed{0.125 \text{ s}}$

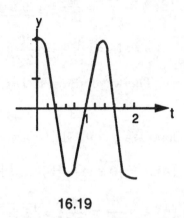

16.19

16.20 Using data from the observations we have $\lambda = 1.2$ m and

$f = (8/12)$ s^{-1}. Therefore $v = f\lambda = [(8/12) \text{ s}^{-1}](1.2 \text{ m}) = \boxed{0.80 \text{ m/s}}$

16.21 $f = \dfrac{40 \text{ vibrations}}{30 \text{ s}} = \dfrac{4}{3} \text{ Hz}$

$v = \dfrac{425 \text{ cm}}{10 \text{ s}} = 42.5 \text{ cm/s}$

$\lambda = \dfrac{v}{f} = \dfrac{42.5 \text{ cm/s}}{(4/3 \text{ Hz})} = 31.9 \text{ cm} = \boxed{0.319 \text{ m}}$

16.22 $v = f\lambda = (4 \text{ Hz})(60 \text{ cm}) = 240 \text{ cm/s} = \boxed{2.40 \text{ m/s}}$

*16.23 $A = \boxed{0.7 \text{ mm}}$

$k = \dfrac{2\pi}{\lambda} = \boxed{31.4 \text{ rad/m}}$

$\omega = 2\pi f = 2\pi \dfrac{v}{\lambda} = \dfrac{2\pi(200 \text{ m/s})}{(0.2 \text{ m})} = \boxed{6.28 \text{ krad/s}}$

16.24 $y = 0.25 \sin(0.3x - 40t)$ m

Compare this with the general expression $y = A\sin(kx - \omega t)$

(a) $A = \boxed{0.25 \text{ m}}$ (b) $\omega = \boxed{40 \text{ rad/s}}$ (c) $k = \boxed{0.3 \text{ m}^{-1}}$

(d) $\lambda = \dfrac{2\pi}{k} = \dfrac{2\pi}{0.3} = \boxed{20.9 \text{ m}}$

(e) $v = f\lambda = \dfrac{\omega}{2\pi}\lambda = (\dfrac{40}{2\pi})(20.9) = \boxed{133 \text{ m/s}}$

(f) The wave moves to the right, along $+x$ direction.

16.25 Compare $y = 0.2 \sin 4\pi(0.4x + t)$ with $y = A\sin(kx + \omega t)$.

(a) $A = \boxed{0.2 \text{ m}}$ (b) $\omega = \boxed{4\pi \text{ rad/s}}$ (c) $k = 1.6\pi = \boxed{5.03 \text{ m}^{-1}}$

(d) $\lambda = \dfrac{2\pi}{k} = \dfrac{2\pi}{5.03} = \boxed{1.25 \text{ m}}$

(e) $v = f\lambda = \dfrac{\omega}{2\pi}\lambda = \dfrac{4\pi}{2\pi}(1.25) = \boxed{2.50 \text{ m/s}}$

(f) The wave moves to the *left*.

16.26 (a) See figure at right.

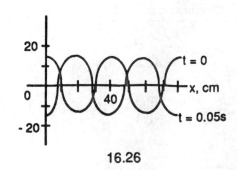

16.26

(b) $c = f\lambda = \dfrac{\omega}{2\pi}\lambda = \dfrac{\omega}{2\pi}\dfrac{2\pi}{k} = \dfrac{\omega}{k}$

$c = \dfrac{\omega}{k} = \dfrac{50.3/\text{s}}{0.157/\text{cm}} = \boxed{320 \text{ cm/s}}$

16.27   (a) $A = y_{max} = 8$ cm $= 0.08$ m; $k = 2\pi/\lambda = 2\pi/(0.8$ m$) = 7.85$ m^{-1}

$\omega = 2\pi f = 2\pi(3) = 6\pi$ rad/s; therefore, $y = A\sin(kx + \omega t)$,

or $y = 0.08\sin(7.85x + 6\pi t)$ m,   (where $y = 0$ at $t = 0$).

(b) In general, $y = 0.08\sin(7.85x + 6\pi t + \phi)$.

Assuming $y(x,0) = 0$ at $x = 0.1$ m,   then we require that

$0 = 0.08\sin(0.785 + \phi)$,   or $\phi = -0.785$ rad.

Therefore, $y = 0.08\sin(7.85x + 6\pi t - 0.785)$ m.

*16.28 $y = (0.12$ m$)\sin\left(\dfrac{\pi}{8}x + 4\pi t\right)$

(a) $v = \dfrac{dy}{dt} = (0.12)(4\pi)\cos\left(\dfrac{\pi}{8}x + 4\pi t\right)$

$v(0.2$ s$, 1.6$ m$) = \boxed{-1.51 \text{ m/s}}$

$a = \dfrac{dv}{dt} = (-0.12$ m$)(4\pi)^2\sin\left(\dfrac{\pi}{8}x + 4\pi t\right)$

$a(0.2$ s$, 1.6$ m$) = \boxed{0}$

(b) $k = \dfrac{\pi}{8} = \dfrac{2\pi}{\lambda}$ $\lambda = \boxed{16 \text{ m}}$

$\omega = 4\pi = \dfrac{2\pi}{T}$ $T = \boxed{500 \text{ ms}}$

$v = \dfrac{\lambda}{T} = \dfrac{16 \text{ m}}{0.5 \text{ s}} = \boxed{32.0 \text{ m/s}}$

16.29 (a) $y(0,0) = A \cos \phi_0 = 0.02$ m

$$\frac{dy}{dt}\big|_{0,0} = -A\omega \, \sin \phi_0 = -2.0 \text{ m/s}$$

Also,

$$\omega = \frac{2\pi}{T} = \frac{2\pi}{0.025 \text{ s}}$$

$$A^2 = (0.02 \text{ m})^2 + \left(\frac{2.0 \text{ m/s}}{2\pi/0.025 \text{ s}}\right)^2$$

$$A = 0.0215 \text{ m} = \boxed{2.15 \text{ cm}}$$

(b) $\phi_0 = \tan^{-1} \dfrac{0.025/\pi}{0.02} = 21.7° = \boxed{0.379 \text{ rad}}$

(c) $v_{y,\text{max}} = A\omega = 2\pi(2.2 \text{ cm})/0.025 \text{ s} = \boxed{541 \text{ cm/s}}$

(d) $\lambda = v_x T = (30 \text{ m/s})(0.025 \text{ s}) = 0.75$ m

$$k = \frac{2\pi}{\lambda} = \frac{2\pi}{0.75} = \frac{8\pi}{3}$$

$$\omega = \frac{2\pi}{0.025} = 80\pi$$

$$y(x,t) = (2.15 \text{ cm}) \cos\left(80\pi t + \frac{8\pi x}{3} + 0.379\right)$$

16.30 (a) Use the form of the wave equation found in part (d) of Problem 29:

$$y = A \sin\left[2\pi\left(\frac{x}{\lambda} - ft\right) + \phi\right]$$

Then $y = (0.08 \text{ m}) \sin[2\pi(x/0.8) - 3t + \phi]$.

Since $y(0,0) = y_{\text{max}} = 0.08$ m; we have $\sin \phi = 1$.

Therefore $\phi = \pi/2$ and $y = (0.08 \text{ m}) \sin[2\pi(x/0.8) - 3t + (\pi/2)]$ or

$y = (0.08 \text{ m}) \cos[2\pi(x/0.8) - 3t]$.

(b) $k = \dfrac{2\pi}{\lambda} = \dfrac{2\pi}{(0.8 \text{ m})} = \boxed{7.85 \text{ m}^{-1}}$

$$v = \frac{\omega}{k} = \frac{(6\pi \text{ s}^{-1})}{(7.85 \text{ m}^{-1})} = \boxed{2.40 \text{ m/s}}$$

*16.31 $\psi = (0.02\text{ m})\sin(2.11x - 3.62t)$ SI units

$A = \boxed{2.00\text{ cm}}$

$k = \boxed{2.11\text{ rad/m}}$

$\lambda = \dfrac{2\pi}{k} = \boxed{2.98\text{ m}}$

$\omega = \boxed{3.62\text{ rad/s}}$

$v = f\lambda = \dfrac{\omega}{2\pi}\dfrac{2\pi}{k} = \dfrac{\omega}{k} = \dfrac{3.62}{2.11} = \boxed{1.72\text{ m/s}}$

*16.32 $\psi = (0.51\text{ cm})\sin(3.1x - 9.3t)$ SI units

$v = \dfrac{w}{k} = \dfrac{9.3}{3.1} = 3.00\text{ m/s}$

$s = vt = \boxed{30.0\text{ m}}$ $\boxed{\text{positive}}$

*16.33   (a) $y = (0.2\text{ mm})\ \sin(16.0x - 3140t)$ (SI units)

(b) $v = 196\text{ m/s} = \sqrt{\dfrac{T}{4.1 \times 10^{-3}\text{ kg/m}}}$

$T = \boxed{158\ N}$

16.34   (a) at $x = 2$ m $y = 10\sin(-20t + 1)$

$y = (0.10\text{ m})\sin(0.5x - 20t)$

(b) $\omega = 20$ rad/s so $f = 3.18$ Hz

At $t = 0$, the phase angle is $+1$ radian.

16.35 $f = \dfrac{v}{\lambda} = \dfrac{30}{0.5} = 60$ Hz; $\omega = 2\pi f = 120\pi$ rad/s

$P = \dfrac{1}{2}\mu\omega^2 A^2 v = \dfrac{1}{2}(\dfrac{0.18}{3.6})(120\pi)^2(0.2)^2(30) = \boxed{1.07\text{ kW}}$

16.42 Eq. 16.26, with $v = \sqrt{F/\mu}$ is

$$\frac{\partial^2 y}{\partial t^2} = \frac{1}{v^2}\frac{\partial^2 y}{\partial t^2}$$

If $y = e^{A(x-vt)}$

Then $\dfrac{\partial y}{\partial t} = -Ave^{A(x-vt)}$ and $\dfrac{\partial y}{\partial x} = Ae^{A(x-vt)}$

$\dfrac{\partial^2 y}{\partial t^2} = A^2 v^2 e^{A(x-vt)}$ and $\dfrac{\partial^2 y}{\partial x^2} = A^2 e^{A(x-vt)}$

Therefore $\dfrac{\partial^2 y}{\partial t^2} = v^2\dfrac{\partial^2 y}{\partial x^2}$, and $e^{A(x-vt)}$ is a solution.

16.43 (a) $y = A\sin(kx - \omega t) + B\cos(kx - \omega t)$

$$\frac{\partial^2 y}{\partial t^2} = -\omega^2 A\sin(kx - \omega t) - \omega^2 B\cos(kx - \omega t)$$

$$\frac{\partial^2 y}{\partial x^2} = -k^2 A\sin(kx - \omega t) - k^2 B\cos(kx - \omega t).$$

Substituting into the general wave equation shows that this is a solution.

(b) $y = A(\sin kx)B(\cos \omega t)$

$$\frac{\partial^2 y}{\partial t^2} = -AB\omega^2(\sin kx)(\cos \omega t)$$

$$\frac{\partial^2 y}{\partial x^2} = -ABk^2(\sin kx)(\cos \omega t)$$

Substitution into the general wave equation shows that this is also a solution.

16.44 Compare the given wave function $y = 4\sin(2.0x - 3.0t)$ cm to the

general form (Eq. 16.11) $y = A\sin(kx - \omega t)$ to find

(a) amplitude $A = 4$ cm = $\boxed{0.04 \text{ m}}$

(b) $k = \dfrac{2\pi}{\lambda} = 2$ cm^{-1} and $\lambda = \pi$ cm = $\boxed{0.031 \text{ m}}$

(c) $\omega = 2\pi f = 3$ s^{-1} and $f = \boxed{0.477 \text{ Hz}}$

(d) $T = \dfrac{1}{f} = \boxed{2.09 \text{ s}}$

(e) The minus sign indicates that the wave is traveling toward the right.

16.45 (a) Let $u = 10\pi t - 3\pi x + \dfrac{\pi}{4}$

$$\frac{du}{dt} = 10\pi - 3\pi \frac{dx}{dt} = 0$$

$$\frac{dx}{dt} = \frac{10}{3} = \boxed{3.33 \text{ m/s}}$$

The velocity is in the positive x-direction.

(b) $y(0.10, 0) = (0.35 \text{ m}) \sin(-0.3\pi + \dfrac{\pi}{4}) = -0.0548 \text{ m} = \boxed{-5.48 \text{ cm}}$

(c) $k = \dfrac{2\pi}{\lambda} = 3\pi$

$\lambda = \boxed{0.667 \text{ m}}$

$\omega = 2\pi f = 10\pi$

$f = \boxed{5.00 \text{ Hz}}$

(d) $v_y = \dfrac{dv}{dt} = (0.35)(10\,\pi)\cos(10\,\pi t - 3\pi t + \dfrac{\pi}{4})$

$v_{y,\text{max}} = (10\,\pi)(0.35) = \boxed{11.0 \text{ m/s}}$

16.46 $\bar{P} = \dfrac{2\pi^2 F A^2 f}{\lambda} = \dfrac{2\pi^2 \mu v^2 A^2 f}{\lambda}$

$= 2\pi^2 \mu v A^2 f^2$

$= 2\pi^2 (0.075 \text{ kg/m})(\dfrac{10}{3} \text{ m/s})(0.35 \text{ m})^2 (5 \text{ s}^{-1})^2 = \boxed{15.1 \text{ W}}$

$E = \bar{P}t = \dfrac{15.1 \text{ W}}{5 \text{ s}^{-1}} = \boxed{3.0 \text{ J}}$

16.47 (a) $v = \sqrt{\dfrac{F}{\mu}} = \sqrt{\dfrac{80 \text{ N}}{(0.005 \text{ kg/2 m})}} = \boxed{179 \text{ m/s}}$

(b) From Eq. 16.21, $P = \dfrac{1}{2}\mu v \omega^2 A^2$ and $\omega = 2\pi(\dfrac{v}{\lambda})$

$P = \dfrac{1}{2}\mu v A^2 (\dfrac{2\pi v}{\lambda})^2 = 2\pi^2 \mu A^2 v^3 (\dfrac{1}{\lambda^2})$

$P = 2\pi^2 (0.005 \text{ kg/2 m})(0.04 \text{ m})^2 (179 \text{ m/s})^3 (\dfrac{1}{0.16 \text{ m}})^2$

$= 1.77 \times 10^4 \text{ W} = \boxed{17.7 \text{ kW}}$

16.48 $v = \sqrt{\dfrac{F}{\mu}}$ and in this case $F = mg$; therefore $m = \dfrac{\mu v^2}{g}$. From

Eq. 16.13, $v = \omega/k$ so that

$$\begin{aligned} m &= \frac{\mu}{g}\left(\frac{\omega}{k}\right)^2 = \frac{0.25 \text{ kg/m}}{9.80 \text{ m/s}^2}\left[\frac{18\pi \text{ s}^{-1}}{0.75\pi \text{ m}^{-1}}\right]^2 \\ &= \boxed{14.7 \text{ kg}} \end{aligned}$$

16.49 $y(0,0) = 15\cos(0)$ and $y(x,0) = 15\cos(0.157x)$

Therefore $0.157x = 60° = \pi/3$ rad or

$$x = \frac{\pi/3}{0.157 \text{ cm}^{-1}} = \boxed{6.67 \text{ cm}}$$

*16.50 $v = f\lambda = \dfrac{8}{(60 \text{ s})}(120 \text{ m}) = \boxed{16.0 \text{ m/s}}$

*16.51 (a) $v = \dfrac{\omega}{k} = \dfrac{15}{3} = \boxed{5.00 \text{ m/s}} + x$

 (b) $v = \dfrac{15}{3} = \boxed{5.00 \text{ m/s}} - x$

 (c) $v = \dfrac{15}{2} = \boxed{7.50 \text{ m/s}} - x$

 (d) $v = \dfrac{12}{1/2} = \boxed{24.0 \text{ m/s}} + x$

16.52 $v = \sqrt{\dfrac{F}{\mu}}$ where $F = \mu x g$, the weight of a length x, of rope.

Therefore $v = \sqrt{gx}$. But $v = \dfrac{dx}{dt}$ so that $dt = \dfrac{dx}{\sqrt{gx}}$ and

$$t = \int_0^\ell \frac{dx}{\sqrt{gx}} = \boxed{2\sqrt{\frac{\ell}{g}}}$$

16.53 Solution:

(a) $\mu = \dfrac{dm}{dL} = \rho A \dfrac{dx}{dx} = \rho A$

$v = \sqrt{F/\mu} = \sqrt{F/\rho A} = \sqrt{F/[\rho(ax+b)]}$

$= \sqrt{F/[\rho(10^{-3}x + 10^{-2})\text{cm}^2]}$.

With all MKS units, $v = \sqrt{F/\rho(10^{-3}x + 10^{-2})10^{-4}}$ m/s

(b) $v = \sqrt{24/[(2700)(0.01)(10^{-4})]} = \boxed{94.3 \text{ m/s}}$

$v = \sqrt{24/[(2700)(0.02)(10^{-4})]} = \boxed{66.7 \text{ m/s}}$

*16.54 (a) $p = (1.27 \text{ Pa}) \sin \pi(x - 340t)$ (SI units)

$\boxed{1.27 \text{ Pa}}$

(b) $\omega = 340\pi = 2\pi f$

$f = \boxed{170 \text{ Hz}}$

(c) $\pi = k = \dfrac{2\pi}{\lambda}$

$\lambda = \boxed{2.00 \text{ m}}$

(d) $v = f\lambda = \boxed{340 \text{ m/s}}$

16.55 Young's modulus, $Y \equiv \dfrac{F/A}{\Delta \ell/\ell}$, mass density, $\rho = \dfrac{\mu}{A}$ and

$v = \sqrt{\dfrac{F}{\mu}} = \sqrt{\dfrac{F/A}{\mu/A}} = \sqrt{\dfrac{Y(\Delta \ell/\ell)}{\rho}} = 100$ m/s

$\dfrac{\Delta \ell}{\ell} = \dfrac{\rho v^2}{Y} = \dfrac{(2700)(10^4)}{7.0 \times 10^{10}} = \boxed{3.86 \times 10^{-4}}$

16.56   (a) For an increment of spring length dx and mass dm, $F = ma$ becomes

$k\,dx = a\,dm$, or $\dfrac{k}{(dm/dx)} = a$. But $\dfrac{dm}{dx} = \mu$ so $a = \dfrac{k}{\mu}$.

Also $a = \dfrac{dv}{dt} = \dfrac{v}{t}$ when $v_0 = 0$. But $\ell = vt$ so $a = \dfrac{v^2}{\ell}$.

Equating the two expressions for a, we have $\dfrac{k}{\mu} = \dfrac{v^2}{\ell}$ or

$$v = \sqrt{\frac{k\ell}{\mu}}.$$

(b) Using the expression from part (a)

$$v = (\frac{k\ell}{\mu})^{1/2} = (\frac{k\ell^2}{m})^{1/2} = [\frac{(100\ \text{N/m})(2\ \text{m})^2}{(0.4\ \text{rmkg})}]^{1/2} = \boxed{31.6\ \text{m/s}}$$

16.57   (a) The speed in the lower half of a rope of length ℓ is the same

function of distance (from the bottom end) as the speed along the

entire length of a rope of length $\ell/2$.

Thus the time required $= 2(\ell'/g)^{1/2}$;   with $\ell' = \ell/2$

the time required $= (1/2)^{1/2}\,2(\ell/g)^{1/2} = (2\ell/g)^{1/2}$

It takes the pulse more than 70% of the total time to cover 50% of

the distance.

(b) By the same reasoning applied in part (a), the distance climbed in a

time τ is given by $g\tau^2/4$. For $\tau = t/2 = (\ell/g)^{1/2}$, we find the

distance climbed $= \ell/4$. In half the total trip time, the pulse has

climbed 1/4 of the total length.

16.58   (a) $v = (F/\mu)^{1/2} = (2F_0/\mu_0)^{1/2} = v_0 2^{1/2}$

$v' = (F/\mu')^{1/2} = (2F_0/3\mu_0)^{1/2} = \boxed{v_0(2/3)^{1/2}}$

(b) $t_{\text{left}} = \dfrac{L/2}{v} = \dfrac{L}{2 \times 2^{1/2} \times v_0} = 0.3536T_0$

$t_{\text{right}} = \dfrac{L/2}{v'} = \dfrac{L}{2(2/3)^{1/2}v_0} = 0.6124T_0$

$t_{\text{left}} + t_{\text{right}} = 0.966T_0$

16.59 (a) $P = \frac{1}{2}\mu\omega^2 A^2 v = \frac{1}{2}\mu\omega^2 A_0^2 e^{-2bx}\left(\frac{\omega}{k}\right) = \frac{\mu\omega^2}{2k} A_0^2 e^{-2bx}$

(b) $P_0 = \frac{\mu\omega^3}{2k} A_0^2$

(c) $\frac{P(x)}{P(0)} = e^{-2bx}$

16.60 $y_1(x,t) = 6(x-3t)^{-2}$, Traveling Right

$y_2(x,t) = -3(x+3t)^{-2}$, Traveling Left

$y = (y_1 + y_2) = 6(x-3t)^{-2} - 3(x+3t)^{-2}$

(a) Choose x_{min} and x_{max}, then set $t = 0$.

(b) Plot the point $[x_{min}, (y_1 + y_2)]$

(c) Then increment x. $x = x + 0.1$ (cm).

(d) Plot $[x, y]$ for the new x value.

(e) Continue in a do loop until $x = x_{max}$.

(f) The plot of $y(x)$ for $t = 0$ is then complete.

Then start a new plot with $t = 0.5$ s ...

CHAPTER 17

17.1 Since $v_{\text{light}} \gg v_{\text{sound}}$,

$$d \cong (343 \text{ m/s})(16.2 \text{ s}) = \boxed{5.56 \text{ km}}$$

17.2 Let d be the distance the stone drops.

$$t = \frac{d}{v_s} + \sqrt{\frac{2d}{g}}$$

$$d + \sqrt{\frac{2}{g}}v_s\sqrt{d} - v_s t = 0$$

$$\sqrt{d} = -\frac{1}{2}\left(\sqrt{\frac{2}{g}}v_s \pm \sqrt{\frac{2v_s^2}{g} + 4v_s t}\right)$$

$$= \frac{1}{2}(-1.50.9 \pm \sqrt{36394})$$

Choose the positive root so that $\sqrt{d} > 0$.

$$\sqrt{d} = 19.9 \sqrt{m}$$

$$d = 397 \text{ m}$$

If the speed of sound is ignored,

$$t = \sqrt{\frac{2d'}{g}}$$

$$d' = \frac{1}{2}gt^2 = 510 \text{ m}$$

The percentage error is given by

$$\frac{d' - d}{d} = 0.28 = 28\%$$

17.3 $v = \sqrt{\dfrac{B}{\rho}} = \sqrt{\dfrac{2.8 \times 10^{10}}{13.6 \times 10^3}} = \boxed{1430 \text{ m/s}}$

17.4 $v = \dfrac{2d}{t}$; $\quad d = \dfrac{vt}{2} = \dfrac{1}{2}(6.5 \times 10^3 \text{ m/s})(1.85 \text{ s}) = \boxed{6.01 \text{ km}}$

17.5 (a) $B = -\dfrac{\Delta P}{\Delta V/V}$ so $[B] = [P] = \text{Pa}$

(b) $v = (B/\rho)^{\frac{1}{2}}$

$$\dfrac{[v]}{[B]^{\frac{1}{2}}/[\rho]^{\frac{1}{2}}} = \dfrac{(\text{N/m}^2)^{\frac{1}{2}}}{(\text{kg/m}^3)^{\frac{1}{2}}}$$

$$= \dfrac{(\text{kg/m} \cdot \text{s}^2)^{\frac{1}{2}}}{(\text{kg/m}^3)^{\frac{1}{2}}}$$

$$= (\text{m}^2/\text{s}^2)^{\frac{1}{2}} = \text{m/s}$$

17.6 $v = (Y/\rho)^{\frac{1}{2}}$; $\quad Y = \rho v^2$

$Y = (2.7 \times 10^2 \text{ kg/m}^3)(5.1 \times 10^3 \text{ m/s})^2 = \boxed{7.02 \times 10^{10} \text{ N/m}^2}$

17.7 Solution: $v(\text{air}) = 343$ m/s and $v(\text{salt water}) = 1533$ m/s. Let d = width of inlet

$$t = \dfrac{d}{v_w}; \quad t + 4.5 = \dfrac{d}{v_a}, \quad \text{so} \quad \dfrac{d}{v_w} + 4.5 = \dfrac{d}{v_a}$$

$$d = \dfrac{4.5 v_w v_a}{v_w - v_a} = \dfrac{(4.5)(1533)(343)}{1533 - 343} = \boxed{1988 \text{ m}}$$

17.8 Solution:

$$B = -6 \times 10^6 (20) + 9.02 \times 10^8 = 7.82 \times 10^8 \text{ N/m}^2$$

$$v = \sqrt{\dfrac{B}{\rho}} = \sqrt{\dfrac{7.82 \times 10^8 \text{ N/m}^2}{792 \text{ kg/m}^3}} = \boxed{994 \text{ m/s}}$$

17.9 Solution:

(a) At 9000 m, $\Delta T = 9000(-1/150) = -60$ C° so $T = -30°$ C

Using the chain rule:

$$\frac{dv}{dt} = \frac{dv}{dT}\frac{dT}{dx}\frac{dx}{dt} = v\frac{dv}{dT}\frac{dT}{dx} = v(0.607)(\frac{1}{150}) = \frac{v}{247}, \quad \text{so} \quad dt = (247 \text{ s})\frac{dv}{v}.$$

$$\int\limits_0^t dt = (247 \text{ s})\int\limits_{v_0}^{v_f} \frac{dv}{v}$$

$$t = (247 \text{ s})\ln(\frac{v_f}{v_0}) = (247 \text{ s})\ln\left(\frac{331.5 + 0.607(30)}{331.5 + 0.607(-30)}\right)$$

$$t = \boxed{27.2\text{s}} \text{ for sound to reach ground}$$

(b) $t = \dfrac{h}{v} = \dfrac{9000}{[331.5 + 0.607(30)]} = \boxed{25.7 \text{ s}}$

It takes longer when the air cools off than if it were at a uniform temperature.

17.10 $\Delta P_m = \rho\omega v s_m = (1.2 \text{ kg/m}^3)(2\pi)(2000 \text{ s}^{-1})(343 \text{ m/s})(2 \times 10^{-8} \text{ m})$

$\Delta P_m = \boxed{0.103 \text{ Pa}} = \boxed{1.02 \times 10^{-6} \text{ atm}}$

17.11 $\Delta P_m = \rho v \omega s_m$

$$s_m = \frac{\Delta P_m}{\rho v \omega} = \frac{(4 \times 10^{-3})}{(1.2)(343)(2\pi)(10^4)} = \boxed{1.55 \times 10^{-10} \text{ m}}$$

17.12 $\Delta P_m = \rho v \omega s_m$

$$f = \frac{\Delta P_m}{2\pi \rho v s_m} = \frac{2.9 \times 10^{-5}}{2\pi(1.2)(343)(2.8 \times 10^{-10})} = \boxed{40 \text{ Hz}}$$

17.13 $\Delta P_m = \rho v \omega s_m = \rho v (2\pi v/\lambda) s_m$

$$\lambda = \frac{2\pi \rho v^2 s_m}{\Delta P_m}$$

$$= \frac{2\pi (1.2)(343)^2 (5.5 \times 10^{-6})}{0.84} = \boxed{5.81 \text{ m}}$$

17.14 (a) $\Delta P = \Delta P_m \sin[kx - \omega t + \phi]$

$\Delta P(0,0) = 0 = \sin\phi; \ \phi = 0; \ \Delta P_m = 4 \text{ Pa}$

$\omega = 2\pi f = 2\pi(5000 \text{ s}^{-1}) = 3.14 \times 10^4 \text{ s}^{-1}$

Therefore, $\Delta P = 4\sin(kx - 3.14 \times 10^4 t)$

$\Delta P(0, 2 \times 10^{-4}) = 4\sin(-3.14 \times 10^4 \times 2 \times 10^{-4}) = \boxed{0}$

(b) $\Delta P = 4\sin[k(0.02)] = \boxed{3.86 \text{ Pa}}$

17.15 Solution:

(a) $A = 2 \ \mu m, \ \lambda = \frac{2\pi}{15.7} = 0.4 \text{ m} = 40 \text{ cm},$

$v = \frac{\omega}{k} = \frac{858}{15.7} = \boxed{54.6 \text{ m/s}}$ probably in vulcanized rubber.

(b) $s = 2\cos[(15.7)(0.05) - (858)(0.003)] = \boxed{-0.433 \ \mu m}$

(c) $v_{\max} = A\omega = (2 \ \mu m)(858 \text{ s}^{-1}) = \boxed{1.72 \text{ mm/s}}$

17.16 $\Delta P = \Delta P_m \sin(kx - \omega t) = (\rho v \omega s_m)\sin[15.7x - 858t)]$

$\Delta P_m = \rho v \omega s_m = (900)(54.6)(858)(2 \times 10^{-6}) = 84.3 \text{ Pa}$

Therefore, at $x = 0$ and $t = \pi/2\omega$,

$\Delta P = (84.3)\sin[-\pi/2] = \boxed{-84.3 \text{ Pa}}$

17.17 $k = \frac{2\pi}{\lambda} = \frac{2\pi}{(0.1 \text{ m})} = 62.8 \text{ m}^{-1}$

$\omega = \frac{2\pi v}{\lambda} = \frac{2\pi(343 \text{ m/s})}{(0.1 \text{ m})} = 2.16 \times 10^4 \text{ s}^{-1}$

Therefore, $\Delta P = (0.2)\sin[62.8x - 2.16 \times 10^4 t] \text{ Pa}$

17.18 $\omega = 2\pi f = \dfrac{2\pi v}{\lambda} = \dfrac{2\pi(343)}{(0.1\text{ m})} = 2.16 \times 10^4$ rad/s

$s_m = \dfrac{\Delta P_m}{\rho v \omega} = \dfrac{(0.2)}{(1.2)(343)(2.16 \times 10^4)} = 2.25 \times 10^{-8}$ m

$k = \dfrac{2\pi}{\lambda} = \dfrac{2\pi}{(0.1)} = 62.8$ m^{-1}

Therefore,

$s = s_m \cos(kx - \omega t) = (2.25 \times 10^{-8}) \cos(62.8x - 2.16 \times 10^4 t)$

17.19 $\beta = 10 \log(\dfrac{I}{I_0}) = 10 \log(\dfrac{4 \times 10^{-6}}{10^{-12}}) = \boxed{66\text{ dB}}$

17.20 $70\text{ dB} = 10 \log(1/10^{-12})$; therefore, $I = 10^{-5}$ W/m$^2 = \boxed{10\mu\text{W/m}^2}$

17.21 (a) $I = \dfrac{\Delta P_m^2}{2\rho v} = \dfrac{(4\text{ N/m}^2)^2}{2(1.2\text{ kg/m}^3)(343\text{ m/s})} = \boxed{1.92 \times 10^{-2}\text{ W/m}^2}$

(b) $\beta = 10 \log\left(\dfrac{0.0194}{10^{-12}}\right) = \boxed{103\text{ dB}}$

17.22 $I = \dfrac{1}{2}\rho \omega^2 s_m^2 v$

(a) At $f = 2500$ Hz, the frequency is increased by a factor of 2.5,

so the intensity (at constant s_m) increases by $(2.5)^2 = 6.25$.

Therefore, $I = 6.25(0.6) = \boxed{3.75\text{ W/m}^2}$

(b) $\boxed{0.6\text{ W/m}^2}$

17.23 $I = \dfrac{\Delta P_m^2}{2\rho v}$ and $\Delta P_m = (2\rho v I)^{\frac{1}{2}}$ also $\beta = 10 \log(\dfrac{I}{10^{-12}})$

so that $I = (10^{-12}\text{ W/m}^2)10^{(\beta/10)} = (10^{-12}\text{ W/m}^2)(10^{12}) = 1$ W/m^2

Therefore, $\Delta P_m = [2(1.2\text{ kg/m}^3)(343\text{ m/s})(1\text{ W/m}^2)]^{\frac{1}{2}} = \boxed{28.7\text{ Pa}}$

17.24 Since intensity is inversely proportional to the square of the distance,

$$I_4 = \frac{1}{100}I_{0.4} \quad \text{and} \quad I_{0.4} = \frac{P^2}{2\rho v} = \frac{10^2}{2(1.29)(343)} = 0.113 \text{ W/m}^2$$

The difference in sound intensity level is

$$\beta = 10 \log(\frac{I_{4\,\text{km}}}{I_{0.4\,\text{km}}}) = 10(-2) = -20 \text{ dB}$$

At 0.4 km,

$$\beta_{0.4} = 10 \log(\frac{0.113 \text{ W/m}^2}{10^{-12} \text{ W/m}^2}) = 110.5 \text{ dB}$$

At 4.0 km

$$\beta_4 = \beta_{0.4} + \beta = (110.5 - 20) \text{ dB} = 90.5 \text{ dB}$$

Allowing for absorption of the wave over the distance travelled,

$$\beta_4' = \beta_4 - (7 \text{ dB/km})(3.6 \text{ km}) = \boxed{65.3 \text{ dB}}$$

This is equivalent to the sound intensity level of very heavy traffic.

*17.25
$$\beta_1 = 10 \log \frac{I_1}{I_0}$$

$$\beta_2 = 10 \log \frac{(1.5)^2 I_2}{I_0}$$

$$\beta_2 - \beta_1 = 10 \log 2.25 = \boxed{3.52 \text{ dB}}$$

17.26 (a) $I_1 = (10^{-12})10^{(\beta/10)} = (10^{-12})(10^{7.5}) = 10^{-4.5} = 31.6 \ \mu\text{W/m}^2$

$$I_2 = (10^{-12})10^8 = 10^{-4} = 100 \ \mu\text{W/m}^2$$

$$I = 100 \times 10^{-6} + 31.6 \times 10^{-6} = 131.6 \times 10^{-6}$$

$$\beta = 10 \log(\frac{131.6 \times 10^{-6}}{10^{-12}}) = \boxed{81.2 \text{ dB}}$$

(b) $I = 131.6 \ \mu\text{W/m}^2 = \boxed{1.316 \times 10^{-4} \text{ W/m}^2}$

17.27 $I = \dfrac{P}{4\pi r^2}$, where $I = 1.2 \text{ W/m}^2$

$P = 4\pi r^2 I = 4\pi(4)^2(1.2) = \boxed{241 \text{ W}}$

*17.28 $40 \; dB = 10 \; dB \; \log\left(\dfrac{I}{10^{-12} \text{ W/m}^2}\right)$

$4 = \log\dfrac{I}{10^{-12}}$

$I = 10^{-12}10^4 = 10^{-8} \text{ W/m}^2$

$P = 4\pi r^2 I = (4\pi)(9)(10^{-8}) = \boxed{1.13 \; \mu\text{W}}$

17.29 $\beta = 10 \; \log(\dfrac{I}{10^{-12}})$; $I = [10^{(\beta/10)}]10^{-12} \text{ W/m}^2$

$I_{(120 \, dB)} = 1 \text{ W/m}^2$; $I_{(100 \, dB)} = 10^{-2} \text{ W/m}^2$; $I_{(10 \, dB)} = 10^{-11} \text{ W/m}^2$

(a) $P = 4\pi r^2$ so that $r_1^2 I_1 = r_2^2 I_2$

$r_2 = r_1(I_1/I_2)^{\frac{1}{2}} = (3 \text{ m})(1/10^{-2})^{\frac{1}{2}} = \boxed{30 \text{ m}}$

(b) $r_2 = r_1(I_1/I_2)^{\frac{1}{2}} = (3 \text{ m})(1/10^{-11})^{\frac{1}{2}} = \boxed{9.49 \times 10^5 \text{ m}}$

*17.30 (a) $E = Pt = 4\pi r^2 It = 4\pi(100 \text{ m})^2 \left(7 \times 10^{-2} \text{ W/m}^2\right)(0.2 \text{ s})$

$= \boxed{1.76 \text{ kJ}}$

(b) $\beta = 10\log\dfrac{7 \times 10^{-2}}{10^{-12}} = \boxed{108 \text{ dB}}$

*17.31 $I = \dfrac{P}{4\pi r^2}$ $I_1 4\pi r_1^2 = I_2 4\pi r_2^2$

$\beta_1 - \beta_2 = 10\left(\log\dfrac{I_1}{I_0} - \log\dfrac{I_2}{I_0}\right) = 10\log\left(\dfrac{I_1}{I_2}\right)$

$= 10\log\left(\dfrac{r_2^2}{r_1^2}\right) = 20\log\left(\dfrac{r_2}{r_1}\right)$

$80 = 20\log\left(\dfrac{r_2}{5 \text{ m}}\right)$ $10^4 = \dfrac{r_2}{5 \text{ m}}$ $r_2 = \boxed{50.0 \text{ km}}$

17.32 Solution:

(a) $\psi_{max} = \dfrac{25.0}{r} = \dfrac{25.0}{4} = \boxed{6.25 \text{ Pa}}$

(b) $v = \dfrac{\omega}{k} = \dfrac{1870}{1.25} = 1496$ m/s, so the material is $\boxed{\text{water}}$

(c) $I = \dfrac{\psi^2}{2\rho v} = \dfrac{(6.25)^2}{(2)(1000)(1496)} = 1.31 \times 10^{-5}$ W/m^2

$\beta = 10 \log(\dfrac{1.31 \times 10^{-5}}{10^{-12}}) = \boxed{71.2 \text{ dB}}$

(d) $\psi = (\dfrac{25}{5}) \sin[(1.25)(5) - (1870)(0.08)] = \boxed{4.59 \text{ Pa}}$

17.33 $\theta = \sin^{-1}\dfrac{v}{v_s} = \sin^{-1}\dfrac{1}{1.38} = \boxed{46.4°}$

17.34 $\sin\theta = v/v_s$; $\quad v_s = \dfrac{v}{\sin\theta} = \dfrac{343}{\sin 40°} = \boxed{534 \text{ m/s}}$

*17.35 $\sin\theta = \dfrac{v_{sound}}{v_{jet}} = \dfrac{v_{sound}}{1.2 v_{sound}} = \dfrac{1}{1.2}$

$\theta = \boxed{56.4°}$

17.35

17.36 (a) $f' = f\dfrac{v}{(v \pm v_s)}$

Approach: $\quad f' = 320\dfrac{(343)}{(343 - 40)} = 362$ Hz

Receding: $\quad f' = 320\dfrac{(343)}{(343 + 40)} = 287$ Hz

The *change* in frequency observed $= 362 - 287 = \boxed{75 \text{ Hz}}$

(b) $\lambda = \dfrac{v}{f'} = \dfrac{343 \text{ m/s}}{362 \text{ Hz}} = \boxed{0.948 \text{ m}}$

17.37 Approaching car $f' = \dfrac{f}{(1 - v_s/v)}$ (Eq. 17.18)

Departing car $f'' = \dfrac{f}{(1 + v_s/v)}$ (Eq. 17.19)

Since $f' = 560$ Hz and $f'' = 480$ Hz,

$560(1 - v_s/v) = 480(1 + v_s/v)$

$1040\,\dfrac{v_s}{v} = 80$

$v = \dfrac{80(343)}{1040}$ m/s = $\boxed{26.4 \text{ m/s}}$

*17.38 $\qquad f_o = f_b \dfrac{v \pm v_0}{v \mp v_s}$

$\qquad\qquad 277 = 262\,\dfrac{340}{340 - v_s}$

$\qquad 340 - v_s = \dfrac{262}{277}(340)$

$\qquad\qquad v_s = (340 \text{ m/s})\left(1 - \dfrac{262}{277}\right) = \boxed{18.4 \text{ m/s}}$

17.39 $f' = f\dfrac{(v \pm v_o)}{(v \pm v_s)}$

(a) $f' = 320\dfrac{(343 + 40)}{(343 + 20)} = \boxed{338 \text{ Hz}}$

(b) $f' = 510\dfrac{(343 + 20)}{(343 + 40)} = \boxed{483 \text{ Hz}}$

*17.40 $f_o = f\left(\dfrac{v}{v + v_s}\right)$

$485 = 512\left(\dfrac{340}{340 + 9.8t_{fall}}\right)$

$485(340) + (485)(9.8t_f) = (512)(340)$

$t_f = \left(\dfrac{512 - 485}{485}\right)\dfrac{340}{9.8} = 1.93$ s

$d_1 = 18.278$ m

$t_{\text{return}} = \dfrac{18.3}{340} = 0.05376$ s   The fork falls some more while sound returns.

$t_{\text{total fall}} = 1.9851$ s

$d_{\text{total}} = \boxed{19.3\text{ m}}$

17.41 The *half angle* of the shock wave cone is given by $\sin\theta = \dfrac{v}{v_s}$

$v_s = \dfrac{v}{\sin\theta} = \dfrac{3 \times 10^8 \text{ m/s}}{\sin(53°)} = \boxed{2.82 \times 10^8 \text{ m/s}}$

17.42 (a) $f_L = \dfrac{f_s(v + v_L)}{(v + v_s)}$ where from L to s is positive.

$f_L = 2500\dfrac{(343 + 25)}{(343 - 40)} = \boxed{3.04\text{ kHz}}$

(b) $f_L = 2500\dfrac{(343 - 25)}{(343 + 40)} = \boxed{2.08\text{ kHz}}$

(c) $f_L = 2500\dfrac{(343 - 25)}{(343 - 40)} = \boxed{2.62\text{ kHz}}$ while police car overtakes

$f_L = 2500\dfrac{(343 + 25)}{(343 + 40)} = \boxed{2.40\text{ kHz}}$ after police car passes

17.43 (a) It takes the plane $t = \dfrac{x}{v_s} = \dfrac{5.66 \times 10^4 \text{ m}}{3 \times 335 \text{ m/s}} = \boxed{56.3 \text{ s}}$

to travel this distance.

(b) $\sin \theta = \dfrac{v}{v_s} = \dfrac{1}{3}$ $\qquad \theta = 19.5°$

$\tan \theta = \dfrac{h}{x}$ $\qquad x = \dfrac{h}{\tan \theta}$

$x = \dfrac{20000 \text{ m}}{\tan 19.5°} = 5.66 \times 10^4 \text{ m} = \boxed{56.6 \text{ km}}$

17.44 $\Delta t = L\left(\dfrac{1}{v_\text{air}} - \dfrac{1}{v_{Cu}}\right) = L\dfrac{v_{Cu} - v_\text{air}}{v_\text{air}\, v_{Cu}}$

$L = \dfrac{v_\text{air}\, v_{Cu}}{v_{Cu} - v_\text{air}}\Delta t = \dfrac{(331 \text{ m/s})(3.56 \times 10^3 \text{ m/s})}{(3560 - 331) \text{ m/s}}(6.4 \times 10^{-3} \text{ s})$

$\boxed{L = 2.34 \text{ m}}$

17.45 $v = \dfrac{4450 \text{ cm}}{9.5 \text{ h}} = 468 \text{ km/h} = \boxed{130 \text{ m/s}}$

$\bar{d} = \dfrac{v^2}{g} = \left(\dfrac{468 \text{ km}}{3600 \text{ s}}\right)^2 \dfrac{10^3}{9.8 \text{ km/s}^2} = \boxed{1.72 \text{ km}}$

*17.46 $I = \frac{1}{2}\rho(\omega s_m)^2 v$ $\qquad$ (Eq. 17.9)

$1 = \frac{1}{2}(1.21)[2\pi \cdot 2000\, s_m]^2(343)$

$s_m = \boxed{5.52 \ \mu\text{m}}$

17.47 $\beta = 10 \log\left(\dfrac{I}{I_0}\right)$ $\quad$ or $\quad I = I_0 10^{\beta/10}$

(a) $I_1 = (10^{-12} \text{ W/m}^2)10^{(130/10)} = 10 \text{ W/m}^2$

$I_2 = (10^{-12} \text{ W/m}^2)10^{(120/10)} = 1 \text{ W/m}^2$

$\dfrac{I_1}{I_2} = \boxed{10}$

(b) $\beta_1 = 10 \log\left[\dfrac{(10^{-4} \text{ W/m}^2)}{(10^{-12} \text{ W/m}^2)}\right] = 80 \text{ dB}$

$\beta_2 = 10 \log\left[\dfrac{(2 \times 10^{-4} \text{ W/m}^2)}{(10^{-12} \text{ W/m}^2)}\right] = 83 \text{ dB}$

Difference in levels: $\beta_2 - \beta_1 = \boxed{3 \text{ dB}}$

17.48 Bulk Modulus, $B = -\dfrac{\Delta P}{\Delta V/V}$ and the *fractional* change in volume is

$\dfrac{\Delta V}{V} = -\dfrac{\Delta P}{B}$. The value of B is found from $v = \sqrt{\dfrac{B}{\rho}}$

Therefore, $\left|\dfrac{\Delta V}{V}\right| = \dfrac{\Delta P}{v^2\rho} = \dfrac{(2\text{ atm})(1.01 \times 10^5\text{ N/m}^2/\text{atm})}{(3560\text{ m/s})^2(8.89 \times 10^3\text{ kg/m}^3)}$

$$= 1.79 \times 10^{-6}$$

The change in volume is $\boxed{1.79\text{ ppm}}$ or $\boxed{1.79 \times 10^{-4}\%}$

17.49 When observer is moving in front of and in the same direction as the

source $f_0 = f_s\dfrac{(v - v_0)}{(v - v_s)}$ where v_0 and v_s are measured

relative to the *medium* in which the sound is propagated. In this case

the ocean current is opposite the direction of travel of the ships and

$v_0 = 45\text{ km/h} - (-10\text{ km/h}) = 55\text{ km/h} = 15.3\text{ m/s}$

$v_s = 64\text{ km/h} - (-10\text{ km/h}) = 74\text{ km/h} = 20.55\text{ m/s}$

Therefore,

$f_0 = (1200\text{ Hz})\dfrac{(1520\text{ m/s} - 15.3\text{ m/s})}{(1520\text{ m/s} - 20.55\text{ m/s})}$

$= \boxed{1204.2\text{ Hz}}$

17.50 $\Delta P_m = \rho\omega v s_m = \rho(\dfrac{2\pi v}{\lambda})v s_m;$ Also ΔP and s are 90° out of phase.

Therefore, $\Delta P = -(\dfrac{2\pi\rho v^2 s_m}{\lambda})\cos(kx - \omega t)$.

17.51 (a) $\theta = \sin^{-1}(\dfrac{v_{\text{sound}}}{v_{\text{obj}}}) = \sin^{-1}[\dfrac{331}{20 \times 10^3}] = \boxed{0.948°}$

(b) $\theta' = \sin^{-1}[\dfrac{1533}{20 \times 10^3}] = \boxed{4.40°}$

*17.52 $P_2 = \frac{1}{20}P_1$ $\beta_1 - \beta_2 = 10\log\frac{P_1}{P_2}$

$$80 - \beta_2 = 10\log 20 = +13.0$$

$$\beta_2 = \boxed{67.0 \text{ dB}}$$

17.53   For the longitudinal wave $v_L = (Y/\rho)^{\frac{1}{2}}$

For the transverse wave $v_T = (F/\mu)^{\frac{1}{2}}$

If we require $\dfrac{v_L}{v_T} = 8$ we have $f = \dfrac{\mu Y}{64\rho}$ where $\mu = m\ell$ and

$\rho = \dfrac{\text{mass}}{\text{volume}} = \dfrac{m}{\pi r^2 \ell}$

This gives $F = \dfrac{\pi r^2 Y}{64} = \dfrac{\pi (0.002 \text{ m})^2 (6.8 \times 10^{10} \text{ N/m}^2)}{64}$

$$= \boxed{1.34 \times 10^4 \text{ N}}$$

*17.54 $\dfrac{d}{v_1} - \dfrac{d}{v_2} = 60 \text{ s}$

$\dfrac{d}{5 \text{ km/s}} - \dfrac{d}{9 \text{ km/s}} = 60 \text{ s}$

$d = \boxed{680 \text{ km}}$

17.55 $P = \frac{1}{2}\rho A v \omega^2 s_m^2$ (See Eq. 17.9) where ρ is found from

$\rho V = (m/M)RT$ or $\rho = \dfrac{m}{V} = \dfrac{pM}{RT}.$

Therefore power $P = \frac{1}{2}(\dfrac{\rho M}{RT})A v \omega^2 s_m^2$

$P = \frac{1}{2}[\dfrac{(1.5 \times 10^5 \text{ N/m}^2)(0.029 \text{ kg/mol})}{(8.314 \text{ J/mol} \cdot \text{K})(293 \text{ K})}]$

$\times (\pi)(0.005 \text{ m})^2 (343 \text{ m/s})(2\pi\, 600 \text{ s}^{-1})^2 (0.001 \text{ m})^2]$

$P = \boxed{34.2 \text{ W}}$

17.56 From Table 17.1, we have: $v = 331$ m/s (air),   1493 m/s (water), and 5130 m/s (iron).

From Table 15.1, we have: $\rho = 1.29$ kg/m^3 (air), 1.00×10^3 kg/m^3 (water), and 7.86×10^3 kg/m^3 (iron).

(a) $\lambda = \dfrac{2\pi v}{\omega}$. $\lambda_{\text{air}} : \lambda_{\text{water}} : \lambda_{\text{iron}} = 331 : 1493 : 5130 = \boxed{1 : 4.5 : 15.5}$

Therefore

$\lambda_{\text{water}} = 4.51\,\lambda_{\text{air}}$;   and $\lambda_{\text{iron}} = 3.44\,\lambda_{\text{water}} = 15.5\,\lambda_{\text{air}}$.

(b) $s_m = [\dfrac{2I_0}{\rho\omega_0^2 v}]^{\frac{1}{2}}$,   so $s_m \sim (\rho v)^{-\frac{1}{2}}$

Therefore

$(s_m)_{\text{air}} : (s_m)_{\text{water}} : (S_m)_{\text{iron}}$
$= (1.29 \times 331)^{-\frac{1}{2}} : (10^3 \times 1493)^{-\frac{1}{2}} : (7.86 \times 10^3 \times 5130)^{-\frac{1}{2}}$
$= 4.84 \times 10^{-2} : 8.18 \times 10^{-4} : 1.57 \times 10^{-4}$
$(s_m)_{\text{water}} = 1.69 \times 10^{-2}(s_m)_{\text{air}}$,

and $(s_m)_{\text{iron}} = 0.192(s_m)_{\text{water}} = 3.24 \times 10^{-3}(s_m)_{\text{iron}}$

or $(s_m)_{\text{air}} : (s_m)_{\text{water}} : (s_m)_{\text{iron}} = 1 : 1.69 \times 10^{-2} : 3.24 \times 10^{-3}$

(c) $\Delta P_m = (2\rho v I_0)^{\frac{1}{2}}$,   so $s_m \sim (\rho v)^{-\frac{1}{2}}$

thus $(\Delta P_m)_{\text{air}} : (\Delta P_m)_{\text{water}} : (\Delta P_m)_{\text{iron}} = 1 : 59.2 : 308$

(d) With $\omega_0 = 2000\,\pi$ rad/s and $I_0 = 10^{-6}$ W/m^2, we find

$\lambda_{\text{air}} = 2\pi\dfrac{331}{2000\pi} = \boxed{0.331\text{ m}}$

$\lambda_{\text{water}} = (4.51)(0.331) = \boxed{1.49\text{ m}}$

$\lambda_{\text{iron}} = 3.44\,\lambda_{\text{water}} = \boxed{5.14\text{ m}}$

$(s_m)_{\text{air}} = (\dfrac{2 \times 10^{-6}}{1.29(2000\pi)^2\,331})^{\frac{1}{2}} = \boxed{1.09 \times 10^{-8}\text{ m}}$

$(s_m)_{\text{water}} = 1.69 \times 10^{-2}(1.09 \times 10^{-8}) = \boxed{1.84 \times 10^{-10}\text{ m}}$

$(s_m)_{\text{iron}} = 3.24 \times 10^{-3}(1.09 \times 10^{-8}) = \boxed{3.53 \times 10^{-11}\text{ m}}$

$(\Delta P_m)_{\text{air}} = (2\rho v I_0)^{\frac{1}{2}} = [2(1.29)(331)(10^{-6})]^{\frac{1}{2}} = \boxed{2.92 \times 10^{-2}\text{ N}}$

$(\Delta P_m)_{\text{water}} = \boxed{1.73\text{ N}}$

$(\Delta P_m)_{\text{iron}} = \boxed{9.00\text{ N}}$

17.57 (a) $f_g = f_e \dfrac{v}{(v - v_{\text{diver}})}$, so $1 - \dfrac{v_{\text{diver}}}{v} = \dfrac{f_e}{f_g}$

$\Rightarrow v_{\text{diver}} = v(1 - \dfrac{f_e}{f_g})$ with $v = 343$ m/s, $f_e = 1800$ Hz and

$f_g = 2150$ Hz, we find $v_{\text{diver}} = 343(1 - \dfrac{1800}{2150}) = \boxed{55.8 \text{ m/s}}$

(b) If the waves are reflected, and the skydiver is moving into them, we have

$f'_{\text{rec}} = f_g \dfrac{(v + v_{\text{diver}})}{v} \Longrightarrow f'_{\text{rec}} = f_e[\dfrac{v}{(v - v_{\text{diver}})}]\dfrac{(v + v_{\text{diver}})}{v}$

so $f'_{\text{rec}} = 1800 \dfrac{(343 + 55.8)}{(343 - 55.8)} = \boxed{2500 \text{ Hz}}$

*17.58 (a) $\quad f_a = \dfrac{fv}{v - u} \qquad f_r = \dfrac{fv}{v + u}$

$f_a - f_r = fv\left(\dfrac{1}{v - u} - \dfrac{1}{v + u}\right)$

$\qquad = \dfrac{fv(v + u - v + u)}{v^2 - u^2} = \dfrac{2uvf}{v^2(1 - u^2/v^2)}$

$\Delta f = \boxed{\dfrac{2uf}{v(1 - u^2/v^2)}}$

(b) 130 km/h $= 36.1$ m/s

$\therefore \quad \Delta f = \dfrac{2(36.1)(400)}{340(1 - 36^2/340^2)} = \boxed{85.9 \text{ Hz}}$

17.59 (a) The time required for a sound pulse to travel a distance L at a speed v is given by $t = \dfrac{L}{v} = \dfrac{L}{(Y/\rho)^{\frac{1}{2}}}$. Using this expression we find

$$t_1 = \frac{L_1}{(Y_1/\rho_1)^{\frac{1}{2}}} = \frac{L_1}{[(7 \times 10^{10} \text{ N/m}^2)/(2.7 \times 10^3 \text{ kg/m}^3)]^{\frac{1}{2}}}$$

$$= 1.96 \times 10^{-4} L_1$$

$$t_2 = \frac{(1.5 - L_1)}{[(1.6 \times 10^{10} \text{ N/m}^2)/(11.3 \times 10^3 \text{ kg/m}^3)]^{\frac{1}{2}}}$$

$$= 1.26 \times 10^{-3} - 8.40 \times 10^{-4} L_1$$

$$t_3 = \frac{(1.5 \text{ m})}{[(11 \times 10^{10} \text{ N/m}^2)/(8.8 \times 10^3 \text{ kg/m}^3)]^{\frac{1}{2}}} = 4.24 \times 10^{-4}$$

17.59

We require $t_1 + t_2 = t_3$, or

$$1.96 \times 10^{-4} L_1 + 1.26 \times 10^{-3} - 8.40 \times 10^{-4} L_1 = 4.24 \times 10^{-4}$$

This gives $L_1 = 1.30$ m and $L_2 = 1.50 - 1.30 = 0.20$ m and the ratio or lengths is $\dfrac{L_1}{L_2} = \boxed{6.5}$

(b) The ratio of lengths L_1/L_2 is adjusted in part (a) so that $t_1 + t_2 = t_3$. Therefore sound travels the two paths in equal time intervals and the phase difference, $\Delta\phi = 0$.

17.60 Use the Doppler formula, and remember that the bat is a moving source.

If the velocity of the insect is v_x

$$40.4 = 40\frac{(340 + 5)(340 - v_x)}{(340 - 5)(340 + v_x)}$$

Solving, $v_x = 3.3$ m/s.

Therefore the bat is gaining on its prey at 1.7 m/s.

17.61 $\sin\beta = \dfrac{v}{v_s} = \dfrac{1}{N_M}$

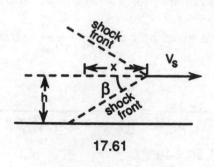

17.61

$h = v(12.8\text{ s})$

$x = v_s(10\text{ s})$

$\tan\beta = \dfrac{h}{x} = 1.28\dfrac{v}{v_s} = \dfrac{1.28}{N_M}$

$\cos\beta = \dfrac{\sin\beta}{\tan\beta} = \dfrac{1}{1.28}$

$\beta = 38.6°$

$N_M = \dfrac{1}{\sin\beta} = \boxed{1.60}$

17.62   Let $\theta = \theta_0 \log R, \quad I = kR$:

$$\begin{aligned}
\beta \;&= 10\,\log\!\left(\dfrac{I}{I_0}\right) = 10\,\log I - 10\,\log I_0 \\[4pt]
&= 10\,\log\,kR - 10\,\log I_0 \\[4pt]
&= 10\,\log\,R + 10(\log\,k - \log\,I_0) \\[4pt]
&= 10\!\left(\dfrac{\theta}{\theta_0}\right) + 10(\log\,k - \log\,I_0)
\end{aligned}$$

$\beta = \left(\dfrac{10}{\theta_0}\right)\theta + 10\log\left(\dfrac{k}{I_0}\right) \longleftarrow$ equation of straight line.

$[y = mx + b]$

CHAPTER 18

18.1 The resultant wave function has the form $y = (2A_0 \sin kx)\cos \omega t$

(a) $A = 2A_0 \cos(\phi/2) = 2(5)\cos[(\pi/4)/2] = \boxed{9.24 \text{ m}}$

(b) $f = \dfrac{\omega}{2\pi} = \dfrac{1200\pi}{2\pi} = \boxed{600 \text{ Hz}}$

18.2 (a) $A = 2A_0 \cos(\phi/2) = 2(6 \text{ m})\cos(\pi/12) = \boxed{11.6 \text{ m}}$

(b) Maximum amplitude for $\phi = 0, 2\pi, 4\pi, \ldots$

18.3 For the resultant wave, $A = 2A_0 \cos(\phi/2)$

$$\phi = 2\cos^{-1}(\frac{A}{2A_0}) = 2\cos^{-1}[\frac{8(3)^{1/2}}{2(8)}] = \pi/3 \text{ rad}$$

Therefore the required wave function is

$y_2 = 8\sin[2\pi(0.1x - 80t - 1/6)]$

18.4 (a) For minimum intensity $\Delta r = (2n-1)(\lambda/2)$. For
the first minimum, $n = 1$, thus
$\Delta r = (1/2)[(343 \text{ m/s})/1500 \text{ s}^{-1}] = 0.114 \text{ m}$.
When the observer is a distance L from the
plane of the sources, then
$y = L\tan\theta = L\tan[\sin^{-1}(\Delta r/d)]$
where d is the distance between the two sources.
From this expression we find
$y = (6 \text{ m})\tan[\sin^{-1}(0.114/2)] = \boxed{0.34 \text{ m}}$

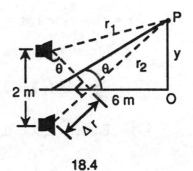

18.4

(b) For maximum we require that $\Delta r = n\lambda$, and for
the first maximum we take $n = 1$. The proce-
dure in part (a) then gives $y = \boxed{0.68 \text{ m}}$

18.5 (a) $\Delta r = r_2 - r_1 = 5.2 - 5.0 = 0.2 \text{ m}$

$\Delta\phi = (\dfrac{2\pi}{\lambda})\Delta r$, where $\lambda = \dfrac{v}{f} = \dfrac{343}{1650} = 0.208 \text{ m}$

$\Delta\phi = (\dfrac{2\pi}{0.208})(0.2) = \boxed{6.04 \text{ rad}}$

(b) $A' = 2A\cos(\phi/2) = \boxed{1.985A}$

*18.6   Path difference $\Delta = 38$ m

   Since $\lambda = 1.39$ m $\Delta = 27.2536\,\lambda$

                         phase diff $=$ 0.2536 cycle

                         $\Delta\phi$ $=$ 0.254 cycle $= \boxed{91.3°}$

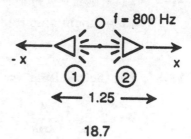

18.6

18.7   For a relative minimum, $\delta = m(\lambda/2)$; $m = 1, 3, 5, \ldots$

   $\delta = x_1 - (1.25 - x_1) = 2x_1 - 1.25$;

   therefore

   $$2x_1 - 1.25 = \frac{1}{2}m\left(\frac{v}{f}\right) = \frac{1}{2}m\left[\frac{343 \text{ m/s}}{800 \text{ Hz}}\right] = m(0.2144)$$

   and

   when $m = 1$, $x_1 = \boxed{0.732 \text{ m}}$ also $1.25 - x_1 = \boxed{0.518 \text{ m}}$

   when $m = 3$, $x_3 = \boxed{0.947 \text{ m}}$ $1.25 - x_3 = \boxed{0.303 \text{ m}}$

   when $m = 5$, $x_5 = \boxed{1.16 \text{ m}}$ $1.23 - x_5 = \boxed{0.09 \text{ m}}$

18.7

18.8 $\Delta r = r_1 - r_2 = 1.20 - 0.80 = 0.40$ m

   (a) Intensity maxima will occur when $\Delta r = n\lambda$ where $n = 1, 2, 3, \ldots$

       For $n = 1$, $\lambda = 0.40$ m and $f_1 = \dfrac{v}{\lambda} = \dfrac{340}{0.4} = 850$ Hz;

       For $n = 2$, $\lambda = 0.20$ m, and $f_2 = \dfrac{340}{0.2} = 1700$ Hz;

       For $n = 3$, $\lambda = 0.1333$ m, and $f_3 = \dfrac{340}{0.1333} = 2550$ Hz.

   (b) Minima will occur when $\Delta r = n\lambda/2$ (for n odd)

       or when $\lambda = \dfrac{2\Delta r}{n} = \dfrac{0.80}{n}$.

       Therefore, $f_n = \dfrac{340}{(0.8/n)} = 425\,n$.

       The highest odd integer to give a frequency $< 20{,}000$ Hz is $n = 47$.

       This corresponds to $f = \boxed{19{,}975 \text{ Hz}}$

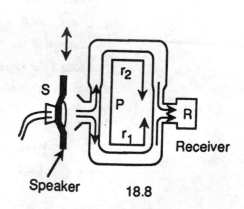

18.8

18.9 $y_1 = 3 \sin \pi(x + 0.6t)\text{cm} \quad y_2 = 3 \sin \pi(x - 0.6t) \text{ cm}$

(a) We can take $t = 0$ to get the maximum y

$$y = y_1 + y_2 = 3\sin(\pi x) + 3\sin(\pi x) = 6\sin(\pi x)$$
At $x = 0.25$ cm, $\quad y = 6\sin(\pi \times 0.25) = \boxed{4.24 \text{ cm}}$

(b) At $x = 0.5$ cm, $y = 6\sin(\pi \times 0.5) = \boxed{6.00 \text{ cm}}$

(c) At $x = 1.5$ cm, $y = 6\sin(\pi \times 1.5) = \boxed{-6.00 \text{ cm}}$

(d) The antinodes occur when $x = n\lambda/4$ $(n = 1, 3, 5\ldots)$. But

$k = 2\pi/\lambda = \pi$, so $\lambda = 2$ cm, and

$x_1 = \lambda/4 = 2/4 = \boxed{0.5 \text{ cm}}$

$x_2 = 3\lambda/4 = 3(2)/4 = \boxed{1.5 \text{ cm}}$

$x_3 = 5\lambda/4 = 5(2)/4 = \boxed{2.5 \text{ cm}}$

18.10 $y_1 = A_0 \sin(kx - \omega t) = A_0 \sin kx \, \cos \omega t - A_0 \cos kx \, \sin \omega t$

$y_2 = A_0 \sin(kx - \omega t) = A_0 \sin kx \, \cos \omega t + A_0 \cos kx \, \sin \omega t$

$y_1 + y_2 = y = 2A_0 \sin kx \cos \omega t$

18.11 The standing wave $y = (2A_0 \sin kx) \cos \omega t$ is formed by the interference of $y_1 = A_0 \sin(kx - \omega t)$ and $y_2 = A_0 \sin(kx + \omega t)$

By comparison with the given wave function we find

$$\lambda = \frac{2\pi}{k} = \frac{2\pi}{(0.25 \text{ m}^{-1})} = \boxed{8\pi \text{ m}} \text{ and } f = \frac{\omega}{2\pi} = \frac{120\pi}{2\pi} = \boxed{60 \text{ Hz}}$$

18.12 $y = 1.5 \sin(0.4x) \cos(200t) = 2A_0 \sin(kx) \cos(\omega t)$

Therefore, $k = \dfrac{2\pi}{\lambda} = 0.4$ or $\lambda = \dfrac{2\pi}{0.4} = \boxed{15.7 \text{ m}}$

$\omega = 2\pi f = 200$, or $f = \dfrac{200}{2\pi} = \boxed{31.8 \text{ Hz}}$

$v = f\lambda = (31.8)(15.7) = \boxed{500 \text{ m/s}}$

18.13   (a) Using the given parameters, the wave function is

$$y = 2\pi \ \sin(\frac{\pi x}{2}) \cos(10\pi t)$$

We need to find values of x for which $\sin(\frac{\pi x}{2}) = 1$

This condition requires that $\frac{\pi x}{2} = \pi(n + \frac{1}{2});\ n = 0, 1, 2, \ldots$

For $n = 0$; $x = 1$ cm and for $n = 1$; $x = 3$ cm;

therefore the distance between antinodes, $\Delta x = \boxed{2 \text{ cm}}$

(b) $A = 2\pi \ \sin(\frac{\pi x}{2})$; when $x = 0.25$ cm, $A = \boxed{2.40 \text{ cm}}$

18.14 $y = 2A_0 \sin \ kx \ \cos \omega t$

$$\frac{\partial^2 y}{\partial x^2} = -2A_0 k^2 \sin \ kx \ \cos \omega t$$

$$\frac{\partial^2 y}{\partial t^2} = -2A_0 \omega^2 \sin \ kx \ \cos \omega t$$

Substitution into the wave equation gives

$$-2A_0 k^2 \sin \ kx \ \cos \omega t = (\frac{1}{v^2})(-2A_0 \omega^2 \sin \ kx \ \cos \omega t)$$

This is satisfied, provided that $v = \frac{\omega}{k}$.

18.15   Solution:

(a) The resultant wave is $y = 2A \sin(kx + \frac{\phi}{2}) \cos(\omega t - \frac{\phi}{2})$

The nodes are located at $kx + \frac{\phi}{2} = n\pi$ so $x = \frac{n\pi}{k} - \frac{\phi}{2k}$ which

means that each node is shifted $\phi/2k$ to the left.

(b) The separation of nodes is $\Delta x = [(n+1)\frac{\pi}{k} - \frac{\phi}{2k}] - [\frac{n\pi}{k} - \frac{\phi}{2k}]$

$\Delta x = \frac{\pi}{k} = \frac{\lambda}{2}$. The nodes are still separated by half a wavelength.

18.16 Solution: $y = 0.03 \cos(\frac{x}{2}) \cos(40t)$

(a) nodes occur where $y = 0$: $\frac{x}{2} = (2n+1)\frac{\pi}{2}$ so $x = (2n+1)\pi = \pi, 3\pi, 5\pi, \ldots$

(b) $y_{max} = 0.03 \cos(\frac{0.4}{2}) = 0.0294$ m

18.17 $L = 120$ cm, $f = 120$ Hz;

(a) For four segments, $L = 2\lambda$, or $\lambda = 60$ cm $\boxed{0.60 \text{ m}}$

(b) $v = \lambda f = 72$ m/s; $f_1 = \frac{v}{2L} = \frac{72}{2(1.2)} = \boxed{30 \text{ Hz}}$

18.18 $v = f\lambda = (F/\mu)^{\frac{1}{2}}$ For the second harmonic, $\lambda = L$.

Therefore $F = f^2 L^2 \mu = (460 \text{ } s^{-1})^2 (1.6 \text{ m})^2 (0.0015 \text{ kg/m}) = \boxed{813 \text{ N}}$

18.19 Touch at the midpoint and pick the string at $L/4$.

18.20 $L = 50$ cm, $\mu = 20 \times 10^{-5}$ kg/m.

(a) $f_1 = \frac{v}{2L} = \frac{v}{(1.0 \text{ m})}$

But $v = (F/\mu)^{\frac{1}{2}}$ and $f_1 = 20$ Hz, so

$(F/\mu)^{\frac{1}{2}} = 20 \implies F = \mu(20)^2 = \boxed{0.08 \text{ N}}$

(b) For $f_1 = 4500$ Hz, $F = \mu(4500)^2 = \boxed{4050 \text{ N}}$

18.21 $L = 30$ m, $\mu = 9 \times 10^{-3}$ kg/m, $F = 20$ N

$f_1 = \frac{v}{2L}$, where $v = (F/\mu)^{\frac{1}{2}} = 47.1$ m/s, so

$f_1 = \frac{47.1}{60} = \boxed{0.786 \text{ Hz}}$

$f_2 = 2f_1 = \boxed{1.57 \text{ Hz}}$, $f_3 = 3f_1 = \boxed{2.36 \text{ Hz}}$, $f_4 = 4f_1 = \boxed{3.14 \text{ Hz}}$

*18.22 d_{NN} $=$ 1 m

$\quad\quad\quad\lambda$ $=$ 2 m

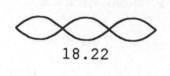

18.22

$\quad\quad\quad v$ $=$ $f\lambda = 400 \text{ m/s} = \sqrt{\dfrac{T}{10^{-3} \text{ kg/m}}}$

$\quad\quad\quad T$ $=$ $\boxed{160 \text{ N}}$

18.23 $L = 16$ m, $\mu = 0.015$ g/cm $= 1.5 \times 10^{-3}$ kg/m, $F = 557$ N

$\quad\quad f_n = \dfrac{nv}{2L}$ where $v = (F/\mu)^{\frac{1}{2}} = 609$ m/s

$\quad\quad f_n = n(\dfrac{609}{32}) = 19n$. Setting $f_n = 20,000 = 19n$ gives $n = \boxed{1050}$

18.24   Identify the wires as ℓ (for long) and s (for short)

$\quad\quad$ then $\dfrac{v_s}{v_\ell} = (\dfrac{F_s}{F_\ell})^{\frac{1}{2}} = (1.4)^{\frac{1}{2}}$ or $v_\ell = 2v_s$

$\quad\quad$ When the longer wire is vibrating in the second harmonic

$\quad\quad (f_\ell)_2 = \dfrac{v_\ell}{\lambda_\ell} = \dfrac{v_\ell}{2L} = \dfrac{2v_s}{2L} = \dfrac{v_s}{L}$ $\quad\quad$ (1)

$\quad\quad$ But when the shorter wire is vibrating in the fundamental mode

$\quad\quad (f_s)_1 = \dfrac{v_s}{\lambda_s} = \dfrac{v_s}{2L}$, therefore $\dfrac{v_s}{L} = 2(f_s)_1 = 120$ Hz.

$\quad\quad$ And from (1), $(f_\ell)_2 = \dfrac{v_s}{L} = \boxed{120 \text{ Hz}}$

*18.25 d_{NN} $=$ 0.7 m

$\quad\quad\quad\lambda$ $=$ 1.4 m

18.25

$\quad\quad\quad f\lambda$ $=$ $v = 308 \text{ m/s} = \sqrt{\dfrac{T}{1.2 \times 10^{-3}/0.7}}$

$\quad\quad$ (a) $T = \boxed{163 \text{ N}}$

$\quad\quad$ (b) $f_3 = \boxed{660 \text{ Hz}}$

18.26 $f_1 = \dfrac{v}{2L}$, where $v = (\dfrac{F}{\mu})^{\frac{1}{2}} = (\dfrac{FL}{m})^{\frac{1}{2}}$

(a) If L is doubled, then $f_1 \propto L^{-1}$ will be reduced by a factor $\dfrac{1}{2}$.

(b) If μ is doubled, then $f_1 \propto \mu^{-\frac{1}{2}}$ will be reduced by a factor $1/\sqrt{2}$.

(c) If F is doubled, then $f_1 \propto F^{\frac{1}{2}}$ will increase by a factor of $\sqrt{2}$.

18.27 $L = 60$ cm $= 0.60$ m, $F = 50$ N, $\mu = 0.1$ g/cm $= 0.01$ kg/m

$f_n = \dfrac{nv}{2L}$, where $v = (\dfrac{F}{\mu})^{\frac{1}{2}} = 70.7$ m/s

$f_n = n(\dfrac{70.7}{1.2}) = 58.9n = 20,000$

Largest $n = 339$ $\implies$ $f = \boxed{19.976 \text{ Hz}}$

*18.28 $\quad f = \dfrac{v}{\lambda} = \sqrt{\dfrac{T}{\mu}}\dfrac{1}{\lambda} = \sqrt{\dfrac{T}{\rho\pi d^2}\dfrac{4}{}}\dfrac{2}{L}$

$\quad\quad \mu = \dfrac{M}{L} = \dfrac{\rho V}{L} = \rho\dfrac{AL}{L}$

$\quad\quad f_{new} = \sqrt{\dfrac{4\,T_{old}\,4}{\rho_{old}\pi(2d_{old})^2}}\dfrac{2}{L_{old}/2}$

$\quad\quad\quad = \sqrt{\dfrac{T_{old}\,4}{\rho_{old}\pi d_{old}^2}}\dfrac{2}{L_{old}/2} \times 2 = 2f_{old} = \boxed{800 \text{ Hz}}$

*18.29 $\quad d_{NN} = 2$ m $\quad\quad \lambda = 4$ m

$\quad\quad v = f\lambda = 260$ m/s $= \sqrt{\dfrac{T}{5 \times 10^{-3} \text{ kg/m}}}$

$\quad\quad T = \boxed{338 \text{ N}}$

18.30 $\lambda_G = 2(0.35 \text{ m}) = \dfrac{v}{f_G}$

$\lambda_A = 2L_A = \dfrac{v}{f_A}$

$L_G - L_A = L_G - \dfrac{f_G}{f_A}L_G = L_G(1 - \dfrac{f_G}{f_A}) = (0.35 \text{ m})(1 - \dfrac{392}{440}) = 0.038 \text{ m}$

The string must be shortened by 3.8 cm.

$L_A = \dfrac{v}{2f_A} = \dfrac{1}{2f_A}\sqrt{\dfrac{F}{\mu}}$

$dL_A = \dfrac{dF}{4f_A\sqrt{F\mu}}$

$\dfrac{dL_A}{L_A} = \dfrac{1}{2}\dfrac{dF}{F}$

$\dfrac{dF}{F} = 2\dfrac{dL_A}{L_A} = 2\dfrac{0.6 \text{ cm}}{(35 - 3.8) \text{ cm}} = \boxed{3.9\%}$

18.31 Since the frequency is fixed, we see that λ is fixed because $f = v/\lambda$.

(a) $L_0 = 1(\lambda/2)$, $L_1 = 2(\lambda/2)$ $L_2 = 3(\lambda/2)\ldots$ all multiples of $\lambda/2$.

For the open pipe, $L_n = n(\dfrac{\lambda}{2}) = n(\dfrac{v}{2f})$ where n is $(1,2,3,\ldots)$

(b) $L_0 = \lambda/4$, $L_1 = 3\lambda/4$ $L_2 = 5\lambda/4\ldots$ all odd multiples of $\lambda/4$.

For the closed pipe, $L_n = [2(n) - 1]\dfrac{\lambda}{4} = [2(n) - 1]\dfrac{v}{4f}$

where n is $(0,1,2\ldots)$

18.32 (a) $L = \dfrac{\lambda}{2}$ \qquad $\lambda = \dfrac{v}{f} = \dfrac{343}{20} = 17.1 \text{ m}$

$L = \boxed{8.55 \text{ m}}$

(b) $L = \dfrac{\lambda}{4} = \dfrac{17.1}{4} = \boxed{4.28 \text{ m}}$

18.33 The length corresponding to the fundamental satisfies $f = \dfrac{v}{4L}$,

giving $L_1 = \dfrac{v}{4f} = \dfrac{343}{4(512)} = 0.617$ m. Since $L > 20$ cm, the

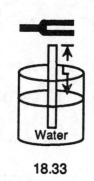

next two modes will be observed, corresponding to $f = \dfrac{3v}{4L_2}$ and

$f = \dfrac{5v}{4L_3}$ or $L_2 = \dfrac{3v}{4f} = \boxed{0.502 \text{ m}}$ and $L_3 = \dfrac{5v}{4f} = \boxed{0.837 \text{ m}}$

18.33

*18.34 $d_{AA} = \dfrac{L}{n} \qquad n = 1, 2, 3, \ldots$

$\lambda = \dfrac{2L}{n}$

$f = \dfrac{v}{\lambda} = 680 \text{ Hz} = \dfrac{344 \text{ m/s}}{2L/n}$

$\dfrac{2L}{n} = \dfrac{344}{680} = 0.506$ m

$L = \dfrac{n}{2}(0.506 \text{ m}) = (0.253 \text{ m})n$

$$\boxed{0.253 \text{ m}, \ 0.506 \text{ m}, \ 0.759 \text{ m}, \ \ldots \ n(0.253) \ \text{m}}$$

18.35 (a) $v = f\lambda \quad L = \dfrac{\lambda}{4}$

$L = \dfrac{v}{4f} = \dfrac{343}{4(240)} = \boxed{0.357 \text{ m}}$

(b) $L = \dfrac{v}{2f} = \dfrac{343}{2(240)} = \boxed{0.715 \text{ m}}$

18.36 $L = 2 \times 10^3 \text{ m} \quad f_1 = \dfrac{v}{2L} = \dfrac{343}{4 \times 10^3} = \boxed{0.0858 \text{ Hz}}$

Since the tunnel is open at each end, all harmonies are present, and it
will resonate at $2f_1$, $3f_1$, $4f_1$, etc.

18.37 $L = 0.7 \text{ m} \quad f_3 = 748 \text{ Hz}$

$f_3 = \dfrac{3v}{2L} \quad \text{so} \quad v = \dfrac{2Lf_3}{3} = \dfrac{2(0.7)(748)}{3} = \boxed{349 \text{ m/s}}$

18.38 (a) $f_0 = \dfrac{v}{\lambda} = \dfrac{v}{4L} = \dfrac{331.5 \text{ m/s}}{4(4.88 \text{ m})} = \boxed{17.0 \text{ Hz}}$

(b) $f_0 = \dfrac{v}{\lambda} = \dfrac{v}{2L} = \boxed{34.0 \text{ Hz}}$

(c) For the closed pipe,

$$f = \frac{v(20^\circ C)}{v(0^\circ C)} f_0 = \sqrt{1 + \frac{20}{273}}\, f_0 = \boxed{17.6 \text{ Hz}}$$

For the open pipe,

$$f = \sqrt{1 + \frac{20}{273}}\, f_0 = \boxed{35.2 \text{ Hz}}$$

18.38

*18.39 $d_{AA} = 0.32 \text{ m} \qquad \lambda = 0.64 \text{ m}$

(a) $f = \dfrac{v}{\lambda} = \boxed{531 \text{ Hz}}$

(b) $\lambda = 0.085 \text{ m} \quad d_{AA} = \boxed{42.5 \text{ mm}}$

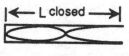

18.39

18.40 (a) $f_1 = \dfrac{v}{2L} = \dfrac{343}{2(0.3)} = \boxed{572 \text{ Hz}} \quad f_2 = 2f_1 = \boxed{1144 \text{ Hz}}$

$f_3 = 3f_1 = \boxed{1716 \text{ Hz}}$

(b) $f_1 = \dfrac{v}{4L} = \dfrac{343}{4(0.3)} = \boxed{286 \text{ Hz}} \quad f_2 = \dfrac{3v}{4L} = 3f_1 = \boxed{858 \text{ Hz}}$

$f_3 = \dfrac{5v}{4L} = 5f_1 = \boxed{1430 \text{ Hz}}$

18.41 $L = 2 \text{ m} \quad f_n = \dfrac{nv}{2L} = 410 \text{ Hz} \quad f_{n+1} = (n+1)\dfrac{v}{2L} = 492 \text{ Hz}$

$\dfrac{f_{n+1}}{f_n} = \dfrac{(n+1)}{n} = \dfrac{492}{410}; \quad n+1 = 1.2n; \quad n = 5$

Therefore, $v = \dfrac{410(2L)}{n} = \dfrac{(410)(4)}{5} = \boxed{328 \text{ m/s}}$

18.42 For the nth harmonic, $L = (2n-1)\dfrac{\lambda}{4}$ or

$$\lambda_n = \frac{4L}{(2n-1)} \quad \text{and} \quad f_n = \frac{v}{\lambda_n} = \frac{v(2n-1)}{4L}$$

Using the given values for L and v we have

$$f_n = \frac{(344\text{ m/s})(2n-1)}{(4)(0.4\text{ m})} = 215(2n-1)\text{ Hz}$$

(a) The lowest frequency corresponds to $n=1$, $f_1 = \boxed{215\text{ Hz}}$

(b) The maximum value of n is the largest integer in the term

$$\frac{2000\text{ Hz}}{(215\text{ Hz}+1)} = 5.15 \text{ or } n_{max} = 5$$

Therefore $f_{max} = 215[2(5)-1]\text{ Hz} = \boxed{1935\text{ Hz}}$

18.43 For resonance in a tube open at one end,

$$f = n\frac{v}{4L} \quad (n=1,3,5,\ldots), \quad \text{Eq. 18.12}$$

(a) Assuming $n=1$ and $n=3$

$$384 = \frac{v}{4(0.228)} \quad \text{and} \quad 384 = \frac{3v}{4(0.683)}$$

In either case $v = \boxed{350\text{ m/s}}$

(b) For the next resonance, $n=5$, and

$$L = \frac{5v}{4f} = \frac{5(350\text{ m/s})}{4(384\text{ s}^{-1})} = \boxed{1.14\text{ m}}$$

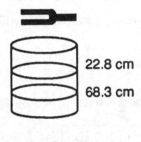

22.8 cm
68.3 cm

18.43

18.44 (a) For open pipes,

$$f = n\frac{v}{2L} \qquad (n = 1, 2, 3, \ldots) \text{ Eq. 18.11}$$

$$L_{max} = \frac{nv}{2f_{min}} = \frac{(1)(343 \text{ m/s})}{(2)(8 \text{ s}^{-1})} = \boxed{21.4 \text{ m}}$$

$$L_{min} = \frac{nv}{2f_{max}} = \frac{(1)(343 \text{ m/s})}{(2)(3 \times 10^4 \text{ s}^{-1})} = \boxed{5.72 \text{ mm}}$$

(b) For a pipe open at one end,

$$f = n\frac{v}{4L} \qquad (n = 1, 3, 5, \ldots) \text{ Eq. 18.12}$$

$$L_{max} = \frac{nv}{4f_{min}} = \frac{(1)(343 \text{ m/s})}{(4)(8 \text{ s}^{-1})} = \boxed{10.7 \text{ m}}$$

$$L_{min} = \frac{nv}{4f_{max}} = \frac{(1)(343 \text{ m/s})}{(4)(3 \times 10^4 \text{ s}^{-1})} = \boxed{2.86 \text{ mm}}$$

18.45 For a closed box, the resonant frequencies will have nodes at both sides, so the permitted wavelengths will be $L = \frac{n\lambda}{2}$, $(n = 1, 2, 3, \ldots)$.

i. e. , $L = \frac{n\lambda}{2} = \frac{nv}{2f}$ and $f = \frac{nv}{2L}$

Therefore with $L = 0.86$ m and $L' = 2.1$ m, the resonant frequencies are

$f_n = \boxed{n(206 \text{ Hz})}$ for $L = 0.86$ m

and $f'_n = \boxed{n(84.5 \text{ Hz})}$ for $L' = 2.1$ m.

18.46 When the rod is clamped at one–quarter of its length the fundamental frequency corresponds to a mode of vibration in which $L = \lambda$.

Therefore $L = \frac{v}{f} = \frac{5100 \text{ m/s}}{4400 \text{ Hz}} = \boxed{1.16 \text{ m}}$

18.47 $v = 4500$ m/s $\quad \lambda_1 = 4L = 240$ cm $= 2.4$ m

so $f_1 = \frac{v}{\lambda_1} = \frac{v}{4L} = \frac{4500}{2.4} = \boxed{1875 \text{ Hz}}$

18.48   (a) permissible vibrations

$$n = 1, \frac{L}{2} = \frac{\lambda_0}{4} \text{ thus } \lambda_0 = 2L \text{ and } f_0 = \frac{v}{\lambda_0} = \frac{v}{2L}$$

$$n = 2, \frac{L}{2} = \frac{3\lambda_1}{4} \text{ thus } \lambda_1 = \frac{2L}{3} \text{ and } f_1 = \frac{v}{\lambda_1} = 3(\frac{v}{2L})$$

$$n = 3, \frac{L}{2} = \frac{5\lambda_1}{4} \text{ thus } \lambda_2 = \frac{2L}{5} \text{ and } f_2 = \frac{v}{\lambda_2} = 5(\frac{v}{2L})$$

Only odd multiples of the fundamental frequency, f_0 are permitted

$$\boxed{[2n - 1]\frac{v}{2L} = f_n}$$

(b) $n = 0, \frac{L}{4} = \frac{\lambda_0}{2} \text{ thus } \lambda_0 = \frac{L}{2} \text{ and } f_0 = \frac{v}{\lambda_0} = \frac{2v}{L}$

$$n = 1, \frac{L}{4} = \frac{3\lambda_1}{2} \text{ thus } \lambda_1 = \frac{L}{6} \text{ and } f_1 = \frac{v}{\lambda_1} = 3(\frac{2v}{L})$$

$$n = 2, \frac{L}{4} = \frac{5\lambda_2}{2} \text{ thus } \lambda_2 = \frac{L}{10} \text{ and } f_2 = \frac{v}{\lambda_2} = 5(\frac{2v}{L})$$

Only odd multiples of the fundamental frequency, f_0 are permitted

$$\boxed{[2n - 1]\frac{2v}{L} = f_n}$$

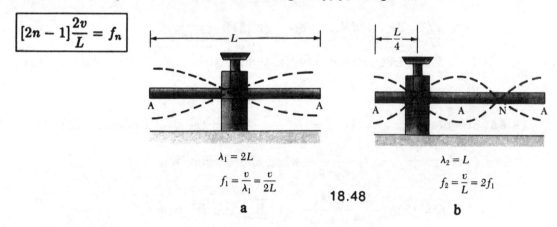

$$\lambda_1 = 2L$$
$$f_1 = \frac{v}{\lambda_1} = \frac{v}{2L}$$

a

$$\lambda_2 = L$$
$$f_2 = \frac{v}{L} = 2f_1$$

b

18.48

18.49   (a) $f = \frac{v}{2L} = \frac{5100}{(2)(1.6)} = \boxed{1594 \text{ Hz}}$

(b) Since it is held in the center there must be a node in the center as well as antinodes at the ends. The even harmonics have an antinode at the center so only the odd harmonics are present: $f, 3f, 5f, \ldots$

(c) $f = \frac{v'}{2L} = \frac{3560}{(2)(1.6)} = \boxed{1113 \text{ Hz}}$

*18.50 $f \; \alpha \; v \; \alpha \; T^{\frac{1}{2}}$

$$f_{\text{new}} = 110\sqrt{\frac{54}{60}} = 104.4 \text{ Hz}$$

$$= \boxed{5.6 \text{ beats/s}}$$

18.51 $y_1 = A_0 \cos \omega_1 t \quad y_2 = A_0 \cos \omega_2 t$

$y = y_1 + y_2 = A_0(\cos \omega_1 t + \cos \omega_2 t)$

$y = 2A_0 [\cos(\frac{\omega_1 - \omega_2}{2})t][\cos(\frac{\omega_1 + \omega_2}{2})t]$

18.52 Solution:

(a) $f_b = |f - f_0|$ so $f = f_0 \pm f_b = \boxed{520 \text{ Hz or } 526 \text{ Hz}}$

(b) $f = \dfrac{1}{2L}\sqrt{\dfrac{F}{\mu}} \dfrac{df}{dF} = \dfrac{1}{2L\sqrt{\mu}}(\dfrac{1}{2\sqrt{F}})$

$\dfrac{df}{f} = \dfrac{dF}{2F}$ so $\dfrac{dF}{F} = 2\dfrac{df}{f} = \dfrac{(2)(3)}{523} = \boxed{1.15\%}$

If the frequency is 520 Hz, tighten string; if 526 Hz reduce tension.

18.53 Solution: For an echo $f = f_0\dfrac{(v + v_s)}{(v - v_s)}$ and the beat frequency $f_b = |f - f_0|$ solving

for f_b gives $f_b = f_0\dfrac{(2v_s)}{(v - v_s)}$ when approaching wall.

(a) $f_b = (256)\dfrac{(2)(1.33)}{(343 - 1.33)} = \boxed{2 \text{ Hz}}$ beat frequency

(b) When moving away from wall, v_s changes sign. Solving for v_s gives

$$v_s = \frac{f_b v}{2f_0 - f_b} = \frac{(5)(343)}{(2)(256) - 5} = \boxed{3.38 \text{ m/s}}$$

18.54 (a) For a piano wire secured at both ends,

$$f = \frac{v}{2L} = \frac{(F/\mu)^{\frac{1}{2}}}{2(1)} = \boxed{261 \text{ Hz}} \text{ (middle C).}$$

(b) For a 1– meter organ pipe closed at the bottom, and open at the top,

$$f = \frac{v_s}{4L} = \frac{340}{4(1)} = \boxed{85 \text{ Hz}} \quad \text{(two E's below middle C).}$$

18.55 Solution:

(a) $\Delta x = \sqrt{(9+4)} - 3 = \sqrt{13} - 3 = 0.606$ m

The wavelength is $\lambda = \dfrac{343}{f} = \dfrac{343}{300} = 1.14$ m

Thus, $\dfrac{\Delta x}{\lambda} = \dfrac{0.606}{1.14} = 0.530$ of a wave or $\Delta\phi = 2\pi(0.530) = \boxed{3.33 \text{ rad}}$

(b) For destructive interference, we want $\dfrac{\Delta x}{\lambda} = 0.5 = f\dfrac{\Delta x}{v}$ where Δx is a constant

in this set up. $f = \dfrac{v}{2\Delta x} = \dfrac{343}{(2)(0.606)} = \boxed{283 \text{ Hz}}$

*18.56 $f = 87$ Hz

speed of sound in air: $v_a = 340$ m/s

(a) $\lambda_b = \ell$

$v = f\lambda_b = (87 \text{ s}^{-1})(0.40 \text{ m})$

$v = \boxed{34.8 \text{ m/s}}$

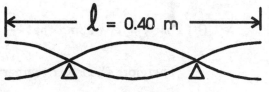

(b) $\left.\begin{array}{l} \lambda_a = 4L \\ v_a = \lambda_a f \end{array}\right\}$ $L = \dfrac{v_a}{4f} = \dfrac{340 \text{ m/s}}{4(87 \text{ s}^{-1})} = \boxed{0.977 \text{ m}}$

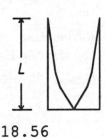

18.56

18.57 Path difference, $\delta = d \sin \theta$; and for $L \gg y$, $\delta \approx d \tan \theta = d(\frac{y}{L})$.

For minimum $\delta_1 = d(\frac{y_1}{L}) = \frac{\lambda}{2}$

For maximum $\delta_2 = d(\frac{y_2}{L}) = \lambda$

Therefore

$$\lambda = 2(y_2 - y_1)\frac{d}{L} = \frac{2(0.4 \text{ m})(1.5 \text{ m})}{(12 \text{ m})} = 0.1 \text{ m}$$

and $f = \frac{v}{\lambda} = \frac{340 \text{ m/s}}{0.1 \text{ m}} = \boxed{3400 \text{ Hz}}$

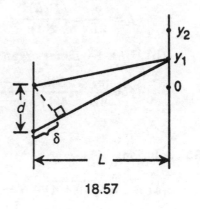

18.57

18.58   (a) $v_1 = (331 \text{ m/s})(\frac{300}{273})^{\frac{1}{2}} = 347 \text{ m/s}$

$v_2 = (331 \text{ m/s})(\frac{305}{273})^{\frac{1}{2}} = 350 \text{ m/s}$

In the fundamental mode, $\frac{\lambda_1}{4} = \frac{\lambda_2}{4}$ or

$$f_2 = f_1(\frac{v_2}{v_1}) = (480 \text{ Hz})(\frac{350}{347}) = 484 \text{ Hz}$$

Therefore the beat frequency is, $f_b = f_2 - f_1 = \boxed{4 \text{ Hz}}$

(b) For $f_1 = f_2$ we find that $\frac{L_2}{L_1} = \frac{v_2}{v_1} = \frac{350}{347} = 1.01$

Therefore the lower temperature pipe should be decreased in length by $\boxed{1\%}$

*18.59 Harmonics...
650 Hz, 550 Hz, 450 Hz, 350 Hz, 250 Hz, 150 Hz, 50 Hz

Closed $f = \boxed{50.0 \text{ Hz}}$, $\lambda = 6.8 \text{ m}$, $L = \boxed{1.7 \text{ m}}$

18.60 Use Eq. 17.21 $f' = f\frac{(v \pm v_0)}{(v - v_s)}$

Let $f_1' = $ frequency of the speaker in front of student and

$f_2' = $ frequency of the speaker behind the student

$f_1' = (456 \text{ Hz})\frac{(331 \text{ m/s} + 1.5 \text{ m/s})}{(331 \text{ m/s} - 0)} = 458 \text{ Hz}$

$f_2' = (456 \text{ Hz})\frac{(331 \text{ m/s} - 1.5 \text{ m/s})}{(331 \text{ m/s} + 0)} = 454 \text{ Hz}$

Therefore $f_b = f_1' - f_2' = \boxed{4 \text{ Hz}}$

18.61 (a) When the string vibrates in three segments fastened at each end

$\lambda = 2L/3 = 0.83$ m. For given tension and linear density the wave

speed is $v = [\frac{F}{(m/\ell)}]^{\frac{1}{2}} = [\frac{10g}{(0.01/1.25)}]^{\frac{1}{2}} = 111$ m/s

Therefore $f = \frac{v}{\lambda} = \frac{111 \text{ m/s}}{0.83 \text{ m}} = \boxed{133 \text{ Hz}}$

(b) In four segments, $\lambda = L/2 = 0.625$ m and $v = f\lambda = 83.1$ m/s

We find the mass of string to be

$M = \frac{\mu v^2}{g} = \frac{(0.01 \text{ kg}/1.25 \text{ m})(83.1 \text{ m/s})^2}{9.80 \text{ m/s}^2} = \boxed{5.64 \text{ kg}}$

18.62 $v = 344$ m/s, $\quad v_s = 20$ km/h $= 5.56$ m/s, $\quad f_b = 4$ Hz

$f' = f(\frac{v}{v - v_s}) \qquad f_b = f' - f$

$f' = f(\frac{344 \text{ m/s}}{338.44 \text{ m/s}}) = 1.0164f$

$f' = f = 0.0164f = 4$ Hz $\qquad f = \boxed{243 \text{ Hz}}$

*18.63 $\quad v = \sqrt{\frac{(48)(2)}{4.8 \times 10^{-3}}} = 141$ m/s

$d_{NN} = 1$ m $\quad \lambda = 2$ m $\quad f = 70.7$ Hz

$\lambda = \frac{c}{f} = \frac{340}{70.7} = \boxed{4.86 \text{ m}}$

18.64 Both, the lower path length r_1 and the top path length r_2, must equal

an integer multiple of wavelengths.

Along the lower path $v = v_1 = (331 \text{ m/s})(\frac{473}{273})^{\frac{1}{2}} = 436 \text{ m/s}$

Along the upper path $v = v_2 = 331 \text{ m/s}$

Using integers n and p we have $n\lambda_1 = r_1$ or $\dfrac{n(436 \text{ s}^{-1})}{f} - 1.75 \text{ m}$

and $p\lambda_2 = r_2$ or $p\dfrac{(331 \text{ m/s}^{-1})}{f} = 1.75 \text{ m}$

The above equations lead to $\dfrac{n}{p} = \dfrac{19}{25}$

and $f = \dfrac{n(436 \text{ m/s})}{(1.75 \text{ m})} = \boxed{4730 \text{ Hz}}$

18.65 Solution: Moving away from station, frequency is depressed: $f' = 180 - 2 = 178 \text{ Hz}$

$178 = 180\dfrac{(343)}{(343 + v)}$. Solving for v gives $v = \dfrac{(2)(343)}{178}$

Therefore, $v = \boxed{3.85 \text{ m/s away from station}}$

Moving towards the station the frequency is enhanced: $f' = 180 + 2 = 182 \text{ Hz}$

$182 = 180\dfrac{(343)}{(343 - v)}$. Solving for v gives $v = \dfrac{(2)(343)}{182}$

Therefore, $v = \boxed{3.77 \text{ m/s towards the station}}$

18.66 (a) $L = \dfrac{v}{4f}$ so $\dfrac{L'}{L} = \dfrac{f}{f'}$. Letting the longest L be 1, the ratio is

$1 : 4/5 : 2/3 : 1/2$ or in integers $30 : 24 : 20 : 15$

(b) $L = \dfrac{343}{(4)(256)} = 33.5 \text{ cm}$. This is the longest pipe so using the ratios the lengths

are: $33.5, 26.8, 22.3$, and 16.7 cm

(c) The frequencies are using the ratio $256, 320, 384$, and 512 Hz. These represent notes C, E, G, and C' on the physical pitch scale.

18.67 (a) Since the first node is at the weld, the wavelength in the thin wire is $2L$ or 80 cm. The frequency and tension are the same in both sections, so

$$f = \frac{1}{2L}\sqrt{\frac{F}{\mu}} = \frac{1}{2(0.4)}\sqrt{\frac{4.6}{0.002}} = 60 \text{ Hz}$$

(b) As the thick wire is twice the diameter, the linear density is 4 times that of the thin wire. $\mu' = 8$ g/m so $L' = \frac{1}{2f}\sqrt{\frac{F}{\mu'}}$

$$L' = [1/(2)(60)]\sqrt{[(4.6)/(0.008)]} = 20 \text{ cm} - \text{half the length of the thin wire.}$$

*18.68 $f_B = f_A$

$$\lambda_B = \tfrac{1}{3}\lambda_A$$

$$v_B = \tfrac{1}{3}v_A$$

$$v_B^2 = \tfrac{1}{9}v_A^2$$

$$v = \sqrt{\frac{T}{\mu}}$$

$$\frac{T_B}{T_A} = \frac{v_B^2}{v_A^2} = \boxed{0.111}$$

18.69 (a) $f = \frac{n}{2L}\sqrt{\frac{F}{\mu}}$ so $\frac{f'}{f} = \frac{L}{L'} = \frac{L}{2L} = 1/2$

The frequency should be halved to get the same number of antinodes for twice the length.

(b) $\frac{n'}{n} = \sqrt{\frac{F}{F'}}$ so $\frac{F'}{F} = (\frac{n}{n'})^2 = [\frac{n}{(n+1)}]^2$

The tension must be $F' = [\frac{n}{(n+1)}]^2 F$

(c) $\frac{f'}{f} = \frac{L}{L'}\sqrt{\frac{F'}{F}}$ so $\frac{F'}{F} = (\frac{f'L'}{fL})^2$

$$\frac{F'}{F} = (\frac{3}{2})^2 = \frac{9}{4}, \text{ to get the same number of antinodes.}$$

$$\boxed{\frac{F'}{F} = \frac{9}{16}}, \text{ to get twice as many antinodes.}$$

18.70   (a) Let f_c be the frequency as seen by the car. Thus

$$f_c = f_0\sqrt{\frac{c+v}{c-v}} \text{ and } f = f_c\sqrt{\frac{c+v}{c-v}}$$

Combining gives $f = f_0\dfrac{(c+v)}{(c-v)}$.

(b) $fc - fv = f_0 c + f_0 v$ which gives $(f - f_0)c = (f + f_0)v \approx 2\,f_0 v$

$$f_b = f - f_0 = \frac{2f_0 v}{c} = \frac{2v}{\lambda}$$

(c) $f_b = \dfrac{(2)(30)(10 \times 10^9)}{3 \times 10^8} = \dfrac{(2)(30)}{(0.03)} = 2000 \text{ Hz} = \boxed{2 \text{ kHz}}$

$$\lambda = 3 \text{ cm} = \frac{c}{f_0} = \frac{(3 \times 10^8)}{(10 \times 10^9)}$$

(d) $v = \dfrac{f_b \lambda}{2}$ so $\Delta v = \dfrac{\Delta f_b \lambda}{2} = \dfrac{5(0.03)}{2} = \boxed{0.075 \text{ m/s} \approx 0.2 \text{ mph}}$

18.71 See approach outlined in solutions manual Chapter 16 problem 60.

18.72   (a) See approach in solutions manual, Chapter 16, problem 60.

(b) To determine the frequency, count the number of complete cycles contained within a given time interval.

(c) To determine the wavelength, measure the distance between *two* successive crossings of the x–axis.

CHAPTER 19

19.1 (a) $T = mP + T_0$ $\quad m = \dfrac{\Delta T}{\Delta P}$

$$m = \frac{78 - (-80)}{(1.635 - 0.900)} = 215.0$$

$$T_0 = T - mP = -80 - 215.0(0.900) = \boxed{-273.5°C} \text{ abs. zero calibration}$$

(b) $P = \dfrac{(T - T_0)}{m} = \dfrac{0 - (-273.7)}{215} = \boxed{1.27 \text{ atm}}$ freezing point

$$P = \frac{100 - (-273.5)}{215} = \boxed{1.74 \text{ atm}} \text{ boiling point.}$$

19.2 $T = aP - 273.15°C$

At $T = 0°C \quad a = \dfrac{273.15°C}{40 \text{ mm Hg}} = 6.829°C/\text{mm Hg}$

$P = \dfrac{T + 273.15°C}{a}$

(a) At $T = 100°C$, $P = \dfrac{373.15°C}{6.829°C/\text{mm Hg}}$ $\boxed{54.6 \text{ mm Hg}}$

(b) At $T = 1064°C$, $P = \dfrac{1337.58°C}{6.829°C/\text{mm Hg}} = \boxed{196 \text{ mm Hg}}$

19.3 (a) $PV = nRT$

$$P_2 = \frac{P_1 T_2}{T_1} = (50 \text{ mm Hg})\left(\frac{273.16°C}{450°C}\right) = \boxed{30.4 \text{ mm Hg}}$$

(b) $T_2 = \dfrac{T_1 P_2}{P_1} = (450 \text{ K})\left(\dfrac{2 \text{ mm Hg}}{50 \text{ mm Hg}}\right) = \boxed{18.0 \text{ K}}$

19.4 $T = aP + b \quad 100°C = a(0.700 \text{ atm}) + b \quad 0°C = a(0.512 \text{ atm}) + b$

$a = 532°C \text{ atm}, \ b = -272°C$

(a) $T = (532°C/\text{atm})(0.0400 \text{ atm}) - 272°C = \boxed{-251°C}$

(b) $P = \dfrac{T - b}{a} = \dfrac{450°C - (-272°C)}{532°C/\text{atm}} = \boxed{1.36 \text{ atm}}$

19.5 $\dfrac{T_1}{P_1} = \dfrac{T_2}{P_2}$

(a) $T_2 = \dfrac{T_1 P_2}{P_1} = \dfrac{(77.34\ \text{K})(45\ \text{kPa})}{25\ \text{kPa}} = \boxed{139\ \text{K}} = \boxed{-134\text{°C}}$

(b) $P_2 = \dfrac{P_1 T_2}{T_1} = \dfrac{(25\ \text{kPa})(20.28\ \text{K})}{77.34\ \text{K}} = \boxed{6.56\ \text{kPa}}$

19.6 The melting point of gold is 1064° C and the boiling point is 2660°C.

(a) Express these temperatures in kelvins. (b) Compute the difference of these temperatures in Celsius degrees and kelvin degrees and compare the two numbers.

(a) $T = 1064 + 273 = \boxed{1337\ \text{K}}$ melting point

$T = 2660 + 273 = \boxed{2933\ \text{K}}$ boiling point

(b) $\Delta T = \boxed{1596\ \text{C°}} = \boxed{1596\ \text{K}}$ The differences are the same.

19.7 (a) $T_F = \dfrac{9}{5}T_C + 32F° = \dfrac{9}{5}(-195.81) + 32 = \boxed{-321\text{°F}}$

(b) $T_R = \dfrac{9}{5}T = \dfrac{9}{5}(77.34) = \boxed{139\text{°R}}$

(c) $T = T_C + 273.15 = -195.81 + 273.15 = \boxed{77.3\ \text{K}}$

19.8 $T_C = \dfrac{5}{9}(T_F - 32.0)$

highest temperature; $T_C = \dfrac{5}{9}(136 - 32.0) = \boxed{57.8\text{°C}}$

lowest temperature; $T_C = \dfrac{5}{9}(-127 - 32.0) = \boxed{-88.3\text{°C}}$

*19.9 $\qquad\qquad 90 - 273 \;=\; -183\text{°C}$

$\qquad\qquad (-183)\dfrac{9}{5} \;=\; -329$

$T(\text{°F}) = 32° - 329° \;=\; \boxed{-297\text{°F}}$

19.10 $T_C = \dfrac{5}{9}(T_F - 32)$

Range: $\boxed{40.6°\text{C to} -31.6°\text{C}}$

19.11 $\Delta T = \dfrac{5}{9}(586) = -325.6°\text{C}$

$T = 444.6 - 325.6 = \boxed{119°\text{C}}$

$T_F = \dfrac{9}{5}T_C + 32 = \dfrac{9}{5}(119) + 32 = \boxed{246°\text{F}}$

$T_F = \dfrac{9}{5}T_C + 32 = \dfrac{9}{5}(444.6) + 32 = \boxed{832°\text{F}}$

19.12 $T_C = \dfrac{5}{9}(T_F - 32)$

$T_C = \dfrac{5}{9}(98.6° - 32°\text{F}) = \boxed{37.0°\text{C}}$

$T_C = \dfrac{5}{9}(102°\text{F} - 32°\text{F}) = \boxed{38.9°\text{C}}$

19.13 (a) $\Delta T_C = \dfrac{5}{9}\Delta T_F = \boxed{90°\text{C}}$

(b) $\Delta T_K = \Delta T_C = \boxed{90\text{ K}}$

19.14 $\Delta T = 350°\text{C} - (-80°\text{C}) = 430°\text{C}$

$\Delta T = \boxed{430\text{ K}}$ (Numerically the same as °C)

$\Delta T = \dfrac{9}{5}(430) = \boxed{774°\text{F}}$

$\Delta T = 774°\text{R}$ (Numerically the same as °F)

19.15 $T_F = \dfrac{9}{5}T_C + 32$

$T_F = \dfrac{9}{5}T_F + 32$

$T_F = \boxed{-40°\text{F} = -40°\text{C}}$

19.16 (a) $\Delta L = \alpha L \Delta T = 24 \times 10^{-6}(\text{C}°)^{-1}(3.0000 \text{ m})(80°\text{C}) = 0.00576 \text{ m}$

$L = \boxed{3.0058 \text{ m}}$

(b) $\Delta L = 24 \times 10^{-6}(\text{C}°)^{-1}(3.0000 \text{ m})(-20°\text{C}) = -0.0014$

$\boxed{L = 2.9986 \text{ m}}$

19.17 The wire is 35 m when $T_C = -20°\text{C}$

$\Delta \ell = \ell_0 \overline{\alpha}(T - T_0)$

$\overline{\alpha} \cong \alpha(20°\text{C}) = 1.67 \times 10^{-5} \text{ deg}^{-1}$ For Cu.

$\Delta \ell = (35 \text{ m})(1.67 \times 10^{-5} \text{ deg}^{-1})(35°\text{C} - (-20°\text{C})) = \boxed{+3.27 \text{ cm}}$

*19.18 $\Delta L = \alpha L \Delta T$

$\qquad = (8.9 \times 10^{-6})(1)(37) = 0.329 \text{ mm}$

$\quad L' = L + \Delta L = \boxed{1.000329 \text{ m}}$

19.19 $\Delta L = L\alpha\Delta T = AL_1 + AL_2 = (15 \text{ m})(11 \times 10^{-6}(\text{C}°)^{-1})(50°\text{C} + 30°\text{C})$

$\qquad = \boxed{1.32 \text{ cm}}$

19.20 $\overline{\alpha} \cong \alpha(20°\text{C}) = 1.1 \times 10^{-5} \text{ deg}^{-1}$ for steel.

$\Delta \ell = (518 \text{ m})(1.1 \times 10^{-5} \text{ deg}^{-1})(35°\text{C} - (-20°\text{C})) = \boxed{0.313 \text{ m}}$

*19.21 $\Delta V = \beta V \Delta T$

$\Delta V = (5.81 \times 10^{-4}/°\text{C})(50 \text{ gal})(20°\text{C}) = \boxed{0.548 \text{ gal}}$

19.22 (a) $\alpha = \dfrac{\Delta L}{L\Delta T} = \dfrac{0.060 \text{ cm}}{(40 \text{ cm})(100°\text{C})} = \boxed{1.50 \times 10^{-5}(\text{C}°)^{-1}}$

(b) $T = \dfrac{\Delta L}{\alpha L} = \dfrac{(-0.025 \text{ cm})}{1.5 \times 10^{-5}(°\text{C})^{-1}(40 \text{ cm})} = \boxed{-41.7°\text{C}}$

*19.23 $\Delta \ell = \alpha \ell \Delta T \qquad \dfrac{F}{A} = Y \dfrac{\Delta \ell}{\ell}$

$\qquad F = \Delta Y \dfrac{\Delta \ell}{\ell} = AY\alpha\Delta T$

$\qquad\quad = \pi (2 \times 10^{-2}\ \text{m})^2 \left(20.6 \times 10^{10}\ \dfrac{\text{N}}{\text{m}^2} \right)(12 \times 10^{-6}/°\text{C})(70°\text{C})$

$\qquad\quad = \boxed{217\ \text{kN}}$

19.24 (a) $L_{\text{Al}}(1 + \alpha_{\text{Al}}\Delta T) = L_{\text{Brass}}(1 + \alpha_{\text{Brass}}\Delta T)$

$\qquad\qquad \Delta T = \dfrac{(L_{\text{Al}} - L_{\text{Brass}})}{(L_{\text{Brass}}\alpha_{\text{Brass}} - L_{\text{Al}}\alpha_{\text{Al}})}$

$\qquad\qquad \Delta T = \dfrac{(10.01 - 10.00)}{[(10.00)(19 \times 10^{-6}) - (10.01)(24 \times 10^{-6})]}$

$\qquad\qquad \Delta T = -199\text{C}° \text{ so } T = \boxed{-179°\text{C This is attainable}}$

$\qquad$ (b) $\Delta T = \dfrac{(10.02 - 10.00)}{[(10.00)(19 \times 10^{-6}) - (10.02)(24 \times 10^{-6})]}$

$\qquad\qquad \Delta T = -396\ \text{C}° \text{ so } T = \boxed{-376°\text{C which is below 0 K so it cannot be reached}}$

19.25 $\Delta L = L\alpha\Delta T = (25\ \text{m})(12 \times 10^{-6}(\text{C}°)^{-1})(40°) = \boxed{1.20\ \text{cm}}$

*19.26 $\Delta A = 2\alpha A \Delta T$

$\qquad\qquad = 2(17 \times 10^{-6}/°\text{C})(64\ \text{cm}^2)(50°\text{C}) = \boxed{+0.109\ \text{cm}^2}$

19.27 (a) $\Delta L = \alpha L_0 \Delta T$

$\qquad\qquad 0.050\ \text{cm} = (24 \times 10^{-6}\ \text{C}°)(5.000\ \text{cm})\Delta T$

$\qquad\qquad \Delta T = 417\ °\text{C}, \text{so } T_f = \boxed{437°\text{C}}$

$\qquad$ (b) $\Delta L_A = \Delta L_B + 0.050\ \text{cm}$

$\qquad\qquad (\alpha L_0)_A \Delta T = (\alpha L_0)_B \Delta T + 0.050$

$\qquad\qquad (24 \times 10^{-6})(5.000)\Delta T = (19 \times 10^{-6})(5.050)\Delta T + 0.05$

$\qquad\qquad \Delta T = 2079°\text{C} , \text{so } T_f = \boxed{2100°\text{C}} \qquad \text{Aluminum melts at 660°C !}$

*19.28 For the dimensions to increase,

$$\Delta L = \alpha L \Delta T$$

$$0.01 \text{ cm} = (1.3 \times 10^{-4}/°\text{C})(2.2\text{cm})(T - 20)$$

$$T = \boxed{55.0°\text{C}}$$

19.29 (a) $\Delta V = V_t\beta_t\Delta T - V_{A1}\beta_{A1}\Delta T = (9.0 \times 10^{-4} - 0.72 \times 10^{-4})(°\text{C})^{-1}(2000 \text{ cm}^3)(60°\text{C})$

$$= 99.4 \text{ cm}^3 \text{ overflows.}$$

(b) The remaining turpentine volume is 1.9006 L. When cooled back to 20°C, the cross-sectional area of the cylinder is again 100 cm². Therefore, the height drops by

$$x = 99\frac{4 \text{ cm}^3}{100 \text{ cm}^2} = 0.994 \text{ cm.}$$ The surface of the turpentine is 0.994 cm below the rim

of the cylinder.

19.30 $\dfrac{\Delta V}{V} = 3\alpha\Delta T = 3(24 \times 10^{-6}/\text{C°})(30 \text{ C°}) = \boxed{2.16 \times 10^{-3}}$

19.31 $\Delta V = \beta\Delta T(V) = 9.6 \times 10^{-4}(\text{ C°})^{-1}(25°\text{C})(45 \text{ L}) = \boxed{1.08 \text{ L}}$

19.32 (a) $V = V_0(1 + \beta\Delta T) = 100[1 + 1.5 \times 10^{-4}(-15)] = \boxed{99.8 \text{ mL}}$

(b) $\Delta V_{\text{acetone}} = (\beta V_0 \Delta T)_{\text{acetone}}$

$$\Delta V_{\text{flask}} = (\beta V_0 \Delta T)_{\text{pyrex}} = (3\alpha V_0 \Delta T)_{\text{pyrex}}$$

for same V_0, ΔT,

$$\frac{\Delta V_{\text{acetone}}}{\Delta V_{\text{flask}}} = \frac{\beta_{\text{acetone}}}{\beta_{\text{pyrex}}} = \frac{1.5 \times 10^{-4}}{3(3.2 \times 10^{-6})} = \frac{1}{6.4 \times 10^{-2}}$$

The volume change of flask is about 6% of the

change in the acetone's volume.

19.33 (a) $\Delta L = \alpha L \Delta T = 9 \times 10^{-6}(\text{C}^\circ)^{-1}(30 \text{ cm})(65^\circ\text{C}) = \boxed{0.176 \text{ mm}}$

(b) $\Delta L = 9 \times 10^{-6}(\text{C}^\circ)^{-1}(1.5 \text{ cm})(65^\circ\text{C}) = \boxed{8.78 \times 10^{-4} \text{ cm}}$

(c) $\Delta V = 3\alpha V \Delta T = 3(9 \times 10^{-6})(\text{C}^\circ)^{-1}\dfrac{(30)(\pi)(1.5)^2}{4} \text{ cm}^3(65^\circ\text{C}) = \boxed{0.0930 \text{ cm}^3}$

19.34 $P_2 = P_1(\dfrac{T_2}{T_1}) = (2.5 \text{ atm})(\dfrac{353 \text{ K}}{283 \text{ K}}) = \boxed{3.12 \text{ atm}}$

*19.35 $\left(\dfrac{PV}{T}\right)_n = \left(\dfrac{PV}{T}\right)_0$

$V = V_0 \dfrac{P_0}{P_n} \dfrac{T_n}{T_0} = 1\left(\dfrac{1}{0.1}\right)\left(\dfrac{233}{293}\right) = \boxed{7.95 \text{ m}^3}$

*19.36 $(1.01 \times 10^5)(6000) = n(8.31)(293)$

$n = 2.49 \times 10^5 \text{ mole}$

$N = \boxed{1.50 \times 10^{29} \text{ molecules}}$

*19.37 $PV = nRT$

$\dfrac{P_n}{P_0} = \dfrac{n_n}{n_0} \qquad \left(\dfrac{P_{\text{drop}}}{P_0}\right) = \left(\dfrac{n_{\text{drop}}}{n_0}\right)$

$\Delta m = (12 \text{ kg})\left(\dfrac{15 \text{ atm}}{41 \text{ atm}}\right) = \boxed{4.39 \text{ kg}}$

*19.38 $PV = nRT$

$\dfrac{(1.2)(1.01 \times 10^5)(8.8 \times 10^{-3})}{(8.31)(358)} = 0.358 \text{ mol}$

$m = \boxed{1.43 \text{ g}}$

*19.39 $\rho_{\text{out}}gV - \rho_{\text{in}}gV - (200 \text{ kg})g = 0$

$(\rho_{\text{out}} - \rho_{\text{in}})(400 \text{ m}^3) = 200 \text{ kg}$

$\left(1.25 \frac{\text{kg}}{\text{m}^3}\right)\left(1 - \frac{283 \text{ K}}{T_{\text{in}}}\right)(400 \text{ m}^3) = 200 \text{ kg}$

$1 - \frac{283}{T_{\text{in}}} = 0.4$

$0.6 = \frac{283}{T_{\text{in}}} \qquad T_{\text{in}} = \boxed{472 \text{ K}}$

19.40 $PV = N P'V' = \frac{4}{3}\pi r^3 N P'$

$N = \frac{3PV}{4\pi r^3 P'} = \frac{(3)(150)(0.1)}{(4\pi)(1.5)^3(1.2)} = \boxed{884 \text{ balloons}}$

19.41 (a) $T_2 = T_1 \frac{(P_2)}{P_1} = (300 \text{ K})(3) = \boxed{900 \text{ K}}$

(b) $T_2 = T_1 \frac{P_2 V_2}{P_1 V_1} = 300(2)(2) = \boxed{1200 \text{ K}}$

19.42 (a) Initially, $P_0 V_0 = n_o R T_0$

$(1 \text{ atm}) V_0 = n_0 R(10 + 273.15)\text{K}$

Finally, $P_f V_f = n_f R T_f \qquad P_f(0.28 V_0) = n_0 R(40 + 273.15) \text{ K}$

Dividing these equations,

$\frac{0.28 \times P_f}{1 \text{ atm}} = \frac{313.15 \text{ K}}{283.15 \text{ K}}$ giving $P_f = 3.95 \text{ atm}$ or

$P_f = \boxed{2.95 \text{ atm gauge} = 4.00 \times 10^5 \text{ Pa(abs.)} = 43.4 \text{ lb/in}^2 \text{ (gauge)}}$

(b) After being driven,

$P_d(1.02)(0.28 V_0) = n_0 R(85 + 273.15) \text{ K}$

$P_d = 1.121 P_f = 4.48 \times 10^5 \text{ Pa} = \boxed{50.4 \text{ lb/in}^2}$

*19.43 $P = \dfrac{nRT}{V} = \left(\dfrac{9\ \text{g}}{18\ \text{g/mol}}\right)\left(\dfrac{8.314\ \text{J}}{\text{mol K}}\right)\left(\dfrac{773\ \text{K}}{2 \times 10^{-3}\ \text{m}^3}\right) = \boxed{1.61\ \text{MPa}} = 16.1\ \text{atm}$

19.44 $PV = nRT = \dfrac{N}{N_A}RT$

$$N = \dfrac{PVN_A}{RT} = \dfrac{(10^{-11}\ \text{mmHg})(\dfrac{1.013 \times 10^5\ \text{N/m}^2}{760\ \text{mm Hg}})(1\ \text{m}^3)(6.02 \times 10^{23}\ \dfrac{\text{molecule}}{\text{mol}})}{(8.31\ \dfrac{\text{J}}{\text{K} \cdot \text{mol}})(300\ \text{K})}$$

$$= \boxed{3.22 \times 10^{11}\ \text{molecules}}$$

19.45 $P = P_g + Pa = (550 + 101) = 651\ \text{kPa}.$

$P_2 = P_1(\dfrac{T_2}{T_1})(\dfrac{V_2}{V_1}) = 651(\dfrac{313}{293})(1) = 695.4\ \text{kPa}$

$P_{2g} = P_2 - Pa = 695.4 - 101 = \boxed{594\ \text{kPa}}$

19.46 $PV = nRT$

$$V = \dfrac{nRT}{P} = (1\ \text{mol})\dfrac{8.31\ \text{J}}{\text{mol} \cdot \text{K}}\ \dfrac{(273\ \text{K})}{1.01 \times 10^5\ \text{N/m}^2} \cdot (\dfrac{10^3\ \text{L}}{1\ \text{m}^3}) = \boxed{22.4\ \text{L}}$$

19.47 $\dfrac{PV}{T} = \dfrac{P'V'}{T'}$ but $V = 2\pi^2 h$ and r does not change

$\dfrac{Ph}{T} = \dfrac{P'h'}{T'}$ $P = P_0 + \rho g d$

$h' = h(\dfrac{T}{T})[\dfrac{P_0}{(P_0 + \rho g h)}]$

$h' = 4(\dfrac{278}{298})\dfrac{1.013 \times 10^5}{\{1.013 \times 10^5 + (1025)(9.8)(220)\}} = 0.164\ \text{m}$

The water comes $4 - 0.164 = \boxed{3.84\ \text{m}}$ up the wall of the bell.

19.48 (a) Initially the air in the bell satisfies $P_0 V_0 = n_0 R T_0$

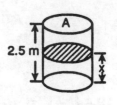

19.48

$$P_{\text{surface}} V_{\text{bell}} = n R T_0 \quad \text{or, (1)} \quad P_{\text{surface}}(2.5 \text{ m} \times A) = n R T_0$$

When the bell is lowered, the air in the bell satisfies

$$(2) \quad P_{\text{bell}}(2.5 \text{ m} - x)A = n R T_f$$

where x is the height the water rises in the bell. Also, the

pressure in the bell, once it is lowered, is equal to the seawater

pressure at the depth of the water level in the bell.

$$(3) \quad P_{\text{bell}} = P_{\text{surface}} + \rho g(82.3 \text{ m} - x)$$

$$\cong P_{\text{surface}} + \rho_{\text{sea}} g(82.3 \text{ m})$$

The approximation is good, as $x < 2.50$ m. Substituting (3) into

(2) and substituting nR from (1) into (2),

$$[P_{\text{surface}} + \rho_{\text{sea}} g(82.3 \text{ m})](2.5 \text{ m} - x)A = P_{\text{surface}} V_{\text{bell}} \frac{T_f}{T_0}$$

Using $P_{\text{surface}} = 1 \text{ atm} = 1.01325 \times 10^5 \text{ Pa}$ and $\rho_{\text{sea}} = 1.025 \times 10^3 \dfrac{\text{kg}}{\text{m}^3}$

$$x = 2.5 \text{ m}[1 - \frac{T_f}{T_0}(1 + \frac{\rho_{\text{sea}} g \times 82.3 \text{ m}}{P_{\text{surface}}})^{-1}]$$

$$= 2.5 \text{ m}[1 - \frac{277.15 \text{ K}}{293.15 \text{ K}}(1 + \frac{1.025 \times 10^3 \frac{\text{kg}}{\text{m}^3} \times 9.8 \frac{\text{m}}{\text{s}^2} \times 82.3 \text{ m}}{1.01325 \times 10^5 \text{ Pa}})^{-1}]$$

$$= \boxed{2.24 \text{ m}}$$

(b) If the water in the bell is to be expelled, the air pressure in

the bell must be raised to the water pressure at the bottom of the bell.

That is,

$$P_{\text{bell}} = P_{\text{surface}} + \rho g(82.3 \text{ m})$$

$$= 1.01325 \times 10^5 \text{Pa} + (1.025 \times 10^3 \frac{\text{kg}}{\text{m}^3})(9.8 \frac{\text{m}}{\text{s}^2})(82.3 \text{ m})$$

$$= 9.28 \times 10^5 \text{ Pa} = \boxed{9.16 \text{ atm}}$$

19.49 At the lake bottom the bubble of marsh gas satisfies (1) $P_0V_0 = nRT_0$

At the bottom of the lake the pressure inside the bubble must be equal to the water pressure there, so   (2) $P_0 = P_{atm} + \rho gh$

h is the lake depth and P_{atm} the surface pressure. Once the bubble is at the surface,

(3) $P_fV_f = nRT_f$ and   (4) $P_f = P_{atm}$

Dividing (3) by (1),

$$\frac{P_fV_f}{P_0V_0} = \frac{T_f}{T_0} \qquad \frac{V_f}{V_0} = \frac{P_0}{P_f}\frac{T_f}{T_0}$$

Substituting from (2) and (4),

$$\frac{V_f}{V_0} = \frac{P_{atm} + \rho gh}{P_{atm}}\frac{T_f}{T_0} = (1 + \frac{\rho gh}{P_{atm}})\frac{T_f}{T_0}$$

$$\frac{\frac{4}{3}\pi r_f^3}{\frac{4}{3}\pi r_0^3} = [1 + \frac{(1.0 \times 10^3 \text{ kg/m}^3)(9.8 \text{ m/s}^2)(4.2 \text{ m})}{1.01325 \times 10^5 \text{ Pa}}]\frac{(12 + 273.15) \text{ K}}{(5 + 273.15) \text{ K}}$$

$$\frac{r_f^3}{r_0^3} = 1.4416 \quad \text{gives} \quad \frac{r_f}{r_0} = \boxed{1.13}$$

19.50   (a) $\dfrac{PV}{T} = \dfrac{P'V'}{T'}$

$V' = V + Ah$

$P' = P + \dfrac{kh}{A}$

$(P + \dfrac{kh}{A})(V + Ah) = PV(\dfrac{T'}{T})$

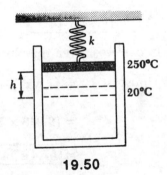

19.50

$(1.013 \times 10^5 \dfrac{\text{N}}{\text{m}^2} + 2 \times 10^5 \dfrac{\text{N}}{\text{m}^3}h)(5 \times 10^{-3} \text{ m}^3 + (0.01 \text{ m}^2)h)$

$= (1.013 \times 10^5 \dfrac{\text{N}}{\text{m}^2})(5 \times 10^{-3} \text{ m}^3)(\dfrac{523 \text{ K}}{293 \text{ K}})$

$2000h^2 + 2013h - 397 = 0$

$h = \dfrac{-2013 \pm 2689}{4000} = \boxed{0.169 \text{ m}}$

(b) $P' = P + \dfrac{kh}{A} = 1.013 \times 10^5 \text{ Pa} + \dfrac{(2 \times 10^3 \text{ N/m})(0.169 \text{ m})}{0.01 \text{ m}^2}$

$= \boxed{1.35 \times 10^5 \text{ Pa}}$

19.51 (a) $R = R_0(1 + AT_c)$

$50 = R_0(1)$

$71.5 = 50(1 + 231.97A)$

$$\boxed{A = 1.85 \times 10^{-3} (\text{C}°)^{-1}} \quad \boxed{R_0 = 50.0 \ \Omega}$$

(b) $T = \dfrac{\dfrac{R}{R_0} - 1}{A} = \boxed{422°\text{C}}$

19.52 (a) $T_1 = 2\pi \sqrt{\dfrac{\ell}{g}}$

$\ell = \dfrac{(15)^2}{4\pi^2} (9.8 \ \text{m/s}^2) = 0.24824 \ \text{m}$

$\Delta \ell = \alpha L \Delta T = 19 \times 10^{-6} (\text{C}°)^{-1} (0.24824 \ \text{m})(10°\text{C}) = 4.717 \times 10^{-5} \ \text{m}$

$T_2 = 2\pi \sqrt{\dfrac{\ell + \Delta \ell}{g}} = 2\pi \sqrt{\dfrac{0.2483 \ \text{m}}{g}} = 1.0000949 \ \text{s}$

$\Delta T = \boxed{9.49 \times 10^{-5} \ \text{s}}$

(b) In one week, the time lost is

time lost $= (1 \ \text{wk})(9.49 \times 10^{-5} \ \text{s lost per second})$

$= (6.048 \times 10^5 \ \text{s})(9.49 \times 10^{-5} \dfrac{\text{s lost}}{\text{s}})$

$= \boxed{57.4 \ \text{s lost}}$

19.53 From the diagram in Figure 19.13 we see that the change in area is

$\Delta A = \ell \Delta w + w \Delta \ell + \Delta w \Delta \ell$. Since $\Delta \ell$ and Δw are each small

quantities, the product $\Delta w \Delta \ell$ will be very small. Therefore, we

assume $\Delta w \Delta \ell \approx 0$. Since $\Delta w = w \alpha \Delta T$ and $\Delta \ell = \ell \alpha \Delta T$,

we then have $\Delta A = \ell w \alpha \Delta T + w \ell \alpha \Delta T$ and since $A = \ell w$, we have

$$\boxed{\Delta A = 2\alpha A \Delta T}$$

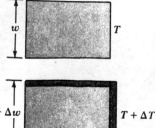

19.53

The approximation assumes $\Delta \omega \Delta \ell \approx 0$, or $\alpha \Delta T \approx 0$. Another way of stating this
is $\boxed{\alpha \Delta T \ll 1}$

19.54 $I = \int r^2 \, dm$ and since $r(T) = r(T_1)(1 + \alpha \Delta T)$ for $\alpha \Delta T \ll$ we find

$$\frac{I(T)}{I(T_0)} = (1 + \alpha \Delta T)^2 \text{ thus } \frac{I(T) - I(T_0)}{I(T_0)} \approx 2\alpha \Delta T$$

(a) With $\alpha = 17 \times 10^{-6}/°C$ and $\Delta T = 100°C$, we find for Cu:

$$\frac{\Delta \ell}{\ell} = 2(17 \times 10^{-6}/°C)(100°C) = \boxed{0.340\%}$$

(b) With $\alpha = 24 \times 10^{-6}/°C$ and $\Delta T = 100°C$, we find for Al:

$$\frac{\Delta \ell}{\ell} = 2(24 \times 10^{-6}/°C)(100°C) = \boxed{0.480\%}$$

19.55 Using the results of Problem 57 and neglecting the expansion of the

glass, $\Delta h = \dfrac{V}{A}\beta \Delta T$

$$\Delta h = \frac{\frac{4}{3}\pi(\frac{0.25 \text{ cm}}{2})^3}{\pi(0.002 \text{ cm})^2}(1.82 \times 10^{-4}/ \text{ C}°)(30°C) = \boxed{3.55 \text{ cm}}$$

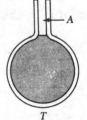

19.55

19.56 (a) $\rho = \dfrac{m}{V}$ and $d\rho = -\dfrac{m}{V^2}dV$. For very small changes in V and ρ,

this can be expressed as $\Delta \rho = -\dfrac{m}{V}\dfrac{\Delta V}{V} = -\rho \beta \Delta T$. The

negative sign means that any increase in temperature causes the

density to decrease and vice versa.

(b) For water we have

$$\beta = |\frac{\Delta \rho}{\rho \Delta T}| = |\frac{(1.0000 \text{ g/cm}^3 - 0.9997 \text{ g/cm}^3)}{(1.0000 \text{ g/cm}^3)(10 - 4)\text{C}°}| = \boxed{5 \times 10^{-5} \text{ °C}^{-1}}$$

19.57 (a) The volume of the liquid increases as $\Delta V_\ell = V\beta\Delta T$. The volume

of the flask increases as $\Delta V_g = 3\alpha V\Delta T$. Therefore the overflow

in the capillary is $V_c = V\Delta T(\beta - 3\alpha)$; and in the capillary

$V_c = A\Delta h$. Therefore $\boxed{\Delta h = \dfrac{V}{A}(\beta - 3\alpha)\Delta T}$

(b) For a mercury thermometer $\beta(Hg) = 1.82 \times 10^{-4}{}^\circ\text{C}^{-1}$ and for

glass, $3\alpha = 3 \times 9 \times 10^{-6}{}^\circ\text{C}^{-1}$. Thus $\beta - 3\alpha \approx \beta$, or $\boxed{\alpha \ll \beta}$

19.58 (a) $B = \rho g V'$ $P' = P_0 + \rho g d$ $P'V' = P_0 V_0$

$B = \dfrac{\rho g P_0 V_0}{P'} = \boxed{\dfrac{\rho g P_0 V_0}{(P_0 + \rho g d)}}$

(b) Since d is in the denominator, B must decrease as the depth increases.

(The volume of the balloon becomes smaller with increasing pressure.)

(c) $\dfrac{1}{2} = \dfrac{B(d)}{B(0)} = \dfrac{\rho g P_0 V_0/(P_0 + \rho g d)}{\rho g P_0 V_0/P_0} = \dfrac{P_0}{P_0 + \rho g d}$

$P_0 + \rho g d = 2P_0$

$d = \dfrac{P_0}{\rho g} = \dfrac{1.013 \times 10^5}{(10^3)(9.8)} = \boxed{10.3 \text{ m}}$

19.59 (a) $n \equiv m/M = \text{g/mol} = $ number of moles

$\rho = \dfrac{m}{V} = \boxed{\dfrac{nM}{V}}$

(b) $V = \dfrac{nRT}{P} = \dfrac{2 \text{ mol}(8.31 \frac{\text{J}}{\text{K} \cdot \text{mol}})(293 \text{ K})}{1.013 \times 10^5 \text{ N/m}^2} = 4.807 \times 10^{-2} \text{ m}^3$

$\rho = \dfrac{nM}{V} = \dfrac{2(32) \text{ mol}}{4.807 \times 10^{-2} \text{ m}^3} \cdot \dfrac{\text{g}}{\text{mol}} = 133 \text{ g/m}^3 = \boxed{0.133 \text{ kg/m}^3}$

19.60 (a) For an ideal gas $PV = nRT$. For small change ΔV and ΔT we have

$P\Delta V = nR\Delta T$. Multiplying each side of the equation by VT we have

$P\Delta V(VT) = nR\Delta T(VT)$ and using $PV = nRT$ this becomes

$T\Delta V = V\Delta T$. But $\beta = \dfrac{\Delta V}{V\Delta T}$ and therefore $\boxed{\beta = \dfrac{1}{T}}$

(b) At $T = 0°$, $\beta = \dfrac{1}{273.15 \text{ K}} = 3.66 \times 10^{-3°}C^{-1}$

$\beta(He) = 3.665 \times 10^{-3°}C^{-1}$ and $\beta(\text{air}) = \boxed{3.67 \times 10^{-3} °C^{-1}}$

Hence, both gases have thermal expansion coefficients very close

to the values predicted by the ideal gas model.

19.61 For each gas alone, $P_1 = \dfrac{n_1 kT}{V}$ and $P_2 = \dfrac{n_2 kT}{V}$ and $P_3 = \dfrac{n_3 kT}{V}$, etc.

For all the gasses

$P_1 V_1 + P_2 V_2 + P_3 V_3 \ldots = (n_1 + n_2 + n_3 \ldots)kT$ and

$(n_1 + n_2 + n_3 \ldots)kT = PV$.

Also $V_1 = V_2 = V_3 = \ldots = V$, and therefore $\boxed{P = P_1 + P_2 + P_3 \ldots}$

19.62   (a) Using the Periodic Table we find the molecular masses of

the air components to be

$M(N_2) = 28.01$ u, $M(O_2) = 32.00$ u, M(Ar) =39.95 u,

and $M(CO_2) = 44.01$ u. Thus, the

number of moles of each gas in the sample is

$$n(N_2) = \frac{75.52 \text{ g}}{28.01 \text{ g/mol}} = 2.6962 \text{ mol}$$

$$n(O_2) = \frac{23.15 \text{ g}}{32.00 \text{ g/mol}} = 0.7234 \text{ mol}$$

$$n(Ar) = \frac{1.28 \text{ g}}{39.95 \text{ g/mol}} = 0.0320 \text{ mol}$$

$$n(CO_2) = \frac{0.05 \text{ g}}{44.01 \text{ g/mol}} = 0.0011 \text{ mol}$$

The total number of moles is $n_o = \sum_i n_i = 3.4527$ mol

Then, the partial pressure of N_2 is

$$P(N_2) = \frac{2.6962 \text{ mol}}{3.4527 \text{ mol}} \cdot (1.01325 \times 10^5 \text{ Pa})$$

$$= 0.791 \times 10^5 \text{ Pa} = 79.1 \text{ kPa}$$

Similarly,

$$P(O_2) = \boxed{21.2 \text{ kPa}} \quad P(Ar) = \boxed{940 \text{ Pa}} \quad P(CO_2) = \boxed{32.3 \text{ Pa}}$$

(b) Solving the ideal gas law equation for V and using $T = 273.15 + 15.00 = 288.15$ K, we find

$$V = \frac{n_o RT}{P} = \frac{(3.4527 \text{ mol})(8.3144 \text{ J/mol} \cdot \text{K})(2.88.15 \text{K})}{1.01325 \times 10^5 \text{ Pa}} = \boxed{8.16 \times 10^{-2} \text{ m}^3}$$

Then,

$$\rho = \frac{m}{V} = \frac{100 \times 10^{-3} \text{ kg}}{8.164 \times 10^{-2} \text{ m}^3} = \boxed{1.23 \text{ kg/m}^3}$$

(c) The 100 g sample must have an appropriate molecular mass to yield n_o moles of gas: that is

$$M(\text{air}) = \frac{100 \text{ g}}{3.4527 \text{ mol}} = \boxed{29.0 \text{ g/mol}}$$

*19.63 $PV = nRT$ $P = 1.01 \times 10^5$ Pa

$\qquad P'V' = nRT$ $P' = (1.01 \times 10^5 + pgh)$ Pa

$$V' = (0.82 \text{ L}) \left(\frac{1 \text{ atm}}{1 \text{ atm} + (1000)(9.8)(10)} \right) = \frac{1.013}{1.993}(0.82) = \boxed{0.417 \text{ L}}$$

19.64 $R_B + \alpha_B R_B(T - 20) = R_s + \alpha_s R_s(T - 20)$

$\qquad 3.99 \text{ cm} + (19 \times 10^{-6}(\text{C}°)^{-1}(3.994 \text{ cm})(\text{T} - 20°\text{C})$

$\qquad\qquad = 4 \text{ cm} + (11 \times 10^{-6})(\text{C}°)^{-1}(4 \text{ cm})(\text{T} - 20°\text{C})$

$\qquad 3.189 \times 10^{-5}T = 0.006638 \quad \boxed{T = 208°\text{C}}$

19.65 $\dfrac{\Delta V}{V} = \dfrac{\beta V \Delta T}{V} = 1.12 \times 10^{-4}(\text{C}°)^{-1}(20°\text{C}) = 22.4 \times 10^{-4}$

$\qquad \dfrac{F}{A} = B\dfrac{\Delta V}{V} = (1 \times 10^9 \text{ N/m}^2)(22.4 \times 10^4) = 22.4 \times 10^5 \text{ N/m}^2 = \boxed{22.1 \text{ atm}}$

19.66   (a) In equilibrium $P_{\text{gas}} = \dfrac{mg}{A} + P_a$. Therefore

$$\frac{nRT}{hA} = \frac{mg}{A} + P_a \text{ or } \boxed{h = \frac{nRT}{(mg + P_aA)}} \text{ where}$$

we have used $V = hA$ as the volume of the gas.

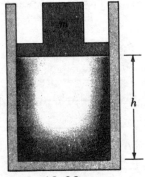

19.66

(b) For the data given $h = \dfrac{(0.2 \text{ mol})(8.314 \text{ J/K} \cdot \text{mol})(400 \text{ K})}{(20 \text{ kg})(9.8 \text{ m/s}^2) + (1.0 \times 10^6 \text{ N/m}^2)(0.008 \text{ m}^2)}$

$\qquad\qquad\qquad\qquad = \boxed{0.662 \text{ m}}$

19.67 (a) $PV = nRT = \text{constant}$

$$P_1 = P_0 + \rho g h; \quad V_1 = \frac{4}{3}\pi(5 \text{ mm})^3 \quad P_2 = P_0; \quad V_2 = \frac{4}{3}\pi(7 \text{ mm})^3$$

$$P_0 + \rho g h = P_0 \left(\frac{7}{5}\right)^3$$

$$\boxed{h = 18.0 \text{ m}}$$

(b) $P = P_0 + \rho g h = 1.01 \times 10^5 \text{ N/m}^2 + (10^3 \text{ kg/m}^3)(9.8 \text{ m/s}^2)(18 \text{ m}) = \boxed{277 \text{ kPa}}$

19.68 The pressure at the free surface of each liquid column is the same

(atmospheric pressure). The system is static(no liquid flow), so the pressure at the bottom of each column is likewise the same. Hence, $\rho_1 g h_1 = \rho_0 g h_0$, or

$\dfrac{\rho_0}{\rho_t} = \dfrac{h_t}{h_0}$. Now the volume V_0 of a unit mass of liquid at 0°C is $V_0 = \dfrac{1}{\rho_0}$, and at $t°C$ it is $V_t = \dfrac{1}{\rho_t}$. Then we have for a unit mass,

$$\frac{\rho_0}{\rho_t} = \frac{V_t}{V_0} = 1 + \bar{\beta}t_c = \frac{h_t}{h_0}$$

Solving for $\bar{\beta}$, we find the desired relationship,

$$\boxed{\bar{\beta} = \frac{h_t - h_0}{h_0 t_c}}$$

19.69   (a) T = constant, so $PV = P'V'$. With constant r, $Ph = P'h'$.

$$P' = 1\ atm + \frac{(20\ kg)(9.8 m/s^2)}{A}$$

$$P' = (1.013 \times 10^5) + \frac{(20 \times 9.8)}{\pi(0.40)^2} = 1.0169 \times 10^5\ Pa$$

$$P = 1\ atm = 1.013 \times 10^5\ Pa$$

$$h_0 = \frac{(50\ cm)(1.013 \times 10^5)}{(1.017 \times 10^5)} = 49.81\ cm\ (piston\ only)$$

$$P'' = 1\ atm + \frac{(95\ kg)(9.8\ m/s^2)}{\pi(0.40)^2} = 1.0315 \times 10^5\ Pa$$

$$h'' = \frac{(50\ cm)(1.013 \times 10^5)}{(1.0315 \times 10^5)} = 49.10\ cm\ (piston + man)$$

$$\Delta h = h_0 - h'' = \boxed{7.06\ mm}$$

(b) P = const, so $\dfrac{V}{T} = V'T'$: $T' = T(\dfrac{V'}{V}) = T(\dfrac{h'}{h})$

$$\therefore T' = 293\ K(\frac{49.81}{49.10}) = \boxed{297\ K}\ (24°C)$$

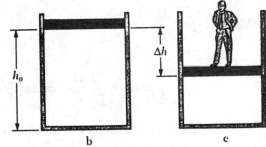

19.69

19.70   (a) $\dfrac{\pi d^2 h}{4} = V$; $h = \dfrac{4V}{\pi d^2} = \dfrac{4(3)(3785)}{(\pi \times 28^2)} = \boxed{18.44\ cm}$

(b) $\dfrac{\pi d^2 h'}{4} = V'$ thus $\dfrac{h'}{h} = (1 + \dfrac{\Delta h}{h}) = \dfrac{V'}{V} = \dfrac{P}{P'} = \dfrac{1.000}{0.965}$

so $\dfrac{\Delta h}{h} = (\dfrac{1.000}{0.965}) - 1 = 0.03627 = \boxed{3.63\%}$

thus $\Delta h = (18.4409)(0.03627) = 0.669\ cm = \boxed{6.69\ mm}$

(c) $\dfrac{\pi d^2 h'}{4} = V'$ thus

$$1 + \frac{\Delta h}{h} = (\frac{\rho}{\rho'})(\frac{d^2}{d'^2}) = (\frac{1.000}{0.965})[\frac{1}{(1 + \alpha\ \Delta T)^2}]$$

so $\dfrac{\Delta h}{h} = (1.03201 - 1) = 0.03201 = \boxed{3.20\%}$ where

$\alpha = 24 \times 10^{-6}/6C°$ and $\Delta T = 86\ C°$; thus

$$\Delta h = (18.4409)(0.03201) = 0.590\ cm = \boxed{5.90\ mm}$$

19.71 (a) $V = \dfrac{4\pi r^3}{3}$

$$n(20°C) = \frac{PV}{RT} = \frac{(4/3)(\pi)(0.1)^3(1.013 \times 10^5)}{(8.314)(293)} = 0.1742 \text{ mol}$$

$$n(100°C) = \frac{PV}{RT} = \frac{(4/3)(\pi)(0.01)^3(1.013 \times 10^5)}{(8.314)(373)} = 0.1368 \text{ mol}$$

$$\Delta n = 0.1742 - 0.1368 = \boxed{0.0374 \text{ mol}}$$

(b) $P = \dfrac{n'RT}{V} = \dfrac{(0.1368)(8.314)(273)}{(4\pi/3)(0.1)^3} = 74.1 \text{ kPa} = \boxed{0.732 \text{ atm}}$

19.72 (a) $\dfrac{dL}{L} = \alpha dT$

$$\int_{T_0}^{T_f} \alpha dT = \int_{L_0}^{L_f} \frac{dL}{L} \Longrightarrow \ln\left(\frac{L_f}{L_0}\right) = \alpha \Delta T \Longrightarrow \boxed{L_f = L_0 e^{\alpha \Delta T}}$$

(b) $L_f = (1)\exp[(2 \times 10^{-5})(100)] = 1.002002$

$L_{f'} = (1)[1 + 2 \times 10^{-5}(100)] = 1.002000$

$$\frac{L_f - L_{f'}}{L_f} = 2 \times 10^{-6} = \boxed{2.00 \times 10^{-4}\%}$$

$L_f = (1)\exp[(0.02)(100)] = 7.389 \quad L_{f'} = (1)[1 + (0.02)(100)] = 3.000$

$$\frac{L_f - L_{f'}}{L_f} = \boxed{59\%}$$

19.73 (a) $\mu = (\frac{\pi d^2}{4})\rho = \frac{\pi(1.00 \times 10^{-3})^2(7.86 \times 10^3)}{4} = \boxed{6.17 \times 10^{-3} \text{ kg/m}}$

(b) $f_1 = \frac{v}{2L}$; $v = \sqrt{\frac{F}{\mu}}$, so $f_1 = \sqrt{\frac{F/\mu}{2L}}$

Therefore $F = \mu(2Lf_1)^2 = (6.173 \times 10^{-3})(2 \times 0.80 \times 2 \times 10^2)^2 = \boxed{632 \text{ N}}$

(c) (Actual length) at 0°C = (natural length) $(1 + \frac{F}{AY})$

$A = (\frac{\pi}{4})(1 \times 10^{-3})^2 = 7.854 \times 10^{-7} \text{m}^2$ and $Y = 20 \times 10^{10} \text{ N/m}^2$

Therefore $\frac{F}{AY} = \frac{632}{(7.854 \times 10^{-7})}(20 \times 20^{10}) = 4.024 \times 10^{-3}$

so the natural length at 0°C $= \frac{(0.800 \text{ m})}{(1 + 4.024 \times 10^{-3})} = 0.79679$ m   and the

unstressed length at 30°C $= (0.79679 \text{ m})[1 + 30)(11 \times 10^{-6})] = 0.79706$ m

Then $0.800 = (0.79706)[1 + \frac{F'}{AY}]$

From this we find $\frac{F'}{AY} = (\frac{0.800}{0.79706}) - 1 = 3693 \times 10^{-3}$

and $F' = AY(3.693 \times 10^{-3})$

$= (7.854 \times 10^{-7})(20 \times 10^{10})(3.693 \times 10^{-3})(1 + \propto \Delta T)^2$

$F' = (580 \text{ N})(1 + 3.3 \times 10^{-4})^2 = 580.4 \text{ N} \approx \boxed{580 \text{ N}}$

also $\frac{f_1'}{f_1} = \sqrt{\frac{F'}{F}}$, therefore $f_1' = 200\sqrt{\frac{580}{632}} = \boxed{192 \text{ Hz}}$

19.74 At 20°C, the unstretched length of the steel and copper wires are

$$\ell_s(20°C) = (2 \text{ m})[1 - (11 \times 10^{-6})(C°)^{-1}(20°C)] = 1.99956 \text{ m}$$

$$\ell_c(20°C) = (2 \text{ m})[1 - (17 \times 10^{-6})(C°)^{-1}(20°C)] = 1.99932 \text{ m}.$$

Under a tension F, the length of the steel and copper wires are

$$\ell_s' = \ell_s[1 + \frac{F}{YA}]_s, \quad \ell_c' = \ell_c[1 + \frac{F}{YA}]_c$$

where $\ell_s' + \ell_c' = 4$ m

Since the tension, F, must be the same in each wire, solve for F :

$$F = \frac{(\ell_s' + \ell_c') - (\ell_s + \ell_c)}{\frac{\ell_s}{Y_s A_s} + \frac{\ell_c}{Y_c A_c}}$$

When the wires are stretched, their areas become

$$A_s = \pi(10^{-3} \text{ m})^2[1 - (11 \times 10^{-6})(20)]^2 = 3.140 \times 10^{-6} \text{ m}^2$$

$$A_c = \pi(10^{-3} \text{ m})^2[1 - (17 \times 10^{-6})(20)]^2 = 3.139 \times 10^{-6} \text{ m}^2$$

Recall $Y_s = 20 \times 10^{10} \text{ N/m}^2$; $Y_c = 11 \times 10^{10} \text{ N/m}^2$

Substituting into the equation for F, we obtain

$$F = \frac{4 \text{ m} - (1.99956 \text{ m} + 1.99932 \text{ m})}{\frac{1.99956 \text{ m}}{(20 \times 10^{10} \text{ N/m}^2)(3.140 \times 10^{-6}) \text{ m}^2} + \frac{1.99932 \text{ m}}{(11 \times 10^{10} \text{ N/m}^2)(3.139 \times 10^{-6}) \text{ m}^2}}$$

$$= 124.8 \text{ N} = \boxed{125 \text{ N}}$$

To find the x -coordinate of the junction,

$$\ell_s' = (1.99956 \text{ m})\left[1 + \frac{125 \text{ N}}{(20 \times 10^{10} \text{ N/m}^2)(3.140 \times 10^{-6} \text{m}^2)}\right] = 1.999958 \text{ m}$$

Thus the x-coordinate is $-2 + 1.999958 = \boxed{-4.20 \times 10^{-5} \text{ m}}$

19.75   (a) $L_1 = r_1\theta = L_0(1 + \alpha\Delta T)$ $L_2 = r_2\theta = L_0(1 + \alpha\Delta T)$

$$\Delta r = r_2 - r_1 = \frac{L_0(\alpha_2 - \alpha_1)\Delta T}{\theta}$$

$$\therefore \; r_2 - r_1 = \frac{1}{\theta}[L_0 + L_0\alpha_2\Delta T - L_0 - L_0\alpha_1]$$

$$\boxed{\theta = L_0(\alpha_2 - \alpha_1)\frac{\Delta T}{(r_2 - r_1)}}$$

(b) $\theta \longrightarrow 0$ as $\Delta T \longrightarrow 0$ $\boxed{\theta \longrightarrow 0 \text{ as } \alpha_1 \longrightarrow \alpha_2}$

$\theta < 0$ when $\Delta T < 0$ cooling means temperature is decreasing.

(c) $\boxed{\text{It bends the other way}}$

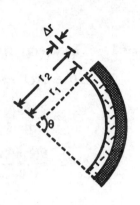

19.75

CHAPTER 20

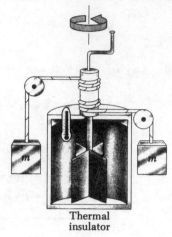

20.1 The energy transformation is represented by

$$\Delta U = \Delta Q \quad \text{or} \quad 2Mgh = (mc\Delta T)_{\text{water}}$$

$$\Delta T = \frac{2Mgh}{mc}$$

$$\Delta T = \frac{2(1.5 \text{ kg})(3 \text{ m})(9.8 \text{ ms}^2)}{(2.00 \text{ g})(4.186 \text{ J/g°C})} = \boxed{0.105 \text{ °C}}$$

Thermal
insulator

20.1

20.2 1 food calorie = 1000 cal and we require $mgh = \dfrac{\Delta Q}{mg} = \Delta Q$ or $h = \dfrac{\Delta Q}{mg}$.

$$h = \frac{7 \times 10^5 \text{ cal}(4.186 \text{ J/cal})}{(80 \text{ kg})(9.8 \text{ m/s}^2)} = \boxed{3.74 \times 10^3 \text{ m}}$$

20.3 Taking $m = 1 \text{ g} = 10^{-3} \text{ kg}$, we have

$$U = mgh = 10^{-3}(9.8)(50) \text{ J} = 0.49 \text{ J} = 0.117 \text{ cal}$$

But $U = Q = mc\Delta T = (1 \text{ g})(1 \text{ cal/g} \cdot {}^\circ\text{C})\Delta T = 0.117 \text{ cal}$ so $\Delta T = 0.117 \text{ C}^\circ$

$$T = T_0 + \Delta T = 10 + 0.117 \approx \boxed{10.12 \text{ °C}}$$

20.4 $Q = cm\Delta T = (900 \text{ J/kg} \cdot \text{C}^\circ)(3 \text{ kg})(50 - 20)°\text{C} \left(\dfrac{1 \text{ cal}}{4.186 \text{ J}}\right) = \boxed{19.4 \text{ kcal}}$

*20.5 $\Delta Q = mc_{\text{silver}}\Delta T$

$1230 \text{ J} = (0.525 \text{ kg}) \ c_{\text{silver}}(10°\text{C})$

$c_{\text{silver}} = \boxed{0.234 \text{ kJ/kg} \cdot °\text{C}}$

20.6 $Q = cm\Delta T; \quad T = 20°\text{C} + \dfrac{400 \text{ cal}}{(50 \text{ g})(0.055 \text{ cal/g} \cdot \text{C}^\circ)} = \boxed{165°\text{C}}$

20.7 $(cm\Delta T)_{\text{milk}} = (cm\Delta T)_{\text{coffee}}$

$(1 \text{ cal/g} \cdot {}^\circ \text{C})(10 \text{ g})(T - 10°\text{C}) = (1 \text{ cal/g} \cdot \text{C}^\circ)(160 \text{ g})(90 - T)°\text{C}$

$\boxed{T = 85.3°\text{C}}$

20.8 Heat gained by water = Heat lost by lead

$$[mc(T_f - T_0)]_{\text{water}} = [mc(T_0 - T_f)]_{\text{lead}}$$

$$500 \text{ g}(1 \text{ cal/ g} \cdot \text{C°})(25 - 20)\text{°C} = m(0.0924 \text{ cal/ g} \cdot \text{C°})(100 - 25)\text{°C}$$

$$m = 361 \text{ g} = \boxed{361 \text{ pellets}}$$

20.9 $(mc\Delta T)_{\text{iron}} = (mc\Delta T)_{\text{water}}$

$$-(1.5 \times 10^3)(0.107)(T - 600) = (20 \times 10^3)(1)(T - 29) \boxed{T = 29.6\text{°C}}$$

*20.10 $1 \text{ m}^3(1000 \text{ kg/m}^3)\left(4.19\dfrac{\text{kJ}}{\text{kg C°}}\right)(1 \text{ C°}) = V\left(1.3\dfrac{\text{kg}}{\text{m}^3}\right)\left(1\dfrac{\text{kJ}}{\text{kg C°}}\right)(1 \text{ C°})$

$$V = \dfrac{4190}{1.3} = \boxed{3220 \text{ m}^3}$$

20.11 Heat Gained by Water + Al = Heat lost by Water

$$200 \text{ g}(1 \text{ cal/g} \cdot \text{° C})(\text{T} - 10)\text{°C} + 300 \text{ g}(0.215 \text{ cal/g} \cdot \text{C°})(\text{T} - 10)\text{°C}$$

$$= 100 \text{ g}(1 \text{ cal/g} \cdot \text{C°})(100 - \text{T})$$

$$\boxed{T = 34.7\text{°C}}$$

*20.12 $\Delta Q = mc_{\text{air}}\Delta T$

$$= \left(\dfrac{10 \text{ breaths}}{\text{min}}\right)\left(\dfrac{1440 \text{ min}}{\text{day}}\right)\left(\dfrac{2 \times 10^{-4}\text{m}^3}{\text{breath}}\right)\left(\dfrac{1.25 \text{ kg}}{\text{m}^3}\right)\left(\dfrac{1000 \text{ J}}{\text{kg°C}}\right)(15\text{°C})$$

$$\Delta Q \cong \boxed{54 \text{ kJ}}$$

20.13 Q = heat to raise to melting point + heat to melt

$$= mc\Delta T + mL = (20 \text{ g})(0.215 \text{ cal/g} \cdot \text{C°})(660\text{°C} - 20\text{°C}) + 20 \text{ g}(94.8 \text{ cal/g})$$

$$= 4.65 \text{ kcal} = \boxed{19.46 \text{ kJ}}$$

20.14 (a) $(m_w c_w + m_c c_c)(T_f - T_c) = m_{Cu} c_{Cu}(T_{Cu} - T_f) + m_{unk} c_{unk}(T_{unk} - T_f)$ where w is for the water, c the calorimeter, Cu the copper sample and unk the unknown. $[(250 \text{ g})(1 \text{ cal/g} \cdot^\circ \text{C}) + (100 \text{ g})(0.215 \text{ cal/g}^\circ\text{C})](20 ^\circ\text{C} - 10^\circ\text{C}) = (50 \text{ g})(0.0924 \text{ cal/g} \cdot^\circ \text{C})(80^\circ\text{C} - 20 \text{ C}) + (70 \text{ g})c_{unk}(100^\circ\text{C} - 20^\circ\text{C})$ $2438 = 5600 c_{unk}$ or $c_{unk} = \boxed{0.435 \text{ cal/g} \cdot \text{C}^\circ}$

(b) The material of the sample is $\boxed{\text{beryllium}}$

20.15 (a) $m_{Hg} c_{Hg}(T - T_{Hg}) = m_{Al} c_{Al}(T_{Al} - T) + m_w c_w(T_w - T)$

$$(200 \text{ g})(0.033 \text{ cal/g} \cdot \text{C}^\circ)(T - 0^\circ\text{C}^\circ) = (50 \text{ g})(0.58 \text{ cal/g} \cdot \text{C}^\circ)(50^\circ\text{C}^\circ - T)$$
$$+(100 \text{ g})(1 \text{ cal/g} \cdot \text{C}^\circ)(100 ^\circ\text{C} - T)$$

$$6.6T = 1450 - 29T + 10000 - 100T \text{ so } 135.6T = 11450$$

$T = \boxed{84.4^\circ\text{C}}$

(b) $Q_{Hg} = (200)(0.033 \text{ cal/g} \cdot \text{C}^\circ)(84.4^\circ\text{C}) = \boxed{557 \text{ cal gained}}$

$Q_{Al} = (50)(0.58 \text{ cal/g} \cdot \text{C}^\circ)(84.4^\circ\text{C} - 50^\circ\text{C}) = \boxed{998 \text{ cal gained}}$

$Q_w = (100)(1 \text{ cal/g} \cdot \text{C}^\circ)(100^\circ\text{C} - 84.4^\circ\text{C}) = \boxed{1560 \text{ cal}}$

*20.16 $\Delta Q = m_{Cu} c_{Cu} \Delta T = m_{N_2}(L_{vap})_{N_2}$

$$(1 \text{ kg}) \left(0.092 \frac{\text{cal}}{\text{g} \cdot \text{C}^\circ}\right)(293 - 77)\text{C}^\circ = m \left(48 \frac{\text{cal}}{\text{g}}\right)$$

$m = \boxed{0.414 \text{ kg}}$

*20.17 $\Delta Q = mL_f + mc\Delta T + mL_{vap}$

$\quad\quad\quad = (1 \text{ g}) \left[80 \frac{\text{cal}}{\text{g}} + 100 \frac{\text{cal}}{\text{g}} + 540 \frac{\text{cal}}{\text{g}}\right]$

$\Delta Q = \boxed{720 \text{ cal}}$

20.18 1 liter $= 1000 \text{ cm}^3$, so 1 liter of water has a mass of 1000 g.

Heat to melt ice + Heat to raise to 10°C = Heat Lost by Water

$(mL)_{ice} + (mc\Delta T)_{water} = (mc\Delta T)_{tea}$

$m(79.7 \text{ cal/g}) + m(1 \text{ cal/g} \cdot \text{C}^\circ)(10^\circ\text{C} - 0^\circ\text{C}) = (1000 \text{ g})(1 \text{ cal/g} \cdot \text{C}^\circ)(30^\circ\text{C} - 10^\circ\text{C})$

$\boxed{m = 223 \text{ g}}$

20.19 $[m_w c_w + m_c c_c][T_f - T_i] = m_s[L_v + c_w(100 - T_f)]$

$[250\ g(1\ cal/g \cdot C°) + 50\ g(0.0924\ cal/g \cdot C°)][50°C - 20°C]$

$$= m_s[540cal/g + (1\ cal/gC°)(100°C - 50°C)]$$

$m_s = \dfrac{7640}{590} = \boxed{12.9g\ steam}$

20.20 $(mL)_{Pb} + (mc\Delta T)_{Pb} = (mc\Delta T)_{Fe}$

$(90\ g)(5.85\ cal/g) + (90\ g)(0.0305\ cal/\ g \cdot° C)(327.3 - T)°C$

$$= (300\ g)(0.107\ cal/g \cdot° C)(T - 20)°C$$

and $T = \boxed{59.4°C}$

20.21 (a) Since the heat required to melt 250 g of ice at 0°C *exceeds* the heat required to cool 600 g of water from 18°C to 0°C, the final temperature of the system (water + ice) must be $\boxed{0°C}$

(b) Heat needed to melt m grams of ice = Heat lost by Water

$mL = (mc\Delta T)_{\text{water}}$

$m(79.7\ cal/g) = 550\ g(1\ cal/g \cdot C°)(16°C - 0)$;

$\quad\quad\quad m = 110\ g$ so the ice remaining $= 300\ g - 110\ g = 190\ g$

$m(79.55\ cal/g) = (600\ g)(1\ cal/gC°)(18°C - 0°C)$

$m = 136\ g$, so the ice remaining $= 250\ g - 136\ g = \boxed{114\ g}$

*20.22 $\Delta Q = m_{\text{ice}} C_v \Delta T = m_{\text{water}} L_f$

$(50g)(+20°C)\left(0.5\dfrac{cal}{g \cdot C°}\right) = m_{\text{water}}\left(80\ \dfrac{cal}{g}\right)$

$m_{\text{water}} = \boxed{6.25\ g}$

*20.23 $\frac{1}{2}mv^2 = \Delta Q = mL_f$

$$\frac{1}{2}(0.5 \text{ kg})(2 \text{ m/s})^2 = m_{\text{ice}}\left(80 \ \frac{\text{cal}}{\text{g}}\right)\left(\frac{4.186 \text{ J}}{\text{cal}}\right)$$

$m_{\text{ice}} = \boxed{2.99 \text{ mg}}$

20.24 (a) To cool the water and calorimeter to 0°C, it will take:

$(m_w c_w + m_c c_c)(T - 0)$
$= [(180 \text{ g})(1 \text{ cal/g} \cdot^\circ \text{C}) + (100 \text{ g})(0.215 \text{ cal/g} \cdot^\circ \text{C})] [30°C - 0°C] = 0.6045 \ \text{cal}$

To melt all the ice would take 100 g(79.7 cal/g) = 7970 cal. Since the ice needs more heat to melt than is available, not all will melt. There is a shortage of 7970 − 6050 = 1920 cal. This represents 1920/79.7 = 24.0 g ice remaining. The final state is 256 g water and $\boxed{24 \text{ g ice at } 0°C}$

(b) To melt 50 g of ice requires 50 g(79.7 cal/g) = 3990 cal. There is 6050 cal of heat available for melting ice. Thus after the ice is melted there is 6050 − 3990 = 2060 cal available to "warm the system".

$T = 2060 \text{ cal}/[180 \text{ cal/g} \cdot^\circ\text{C} + 50 \text{ cal/g} \cdot^\circ\text{C} + 100 \text{ g}(0.215 \text{ cal/g} \cdot^\circ\text{C})] = \boxed{8.22°C}$

20.25 (a) $(f)(mgh) = mc\Delta T$

$$\frac{(0.60)(3 \times 10^{-3} \text{ kg})(9.8 \text{ m/s})(50 \text{ m})}{4.186 \ \text{J/cal}} = 3 \text{ g}(0.0924 \text{ cal/gC°})(\Delta T)$$

$\Delta T = 0.760°C; \quad \boxed{T = 25.8°C}$

(b) $\boxed{\text{No}}$ Both the change in potential energy and the heat absorbed

are proportional to the mass; hence, the mass cancels in the energy

relation.

*20.26 $m = (4 \times 10^{11} \text{ m}^3)(1000 \text{ kg/m}^3)$

(a) $\Delta Q = mc\Delta T = Pt$
$\qquad\quad = (4 \times 10^{14} \text{ kg})(4186 \text{ J/kg°C})(1°C)$
$\ \Delta Q \ = \ \boxed{1.68 \times 10^{18} \text{ J}} = Pt$

(b) $t = \dfrac{1.68 \times 10^{18} \text{ J}}{10^9 \text{ J/s}} = 1.68 \times 10^9 \text{ s} = \boxed{53.1 \text{ y}}$

*20.27 $\frac{1}{2}mv^2 = \Delta Q = m_{ice}L_f$

$\frac{1}{2}(0.003 \text{ kg})(240 \text{ m/s})^2 = m_{ice}(336,000 \text{ J/kg})$

$m_{ice} = \boxed{0.26 \text{ g}}$

20.28 1 atm $= 1.013 \times 10^5$ N/m^2

1 liter·atm $= (10^3 \text{ cm}^3)(1.013 \times 10^5 \text{ N/m}^2) = (10^{-3})(1.013 \times 10^5 \text{ N/m}^2)$

$= 1.013 \times 10^2 \text{ N} \cdot \text{m} = 101.3 \text{ J} = 24.2 \text{ cal}$

20.29 (a) Along IAF, $W = (4 \text{ atm})(2 \text{ liter}) = 8L \cdot \text{atm} = \boxed{810 \text{ J}}$

(b) Along IF, $W = 5L \cdot \text{atm} = \boxed{507 \text{ J}}$

(c) Along IBF, $W = 2L \cdot \text{atm} = \boxed{203 \text{ J}}$

20.30 (a) $W = \int PdV = P\Delta V = (1.5 \text{ atm})(4 \text{ m}^3) = \boxed{6.08 \times 10^5 \text{ J}}$

(b) $W = \int PdV = P\Delta V = (1.5 \text{ atm})(1 - 4)\text{m}^3 = \boxed{-4.56 \times 10^5 \text{ J}}$

20.31 $W = P\Delta V = P(\frac{nR}{P})(T_h - T_c) = nR\Delta T = 0.2(8.314)(280) = \boxed{466 \text{ J}}$

*20.32 (a) $W = \int PdV$

$= (6 \times 10^6 \text{Pa})(2 - 1) \text{ m}^3 + (4 \times 10^6 \text{ Pa})(3 - 2) \text{ m}^3$

$+ (2 \times 10^6 \text{Pa})(4 - 3) \text{ m}^3$

$W_{i \to f} = \boxed{-12.0 \text{ MJ}}$

(b) $W_{f \to i} = \boxed{+12.0 \text{ MJ}}$

20.33 $W_{ab} = \int_a^b P\, dV$

The work done by the gas is just the area under the curve $P = \alpha V^2$ between V_a and V_b.

$$W_{ab} = \int_a^b \alpha V^2 dV = \frac{1}{3}\, \alpha (V_b^3 - V_a^3)$$

$$V_b = 2V_a = 2(1\ m^3) = 2\ m^3$$

$$W_{ab} = \frac{1}{3}(5.0\ \frac{atm}{m^6} \times 1.01325 \times 10^5\ \frac{Pa}{atm})[(2\ m^3)^3 - (1\ m^3)^3] = \boxed{1.18 \times 10^6\ J}$$

20.34 (a) $T = 273\ K,\quad P = 1\ atm = 1.013 \times 10^5\ Pa,\quad V = 25\ L = 25 \times 10^{-3}\ m^3.$

$$a = 2PV^2 = 2(1.013 \times 10^5)(25 \times 10^{-3})^2 = 127\ Pa \cdot m^6 = \boxed{127\ N \cdot m^4}$$

(b) $P_f = 0.5\, aV_f^{-2} = 0.5(127)(80 \times 10^{-3})^{-2} = \boxed{9920\ Pa}$

$$T_f = \frac{P_f V_f T_i}{P_i V_i} = \frac{(9920)(0.080)(273)}{(1.013 \times 10^5)(0.025)} = \boxed{85.5\ K}$$

(c) $W = \int P dV = \frac{a}{2}\int_{V_i}^{V_f} V^{-2} dV = \boxed{\frac{a}{2}(\frac{1}{V_i} - \frac{1}{V_f})}$

(d) $W = -\frac{127}{2}(\frac{1}{0.080} - \frac{1}{0.025}) = \boxed{1.74\ \ kJ}$

20.35 (a) $W = nRT\, \ln(\frac{V_f}{V_i}) = P_f V_f \ln\frac{V_f}{V_i}$ so $V_i = V_f \exp(-\frac{W}{P_f V_f})$

$$V_i = (0.025)\exp[-\frac{3000}{(0.025)(1.013 \times 10^5)}] = 7.65\ L = \boxed{0.00765\ m^3}$$

(b) $T = \frac{P_f V_f}{nR} = \frac{(1.013 \times 10^5 N/m^2)(0.025\ m^3)}{(1\ mol)(8.314\ J/K \cdot mol)} = \boxed{305\ K = 32^\circ C}$

20.36 (a) $\Delta U = Q - W = 400 \text{ J} - \int P dV$

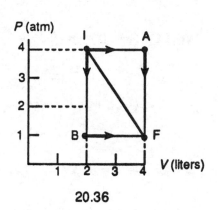

20.36

$$= 400 \text{ J} - [\tfrac{1}{2}(2)(3) + (1)(2)] \text{ atm} \cdot \text{L}$$

$$= 400 \text{ J} - 5(1.013 \times 10^5 \text{ N/m}^2)(\frac{\text{m}^3}{10^3 \text{ L}}) = \boxed{-107 \text{ J}}$$

(b) $Q = \Delta U + W = -107 \text{ J} + 8 \text{ atm} \cdot \text{L} = \boxed{703 \text{ J}}$

20.37 (a) $W = P\Delta V = (0.8 \text{ atm})(7 \text{ L}) = \boxed{-567 \text{ J}}$

(b) $\Delta U = Q - W = -400 \text{ J} + 567 \text{ J} = \boxed{167 \text{ J}}$

20.38 $\Delta U = Q - W$

$Q = \Delta U + W = -500 \text{ J} - 200 \text{ J} = \boxed{-720 \text{ J}}$

Heat is transferred *from* the system.

20.39 (a) $Q = $ Area of triangle $= \dfrac{1}{2}(4 \text{ m}^3)(6 \text{ kPa}) = \boxed{12.0 \text{ kJ}}$

(b) $W = \boxed{-12.0 \text{ kJ}}$

20.40

	Q	W	ΔU	
BC	–	0	–	($Q = \Delta U$ since $W_{BC} = 0$)
CA	–	–	–	$\Delta U < 0$ and $W < 0$, so $Q < 0$)
AB	+	+	+	($W > 0, \Delta U > 0$ since $\Delta U < 0$ for $B \to C \to A$; so $Q > 0$)

20.41 (a) $W = \int P dV = \int \frac{nRT}{V} dV = nRT \ln(\frac{V_f}{V_i}) = (5 \text{ mol})(8.314 \frac{\text{J}}{\text{K} \cdot \text{mol}})(400 \text{ K}) \ln(4)$

$= \boxed{23.1 \text{ kJ}}$

(b) Since $T = $ constant, $\Delta U = 0$ so $Q = W = \boxed{23.1 \text{ kJ}}$

20.42 $W = P\Delta V = P(V_s - V_w) = \frac{P(nRT)}{P} - n\left[\frac{(18 \text{ g/mol})P}{(1 \text{ g/cm}^3)(10^6 \text{cm}^3/\text{m}^3)}\right]$

$= (1 \text{ mol})(8.314 \text{ J/K} \cdot \text{mol})(373 \text{ J}) - (1.013 \times 10^5 \text{ N/m}^2)(1 \text{ mol})(\frac{18 \text{ g/mol}}{10^6 \text{ g/m}^3}) = \boxed{3.10 \text{ kJ}}$

$Q = mLV = (18 \text{ g})(2.26 \times 10^6 \text{ J/kg}) = 40.7 \text{ kJ}$

$\Delta U = Q - W = \boxed{37.6 \text{ kJ}}$

20.43 $U_i = 91 \text{ J}$ $U_f = 182 \text{ J}$

(a) $W_{IAF} = W_{IA} + W_{AF} = 0 + 1.5(0.5) = 0.75 \text{ L} \cdot \text{atm} = \boxed{76.0 \text{ J}}$

$W_{IBF} = W_{IB} + W_{BF} = 2(0.5) + 0 = 1 \text{ L} \cdot \text{atm} = \boxed{101 \text{ J}}$

$W_{IF} = (1/2)(0.5)(0.5) + (1.5)(0.5) = 0.875 \text{ L} \cdot \text{atm} = \boxed{88.6 \text{ J}}$

(b) $IAF: Q = \Delta U + W = 91 \text{ J} + 76 \text{ J} = \boxed{167 \text{ J}}$

$IBF: Q = \Delta U + W = 91 \text{ J} + 101 \text{ J} = \boxed{192 \text{ J}}$

$IF: Q = \Delta U + W = 91 \text{ J} + 89 \text{ J} = \boxed{180 \text{ J}}$

20.44 $Q_{N_2} = +25.0$ cal; $\Delta U_{N_2} = +8.0$ cal

$m_{N_2} = 1.00$ kg; $P = $ constant (isobaric)

(a) The first law of thermodynamics is

$Q = W + \Delta U$ between equilibrium states.

$W = $ work done by gas $= Q - \Delta U$

$= 25.0$ cal $- 8.0$ cal $= 17.0$ cal $= \boxed{71.2 \text{ kJ}}$

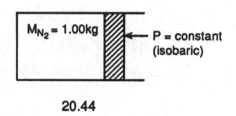

20.44

(b) $W = P\Delta V$ for an isobaric process.

Therefore

$$\Delta V = \frac{W}{P} = \frac{7.116 \times 10^4 \text{ J}}{1.01325 \times 10^5 \text{ Pa}} = \boxed{0.702 \text{ m}^3}$$

20.45 (a) $\Delta U = Q = P\Delta V = 12{,}500$ J $= (2{,}500$ Pa$)(3-1)$ m$^3 = \boxed{7{,}500 \text{ J}}$

(b) $\dfrac{V_1}{T_1} = \dfrac{V_2}{T_2}$; $\quad T_2 = \dfrac{V_2}{V_1}T_1 = \dfrac{3}{1}(300 \text{ K}) = \boxed{900 \text{ K}}$

20.46 (a) $P_i V_i = P_f V_f = nRT = 2 \text{ mol}(8.31 \text{ J/K} \cdot \text{mol})(300 \text{ K}) = 4986$ J

$$V_i = \frac{nRT}{P_i} = \frac{4986 \text{ J}}{1.2 \text{ atm}} = 0.123 \text{ m}^3$$

$$V_f = \frac{nRT}{P_i} = \frac{4986 \text{ J}}{1.2 \text{ atm}} = \frac{1}{3}V_i = \boxed{0.0410 \text{ m}^3}$$

(b) $W = \displaystyle\int P dV = nRT \ln\left(\frac{V_f}{V_i}\right) = 4986 \ln\left(\frac{1}{3}\right) = \boxed{-5.48 \text{ kJ}}$

(c) $\Delta U = 0 = Q - W$

$Q = \boxed{-5.48 \text{ kJ}}$

20.47   (a)   (b)

$n = 1$ mol $n = 1$ mol

$P = 1$ atm $P = 1$ atm

$T = 300$ K $T = 400$ K

The gas is heated isobarically so that the pressure is constant.

(a) $W_{ab} = \displaystyle\int_a^b P\,dV = (1\text{ atm})(V_b - V_a)$

Since $PV = nR'T$, $V = \dfrac{nR'T}{P}$ with $R' = 0.99967R$

$V_b - V_a = \dfrac{nR'}{P}(T_b - T_a)$.

$W_{ab} = P(V_b - V_a) = nR'(T_b - T_a)$

$= (1\text{ mol})(0.99967R)(400\text{ K} - 300\text{ K}) = (99.97R)\text{ J} = \boxed{(100\,R)\text{ J}}$

(b) $Q_{ab} = nc_p\Delta T$ as the pressure is constant

$= (1\text{ mol})(2.5043R)(400\text{ K} - 300\text{ K}) = (250.43R)\text{ J} = \boxed{(250R)\text{ J}}$

(c) $U_{ab} = Q_{ab} - W_{ab} = (250.43 - 99.97)R = \boxed{(150R)\text{ J}}$

*20.48 $P = 12e^{-bV}\text{atm};\quad b = \dfrac{1}{12}\text{ m}^{-3}$

$W = \displaystyle\int_{V_i}^{V_f} P\,dV = \int_{12}^{36} (12\text{ atm})e^{-bV}\,dV$

$= -(12\text{ atm})(12\text{ m}^3)(e^{-3} - e^{-1})$

$= 144(1.013 \times 10^5)(e^{-1} - e^{-3})$

$W = \boxed{4.64\text{ MJ}}$

20.49 (a) $W = P\Delta V = P[3\alpha V \Delta T]$

$$= (1.013 \times 10^5 \text{ N} \cdot \text{m}^2)(3)(24 \times 10^{-6})(\text{C}°)^{-1}(\frac{1 \text{ kg}}{2.7 \times 10^3 \text{ kg/m}^3})(18°\text{C})$$

$$= \boxed{48.6 \text{ mJ}}$$

(b) $Q = cm\Delta T = (900 \text{ J/kg} \cdot °\text{C})(1 \text{ kg})(18°\text{C}) = \boxed{16.2 \text{ kJ}}$

(c) $\Delta U = Q - W = 16.2 \text{ kJ} - 48.6 \text{ mJ} = \boxed{16.2 \text{ kJ}}$

20.50 $\Delta U_{ABC} = \Delta U_{AC}$ (Conservation of energy)

$\Delta U_{ABC} = Q_{ABC} - W_{ABC}$ (First Law)

(a) $Q_{ABC} = 800 \text{ J} + 500 \text{ J} = \boxed{1300 \text{ J}}$ (+ means heat is added to the system)

(b) Since $W_{BC} = W_{DA} = 0$ (Isochors $\Delta V = 0$) and $W_{AB} = P_A \Delta V_{AB}$,

$W_{CD} = P_C \Delta V_{CD}$, $\Delta V_{AB} = \Delta V_{CD}$, and $P_A = 5P_C$, then

$W_{CD} = \frac{1}{5}P_A \Delta V_{AB} = \frac{1}{5}W_{AB} = \boxed{-100 \text{ J}}$ (- means that the work done

by the system is negative-work is done on the system)

(c) $W_{CDA} = W_{CD}$ so that $Q_{CA} = \Delta U_{CA} + W_{CDA} = -800 \text{ J} - 100 \text{ J} = \boxed{-900 \text{ J}}$

(− means that heat must be removed from the system)

(d) $\Delta U_{CD} = \Delta U_{CDA} - \Delta U_{DA} = -800 \text{ J} - 500 \text{ J} = -1300 \text{ J}$

and $Q_{CD} = \Delta U_{CD} + W_{CD} = -1300 \text{ J} - 100 \text{ J} = \boxed{-1400 \text{ J}}$

*20.51 (a) PV =   constant

For P_1 = 10 atm, $V_1 = 1$ L, $PV = \text{constant} = \boxed{10 \text{ L} \cdot \text{atm}}$

(b) $P_1 V_1$ = $10 \text{ L} \cdot \text{atm} = P_2 V_2$

P_2 = $\dfrac{10 \text{ L} \cdot \text{atm}}{10^3 \text{ L}} = \boxed{10^{-2} \text{ atm}}$

(c) W = $\int P dV = \int_{10^{-3}\text{m}^3}^{1 \text{ m}^3} \dfrac{10 \text{ L} \cdot \text{atm}}{V} dV$

$= 10 \text{ L} \cdot \text{atm}(\ln V) \Big|_{10^{-3}}^{1}$

$= (1.013 \times 10^3 \text{ J})(\ln 1 - \ln 10^{-3})$

$= \boxed{7.00 \text{ kJ}}$

20.52 $\dfrac{dQ}{dt} = kA\dfrac{\Delta T}{\Delta x} = (0.8\text{ W/mC}°)(3\text{ m}^2)(\dfrac{25°\text{C}}{0.6 \times 10^{-2}\text{ m}^2})(\dfrac{3600\text{ s}}{\text{h}}) = \boxed{36.0 \times 10^6 \ \text{J/h}}$

*20.53 $\dfrac{\Delta Q}{\Delta t} = \dfrac{A\Delta T}{\sum\limits_i \dfrac{L_i}{k_i}} = \dfrac{(6\text{ m}^2)(50°\text{ C})}{\dfrac{2(4 \times 10^{-3}\text{ m})}{0.8\text{ W/mC}°} + \dfrac{5 \times 10^{-3}\text{ m}}{0.0234\text{ W/mC}°}} = \boxed{1.34\text{ kW}}$

*20.54 $\quad Q = \dfrac{k\,A\,\Delta T}{L}t$

$\qquad\quad = \left(427\ \dfrac{W}{m\cdot°\,C}\right)\left(\dfrac{10^{-4}\text{ m}^2}{0.3\text{ m}}\right)(100°\text{C})(1\text{ s}) = \boxed{14.2\text{ W}}$

20.55 In the steady state condition, $\left(\dfrac{dQ}{dt}\right)_{Au} = \left(\dfrac{dQ}{dt}\right)_{Ag}$ so that

$\quad k_{Au}A_{Au}\left(\dfrac{\Delta T}{\Delta x}\right)_{Au} = k_{Ag}A_{Ag}\left(\dfrac{\Delta T}{\Delta x}\right)_{Ag}.$

In this case $A_{Au} = A_{Ag}$, $\Delta x_{Au} = \Delta x_{Ag}$, $\Delta T_{Au} = (80 - T)$

and $\Delta T_{Ag} = (T - 30)$

where T is the temperature of the junction. Therefore

$\quad k_{Au}(80 - T) = k_{Ag}(T - 30)$ and $\boxed{T = 51.2°\text{C}}$

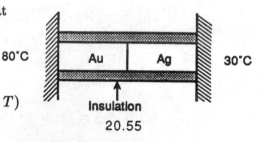

20.55

20.56 Two rods $\dfrac{dQ}{dt} = (k_1 A_1 + k_2 A_2)\dfrac{dT}{dx} = \boxed{(k_1 A_1 + k_2 A_2)\left(\dfrac{T_k - T_c}{L}\right)}$

In general $\dfrac{dQ}{dt} = (\Sigma k_i A_i)\dfrac{dT}{dx} = \boxed{(\Sigma k_i A_i)\left(\dfrac{T_k - T_c}{L}\right)}$

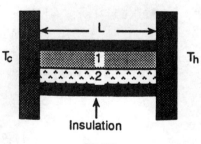

20.56

*20.57 Ignoring boundary layers,

$\quad Q = \dfrac{kA\Delta T}{L}t = \left(\dfrac{0.8\ W}{m\cdot°\,C}\right)\left(\dfrac{40\text{ m}^2}{0.15\text{ m}}\right)(15°\text{C})12(3600\text{ s})$

$\quad Q = \boxed{138\text{ MJ}}$

20.58 (a) $\dfrac{dQ}{dt} = -kA\dfrac{dT}{ds} = -k\pi r^2\dfrac{\Delta T}{L} = (0.19)(\pi)(0.5)^2\dfrac{(100)}{20} = \boxed{3.12\ \text{J/s}}$

(b) $m = \dfrac{Q}{L_f}$ so $\dfrac{dm}{dt} = \dfrac{dQ/dt}{L_f} = \dfrac{0.746}{79.7} = \boxed{9.36\ \text{mg/s}}$

(c) $m = \dfrac{Q}{L_v}$ so $\dfrac{dm}{dt} = \dfrac{(dQ/dt)}{L_v} = \dfrac{0.746}{540} = 0.00138\ \text{g/s} = \boxed{1.38\ \text{mg/s}}$

(d) Thermal gradient $= \dfrac{dT}{dx} = \dfrac{\Delta T}{L} = \dfrac{100}{0.20} = \boxed{500\ \text{C}^\circ/\text{m}}$

*20.59 $P = \dfrac{Q}{t} = kA\dfrac{\Delta T}{L}$

$k = \dfrac{PL}{A\,\Delta T} = \dfrac{(10\ \text{W})(0.04\ \text{m})}{(1.2\ \text{m}^2)(15\ \text{C}^\circ)}$

$k = \boxed{2.22\times 10^{-2}\ \dfrac{\text{W}}{\text{m}\cdot{}^\circ\text{C}}}$

*20.60 Ignoring convection,

$P = e\sigma A T^4$ \quad (Eq. 20.19)

$100\ \text{W} = (1)\left(5.67\times 10^{-8}\dfrac{\text{W}}{\text{m}^2\text{K}^4}\right)(1\ \text{m}^2)(T^4)$

$T = 364\ \text{K} = \boxed{91.4\ ^\circ\text{C}}$

*20.61 (a) $E = \left(840\ \dfrac{\text{W}}{\text{m}^2}\right)(70\ \text{m}^2)(\sin 60^\circ)(0.15)(8\ \text{h}) = \boxed{61.1\ \text{kWh}}$

(b) At 6¢/kWh \quad Savings $= \boxed{\$3.67}$

20.62 $P = \sigma A T^4 = (5.6696\times 10^{-8}\ \text{W/m}^2\cdot\text{K}^4)(4\pi)(6.96\times 10^8\ \text{m}^2)(5800\ \text{K})^4 = 3.91\times 10^{26}\ \text{W}$

$Q = P\Delta t = (3.91\times 10^{26}\ \text{W})(8.64\times 10^4\ \text{s}) = \boxed{3.38\times 10^{31}\ \text{J}}$

20.63 $T_e = T_s + (30\text{C}^\circ/\text{km})(6400 \text{ km}) = \boxed{192 \times 10^3 \text{ }^\circ\text{C}}$ which is unreasonable.

20.64 (a) The volume change is $\left(\dfrac{2 \text{ kg}}{999.02 \text{ kg/m}^3}\right) - \left(\dfrac{2 \text{ kg}}{99.17 \text{ kg/m}^3}\right) = 3.00 \times 10^{-7} \text{ m}^3$

Hence the work done is

$$P\Delta V = (1.013 \times 10^5 \text{ N/m}^3)(3.00 \times 10^{-7} \text{ m}^3) = \boxed{3.04 \times 10^{-2} \text{ J}}$$

(b) $\dfrac{3.04 \times 10^{-2} \text{ J}}{8370 \text{ J}} = \boxed{3.63 \times 10^{-6} \text{ times as large}}$

*20.65 $\dfrac{1}{2} m_{\text{meteor}} (600 \text{ m/s})^2 = (75 \text{ kg})\left(0.8 \dfrac{\text{kcal}}{\text{kg C}^\circ}\right)(500 \text{ C}^\circ) + (75 \text{ kg})\left(48 \dfrac{\text{kcal}}{\text{kg}}\right)$

$$= 3.36 \times 10^4 \text{ kcal} = 1.41 \times 10^8 \text{ J}$$

$m_{\text{meteor}} = \boxed{781 \text{ kg}}$

20.66 $Q = cm\Delta T; \quad m = \rho V; \quad \dfrac{dQ}{dt} = \rho c \Delta T\left(\dfrac{dV}{dt}\right)$

$$c = \dfrac{dQ/dt}{\rho \Delta T (dV/dt)} \dfrac{(30 \text{ J/s})\left(\dfrac{1 \text{ cal}}{4.186 \text{ J}}\right)}{(0.78 \text{ g/cm}^2)(4.8^\circ\text{C})(4 \text{ cm}^3/\text{s})} = 0.479 \text{ cal/g} \cdot \text{C}^\circ$$

$$= \boxed{2.00 \text{ kJ/kg} \cdot \text{C}^\circ}$$

20.67 (a) Work done by the gas is the area under the PV curve, and

$$W = P_0(\frac{V_0}{2} - V_0) = \boxed{-\frac{P_0 V_0}{2}}$$

(b) In this case the area under the curve is $W = \int P dV$. Since the process is isothermal, $PV = P_0 V_0 = 4 P_0 (\frac{V_0}{4}) = nRT_0$ and

$$W = \int_{V_0}^{V_0/4} (\frac{dV}{V})(P_0 V_0) = P_0 V_0 \ln(\frac{V_0/4}{V_0}) = -P_0 V_0 \ln 4 = \boxed{-1.39 P_0 V_0}$$

(c) The area under the curve is 0 and $\boxed{W = 0}$

20.68 Work is area under the curve and

(a) $W_{IAF} = (1 \times 10^5 \text{ N/m}^2)[(6 - 2) \text{ m}^3]$

$\quad + \frac{1}{2}[(2 \times 10^5 - 1 \times 10^5) \text{ N/m}^2][(6 - 2) \text{ m}^3]$

$\quad = \boxed{600 \text{ kJ}}$

(b) $W_{IF} = (1 \times 10^5 \text{ N/m}^2)[(6 - 2) \text{ m}^3] = \boxed{400 \text{ kJ}}$

(c) $\Delta U_{IF} = \Delta U_{IAF}$ since the temperature

change is independent of the path taken

$\quad \Delta U_{IAF} = (Q - W)_{IAF} = (4 \times 10^5 \text{ cal})(4.186 \text{ J/cal}) - 6 \times 10^5 \text{ J} = \boxed{1.07 \times 10^6 \text{ J}}$

(d) $\Delta U_{IAF} = Q_{IF} - W_{IF}$ and $Q_{IF} = \Delta U_{IF} + W_{IF} = (10.7 + 4) \times 10^5 \text{ J} = \boxed{1.47 \times 10^6 \text{ J}}$

20.68

20.69   (a) During any time interval the heat energy lost by the rod equals the heat energy gained by the helium. Therefore

$$(mL)_{He} = (mc\Delta T)_{Al} \text{ or } (\rho VL)_{He} = (\rho Vc\Delta T)_{Al} \text{ so that } V_{He} = \frac{(\rho Vc\Delta T)_{Al}}{(\rho L)_{He}}$$

$$V_{He} = \frac{(2.79 \text{ g/cm}^3)(62.5 \text{ cm}^3)(0.21 \text{ cal/g}°\text{C})(295.8°\text{C})}{(0.125 \text{ g/cm}^3)(4.99 \text{ cal/g})} = \boxed{16.8 \text{ L}}$$

(b) The rate at which energy is supplied to the rod in order to maintain constant temperature is given by

$$\frac{dQ}{dt} = kA\frac{dT}{dx} = (31 \text{ J/s} \cdot \text{cm} \cdot \text{K})(2.5 \text{ cm}^2)[\frac{295.8 \text{ K}}{25 \text{ cm}}] = 219 \text{ cal/s}$$

This power supplied to the helium will produce a "boil-off"

rate given by $\frac{dQ}{dt} = \frac{d}{dt}(\rho VL) = \rho L\frac{dV}{dt}$

$$\frac{dV}{dt} = \frac{dQ/dt}{\rho L} = \frac{219 \text{ cal/s}}{(0.1259 \text{ g/cm}^3)(4.99 \text{ cal/g})} = \boxed{0.351 \text{ L/s}}$$

*20.70 $Q = \frac{k \ A \ \Delta T \ t}{L}$

$= \left(\frac{427 \text{ W}}{\text{m} \cdot \text{C}°}\right)\frac{\pi(0.0125 \text{ m})^2(10 \text{ C}°)(1 \text{ s})}{0.30 \text{ m}}$

$= 6.99 \text{ J}$

$\boxed{515 \text{ times better}}$

*20.71 The total (kinetic) energy content of the bullet before impact is $\frac{1}{2}mv^2 = 225$ J. This is converted in to heat energy on inelastic impact.

Time to do some bookkeeping:

1. It takes $Q = mc\Delta T = 5(0.122)330 = 201$ J to heat the lead to melt temp.

2. It will take $Q = mH_f = 5(24.7) = 123.5$ J to then melt the lead.

3. Since only 225 J is available, the bullet will partially melt.

20.72 (a) $\dfrac{\Delta Q}{\Delta t} = \dfrac{kA\Delta T}{L} = \dfrac{(238 \text{ W/m} \cdot \text{C}°)(\pi)(0.08 \text{ m})^2(1°\text{C})}{0.3 \times 10^{-2} \text{ m}} = \boxed{1.60 \text{ kW}}$

(b) $t = \dfrac{Q}{dQ/dt} = \dfrac{mL}{dQ/dt} = \dfrac{(1 \text{ kg})(2.26 \times 10^6 \text{ J/kg})}{1.60 \text{ kW}} = \boxed{1.41 \text{ ks}}$

20.73 The heat added to the system is used to boil the liquid He at a constant temperature of 4.2 K and then increase the temperature of the gas to 273.15 K. Therefore

$Q = mL + nC_p\Delta T$;

$m = \rho V = (0.125 \text{ g/cm}^3)(2 \text{ cm}^3) = 0.250 \text{ g}$ and $\dfrac{m}{M} = \dfrac{0.250 \text{ g}}{4 \text{ g/mol}} = 6.25 \times 10^{-2}$ mol

Therefore,

$Q = (0.25 \text{ g})(4.99 \text{ cal/g})(4.186 \text{ J/cal})$

$\qquad + (6.25 \times 10^{-2} \text{ mol})(24.9 \text{ J/mol} \cdot \text{K})(273.15 - 4.2)\text{K} = 423.7$ J

$W = \displaystyle\int P\,dV$ and at constant pressure, $W = P\Delta V = nR\Delta T$. Therefore,

$W = (6.25 \times 10^{-2} \text{ mol})(8.314 \text{ J/mol} \cdot \text{K})(273.15 - 4.2) \text{ K} = 138.6$ J

$\Delta U = Q - W = (423.7 - 138.6) \text{ J} = \boxed{285 \text{ J}}$

20.74 (a) The work done during each step of the cycle

equals the area under that segment of the PV curve

$$W = W_{DA} + W_{AB} + W_{BC} + W_{CD}$$

$$W = P_0(V_0 - 3V_0) + 0 + 3P_0(3V_0 - V_0) + 0 = \boxed{4P_0V_0}$$

(b) The initial and final values of T for the system are equal.

Therefore $\Delta U = 0$, and $Q = W = \boxed{4P_0V_0}$

(c) $W = 4P_0V_0 = 4nRT_0 = 4(1)(8.314)(273) = \boxed{9.08 \times 10^3 \text{ J}}$

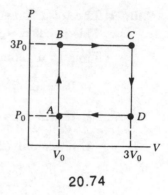
20.74

20.75 $4\pi r_1^2 k_1 \dfrac{(T_{in} - T_m)}{\Delta r_1} = \dfrac{dQ}{dt}$ and $4\pi r_2^2 k_2 \dfrac{(T_m - T_{out})}{\Delta r_2} = \dfrac{dQ}{dt}$

$$\implies T_{in} - T_{out} = T_{in} - T_m + T_m - T_{out}$$

$$= (\frac{dQ}{dt})[\frac{\Delta r_1}{4\pi r_1^2 k_1} - \frac{\Delta r_2}{(4\pi r_2^2 k_2)}]$$

so $T_{in} = T_{out} + (\dfrac{1}{4\pi})[\dfrac{\Delta r_1}{(r_1^2 k_1)} - \dfrac{\Delta r_2}{(r_2^2)}\dfrac{dQ}{dt}]$

with $T_{out} = 0°C$, $\Delta r_1 = \Delta r_2 = 2$ cm, $r_1 = 147$ cm, $r_2 = 149$ cm,

$k_1 = 5 \times 10^{-4}$ cal/s $\cdot$ cm $\cdot$ °C, $k_2 = 0.19$ cal/s $\cdot$ cm $\cdot$° C and

$\dfrac{dQ}{dt} = 1500$ W $= 358.3$ cal/s. Then

$$T_{min} = \frac{(358 \text{ cal/s})(2 \text{ cm})}{4\pi} \times$$

$$\left[\frac{1}{(147 \text{ cm})^2(5 \times 10^{-4} \text{ cal/s} \cdot \text{cm} \cdot° \text{C})} - \frac{1}{(149 \text{ cm})^2(0.19 \text{ cal/s} \cdot \text{cm} \cdot °\text{C})}\right]$$

$$= \boxed{5.26 °\text{C}}$$

20.76 (a) $Fv = (50 \text{ N})(40 \text{ m/s}) = \boxed{2000 \text{ W}}$

(b) Energy received by each object is $(1000 \text{ W})(10 \text{ s}) = 10^4$ J $= 2389$ cal The
specific heat of iron is 0.107 cal/g $\cdot$ °C, so the heat capacity of each object is
$5 \times 10^3 \times 0.107 = 535.0$ cal/°C

$$\Delta T = \frac{2389 \text{ cal}}{535.0 \text{ cal/°C}} = \boxed{4.47°\text{C}}$$

20.77 $\dfrac{dQ}{dt} = kA\dfrac{dT}{dx}$. For a spherical shell of radius r and thickness dr,

$\dfrac{dQ}{dt} = -k(4\pi r^2)\dfrac{dT}{dr}$. Since the rate of heat transfer, $\dfrac{dQ}{dt}$, is constant, we can integrate over r to find the difference in temperature across the wall of the shell:

$$-4\pi k(T_2 - T_1) = \frac{dQ}{dt}\int_a^b \frac{dr}{r^2} = \frac{dQ}{dt}\Big(\frac{1}{a} - \frac{1}{b}\Big) \text{ and}$$

$$\boxed{\frac{dQ}{dt} = \frac{4\pi k(T_1 - T_2)ab}{b - a}}$$

20.78 For a cylindrical shell of radius r, height L, and thickness dr, Eq. 20.8, $\dfrac{dQ}{dt} = -kA\dfrac{dT}{dx}$, becomes

$\dfrac{dQ}{dt} = -k(2\pi rL)\dfrac{dT}{dr}$. Under equilibrium conditions

$\dfrac{dQ}{dt}$ is constant, therefore $dT = -\dfrac{dQ}{dt}\Big(\dfrac{1}{2\pi kL}\Big)\dfrac{dr}{r}$ and

$$T_2 - T_1 = -\frac{dQ}{dt}\Big(\frac{1}{2\pi kL}\Big)\ln\Big(\frac{b}{a}\Big)$$

but $T_1 > T_2$ therefore, $\boxed{\dfrac{dQ}{dt} = \dfrac{2\pi kL(T_1 - T_2)}{\ln(b/a)}}$

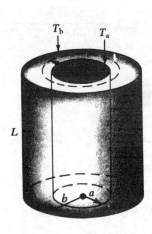

20.78

20.79 From problem 78; the rate of heat flow through the wall is

$$\frac{dQ}{dt} = \frac{2\pi kL(T_1 - T_2)}{\ln(b/a)}$$

$$\frac{dQ}{dt} = \frac{+2\pi(4\times 10^{-5}\ \text{cal/s})(3500\ \text{cm})(60°\text{C})}{\ln\Big(\dfrac{2.56}{2.50}\Big)} = 2.23 \times 10^3 \text{cal/s} = \boxed{9.32\ \text{kW}}$$

This is the rate of heat loss from the plane, and consequently the rate at which energy must be supplied in order to maintain an equilibrium temperature.

20.80 Heat energy is lost from the thermos at a rate

$$\frac{dQ}{dt} = 2\pi kL[\frac{(T_1 - T_2)}{\ln(b/a)}] \quad \text{(see Problem 78)}.$$

$$\frac{dQ}{dt} = 2\pi(30 \text{ cm})(2 \times 10^{-5} \text{ cal/s} \cdot \text{cm}^\circ\text{C})\frac{(T - 20)}{\ln(\frac{4.5}{4})}$$

$$\frac{dQ}{dt} = 0.0032(T - 20) \text{ cal/s} \cdot^\circ \text{C}$$

Energy must be lost by the coffee at this same rate; $Q = mc(T - 50)$

$dQ = mcdT$; but for Q loss, $dT < 0$; $dQ = -mcdT$

$$\frac{mcdT}{(0.032 \text{ cal/s} \cdot {}^\circ\text{C})(T - 20)} = -dt; \quad \text{Since 1 liter} = 1000 \text{ cm}^3,$$

$m = (1 \text{ g/cm}^3)(1000 \text{ cm}^3) = 1000 \text{ g}$; If we assume that $c = 1 \text{ cal/g} \cdot {}^\circ\text{C}$,

we find

$$\Delta t = (3.12 \times 10^4)\int_{50}^{90} \frac{dT}{(T - 20)} = 2.65 \times 10^4 \text{ s} = \boxed{441 \text{ min}}$$

20.81 The power incident on the solar collector is

$$P_i = JA = (600 \text{ W/m}^2)\pi(0.3 \text{ m})^2 = 169.65 \text{ W} = 40.53 \text{ cal/s}$$

For a 40% reflector, the collected power is $P_c = 16.21 \text{ cal/s}$.

The total energy required to increase the temperature of the

cooker to the boiling point and to evaporate it is

$$Q = cm\Delta T + mL_V = (500 \text{ g})[(1 \text{ cal/g} \cdot^\circ \text{C})(80^\circ\text{C}) + 540 \text{ cal/g}]$$

$$= 3.10 \times 10^5 \text{ cal}$$

20.81

The time required is $\Delta t = \frac{Q}{P_c} = \frac{3.10 \times 10^5 \text{ cal}}{16.21 \text{ cal/s}} = \boxed{5.31 \text{ h}}$

*20.82
$$\frac{L\rho A dx}{dt} = kA\frac{\Delta T}{x}$$

$$L\rho \int_4^8 x\,dx = k\Delta T \int_0^t dt$$

$$L\rho \left.\frac{x^2}{2}\right|_4^8 = k\Delta T t$$

$$\left(3.33 \times 10^5 \frac{J}{kg}\right)\left(0.917 \times 10^3 \frac{kg}{m^3}\right)\left(\frac{(0.08\ m)^2 - (0.04\ m)^2}{2}\right) = \left(2\frac{W}{m \cdot {}^\circ C}\right)(10\ C^\circ)t$$

$$t = 3.66 \times 10^4\ s = \boxed{10.2\ h}$$

*20.83 $\Delta Q_{water} + \Delta Q_{calo} = \Delta Q_{Al} = c_{Al}M_{Al}\Delta T_{Al}$

$$(0.4\ kg)\left(4186\frac{J}{kg \cdot C^\circ}\right)(3.7\ C^\circ) + (0.04\ kg)\left(630\frac{J}{kg \cdot C^\circ}\right)(3.7\ C^\circ)$$

$$= c_{Al}(0.2\ kg)(39.3\ C^\circ)$$

$$c_{Al} = \frac{(6289)}{(0.2)(39.3)} = \boxed{800\ \frac{J}{kg \cdot C^\circ}}$$

CHAPTER 21

21.1 $PV = N m v_{av}^{2/3} = n M v_{av}^{2/3}$

where $n = 1, P = 1.013 \times 10^5 \, \text{N/m}^2, M = 28 \, \text{g/mol} = 28 \times 10^{-3} \, \text{kg/mol}$

and $V = 22.4 \, \text{liters} = 22.4 \times 10^{-3} \, \text{m}^3$

$$v_{av}^2 = \frac{3PV}{nM} = \frac{3(1.013 \times 10^5)(22.4 \times 10^{-3})}{(1)(28 \times 10^{-3})} = \boxed{2.43 \times 10^5 \, \text{m}^2/\text{s}^2}$$

21.2   Use Eq. 21.5, $P = \frac{2N}{3V}[\frac{mv^2}{2}]$, so that

$$K_{av} = \frac{mv^2}{2} = \frac{3PV}{2N} \text{ where } N = nN_A = 2N_A$$

$$K_{av} = \frac{3PV}{2(2N_A)} = \frac{3(8 \, \text{atm})(1.01 \times 10^5 \, \text{Pa/atm})(5 \times 10^{-3} \, \text{m}^3)}{2(2 \, \text{mol})(6.03 \times 10^{23} \, \text{molecules/mol})}$$

$$K_{av} = \boxed{5.02 \times 10^{-21} \, \text{J/molecule}}$$

*21.3   Since all real gases behave very nearly as an ideal gas, the equation of state of an ideal gas, $PV = nRT$, relates the parameters for any given conditions. The first step is to convert all data into a consistent system of units. We choose SI units and $R = 8.31 \, \text{J/mol} \cdot \text{K}$. As mentioned, temperature must be expressed in kelvins. Therefore, from Equation (19.4),

$$T = T_C + 273° = (-50°C) + 273° = 223 \, \text{K}$$

The units of pressure must be changed to SI units of *pascals*. At standard pressure, 760 mm of Hg corresponds to 1.013×10^5 Pa, we therefore have

$$(40 \, \text{mm Hg}) \underbrace{\left(\frac{1.013 \times 10^5 \, \text{Pa}}{760 \, \text{mm of Hg}}\right)}_{\text{Conversion ratio}} = 5.33 \times 10^3 \, \text{Pa}$$

Finally, from $PV = nRT$ we obtain:

$$n = \frac{PV}{RT} = \frac{(5.33 \times 10^3 \, \text{Pa})(800 \, \text{m}^3)}{(8.31 \, \text{J/mol} \cdot \text{K})(223 \, \text{K})} = \boxed{2300 \, \text{mol}}$$

*21.4 (a) The molecular weight of helium is 4, so one mole of helium has a mass of 4.00 g. Therefore, 2300 moles have a mass of

$$m = (4.00 \text{ g/mol})(2300 \text{ mol}) = 9200 \text{ g} = \boxed{9.20 \text{ kg}}$$

(b) Using the ideal gas law (letting subscripts 1 represent values at ground level)

$$V_1 = \left(\frac{T_1}{T_2}\right)\left(\frac{P_2}{P_1}\right) V_2 = \left(\frac{273 \text{ K}}{223 \text{ K}}\right)\left(\frac{40 \text{ mm of Hg}}{760 \text{ mm of Hg}}\right)(800 \text{ m}^3) = \boxed{51.3 \text{ m}^3}$$

(c) Let subscripts 2 represent values in the tank and subscripts 1 be at STP. Here, $T_2 = 27°C + 273° = 300$ K. Thus:

$$V_2 = \left(\frac{T_2}{T_1}\right)\left(\frac{P_1}{P_2}\right) V_1 = \left(\frac{300 \text{ K}}{273 \text{ K}}\right)\left(\frac{1 \text{ atm}}{170 \text{ atm}}\right)(51.3 \text{ m}^3) = \boxed{0.332 \text{ m}^3}$$

21.5 $P = \dfrac{2}{3}\dfrac{N}{V}(\overline{KE})$ Eq. 21.5

$$N = \frac{3}{2}\frac{PV}{(\overline{KE})} = \frac{3}{2}\frac{(1.2 \times 10^5)(0.004)}{(3.6 \times 10^{-22})} = 2 \times 10^{24} \text{ molecules}$$

$$n = \frac{N}{N_A} = \frac{2 \times 10^{24} \text{ molecules}}{6 \times 10^{23} \text{ molecules/mol}} = \boxed{3.32 \text{ mol}}$$

21.6 $F = m\dfrac{\Delta v}{\Delta t} = \dfrac{(0.005)(2/2^{1/2})(8)}{(30/500)} = \boxed{0.943 \text{ N}}$

$P = \dfrac{F}{A} = \boxed{1.57 \text{ N/m}^2}$

21.7 $K_{av} = \dfrac{3}{2}kT = \dfrac{3}{2}(1.38 \times 10^{-23} \text{ J/K})(423 \text{ K}) = \boxed{8.76 \times 10^{-21} \text{ J}}$

21.8 $v_{rms} = \sqrt{\dfrac{3RT}{M}} = \sqrt{\dfrac{3(8.314)(250 + 273)}{0.002}} = \boxed{2.54 \times 10^3 \text{ m/s}}$

21.9 $v_{rms} = \sqrt{\dfrac{3kT}{m}}$

(a) $T = \dfrac{mv_{rms}^2}{3k} = \dfrac{4(1.66 \times 10^{-27})(500)^2}{(3)(1.38 \times 10^{-23})} = \boxed{40.1 \text{ K}}$

(b) $v_{rms} = \sqrt{\dfrac{3(1.38 \times 10^{-23})(5800)}{(4)(1.66 \times 10^{-27})}} = \boxed{6.01 \times 10^3 \text{ m/s}}$

*21.10 Following Equation 21.27,

$v_{mp} = \sqrt{\dfrac{2kT}{m}} = \sqrt{\dfrac{2(1.38 \times 10^{-23} \text{ J/K})(4.2 \text{ K})}{(6.65 \times 10^{-27} \text{ kg})}} = \boxed{132 \text{ m/s}}$

*21.11 $v = \sqrt{\dfrac{3kT}{m}}$

$\dfrac{v_0}{v_{\text{He}}} = \sqrt{\dfrac{M_{\text{He}}}{M_0}} = \sqrt{\dfrac{4}{32}} = \sqrt{\dfrac{1}{8}}$

$v_0 = \dfrac{1350 \text{ m/s}}{\sqrt{8}} = \boxed{477 \text{ m/s}}$

21.12 (a) $PV = nRT = \dfrac{Nmv^2}{3} \qquad K = \dfrac{Nmv^2}{2}$

$K = \dfrac{3PV}{2} = \dfrac{3}{2}(3 \times 1.01 \times 10^5)(5 \times 10^{-3}) = \boxed{2.27 \times 10^3 \text{ J}}$

(b) $\dfrac{mv^2}{2} = \dfrac{3kT}{2} = \dfrac{3RT}{2N_A} = \dfrac{3}{2}\dfrac{(8.314)(300)}{(6.02 \times 10^{23})} = \boxed{6.21 \times 10^{-21} \text{ J}}$

21.13 $PV = nRT$ (Perfect Gas Law)

$$P = \frac{(1\,\text{mol})(8.31\ \text{J/mol}\cdot\text{K})(293\ \text{K})}{0.0224\ \text{m}^3} = \boxed{1.09 \times 10^5\ \text{Pa}}$$

21.14 (a) $PV = NkT$

$$N = \frac{PV}{kT} = \frac{(1.01 \times 10^5\ \text{Pa})\frac{4}{3}\pi(0.15\ \text{m})^3}{(1.38 \times 10^{-23}\ \text{J/K})(293\ \text{K})} = \boxed{3.53 \times 10^{23}\ \text{molecules}}$$

(b) $\overline{KE} = \frac{3}{2}kT = \frac{3}{2}(1.38 \times 10^{-23})(293)\ \text{J} = \boxed{6.07 \times 10^{-21}\ \text{J}}$

(c) $\frac{1}{2}m\overline{v^2} = \frac{3}{2}kT \qquad \therefore \quad \overline{v} = \sqrt{\frac{3kT}{m}} = \boxed{1350\ \text{m/s}}$

21.15 $U = \frac{3}{2}nRT$

$$\Delta U = \frac{3}{2}nR\Delta T = \frac{3}{2}(3\ \text{mol})(8.31\ \text{J/mol}\cdot\text{K})(2\ \text{K}) = \boxed{75.0\ \text{J}}$$

21.16 $n = 2\ \text{mol}, \quad \Delta T = 320 - 300 = 20\ \text{K}, \quad C_v = 5.02\ \text{cal/mol}\cdot\text{K} \quad C_p = 7.03\ \text{cal/mol}\cdot\text{K}$

(a) $Q = nC_v\Delta T = 2(5.02)(20) = \boxed{201\ \text{cal}}$

(b) $Q = nC_p\Delta T = 2(7.03)(20) = \boxed{281\ \text{cal}}$

21.17 $C_p' = 14.9\ \text{cal/K} = nC_p = n(\frac{5R}{2})$ for a monatomic gas

$$n = \frac{2C_p'}{5R} = \frac{2(14.9)}{(5)(1.99)} = \boxed{2.99\ \text{mol}}$$

(b) $C_v' = nC_v = (2.99)(\frac{3R}{2}) = (2.99)(2.985) = \boxed{8.93\ \text{cal/K}}$

(c) $U = \frac{3}{2}nRT = (1.5)(2.99)(1.99)(350) = 3.12 \times 10^3\ \text{cal} = \boxed{1.31 \times 10^4\ \text{J}}$

21.18 $n = 3$

    (a) $C'_p = nC_p = 3(\frac{5R}{2})$ $\boxed{14.9 \text{ cal/K}}$

        $C'_v = nC_v = 3(\frac{3R}{2}) = \boxed{8.96 \text{ cal/K}}$

    (b) $C'_p = 3(\frac{7R}{2}) = \boxed{20.9 \text{ cal/K}}$

        $C'_v = 3(\frac{5R}{2}) = \boxed{14.9 \text{ cal/K}}$

21.19 Use C_p data from Table 21.2

    (a) $Q = nC_p\Delta T = (1)(28.8)(420 - 300) = \boxed{3460 \text{ J}}$

    (b) $\Delta U = \frac{5}{2}nR\Delta T = (2.5)(1)(8.31)(120) = \boxed{2450 \text{ J}}$

    (c) $W = Q - \Delta U = 3460 - 2450 = \boxed{1.01° \text{ kJ}}$

21.20 $n = 1,\ T_i = 300 \text{ K} = 27°\text{C}$

    (a) $\Delta U = Q = 50 \text{ cal} = \boxed{209 \text{ J}}$

    (b) $W = \boxed{0}$ since $V = $ constant

    (c) $\Delta U = \frac{3}{2}nR\Delta T = 50 \text{ cal}$ $\Delta T = \dfrac{50}{(1.5)(1)(1.99)} \approx 17 \text{ K}$

        $T = T_i + \Delta T = \boxed{317 \text{ K}}$

21.21   (a) $U = \frac{3}{2}nRT = \frac{3}{2}(25)(8.31)(77) \text{ J} = \boxed{24.0 \text{ kJ}}$

    (b) Assuming constant volume,

        $\Delta U = nC_v\Delta T = (25 \text{ mol})(12.5 \text{ J/mol} \cdot \text{K})(220 \text{ K}) = \boxed{68.7 \text{ kJ}}$

21.22 $U = \frac{3}{2}nRT = \frac{3}{2}(\frac{1}{0.0224})(8.31)(273) \text{ J} = \boxed{151 \text{ kJ}}$

21.23 For an ideal gas, $C_v = \frac{3}{2}R = 2.98$ cal/mol $\cdot$ K. Since the specific heat of neon is 0.149 cal/g$\cdot$K, then its molecular weight is 20 g/mol.

$\therefore$ The mass of a neon atom is $\dfrac{20 \text{ g/mol}}{6.023 \times 10^{23} \text{ atoms/mol}} = \boxed{3.33 \times 10^{-26} \text{ kg}}$

21.24 (a) $U = \frac{3}{2}nRT = \frac{3}{2}(\frac{20}{0.0224})(8.31)(273) = \boxed{3.00 \times 10^6 \text{ J}}$

(b) $U = \frac{3}{2}nRT = \frac{3}{2}(\frac{20}{0.0240})(8.31)(293) = 3.00 \times 10^6$ J

21.25 (a) $P_1 V_1^\gamma = P_2 V_2^\gamma$, $P_2 = (\frac{V_1}{V_2})^\gamma P_1 = (\frac{12}{30})^{1.40}(5 \text{ atm}) = \boxed{1.39 \text{ atm}}$

(b) $T_1 = \dfrac{P_1 V_1}{nR} = \dfrac{(5)(1.01 \times 10^5)(12 \times 10^{-3})}{(2)(8.31)} = \boxed{365 \text{ K}}$

$T_2 = \dfrac{P_2 V_2}{nR} = \boxed{254 \text{ K}}$

21.26 $P_i V_i^\gamma = P_f V_f^\gamma$

Direct substitution of $P = \dfrac{nRT}{V}$ into the first equation gives $T_i V_i^{\gamma-1} = T_f V_f^{\gamma-1}$

21.27 (a) $T_1 V_1^{\gamma-1} = T_2 V_2^{\gamma-1}$, $(\frac{V_2}{V_1})^{\gamma-1} = \dfrac{T_1}{T_2}$

$\dfrac{V_2}{V_1} = (\frac{T_1}{T_2})^{1/\gamma-1} = (3)^{2.5} = \boxed{15.6}$

(b) $P_1 V_1^\gamma = P_2 V_2^\gamma$, $\dfrac{P_2}{P_1} = (\frac{V_1}{V_2})^\gamma = (15.58)^{-1.4} = \boxed{0.0214}$

21.28 $P_i V_i^\gamma = P_f V_f^\gamma$

$$P_f = P_i(\frac{V_i}{V_r})^\gamma = (1 \text{ atm})(\frac{V_i}{V_i/4})^{1.67} = (1 \text{ atm})(4)^{1.67} = \boxed{10.1 \text{ atm}}$$

$$T_f = T_i(\frac{V_i}{V_f}) = (300 \text{ K})(4)^{0.67} = \boxed{759 \text{ K}}$$

21.29   (a) $\dfrac{V_f}{V_i} = (\dfrac{P_i}{P_f})^{1/\gamma} = (\dfrac{1}{20})^{1/140} = 0.118$ or $\boxed{V_i = 8.50 V_f}$

(b) $T_f = T_i(\dfrac{V_i}{V_f})^{\gamma-1} = T_i(8.50)^{0.40} = \boxed{2.35 T_i}$

21.30 $T_1 V_1^{\gamma-1} = T_2 V_2^{\gamma-1}$ (Eq. 21.20) $\gamma_{He} = 1.67$

$$T_2 = T_1(\frac{V_1}{V_2})^{\gamma-1} = (293 \text{ K})(5)^{0.67} = \boxed{861 \text{ K}}$$

(b) From Table 21.2, $\gamma_{\text{air}} = 1.40$

$$T_2 = T_1(\frac{V_1}{V_2})^{\gamma-1} = (293 \text{ K})(5)^{0.4} = \boxed{558 \text{ K}}$$

21.31 $\dfrac{T_f}{T_i} = (\dfrac{V_i}{V_f})^{\gamma-1} = (\dfrac{1}{2})^{0.4}$

If $T_i = 300$, K then $T_f = \boxed{227 \text{ K}}$

21.32

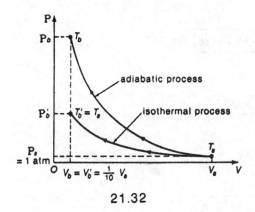

21.32

(a) The work done on the gas is $-W_{ab}$. For the isothermal process, we use Eq. 20.13.

$$-W_{ab} = -nRT\ln\frac{V_b'}{V_a} = -(5\text{ mol})(8.314\text{ J/mol}\cdot\text{K})(293\text{ K})\ln\frac{1}{10} = \boxed{2.80\times10^4\text{ J}}$$

(b) For the adiabatic process, let us use Eq. 21.18. We must first determine the final temperature T_b. From Eq. 25-17, we have $P_bV_b^\gamma = P_aV_a^\gamma$

and from the ideal gas law equation, we have

$$\frac{P_bV_b}{T_b} = \frac{P_aV_a}{T_a}.$$

Dividing the first of these two equations by the second gives

$$T_b = T_a(\frac{V_a}{V_b})^{\gamma-1} = (293\text{ K})(10)^{0.403} = 741\text{ K}$$

where we have used $\gamma(\text{air}) = 1.403$ (see Table 21-2). Thus, the work done on the gas is (Eq. 21.14).

$$-W_{ab} = nC_v(T_b - T_a) = (5\text{ mol})(20.68\text{ J/mol}\cdot\text{K})(741\text{ K} - 293\text{ K}) = \boxed{4.63\times10^4\text{ J}}$$

where we have used the value of C_v for air (N_2, O_2) given in Table 21-2

(c) For the isothermal process, we have $P_b'V_b' = P_aV_a$; thus,

$$P_b' = P_a(\frac{V_a}{V_b'}) = (1\text{ atm})(10) = \boxed{10.1\text{ atm}}$$

For the adiabatic process, we have $P_b'V_b^\gamma = P_aV_a^\gamma$; thus

$$P_b = P_a(\frac{V_a}{V_b})^\gamma = (1\text{ atm})(10)^{1.403} = \boxed{25.3\text{ atm}}$$

21.33 $v = \sqrt{\dfrac{\gamma RT}{m}} = \sqrt{\dfrac{1.31(8.314)(288)}{0.016}} = \boxed{443 \text{ m/s}}$

21.34   In He, $v = \sqrt{\dfrac{\gamma RT}{M}} = \sqrt{\dfrac{1.66 \times 8.314 \times 288}{4 \times 10^{-3}}} = 997 \text{ m/s}$

For $CH_4, \gamma = 1.31$ and $M = 16 \times 10^{-3}$ kg/mol, so $\dfrac{\gamma RT}{M} = (997)^2$

$T = \dfrac{M(997)^2}{\gamma R} = \dfrac{(16 \times 10^{-3})(997)^2}{(1.31)(8.314)} = \boxed{1460 \text{ K}}$

21.35 $v = \sqrt{\dfrac{\gamma P}{\rho}}$ (Eq. 21.21) $\gamma_{He} = 1.67,$ $\gamma_{air} = 1.40$ (Table 21.2)

$\rho_{He} = \dfrac{4}{29}\rho_{air}$, from molecular weights: Air $= 77\% \ N_2, 23\% \ O_2$

$\dfrac{v_{He}}{v_{air}} = \dfrac{\sqrt{\dfrac{(1.67)(1.01 \times 10^5)}{(4/29)(1.25)}}}{\sqrt{\dfrac{(1.40)(1.01 \times 10^5)}{(1.25)}}} = \dfrac{989 \text{ m/s}}{336 \text{ m/s}} = \boxed{2.94}$

21.36   In air, $t_1 = \dfrac{d}{v_1} = \dfrac{1.61 \times 10^3 \text{ m}}{343 \text{ m/s}} = 4.69 \text{ s}$

In iron, $t_2 = \dfrac{d}{v_2} = \dfrac{1.61 \times 10^3 \text{ m}}{5200 \text{ m/s}} = 0.31 \text{ s}$

$\Delta t = t_1 - t_2 = \boxed{4.38 \text{ s}}$

21.37   (a) $v = \sqrt{\dfrac{\gamma P}{\rho}} = \sqrt{\dfrac{1.67(1.01 \times 10^5 \text{ N/m}^2)}{5.9 \text{ kg/m}^3}} = \boxed{169 \text{ m/s}}$

(b) $B = \rho v^2 = (5.9)(169)^2 = \boxed{1.69 \times 10^5 \text{ Pa}}$

21.38 $\lambda_0 = \frac{1}{f}(\frac{\gamma R T_0}{M})^{1/2} : \lambda = \frac{1}{f}(\frac{\gamma R T}{M})^{1/2}$

$\Delta\lambda = \lambda - \lambda_0 = \frac{1}{f}(\frac{\gamma R}{M})^{1/2}(T^{1/2} - T_0^{1/2})$

$\frac{\Delta\lambda}{\lambda_0} = \frac{\lambda - \lambda_0}{\lambda_0} = \frac{T^{1/2} - T_0^{1/2}}{T_0^{1/2}} = \frac{283^{1/2} - 300^{1/2}}{300^{1/2}} = 0.0287$

Fractional change in wavelength = $\boxed{2.87\%}$

21.39 Let d be the distance the stone drops, then $t = \frac{d}{v} + \sqrt{\frac{2d}{g}}$

Let $v = 340$ m/s and $t = 10$.

Utilize the quadratic equation, $\boxed{d = 385 \text{ m}}$

21.40 (1) $U = Nf[\frac{kT}{2}] = \frac{1}{2}fnRT$

(2) $C_v = \frac{1}{n}(\frac{dU}{dT}) = \frac{1}{2}fR$

(3) $C_p = C_v + \frac{1}{2}R[(f+2)R]$

(4) $\gamma = \frac{C_p}{C_v} = \frac{(f+2)}{f}$

21.41 A complex molecule like SO_2 contains more rotational and vibrational energy states.

21.42 A more complicated molecule has more rotational and vibrational energy states. (See Section 21.3).

21.43 Rotational Kinetic Energy $= \frac{1}{2}I\omega^2$

$I = 2mr^2$, $m = 35 \times 1.67 \times 10^{-27}$ kg, $r = 10^{-10}$ m.

$I = 1.17 \times 10^{-45}$ kg $\cdot$ m^2, $\omega = 2 \times 10^{12}$ s^{-1}

$\therefore K_{\text{rot}} = \frac{1}{2}I\omega^2 = \boxed{2.33 \times 10^{-21} \text{ J}}$

21.44   (a) $C_v' = \frac{5}{2}nR = \boxed{9.95 \text{ cal/K}}$; $C_p' = \frac{7}{2}nR = \boxed{13.9 \text{ cal/K}}$

   (b) $C_v' = \frac{7}{2}nR = \boxed{13.9 \text{ cal/K}}$; $C_p' = \frac{9}{2}nR = \boxed{17.9 \text{ cal/K}}$

21.45   (a) $v_{rms} = \sqrt{\frac{3RT}{m}} = \sqrt{\frac{3(8.31)(400)}{0.032}} = \boxed{558 \text{ m/s}}$

   (b) $v_{avg} = \sqrt{\frac{8RT}{\pi m}} = \boxed{514 \text{ m/s}}$

   (c) $v_{mp} = \sqrt{\frac{2RT}{m}} = \boxed{456 \text{ m/s}}$

21.46   (a) $v_{av} = \frac{\sum n_i v_i}{N} = \frac{1}{15}[1(2) + 2(3) + 3(5) + 4(7) + 3(9) + 2(12)] = \boxed{6.80 \text{ m/s}}$

   (b) $(v^2)_{av} = \frac{\sum n_i v_i^2}{N} = 54.9 \text{ m}^2/\text{s}^2$

   so $v_{rms} = \sqrt{(v^2)_{av}} = \sqrt{54.9} = \boxed{7.41 \text{ m/s}}$

   (c) $v_{mp} = \boxed{7.00 \text{ m/s}}$

21.47 Use Equations 21.25, 21.26 and 21.27 with

   $m = 28(1.66 \times 10^{-27} \text{ kg})$ for N_2, to find $v_{mp} = \boxed{731 \text{ m/s}}$, $v_{av} = \boxed{825 \text{ m/s}}$

   and $v_{rms} = \boxed{895 \text{ m/s}}$

21.48 $v_{rms} = \sqrt{\frac{3kT}{m}}$ (Eq. 21.25)

   20°C (a) 511 m/s (N_2),   637 m/s (H_2O),   478 m/s (O_2)

   100°C (b) 576 m/s (N_2),   719 m/s (H_2O),   539 m/s (O_2)

21.49 The estimates of the total number with these speeds is made by measuring the areas under the two curves in the speed interval 400 m/s to 600 m/s. To a first approximation, the curves can be taken to be linear over this range of speeds. We estimate the following results: (a) 3.6×10^4 molecules; (b) 1.8×10^4 molecules.

21.50 Use Eq. 21.24 take $\dfrac{dN_v}{dv} = 0$, and solve for v_{mp} to get Eq. 21.27.

21.51 Equate the initial kinetic energy, $mv^2/2$, to $3kT/2$.

In part (a), take $v = 1.12 \times 10^4$ m/s and
$m = 4(1.66 \times 10^{-27} \text{kg})$ to find $T = \boxed{2.37 \times 10^4 \text{ K}}$

In part (b), take $v = 2.37 \times 10^3$ m/s to find $T = \boxed{1.06 \times 10^3 \text{ K}}$

21.52 The fraction $f = \displaystyle\int_{1000}^{1200} \dfrac{N_v dv}{N}$

$= \text{[area under curve between } v = 1000 \text{ and } v = 12000]$

$\approx \dfrac{15000}{10^5} = \boxed{0.15} \text{ or } \boxed{15\%}$

21.53 (a) $PV = \left(\dfrac{N}{N_A}\right)RT$ and $N = \dfrac{PVN_A}{RT}$, so that

$$N = \frac{(10^{-10})(133)(1)(6.02 \times 10^{23})}{(9.31)(300)} = \boxed{3.21 \times 10^{12} \text{ molecules}}$$

(b) $\ell = \dfrac{1}{n\sigma 2^{1/2}} = \dfrac{V}{N\sigma 2^{1/2}}$

$= 1 \text{ m}^3/(3.21 \times 10^{12} \text{ molecules})\pi(3 \times 10^{-10} \text{ m})^2(2)^{1/2} = \boxed{7.78 \times 10^5 \text{ m}}$

(c) $f = \dfrac{v}{\ell} = \boxed{6.42 \times 10^{-4} \text{ s}^{-1}}$

21.54 From Eq. 21.28, $\ell = \dfrac{1}{\sqrt{2}\pi d^2 n_v}$ For an ideal gas, $n_v = \dfrac{N}{V} = \dfrac{P}{kT}$

Therefore $\ell = \dfrac{kT}{\sqrt{2}\pi d^2 P}$, as required.

21.55 $\ell = [\sqrt{2}\pi d^2 n_v]^{-1}$, $n_v = \dfrac{P}{kT}$

$d = 3.6 \times 10^{-10}$ m, $n_v = \dfrac{1.01 \times 10^5}{(1.38 \times 10^{-23})(293)} = 2.5 \times 10^{25}/\text{m}^3$

$\therefore \ell = 6.95 \times 10^{-8}$ m, or about $\boxed{193 \text{ molecular diameters}}$

21.56 Using $P = N_v kT$, Eq. 21.28 becomes $\ell = \dfrac{kT}{\sqrt{2}\pi P d^2}$ (1)

(a) $\ell = \dfrac{(1.381 \times 10^{-23}\ \text{J/K})(293\ \text{K})}{\sqrt{2}\pi(1.013 \times 10^5\ \text{Pa})(3.10 \times 10^{-10}\ \text{m})^2} = \boxed{9.36 \times 10^{-8}\ \text{m}}$

(b) Equation (1) shows that $P_1\ell_1 = P_2\ell_2$. Taking $P_1\ell_1$ from (a) and with $\lambda_2 = 1$ m, we find

$P_2 = \dfrac{(1\ \text{atm})(9.36 \times 10^{-8}\ \text{m})}{1\ \text{m}} = \boxed{9.36 \times 10^{-8}\ \text{atm}}$

(c) For $\ell_2 = 3.1 \times 10^{-10}$ m, we have $P_2 = \dfrac{(1\ \text{atm})(9.36 \times 10^{-8}\ \text{m})}{3.1 \times 10^{-10}\ \text{m}} = \boxed{302\ \text{atm}}$

21.57 Van der Waals equation (Eq. 21.30) is $\left(P + \dfrac{a}{V^2}\right)(V - b) = RT$,   per mol of gas.

$(V - b)$ is the empty volume available to the gas, where

b is the (number of molecules) $\times$ (the volume per molecule)

$\therefore$ If $b = 31.8$ cm^3/mol, then $\dfrac{4\pi}{3}r^3 = \dfrac{31.8\ \text{cm}^3}{6 \times 10^{23}\ \text{mol}}$

$r_{\text{molecule}} = 2.327 \times 10^{-8}$ cm $d_{\text{molecule}} = \boxed{4.65 \times 10^{-8}\ \text{cm}}$

21.58 $v = \sqrt{\dfrac{\gamma RT}{M_{av}}}$ where $M_{av} = \dfrac{M_0(0.6) + M_n(0.4)}{(0.4 + 0.6)}$

$M_{av} = (32)(0.6) + (28)(0.4) = 30.4 \text{ g/mol}$ and $\gamma = 1.4$;

so $v = \sqrt{\dfrac{(1.4)(8.314)(313)}{0.0304}} = \boxed{346 \text{ m/s}}$

21.59 $\Delta t = t_a - t_m = \dfrac{\ell}{v_a} - \dfrac{\ell}{v_m} = \dfrac{\ell(v_m - v_a)}{v_a v_m}$

21.60 $W = \displaystyle\int_{V_i}^{V_f} P\,dV = \int_{V_i}^{V_f} [\dfrac{RT}{(V-b)} - \dfrac{a}{V^2}]dV$

Integrating, $W = RT\ln(\dfrac{V_f - b}{V_i - b}) + a(V_f^{-1} - V_i^{-1})$

21.61 The root-mean-square speed of a gas is given by $v_{rms} = \sqrt{\dfrac{3kT}{m}}$.

For 2 different gases at a common temperature this ratio becomes

$\dfrac{(v_1)_{rms}}{(v_2)_{rms}} = \dfrac{\sqrt{3kT/m_1}}{\sqrt{3kT/m_2}} = \sqrt{\dfrac{m_2}{m_1}}$

21.62 (a) $PV^\gamma = k$. So $W = \displaystyle\int_i^f P\,dV = k\int_i^f \dfrac{dV}{V^\gamma} = \dfrac{P_iV_i - P_fV_f}{\gamma - 1}$

(b) $dU = dQ - dW$ and $dQ = 0$ for an adiabatic process.

Therefore, $W = -\Delta U = -\dfrac{3}{2}nR\Delta T = nC_v(T_i - T_f)$.

To show consistency between these 2 equations, consider that $\gamma = C_p/C_v$ and $C_p - C_v = R$.

Therefore $1/(\gamma - 1) = C_v/R$. Using this, the result found in part (a) becomes

$W = (P_iV_i - P_fV_f)\dfrac{C_v}{R}$. Also, for an ideal gas $\dfrac{PV}{R} = nT$ so that

$W = nC_v(T_i - T_f)$.

21.63 (a) The average speed v_{av} is just the weighted average of all the speeds.

$$v_{av} = \frac{[2(v) + 3(2v) + 5(3v) + 4(4v) + 3(5v) + 2(6v) + 1(7v)]}{(2+3+5+4+3+2+1)} = \boxed{365v}$$

(b) First find the average of the square of the speeds,

$$v_{av}^2 = \frac{[2(v)^2 + 3(2v)^2 + 5(3v)^2 + 4(4v)^2 + 3(5v)^2 + 2(6v)^2 + 1(7v)^2]}{2+3+5+4+3+2+1}$$
$$= 15.95v^2$$

The root-mean square speed is then $v_{rms} = \sqrt{v_{av}^2} = \boxed{3.99v}$

(c) The most probable speed is the one that most of the particles have, i.e., five particles have speed $\boxed{3.00v}$

(d) $PV = \frac{1}{2}Nmv_{av}^2$. Therefore, $P = \frac{20}{3}\frac{[m(15.95)v^2]}{V} = \boxed{106(\frac{mv^2}{V})}$

(e) The average kinetic energy for each particle is

$$K = \frac{1}{2}mv_{av}^2 = \frac{1}{2}m(15.95v^2) = \boxed{7.98mv^2}$$

21.64 (a) Using Maxwell's speed distribution,

$$N_v = 4\pi(10^4)[32(1.67 \times 10^{-27}) \div 2\pi(1.38 \times 10^{-23})(500)]^{3/2}$$
$$\times v^2 \exp -\{32(1.67 \times 10^{-27})v^2/[2(1.38 \times 10^{-23})(500)]\}$$
$$N_v = (1.72 \times 10^{-4})v^2 \exp -(3.87 \times 10^{-6}v^2).$$

We use this equation to plot N_v vs v for $0 \le v \le 1200$.

(b) The most probable speed occurs for N_v maximum. From the graph $v_{mp} = 500$ m/s.

(c) $v_{av} = \sqrt{\frac{8RT}{\pi m}} = \sqrt{\frac{8(8.31)(500)}{\pi(0.032)}} = \boxed{575 \text{ m/s}}$

Also, $v_{rms} = \sqrt{\frac{3RT}{m}} = \sqrt{\frac{3(8.31)(500)}{0.032}} = \boxed{624 \text{ m/s}}$

(d) The fraction of particles in the range $300 \le v \le 600$ is

$$\int_{300}^{600} N_v dv/N \text{ where } N = 10^4 \text{ and the integral of } N_v \text{ is read from the graph as the}$$

area under the curve. This is approximately 4400 and the fraction is 0.44 or $\boxed{44\%}$

21.65 The Maxwell speed distribution for molecules of varying velocity is

$N_v = 4\pi N[m/2\pi kT]^{3/2}v^2 e^{-mv^2/2kT}$. For 1 mol of gas $N = N_A = 6.02 \times 10^{23}$. The mass m of a helium atom is approximately 4 u, or $m = 4(1.67 \times 10^{-27}$ kg). The number of molecules with a speed in the range dv is $N_v dv$ which is $\approx N_v \Delta v$. In this case N_v is calculated for the average of the two velocity extremes in the interval. That is, $N_v \to N_{405}$. Substituting these values into the speed distribution function gives

$$(N_{405})(10) = 4\pi(6.03 \times 10^{23}) \times \{4(1.67 \times 10^{-27})/[2\pi(1.38 \times 10^{-23})(300)]\}^{3/2}(405)^2$$
$$\exp\{(6.68 \times 10^{-27})(405)^2/[2(2.381 \times 10^{-23})(300)]\}(10)$$
$$= \boxed{1.41 \times 10^{21} \text{ molecules}}$$

*21.66 (a) $PV = nRT$

$$\left(\frac{P_{\text{down}}}{1 \text{ atm}}\right)\left(\frac{1.5 \text{ m}}{4 \text{ m}}\right) = \frac{281 \text{ K}}{293 \text{ K}}$$

$$P_{\text{down}} = (1 \text{ atm})\left(\frac{4}{1.5}\right)\frac{281}{293} = \boxed{2.56 \text{ atm}}$$

(b) $\Delta P = \rho g h$

$$\left(1.013 \times 10^5 \frac{Pa}{\text{atm}}\right)(1.56 \text{ atm}) = (1000 \text{ kg/m}^3)(9.8 \text{ m/s}^2)h$$

$$h = \boxed{16.1 \text{ m}}$$

21.67 Oxygen at pressures much above 1 atm, become toxic to lung cells. What ratio, by weight, of helium gas (He) to oxygen (O_2) must be used by a scuba diver who is to descend to an ocean depth of 50 m?

50 m depth = 6 atm (5 atm Hydrostatic + 1 atm)

$\therefore$ 5 moles He per 1 mole O_2 or 20 grams He per 32 grams O_2.

21.68   (a) Since pressure increases as volume decreases (and vice versa),

$$\frac{dV}{dP} < 0 \text{ and } -\frac{1}{V}[\frac{dV}{dP}] > 0.$$

(b) For an ideal gas $V = \frac{nRT}{P}$ and $\kappa_1 = -\frac{1}{V}\frac{d}{dP}\frac{nRT}{P}$.

If the compression is isothermal, T is constant and

$$\kappa_1 = -\frac{nRT}{V} - \frac{1}{P^2} = \frac{1}{P}.$$

(c) For an adiabatic compression, $PV^\gamma = C_1$ (where C is a constant) and

$$\kappa_2 = -\frac{1}{V}\frac{d}{dP}(\frac{C}{P})^{1/\gamma} = \frac{1}{V}(\frac{1}{\gamma})\frac{C^{1/\gamma}}{P^{(1/\gamma)+1}} = \frac{P^{1/\gamma}}{V\gamma P^{(1/\gamma)}+1} = \frac{1}{1/\gamma P}$$

(d) $\kappa_1 = \frac{1}{P} = \frac{1}{(2 \text{ atm})} = \boxed{0.5 \text{ atm}^{-1}}$

$\gamma = \frac{C_p}{C_v}$ and for a monatomic ideal gas, $\gamma = 5/3$, so that

$\kappa_2 = \frac{1}{\gamma P} = \frac{1}{(5/3)(2 \text{ atm})} = \boxed{0.3 \text{ atm}^{-1}}$

21.69   Van der Waals' equation is $(P + \frac{a}{V^2})(V - b) = RT$ (1)

Holding T constant, take the partial derivative $\partial/\partial V$ of each side to get

$$[\frac{\partial P}{\partial V} - \frac{2a}{V^3}](V - b) + (P + \frac{a}{V^2}) = 0.$$

Setting $\frac{\partial P}{\partial V} = 0$ gives $(P + \frac{a}{V^2}) = \frac{2a}{V^3}(V - b)$ (2)

Taking the second derivative $\partial^2/\partial V^2$ of Eq. (1) we get

$$\frac{\partial^2}{\partial V^2}P + \frac{6a}{V^4}(V - b) + 2[\frac{\partial P}{\partial V} - \frac{2a}{V^3}] = 0.$$

Setting $\frac{\partial^2}{\partial V^2}P = \frac{\partial P}{\partial V} = 0$ gives $\frac{2a}{V^3} - \frac{6ab}{V^4} = 0$ and $\frac{3b}{V} = 1$ (3)

Solving equations (1), (2), and (3) gives

$$P_c = \frac{a}{27b^2}, \quad V_c = 3b, \quad \text{and } T_c = \frac{8a}{27Rb}$$

*21.70 (a) $\frac{1}{2}m\overline{v^2} = \frac{3}{2}kT$ (Eq. 21.7)

$$= \frac{3}{2}(1.38 \times 10^{-23} \text{ J/K})(2 \times 10^7 \text{ K})$$

$$= \boxed{4.14 \times 10^{-16} \text{ J}}$$

(b) $v_{rms} = \sqrt{\dfrac{2(4.14 \times 10^{-16} \text{ J})}{1.67 \times 10^{-27} \text{ kg}}} = \boxed{704 \text{ km/s}}$

21.71 (a) $v = \sqrt{\dfrac{\gamma RT}{m}} = \sqrt{\dfrac{\gamma R(273)}{m}}\sqrt{\dfrac{T}{273}} = v_0\sqrt{\dfrac{T}{273}}$

where $T \equiv$ Temperature in Kelvin. If $t \equiv$ temperature in Celsius,

then $v = v_0\sqrt{\dfrac{t}{273} + 1} \approx v_0[1 + \dfrac{t}{546}]$

(b) For air, $v_0 = 331$ m/s and $v = (331 + 0.61t)$ m/s.

21.72 First find v_{av}^2 as $v_{av}^2 = \dfrac{1}{N}\displaystyle\int_0^\infty v^2 N_v dv$. Let $a = \dfrac{m}{2kT}$.

Then $v_{av}^2 = \dfrac{1}{N}\displaystyle\int_0^\infty v^2 dv[4N\pi^{-1/2}a^{3/2}e^{-av^2}]$

$$= [4a^{3/2}\pi^{-1/2}]\dfrac{(\pi/a)(3)}{8a^2} = \dfrac{3kT}{m}.$$

The root-mean square speed is then $v_{rms} = \sqrt{v_{av}^2} = \sqrt{\dfrac{3kT}{m}}$.

To find the average speed, we have

$$v_{av} = (1/N)\int_0^\infty vdv[(4N\pi^{-1/2})a^{3/2}e^{-av^2}] = \dfrac{4a^{3/2}\pi^{-1/2}}{2a^2} = \sqrt{\dfrac{8kT}{\pi m}}.$$

*21.73 (a) $n = 10$ moles, $R = 8.314$ J/mol· K, $T = 298$ K, $V = 0.5$ m^3

$$P = \dfrac{(10)(8.314)(298)}{(0.5)} = \boxed{49.6 \text{ kPa}} = 0.489 \text{ atm}$$

(b) $\rho = (10 \text{ mol})\dfrac{(44 \text{ g/mol})}{(0.5 \text{ m}^3)} = \boxed{0.880 \text{ kg/m}^3}$

*21.74 (a) The number of moles in 1 m³ of air at standard conditions (1 atm, 0°C) is

$$n = \frac{(1.013 \times 10^5)(1\ \text{m}^3)}{(8.314)(273)} = 44.6\ \text{mol}$$

$$m = 44.6(\underbrace{(0.78)28 + (0.21)32}_{28.56\ \text{g/mol}}) = \boxed{1.27\ \text{kg}}$$

(b) The mass of 1 m³ of He at standard conditions is

$$m = (44.631)(4\ \text{g/mol}) = 0.179\ \text{kg}$$

For He Lift $= (1.27\ \text{kg} - 0.179\ \text{kg})(9.8\ \text{m/s}^2) = \underline{10.74\ \text{N}}$

For H₂ Lift $= (1.27\ \text{kg} - 0.089\ \text{kg})(9.8\ \text{m/s}^2) = \underline{11.6\ \text{N}}$

(c) $\dfrac{\text{Lift 1 m}^3\ \text{He}}{\text{Lift 1 m}^3\ \text{H}_2} = \dfrac{10.74\ \text{N}}{11.6\ \text{N}} = \boxed{0.925}$

*21.75 (a) $(10^{59})(10^{11})(10^3)(10^9) \cong \boxed{10^{82}}$ protons and neutrons

(b) $(10^{82})(10^{-45})(\text{m}^3) = \dfrac{4}{3}\pi r^3$

$r \cong \boxed{10^{12}\ \text{m}}$ (about the distance of Saturn from the sun)

(c) $(10^{82})\left(\dfrac{1\ \text{mole}}{6.023 \times 10^{23}\ \text{nucleons}}\right) \cong \boxed{10^{58}\ \text{moles}}$

*21.76 (a) For escape, $\dfrac{1}{2}mv^2 = \dfrac{GmM}{R}$

where $g = \dfrac{GM}{R^2}$ and $\dfrac{1}{2}mv^2 = \dfrac{mgR^2}{R} = mgR$

(b) If $\dfrac{1}{2}mv^2 = mgR = 10\left(\dfrac{3}{2}kT\right)$

Then, for O_2, $\dfrac{32\ \text{g}}{6.02 \times 10^{23}}(9.8\ \text{m/s}^2)(6.4 \times 10^6\ \text{m}) = 15(1.38 \times 10^{-23}\ \text{J/mol}\cdot\text{K})T$

$\dfrac{(32 \times 10^{-3}\ \text{kg})}{\text{mol}}(9.8\ \text{m/s}^2)(6.4 \times 10^6\ \text{m}) = 15(8.314\ \text{J/mol}\cdot\text{K})T$

$T = \boxed{1.61 \times 10^4\ \text{K}}$

*21.77 For sodium atoms (with a mass M = 23 g/mol),

$$\frac{1}{2}mv^2 = \frac{3}{2}kT$$

$$\frac{1}{2}\frac{M}{N_A}v^2 = \frac{3}{2}kT \qquad\qquad \text{(Eq. 21.10)}$$

(a) $v_{rms} = \sqrt{\dfrac{3RT}{M}} = \sqrt{\dfrac{(8.314 \text{ J/mol K})(2.4 \times 10^{-4} \text{ K})}{(23 \times 10^{-3} \text{ kg})}} = \boxed{0.51 \text{ m/s}}$

(b) $\overline{T} = \dfrac{d}{\overline{v}} = \dfrac{0.01 \text{ m}}{0.51 \text{ m/s}} \cong \boxed{20 \text{ ms}}$

21.78 Referring to Eq. 21.24

$$\frac{N_v(v)}{N_v(v_{mp})} = \left(\frac{v}{v_{mp}}\right)^2 e^{-(mv^2/2kT - mv_{mp}^2/2kT)} = \left(\frac{v}{v_{mp}}\right)^2 e^{-[(v/v_{mp})^2 - 1]},$$

since $v_{mp}^2 = 2kT/m$, some numerical values of this ratio are given below:

v/v_{mp}	$e^{-[(v/v_{mp})^2 - 1]}$	$N_v(v)/N_v(v_{mp})$
1/50	2.7172	1.09×10^{-3}
1/10	2.6959	2.70×10^{-2}
1/2	2.1170	0.529
2	4.9787×10^{-2}	0.199
10	1.0112×10^{-43}	1.01×10^{-41}

21.79 The Maxwell Distribution function is

$$N_v = 4\pi N \left(\frac{m}{2\pi kT}\right)^{3/2} v^2 e^{-mv^2/2kT}$$

$N = 10^4$ molecules, $m = 32 \times 1.67 \times 10^{-27}$ kg,

$k = 1.38 \times 10^{-23}$ J/K, $\quad T_A = 300$ K and $T_B = 1000$ K.

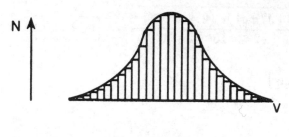

21.79

General Shape of Maxwell Curve

In plotting, note that $N_v(v = 0) = 0$. Then evaluate $N_v(v = 100)$. Plot.

Evaluate $N_v(v = 200)$. Plot, $\cdots$

The computer can keep track of number of molecules in each velocity interval.

CHAPTER 22

22.1 (a) $e = \dfrac{W}{Q_h} = \dfrac{25 \text{ J}}{360 \text{ J}} = \boxed{6.94 \text{ \%}}$

(b) $Q_c = Q_h - W = (360 - 25) \text{ J} = \boxed{335 \text{ J}}$

22.2 $W = 200 \text{ J} \quad e = 30\%$

(a) $e = \dfrac{W}{Q_h}$ (Eq. 22.2) $\quad Q_h = \dfrac{W}{e} = \dfrac{200}{0.3} = \boxed{667 \text{ J}}$

(b) A heat $Q_c = Q_h - W = \boxed{467 \text{ J}}$ is rejected.

22.3 $COP \text{ (refrigerator)} = \dfrac{Q_c}{W}$ (Eq. 22.7)

(a) If $Q_c = 120 \text{ J}$ and $COP = 5$, then $\boxed{W = 24 \text{ J}}$

(b) Heat expelled = Heat removed + Work done.

$Q_h = Q_c + W = 120 \text{ J} + 24 \text{ J} = \boxed{144 \text{ J}}$

*22.4 (a) $\Delta U = \Delta Q - W = [500(4.186) - 800] \text{ J} = \boxed{1290 \text{ J}}$

(b) $\Delta U = \Delta Q + W = [500(4.186) + 500] \text{ J} = \boxed{2590 \text{ J}}$

(c) $\Delta U = (-1000)(4.186) \text{ J} = \boxed{-4186 \text{ J}}$

*22.5 (a) $\Delta U = 0 = Q - W$

If $Q = 1000 \text{ J}$, then $W = \boxed{1000 \text{ J}}$

(b) If the temperature remains constant,

$\Delta U = \boxed{0}$

22.6 In a refrigerator, heat expelled = heat removed + work done.

$\therefore W = Q_h - Q_c = 30$ J

(a) At 60 cycles/sec, $P = \boxed{1.8 \text{ kW}}$

(b) $COP = \dfrac{\text{heat removed}}{\text{Work done}} = \dfrac{Q_c}{W} = \dfrac{100 \text{ J}}{30 \text{ J}} = \boxed{3.33}$

22.7 (a) $e = \dfrac{Q_h - Q_c}{Q_h} = \dfrac{1600 - 1000}{600} = 0.375$ or $\boxed{37.5\%}$

(b) $Q = Q_h - Q_c = \boxed{600 \text{ J}}$

(c) $P_{av} = \dfrac{W}{t} = \dfrac{600 \text{ J}}{0.3 \text{ s}} = \boxed{2000 \text{ W}}$

22.8 $e_c = 1 - \dfrac{T_c}{T_h} = 1 - \dfrac{293}{573} = 0.489$ or $\boxed{48.9\%}$

*22.9 $e_c = 1 - \dfrac{T_c}{T_h} = 1 - \dfrac{287}{413} = \boxed{0.305}$

From Eq. 22.2,

$Q_c = Q_h(1-e)$

$Q_c = (24 \text{ MJ})(1 - 0.305) = \boxed{16.7 \text{ MJ}}$

22.10 When $e = e_c$, $1 - \dfrac{T_c}{T_h} = \dfrac{W}{Q_h}$, and $(\dfrac{W}{t})/(\dfrac{Q_h}{t}) = 1 - \dfrac{T_c}{T_h}$

(a) $Q_h = \dfrac{(W/t)t}{1 - (T_c/T_h)} = \dfrac{(1.5 \times 10^5 \text{ W})(3600 \text{ s})}{1 - (293/773)}$

$Q_h = \boxed{8.69 \times 10^8 \text{ J}} = 2.08 \times 10^8$ cal

(b) $Q_c = Q_h - (\dfrac{W}{t})t = 8.69 \times 10^8 - (1.5 \times 10^5)(3600) = \boxed{3.3 \times 10^8 \text{ J}}$

22.11 $T_h = 293$ K , $T_c = 278$ K.

(a) $e = 1 - \dfrac{T_c}{T_h}$ $e = \dfrac{15}{293} = 5.12\%$

(b) $Q_h = \dfrac{W}{e} = \dfrac{(75 \times 10^6)(3600)\ \text{J}}{0.0512} = 5.27 \times 10^{12}\ \text{J}$

(c) Such a huge area would be required for heat absorption that the feasibility is doubtful at best.

22.12 $T_c = 353$ K, $T_h = 623$ K, $e = \dfrac{\Delta T}{T_h} = 0.433$

$Q_c = 2 \times 10^4$ J, $t = 1$ s

(a) $P = \dfrac{W}{t} = \dfrac{eQ_h}{1\ \text{s}} = \dfrac{(0.433)(2 \times 10^4)\ \text{J}}{1\ \text{s}} = \boxed{8.67\ \text{kW}}$

(b) $Q_c = Q_h - W = 20\ \text{kJ} - 8.67\ \text{kJ} = \boxed{11.33\ \text{kJ}}$

22.13 $T_c = 703$ K , $T_h = 2143$ K

(a) $e = \dfrac{\Delta T}{T_h} = \dfrac{1440}{2143} = \boxed{67.2\%}$

(b) $Q_h = 1.4 \times 10^5$ J , $W = 0.42 Q_h$

$P = \dfrac{W}{t} = \dfrac{5.88 \times 10^4\ \text{J}}{1\ \text{s}} = \boxed{58.8\ \text{kW}}$

22.14 $e = \dfrac{\Delta T}{T_h} = \dfrac{680}{1073} = \boxed{63.3\%}$

22.15 $\dfrac{dQ}{dt} = \dfrac{dm}{dt} c \Delta T$

$2 \times 10^9 = (10^6)(4200\ \text{J/kg}) \Delta T$

$\Delta T = 0.48\ ^\circ\text{C}$

22.16 $P = 5 \times 10^8 \text{ W} : T_h = 473 \text{ K}, T_c = 313 \text{ K}$

$$e = \frac{1}{2}\left(\frac{\Delta T}{T_h}\right) = \frac{80}{473} = 16.9\%$$

(a) $Q_c = Q_h - W = \frac{W}{e} - W = \left(\frac{1}{e} - 1\right)(5 \times 10^8 \text{ J/s})$

$Q_c = \boxed{2.46 \times 10^9 \text{ J}}$ per second

(b) This amount of heat would raise the

temperature of 1.2×10^6 kg of water by

$$\Delta T = \frac{\Delta Q}{mC_v} = \frac{2.46 \times 10^9 \text{ J}}{(1.2 \times 10^6)(4186)} = \boxed{+0.49 \text{ °C}}$$

*22.17 From Eq. 22.4,

(a) $e = \dfrac{\Delta T}{T_h} = \dfrac{100}{373} = \boxed{0.268}$

(b) $e = \dfrac{\Delta T}{T_h} = \dfrac{200}{473} = \boxed{0.423}$

*22.18 The Carnot efficiency of the engine is

$$e_c = \frac{\Delta T}{T_h} = \frac{120 \text{ K}}{473 \text{ K}} = 0.253$$

At 20% of this maximum efficiency,

$e = (0.2)(0.253) = 0.0506$

From Eq. 22.2,

$$W = Q_h e \quad \text{and} \quad Q_h = \frac{W}{e} = \frac{10^4 \text{ J}}{0.0506} = \boxed{197 \text{ kJ}}$$

22.19 Isothermal expansion at $T_h = 523$ K

Isothermal compression at $T_c = 323$ K

Gas absorbs 1200 J during expansion

(a) $Q_c = Q_h \dfrac{T_c}{T_h} = (1200 \text{ J})(\dfrac{323}{523}) = \boxed{741 \text{ J}}$

(b) $W = Q_h - Q_c = (1200 - 741) \text{ J} = \boxed{459 \text{ J}}$

22.20 Compression ratio $= 6$, $\gamma = 1.4$

(a) Efficiency of an Otto-engine $e = 1 - (\dfrac{V_2}{V_1})^{\gamma - 1}$

$e = 1 - (\dfrac{1}{6})^{0.4} = \boxed{51.2\%}$

(b) If actual efficiency $e' = 15\%$, then

losses in system are $e - e' = \boxed{36.2\%}$

22.21 $\gamma = 1.4$ $T_A = 300$ K, $T_c = 1500$ K. Find $\dfrac{V_1}{V_2}$ if $e = 0.20$

(a) Since $e = 1 - \dfrac{T_A}{T_B} = 0.2$, $\dfrac{T_A}{T_B} = 0.8 = (\dfrac{V_2}{V_1})^{\gamma - 1}$.

Thus $(\dfrac{V_1}{V_2})^{-0.4} = 0.8$ and $\dfrac{V_1}{V_2} = (0.8)^{-2.5} = \boxed{1.75}$

(b) Carnot efficiency $= \dfrac{\Delta T}{T_h} = \dfrac{1200}{1500} = \boxed{0.80}$

22.22 $P_1 V_1^{\gamma} = P_2 V_2^{\gamma}$

$P_2 = P_1(\dfrac{V_1}{V_2})^{\gamma} = (3 \times 10^6)(\dfrac{1}{6})^{1.4} \text{ Pa} = \boxed{244 \text{ kPa}}$

22.23 $W = \int_{V_1}^{V_2} PdV, \quad P = P_1(\frac{V_1}{V})^\gamma$

Integrating,

$$W = (\frac{1}{\gamma - 1})P_1V_1[1 - (\frac{V_1}{V_2})^{\gamma - 1}]$$

$$= (2.5)(3 \times 10^6)(5 \times 10^{-5})[1 - (\frac{1}{6})^{0.4}] \text{ J} = \boxed{192 \text{ J}}$$

22.24   (a) For a complete cycle, $\Delta U = 0$ and $W = Q_h - Q_c = Q_c[\frac{Q_h}{Q_c} - 1]$.

We have already shown that for a Carnot cycle (and only for a

Carnot cycle) that $\frac{Q_h}{Q_c} = \frac{T_h}{T_c}$. Therefore, $W = Q_c[\frac{T_h - T_c}{T_c}]$

(b) We have from Eq. 22.7 $COP = \frac{Q_c}{W}$. Using the result from part (a),

this becomes $COP = \frac{T_c}{T_h - T_c}$.

22.25 $(COP)_{\text{refrig}} = \frac{T_c}{\Delta T} = \frac{270}{30} = \boxed{9}$

22.26 $(COP)_{\text{heatpump}} = \frac{Q + W}{W} = \frac{T_h}{\Delta T} = \frac{295}{25} = \boxed{11.8}$

22.27 $(COP)_{\text{He refrig}} = \frac{T_c}{\Delta T} = \frac{4}{289} \quad \therefore W = \boxed{72.25 \text{ J}}$ per 1 J heat removed.

22.28   (Table 20.2) $\Delta S = \frac{(8.82 \times 10^4)(0.108)}{1234} = \boxed{7.72 \text{ J/K}}$

22.29 $\Delta S = \frac{mg\Delta h}{T} = \frac{(1000)(9.8)(200)}{270} \text{ J/K} = \boxed{7260 \text{ J/K}}$

22.30 $\quad \Delta S = \int_{T_1}^{T_2} \frac{dQ}{T} = \int_{T_1}^{T_2} \frac{nC_P dT}{T} = nC_P \ln \frac{T_2}{T_1}$

$\qquad\qquad = 21 \ln(\frac{4}{293}) \text{ J/K} = \boxed{-90.2 \text{ J/K}}$

22.31 $\quad \Delta S = \int_{i}^{f} \frac{dQ_r}{T} = \int_{T_1}^{T_2} \frac{mc\, dT}{T} = mc \ln \frac{T_2}{T_1}$

$\qquad\qquad \Delta S = (250 \text{ g})(1 \text{ cal/g·C}^\circ) \ln(\frac{353}{293}) = 46.6 \text{ cal/K} = \boxed{195 \text{ J/K}}$

22.32 For a freezing process,

$\qquad\qquad \Delta S = \frac{\Delta Q}{T} = \frac{-(0.5 \text{ kg})(3.33 \times 10^5 \text{ J/kg})}{273 \text{ K}} = \boxed{-610 \text{ J/K}}$

22.33 $\quad \Delta S = \int_{T_1}^{T_2} \frac{nC_v dT}{T} = nC_v \ln(\frac{T_2}{T_1})$ and $C_v = \frac{3R}{2}$, so that

$\qquad\qquad \Delta S = n(\frac{3R}{2}) \ln(\frac{T_2}{T_1}) = (1)(\frac{3}{2})(8.31)\, ln(\frac{400}{300}) = \boxed{3.59 \text{ J/K}}$

*22.34 At a constant temperature of 4.2 K,

$\qquad\qquad \Delta S = \frac{\Delta Q}{T} = \frac{H_{vap}}{4.2 \text{ K}} = \frac{20.5 \text{ kJ/kg}}{4.2 \text{ K}}$

$\qquad\qquad \Delta S = \boxed{4.88 \text{ kJ/kg} \cdot \text{K}}$

22.35 $\quad \Delta S = \frac{\frac{1}{2}mv^2}{T} = \frac{750(20)^2}{293} \text{ J/K} = \boxed{1.02 \times 10^3 \text{ J/K}}$

22.36 $\quad \Delta S = \frac{Q_2}{T_2} - \frac{Q_1}{T_1} = (\frac{1000}{290} - \frac{1000}{5700}) \text{ J/K} = \boxed{3.27 \text{ J/K}}$

22.37 $\Delta S = \int_{T_1=268}^{T_2=273} \frac{mC_{ice}dT}{T} + \frac{mL_{ice}}{273}$

$= (10^5 \text{ kg})(2010 \frac{\text{J}}{\text{kg°C}})\ln(\frac{273}{268}) + \frac{(10^5)(3.3 \times 10^5)}{273} \text{ J/K} = \boxed{1.245 \times 10^8 \text{ J/K}}$

22.38 (a) $\Delta S = nR\ln(\frac{V_2}{V_1}) = R\ln 2 = \boxed{1.38 \text{ cal/K}}$

(b) There is no change in temperature.

22.39 $\Delta S = nR\ln(\frac{V_2}{V_1}) = (0.044)(2)R\ln 2 = (0.088)(8.31)\ln 2 = \boxed{0.507 \text{ J/K}}$

22.40 3200 J flows from $T_h = 500$ K to $T_c = 300$ K.

(a) $\Delta S_h = \frac{\Delta Q_h}{T_h} = \frac{-3200 \text{ J}}{500 \text{ K}} = \boxed{-6.4 \text{ J/K}}$

(b) $\Delta S_c = \frac{\Delta Q_c}{T_c} = \frac{+3200 \text{ J}}{300 \text{ K}} = \boxed{+10.7 \text{ J/K}}$

(c) $\Delta S_{rod} = \frac{\Delta Q_{rod}}{T_{rod}} = \frac{0}{T_{rod}} = \boxed{0}$

(d) $\Delta S_{universe} = \frac{\Delta Q_h}{T_h} + \frac{\Delta Q_c}{T_c} = \boxed{+4.3 \text{ J/K}}$

22.41 $\Delta S_{universe} = \frac{\Delta Q}{T} = \frac{\frac{1}{2}mv^2}{293} = \frac{\frac{1}{2}(2)(5)^2}{293} = \boxed{+0.085 \text{ J/K}}$

22.42 $\Delta S = \frac{Q}{T} = \frac{mgh}{T} = \frac{(70 \text{ kg})(9.80 \text{ m/s}^2)(25 \text{ m})}{300 \text{ K}} = \boxed{57.2 \text{ J/K}}$

*22.43 $\Delta S = \frac{\Delta Q}{T} = \frac{H_{vap}\, m}{T}$

$\Delta S = \frac{(1120 \text{ J/g})(1 \text{ g})}{300 \text{ K}} = \boxed{3.73 \text{ J/K}}$

*22.44 AB $\quad Q_h$ in at $T_h \quad S\uparrow \dfrac{Q_h}{T_h} \quad T\to$ at T_h

BC $\quad$ rev. adiabatic $\quad S\to \quad T\downarrow$

CD $\quad Q_c$ out at $T_c \quad S\downarrow \dfrac{Q_c}{T_c} \quad T\to$ at T_c

DA $\quad$ rev. adiabatic $\quad S\to$

(a)

(b) $\text{area} = (T_h - T_c)\dfrac{Q_h}{T_h}$

$\qquad\quad = \left(1 - \dfrac{T_c}{T_h}\right)Q_h$

$\qquad\quad = e_c Q_h = \underline{\text{work out}}$

22.45 (a) $\Delta Q_1 = \Delta Q_2$ or $(mc\Delta T)_1 = (mc\Delta T)_2,$ and

$(200\text{ g})(T - 20°\text{C}) = (300\text{ g})(75°\text{C} - T)$

This gives $T = \boxed{53°\text{C}}$ or $\boxed{326\text{ K}}$

(b) $\Delta S = mc\ln\left(\dfrac{T_2}{T_1}\right)$ for each material

$\Delta S = (200\text{ g})(1\text{ cal/g}\cdot\text{C}°)\ln\left[\dfrac{(53+273)}{(20+273)}\right]$

$\qquad + (300\text{ g})(1\text{ cal/g}\cdot\text{C}°)\ln\left[\dfrac{(53+273)}{(75+273)}\right]$

$\Delta S = 1.75\text{ cal/deg} = \boxed{7.33\text{ J/deg}}$

22.45

22.46 (a) $\Delta S = 0.018\left[\dfrac{3.33\times10^5}{273} + \displaystyle\int_{T=273}^{373}\dfrac{C_v dT}{T} + \dfrac{22.6\times10^5}{373}\right]$ J/K

$\qquad = 0.018\left[1220 + 4186\ln\dfrac{373}{273} + 6059\right]$ J/K $= \boxed{154.5\text{ J/K}}$

(b) $\Delta E = 0.018(3.33\times10^5 + 4.18\times10^5 + 22.6\times10^5)$ J $= \boxed{54.2\text{ kJ}}$

*22.47 $\Delta S_{\text{hot}} = \dfrac{-1000}{600}\dfrac{\text{J}}{\text{K}}$

$\qquad\quad \Delta S_{\text{cold}} = \dfrac{+750}{350}\dfrac{\text{J}}{\text{K}}$

(a) $\Delta S_{\text{univ}} = \Delta S_{\text{hot}} + \Delta S_{\text{cold}} = \boxed{0.476 \text{ J/K}}$

(b) $e_c = 1 - \dfrac{T_1}{T_2} = 0.417$

$\qquad W = Q_h e_c = (1000 \text{ J})(0.417) = \boxed{417 \text{ J}}$

(c) $W_{\text{net}} = 417 \text{ J} - 250 \text{ J} = \underline{167 \text{ J}}$

$\qquad T_1 \Delta S_{\text{univ}} = (350 \text{ K})(0.476 \text{ J/K}) = \boxed{167 \text{ J}}$

22.48 This is the same as extracting heat from a refrigerator.

$(COP)_{\text{refrig}} = \dfrac{T_c}{\Delta T} = \dfrac{273}{20} = 13.65$

$W = \dfrac{400 \text{ J}}{13.65} = \boxed{29.3 \text{ J}}$

22.49 $\dfrac{dQ}{dt} = 5000 \text{ W} \qquad T_i = 295 \text{ K} \qquad T_0 = 268 \text{ K}$

(a) If $\dfrac{\Delta Q}{\Delta t} = \dfrac{\Delta E}{\Delta t}$ then $\boxed{P_{El} = 5000 \text{ W}}$

(b) For a heat pump,

$(COP)_{\text{Carnot}} = \dfrac{T_h}{\Delta T} = \dfrac{295}{27} = 10.92$

Actual $COP = (0.6)(10.92) = 6.55$

Therefore to bring 5000 W of heat into the house only requires $\boxed{763 \text{ W}}$

*22.50 Define T_1 = Temp Cream = 5°C = 278 K.

Define T_2 = Temp Coffee = 60°C = 333 K.

The final temperature of the mixture is

$T_f = (T_1 + 10\,T_2)/11 = 55°C = 328$ K.

The entropy change due to this mixing is

$$\Delta S = 20 \int_{T_f}^{T_1} c_v dT/T + 200 \int_{T_f}^{T_1} c_v dT/T$$
$$= 84\ln(T_f/T_1) + 840\ln(T_f/T_2)$$
$$= 84\ln(328/278) + 840\ln(328/333)$$

$\Delta S = \boxed{+1.18 \text{ J/K}}$

22.51 (a) For the isothermal process AB, $W_{AB} = P_A V_A \ln(\frac{V_B}{V_A})$

$W_{AB} = (5)(1.013 \times 10^5 \text{ Pa})(10 \times 10^{-3} \text{ m}^3)\ln(\frac{50}{10})$

$W_{AB} = 8.15 \times 10^3$ J, where we used 1 atm = 1.03×10^5 Pa and $1 \text{ L} = 10^{-3} \text{ m}^3$.

$W_{BC} = P_B \Delta V = (1.01 \times 10^5 \text{ Pa})[(10 - 50) \times 10^{-3}] \text{ m}^3$

$W_{BC} = -4.05 \times 10^3$ J

$W_{CA} = 0$ and $W = W_{AB} + W_{BC} = \boxed{4.11 \times 10^3 \text{ J}}$

(b) Since AB is an isothermal process, $\Delta U_{AB} = 0$, and

$Q_{AB} = W_{AB} = 8.15 \times 10^3$ J. For an ideal monatomic gas

$C_V = 3R/2$ and $C_P = 5R/2$.

$T_B = T_A = P_B V_B/(nR) = (1.01 \times 10^5)(50 \times 10^{-3})/R = 5.05 \times 10^3/R$.

Also $T_c = P_C V_C/(nR) = (1.01 \times 10^5)(10 \times 10^{-3})/R = 1.01 \times 10^3/R$.

(c) Therefore $Q_{BC} = nC_P\Delta T = \frac{5}{2}(1.01 \times 10^3)(1 - 5) = \boxed{-1.01 \times 10^4 \text{ J}}$

(d) $e = \dfrac{W}{Q_h} = \dfrac{4.1 \times 10^3}{1.42 \times 10^4} = 0.289$ or $\boxed{28.9\%}$

22.52   (a) $35°F = \dfrac{5}{9}(35 - 32)°C = (1.67 + 273.15) \text{ K} = 274.82 \text{ K}$

$$98.6°F = \dfrac{5}{9}(98.6 - 32)°C = (37 + 273.15) \text{ K} = 310.15 \text{ K}$$

$$\Delta S_{\text{ice water}} = \int \dfrac{dQ}{T} = (453.6 \text{ g})(1 \text{ cal/g} \cdot \text{K}) \times \int_{274.82}^{310.85} \dfrac{dT}{T}$$

$$= 453.6 \ln\left(\dfrac{310.15}{274.82}\right) = 54.86 \text{ cal/K}$$

$$\Delta S_{\text{body}} = -\dfrac{|Q|}{T_{\text{body}}} = -(453.6)(1)\dfrac{(310.15 - 274.82)}{310.15} = -51.67 \text{ cal/K}$$

$$\Delta S_{\text{system}} = 54.86 - 51.67 = 3.19 \text{ cal/K} = \boxed{13.4 \text{ J/K}}$$

(b) $(453.6)(1)(T_F - 274.82) = (70 \times 10^3)(1)(310.15 - T_F)$. Thus

$$(70.0 + 0.4536) \times 10^3 \, T_F = [(70)(310.15) + (0.4536)(274.82)] \times 10^3$$

and $T_F = 309.92 \text{ K} = 36.77 \, °C = \boxed{98.19°F}$

$$\Delta S'_{\text{icewater}} = 453.6 \ln\left(\dfrac{309.92}{274.82}\right) = 54.52 \text{ cal/K}$$

$$\Delta S'_{\text{body}} = -(70 \times 10^3) \ln\left(\dfrac{310.15}{309.92}\right) = -51.93 \text{ cal/K}$$

$\Delta S'_{\text{sys}} = 54.52 - 51.93 = \boxed{2.59 \text{ cal/K}}$ which is less than the

estimate in part (a).

22.53   (a) For an isothermal process, $Q = nRT \ln(V_2/V_1)$. Therefore

$Q_1 = nR(3T_0) \ln 2$ and $Q_3 = nR(T_0) \ln(1/2)$. For the constant

volume processes we have $Q_2 = nC_V(T_0 - 3T_0)$ and

$Q_4 = nC_V(3T_0 - T_0)$. The net heat transferred is then

$Q = Q_1 + Q_2 + Q_3 + Q_4$ or $Q = 2nRT_0 \ln 2$.

(b) Heat > 0 is the heat added to the system. Therefore

$Q_h = Q_1 + Q_4 = 3nRT_0(1 + \ln 2)$. Since the change in temperature

for the complete cycle is zero, $\Delta U = 0$ and $W = Q$. Therefore,

the efficiency is $e_c = \dfrac{W}{Q_h} = \dfrac{Q}{Q_h} = \dfrac{2 \ln 2}{3(1 + \ln 2)} = \boxed{0.273}$

*22.54   (a) +3.00 kJ

(b) −1.00 kJ

(c) +2.00 kJ

(d) +1.00 kJ

(e) +1.00 kJ

(f) 0.333

	Q	W	ΔU
AB	+3	+3	0
BC	0	+1	−1
CD	−2	−2	0
DA		1	+1

22.55 At point A, $P_0V_0 = nRT_0$, $n = 1$;   At point B, $3P_0V_0 = RT_B$ and

$T_B = 3T_0$; At point C, $(3P_0)(2V_0) = RT_c$ and $T_c = 6T_0$;

At point D, $P_0(2V_0) = RT_0$ and $T_D = 2T_0$

The heat transfer for each step in the cycle is found using

$C_V = 3R/2$ and $C_P = 5R/2$. $Q_{AB} = C_V(3T_0 - T_0) = 3RT_0$;

$Q_{BC} = C_P(6T_0 - 3T_0) = 7.5RT_0$; $Q_{CD} = C_V(2T_0 - 6T_0) = -6RT_0$;

$Q_{DA} = C_P(T_0 - 2T_0) = -2.5RT_0$; Therefore

(a) $Q_{(entering)} = Q_h = Q_{AB} + Q_{DA} = \boxed{10.5RT_0}$

(b) $Q_{(leaving)} = Q_c = |Q_{CD} + Q_{DA}| = \boxed{8.5RT_0}$

(c) Eff, $e = \dfrac{Q_h - Q_c}{Q_h} = \boxed{0.190}$

(d) Carnot Eff, $e_c = 1 - \dfrac{T_c}{T_h} = 1 - \dfrac{T_0}{6T_0} = \boxed{0.83}$

*22.56 (a) $\displaystyle\int P\,dV = \int \frac{nRT}{V}\,dV = nRT\ln V\,|_1^2 = \underline{RT\ln 2}$

(b) The second law refers to cycles.

22.57 The isobaric process (AB) is shown along with an isotherm (AC) and
an adiabat (CB) in the PV diagram. Since the change in entropy is path
independent, $\Delta S_{AB} = \Delta S_{AC} + \Delta S_{CB}$ and $\Delta S_{CB} = 0$ for an
adiabatic process. For isotherm (AC), $P_A V_A = P_C V_C$
and for adiabat (CB), $P_C V_C^\gamma = P_B V_B^\gamma$. Combining these gives
$V_C = [\dfrac{P_B V_B^\gamma}{P_A V_A}]^{1/(\gamma-1)} = [(\dfrac{P_0}{P_0})\dfrac{(3V_0)^\gamma}{V_0}]^{1/(\gamma-1)} = 3^{\gamma/\gamma-1}V_0$. Therefore
$\Delta S_{AC} = \dfrac{P_A V_A}{T}\ln(\dfrac{V_C}{V_A}) = nR\ln[3^{(\gamma/\gamma-1)}] = \boxed{nR\gamma\dfrac{\ln 3}{(\gamma-1)}}$

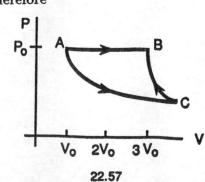

22.57

22.58 (a) $W/t = 1.5 \times 10^8 \ W_{(\text{electrical})}, \quad Q = mL = [\frac{W/t}{0.15}]\Delta t$ and

$L = 7.8 \times 10^3 \ \text{cal/g} = 7.8 \times 10^6 \ \text{cal/kg}.$

$m = [\frac{W/t}{0.15}]\Delta t/L$

$m = (1.5 \times 10^5 \ \text{W})(86,400 \ \text{s/day})$

$\div [0.15(7.8 \times 10^6 \ \text{cal/kg})(4.184 \ \text{J/cal})]$

$m = 2.65 \times 10^6 \ \text{kg/day} = \boxed{2.65 \times 10^3 \ \text{metric tons/day}}$

(b) $\text{Cost} = (\$8/\text{metric ton})(2.65 \times 10^3 \ \text{metric tons/day})(365 \ \text{days/y})$

$\text{Cost} = \boxed{\$7.74 \times 10^6/\text{y}}$

(c) First find the rate at which heat energy must be discharged to the water.

$e = \frac{W}{Q_h} = \frac{W}{W + Q_c} = \frac{W/t}{(W/t) + (Q_c/t)}$, and

$Q_c/t = (W/t)(1/e - 1) = (1.5 \times 10^8 \ \text{W})(1/0.15 - 1) = \boxed{8.5 \times 10^8 \ \text{W}}$

$Q_c/t = \boxed{2.03 \times 10^8 \ \text{cal/s}}$ Now require $\frac{Q_c}{t} = \frac{mc\Delta T}{t}$ and find

$\frac{m}{t} = \frac{Q_c/t}{c\Delta T} = \frac{2.03 \times 10^8 \ \text{cal/s}}{(1 \ \text{cal/g} \cdot \text{C}^\circ)(5 \ \text{C}^\circ)}$

$\frac{m}{t} = \boxed{4 \times 10^4 \ \text{kg/s}}$

*22.59 (a) $Q_{\text{out}} = W + Q_{\text{in}}$

$480 \ \text{kJ} = W + 360 \ \text{kJ}$

$W = \boxed{120 \ \text{kJ}}$

(b) COP (refrigerater) $= \frac{Q_c}{W} = \frac{360 \ \text{kJ}}{120 \ \text{kJ}} = \boxed{3.0}$

*22.60 Simply evaluate the maximum (Carnot) efficiency

$$e_c = \frac{\Delta T}{T_h} = \frac{4 \text{ K}}{277 \text{ K}} = \boxed{0.0144}$$

The proposal does not merit serious consideration.

22.61   (a) The heat transfer over the paths CD and BA are zero since they are

adiabats. Over path BC: $Q_{BC} = nC_P(T_C - T_B) > 0$.

Over path DA: $Q_{DA} = mC_V(T_A - T_D) < 0$. Therefore, $Q_C = |Q_{DA}|$

and $Q_h = Q_{BC}$. The efficiency is then:

$$e = 1 - \frac{Q_C}{Q_h} = 1 - \frac{(T_D - T_A)}{(T_C - T_B)}\frac{C_V}{C_P}$$

$$e = 1 - \frac{1}{\gamma}\left[\frac{(T_D - T_A)}{(T_C - T_B)}\right]$$

22.62 (a) Use the equation of state for an ideal gas $V_A = nRT_A/P_A$

$$V_A = \frac{(1)(8.318)(600)}{(25)(1.0 \times 10^5)} = \boxed{1.98 \times 10^{-3} \text{ m}^3}$$

$$V_C = \frac{ndRT_C}{P_C} = \frac{(1)(8.318)(400 \text{ K})}{1.01 \times 10^5} = \boxed{32.8 \times 10^{-3} \text{ m}^3}$$

Since AB is isothermal, $P_A V_A = P_B V_B$, and since BC is adiabatic,

$P_B V_B^\gamma = P_C V_C^\gamma$. Combining these two expressions we have

$$V_B = [\frac{P_C V_C}{P_A V_A}]^{1/(\gamma - 1)}$$

$$V_B = [(1/25)(32.8 \times 10^{-3} \text{ m}^3)^{1.4}/(1.98 \times 10^{-3} \text{ m}^3)]^{(1/0.4)} = \boxed{11.8 \times 10^{-3} \text{ m}^3}$$

$$V_D = [(25/1)(1.98 \times 10^{-3} \text{ m}^3)^{1.4}/(32.9 \times 10^{-3} \text{ m}^3)]^{(1/0.4)} = \boxed{5.46 \times 10^{-3} \text{ m}^3}$$

Pressure values are found using the ideal gas law $P_B = nRT_B/V_B$

and $P_D = nRT_D/V_D$. Using given temperatures (recall the

processes $A \rightarrow B$ and $C \rightarrow D$ are isothermal) and calculated

volumes, the pressure values are $P_B = \boxed{4.17 \text{ atm}}$ and $P_D = \boxed{6.01 \text{ atm}}$

(b) $W = eQ_h = \dfrac{0.333}{8.93 \times 10^3 \text{ J}} = \boxed{2.98 \times 10^3 \text{ J}}$

(c) Heat energy is added to the gas during the process $A \rightarrow B$ and

$$Q_h = W_{AB} - P_A V_A \ln(\frac{V_B}{V_A}) = 8.93 \times 10^3 \text{ J}$$

The efficiency $e = \dfrac{W}{Q_h} = 1 - \dfrac{T_C}{T_h} = 1 - \dfrac{400}{600} = \boxed{0.333}$

22.63 From the first law of thermodynamics $dQ = dU + PdV$ or

$CdT = C_V dT + PdV$. Also, $PdV + VdP = RdT$. Solving for dT in the

first equation and substituting into the second gives

$PdV + VdP = \dfrac{RdV}{C - C_V}$. Rearranging terms and using the fact that

$R = C_P - C_V$ we get $\dfrac{(C - C_P)}{(C - C_V)}\dfrac{dV}{V} + \dfrac{dP}{P} = 0$ and since

$\dfrac{dx}{x} = d(\ln x)$ we have $\ln V^{\gamma'} + \ln P = \ln(k)$ and $PV^{\gamma'} = k$ where

k is constant.

22.64   (a) $\dfrac{dQ}{dt} = (2 \times 10^6 \text{ cal} \times 4.186 \text{ J/cal})/(24 \text{ h} \times 3600 \text{ s/h})$

$\qquad = \boxed{96.9 \text{ W}} = \boxed{8.33 \times 10^4 \text{ cal/h}}$

(b) $\dfrac{dT}{dt} = \dfrac{dQ/dt}{mc} = \dfrac{8.33 \times 10^4 \text{ cal/h}}{(70 \times 10^3 \text{ g})(1 \text{ cal/g} \cdot \text{°C})}$

$\qquad = \boxed{1.19 \text{ °C/h}} = 2.14 \text{ °F/h}$

(c) $\dfrac{dS}{dt} = \dfrac{1}{T}\left(\dfrac{dQ}{dt}\right) = \dfrac{8.33 \times 10^4 \text{ cal/h}}{293.15 \text{ K}} = = \boxed{284 \text{ cal/K} \cdot \text{h}}$

*22.65 The efficiency e is

$$e = \frac{\text{Work done}}{\text{Energy input}} = \frac{\text{Heat input} - \text{Heat exhaust}}{\text{Heat input}}$$

Heat input at T_2 isotherm : $Q_2 = nRT_2 \ln(V_2/V_1)$

Heat exhaust at V_2 isochor : $Q_3 = nC_v(T_2 - T_1)$

Heat exhaust at T_1 isotherm : $Q_1 = nRT_1 \ln(V_2/V_1)$

Heat input at V_1 isochor : $Q_4 = nC_v(T_2 - T_1)$

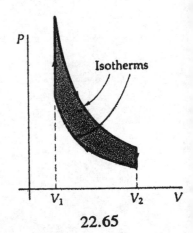

22.65

Noting that $Q_3 = Q_4$, we find the efficiency e to be

$$e = \frac{(Q_2 + Q_4) - (Q_1 + Q_3)}{(Q_2 + Q_4)}$$

$$e = \frac{nR(T_2 - T_1)\ln(V_2/V_1)}{nRT_2 \ln(V_2/V_1) + nC_v(T_2 - T_2)} = \boxed{\frac{2(T_2 - T_1)\ln(V_2/V_1)}{3(T_2 - T_1) + 2T_2 \ln(V_2/V_1)}}$$

$$\uparrow$$
$$(\tfrac{3}{2}R)$$

*22.66 (a) $\boxed{20.0\ ^\circ\text{C}}$

(b) $\Delta S = mc \ln\dfrac{T_f}{T_1} + mc \ln\dfrac{T_f}{T_2}$

$\qquad = (1\ \text{kg})(4.19\ \text{kJ/kg} \cdot \text{K}) \left[\ln\dfrac{T_f}{T_1} + \ln\dfrac{T_f}{T_2} \right]$

$\qquad \Delta S = (4.19\ \text{kJ/K}) \ln\left(\dfrac{293}{283} \cdot \dfrac{293}{273} \right)$

(c) $\Delta S = \boxed{+4.88\ \text{J/K}}$

(d) $\boxed{\text{Yes}}$ Entropy has increased.

ANSWERS TO EVEN-NUMBERED PROBLEMS

CHAPTER 1

2. 2.33 cm

*4. 0.242

6. (a) 3.83×10^{-16} g; (b) 1.06×10^7 atoms

8. 3.74 cm

10. $m = 1; n = 2m = 2$

18. 1.39×10^{-4} m^3

20. 7.46×10^{-4} m^3

22. 4045 m^2

24. 9.82 cm

*26. 1.2×10^{57}

28. 384 ft^2; 35.7 m^2

30. (a) 3.156×10^7 s; (b) 6×10^{10} y

32. 2.57×10^6 m^3

*34. 200 km

36. (a) 13.4 (b) 49.1

*38. 10^6 m^2

40. 2.2×10^9

42. $1 Billion

44. 10^9

*46. 1500 times larger

48. 40,000 pitches

50. (a) 2 (b) 4 (c) 3 (d) 2

52. (a) 797 (b) 11 (c) 18

54. 1.61×10^3 kg/m^3

56. 115.9 m

58. 24

*60. 24.6°

*62. 5×10^9 gallons

CHAPTER 2

2. (5.83 m, 121°)

4. (b) 4.55 m

6. $\sqrt{5}$ m; 26.5°

8. 25 m@ ± 37° *or* 61.8 m@ ± 14°

10. 14.3 km ; 65.2° N of E

*12. (a) 6.1 at 112° from x-axis;

    (b) 14.8 at 22.5° from x-axis

*14. 9.54 N at 57°

16. 7.92 at 4.3° N of W

*18. 5.24 km at 154°

*20. (a) 7 blocks; (b) 5 blocks at 143°

22. 358.2 m

*24. | B | = 7.81

26. −25 m ; 43.3 m

28. 7.3 cm; −7.2 cm

30. (b) 9.22; 49.4°

*32. (a) 4.47 at 63.4°; (b) 8.49 at 135°

34. 42.7 yards

*36. 4.65 m at 78.6°

38. 196 cm; −14.3°

*40. (a) 2.24   (b) 8.77

42. − 4i + 15.4j

*44. 656 km

48. (a)   2; 1; 3   (b) 3.74;

    (c) 57.7° from + x;

50. (a) | F | = 185 N;   (b) (-39i − 181j)N

CHAPTER 3

2. (a) 180 km; (b) 63.4 km/h; (c) 180 km

4. (a) 1920 m; (b) $\dfrac{32}{7}$ m/s

*6. (a) 50 m/s;   (b) 41 m/s

8. (a) − 0.60 m/s;   (b) −0.8 m/s

16. − 2.5 m/s²

18. (a) 0.6 m/s²

*22. 26,500 m/s²

24. (a) 0 m/s²; (b) 6 m/s²;

    (c) 825 m; (d) 65 m/s

26. 870 m

28. (a) 1875 m; (b) 1457 m; (e) 37.5 m/s

30. (a) a = −2.25 ×10⁻² m/s²; (b) 133 s;

    (c) v = 1.5 m/s

*32. The train leads the car by 1375 m.

*34. 234 m

36. (a) 0.494 m/s²;(b) 11,330 m ahead;

    (c) 13.33 km

38. 23.8 s

40. (a) 3 ×10⁻¹⁰ s; (b) 1.26 ×10⁻⁴ m

42. (a) − 4.9 ×10⁵ m/s;   (b) 3.57 ×10⁻⁴ s;

    (c) 1.8 thicknesses

44. (a) 8.2 s; (b) 134 m

46. t = 1.79 s

48. (a) 2.64 s;   (b) −2.09 m/s   (c) 1.62 s

50. (a) v_0 = 98 m/s; (b) 490 m

*52. On moon t = 1.11 s; on earth t = 0.45 s

54. 73.9 m

*56. 420 m

*58. 14.0 m

60. 0.22 s

62. (a) 0.117 s; (b) 5.53 m/s

*64. (b) 29.5 m/s²;   (b) 24.5 m/s²

66. (a) a = 2.41 m/s²; (b) t = 14.4s;

    (c) 60.25 m/s

68. 38.16 m

70. (a) 7210 ft/s²; (b) 140 ft; (c) 3.75 s

*72. (a) 15 s;   (b) 30 m/s;   (c) 225 m

*74. (a) 26.4 m

76. (a) 41 s;   (b) 1735 m;   (c) −184 m/s

78. (a) 3.92v; (b) 0.784v

CHAPTER 4

2. 1.12 m/s

6. (a) 2t m/s; 4t m/s; (c) 4.47t m/s

10. 3.19 s; 36.1 m/s; −60.1°

12. 14.6 m/s

*14. 74.5 m/s

16. (a) 1.03 s;

   (b) $v_x = 8.67$m/s $v_y = 4.2$m/s

   (c) $\theta = 25.8°$

*18. 18.7 m

20. (a) 0.784 m; (b) $\theta = 0.225°$

22. 38.3 m/s; 96.4 m

24. (b) $2\sqrt{\dfrac{2h}{g}}$; $2\sqrt{\dfrac{h}{g}}$

*26. (a) 22.6 m;   (b) 52.3 m;   (c) 1.18 s

28. (a) 6 rev/s; (b) 1.52×10^3 m/s;

   (c) 1.28×10^3 m/s^2

30. 0.0337 m/s^2

32. 19.8 m/s

34. 10.47 m/s; 219 m/s^2 (inward)

*36. (a) 0.6 m/s^2;   (b) 0.8 m/s^2;

   (c) 1.0 m/s^2

38. (a) 25 m/s^2;   (c) 26.8 m/s^2; 21.4°

40. (a) 32 m/s^2; (b) 55.4 m/s^2; (c) 64 m/s^2

44. $v = 0.85$ m/s

46. 120 m

48. (a) 14.5°; (b) 194 km/h

50. (a) 36.9°; (b) 41.6°; (c) 3 min

52. 15.3 m

54. 18.2 m

56. 15.6 m/s

58. (a) 14.7° or 75.3°; (b) 10.3 s; 39.6 s

*60. (a) 2.83 m;   (b) 14.4 m

62. (b) 9.80 m/s; (d) 9.80 m/s;

   45.6° north of the vertical; $v_0 = 14$ m/s

64. (a) 1530 m; (b) 36.2 s; (c) 4040 m

66. (a) and (b) 3.81 s; 41.7 m/s; (c) 36.6 m/s

*68. $t = 0$ s and 1.73 s

70. 7.52 m/s

72. (a) 55.5 s; (b) 33.4 s

74. 0.139 m/s

*76. (a) $c = 2$ km/h;   (b) $v = (4\mathbf{i} + 3\mathbf{j})$km/h

78. (a) 7.14 m/s; -12.1 m/s; (b) 2.47 s ;

   (c) 4.90 m

80. (a) $\tan\theta = \dfrac{2h}{b}$; (b) $v_0 = \sqrt{\dfrac{(4h^2 + b^2)g}{2h}}$

82. 3065 m; 6276 m;

   < 265 m *or* > 3476 m

84. (a) 22.9 m/s ; 3.06 s; (b) 360 m; 4.52 s;

   (c) 114 m/s; $- 44.3$ m/s

CHAPTER 5

2. (a) 12 N; (b) 3 m/s^2

4. 6 N

6. (a) 1.44 m; (b) 50.8 N

8. (a) 10^5 dynes   (b) 0.225 lb

10. 1.8 N

12. 2376 N

*16. 5.15 m/s^2 at 14° S of E

18. (a) $a = 5$ m/s^2; $a = 6.08$ m/s^2

20. 7 N to the left

*22. 600 N

24. (a) 3.6×10^{-18} N; (b) 8.9×10^{-30} N

26. (a) $T_1 = 31.5$ N; $T_2 = 37.5$ N; $T_3 = 49$ N

    (b) $T_1 = 113$ N; $T_2 = 56.6$ N; $T_3 = 98$ N

30. (a) 49 N; (b) 98 N; (c) 24.5 N

32. (a) $\theta = 55.15°$; (b) $N = 167.3$ N

34. −6400 N

*36. 1.59 m/s^2

40. (a) 2.54 m/s^2; (b) 3.18 m/s;

42. (a) 3.57 m/s^2; (b) 26.7 N; (c) 7.14 m/s

44. 112 N

48. $\mu_s = 0.306$; $\mu_k = 0.245$

50. 0.456

52. (a) 256 m; (b) 42.7 m

54. (a) 16.3 N; (b) 8.07 N

*56. 7.0 s

*62. 28.7 m

*64. $\Delta x = 37.0$ m

66. 80 lb

70. (a) 1.02 m/s^2; (b) 2.04 N; 3.06 N; 4.08 N

    (c) 14 N; 8 N

*72. it is impossible

74. (b) 9.8 N; 0.58 m/s^2

*76. (a) 600 N;   (b) 1110 N;   (c) 1 m/s^2

*82. $\bar{a} = 14.4$ cm/s^2, $a' = 13.7$ cm/s^2

86. (b) $T_1 = 17.4$ N; $T_2 = 40.5$ N;

    $a = 5.75$ m/s^2

88. 0.202; 17.5 N

*90. 3.34

CHAPTER 6

2. 6.22×10^{-12} N

4. 6.56×10^{15} rev/s

6. (a) 5.59×10^3 m/s; (b) 239 min;

    (c) 735 N

*8. 13.3 m/s

*10. 0.283

12. (a) 0.105 m/s; (b) 1.11×10^{-2} m/s^2

14. (a) 149 N; (b) 10.4 m/s

*16. (a) 1.33 m/s^2;   (b) 1.79 m/s^2

*18. 8.88 N

20. (a) 2.49×10^4 N; (b) 12.1 m/s

22. (a) 8.62 m;   (b) Mg, downward;

    (c) 8.45 m/s^2;   (d) $v > 14$ m/s

24. 2.42 m/s^2

26. (a) 3.60 m/s^2 ; (b) 0

28. $\theta = \arctan \dfrac{a_x}{a_y} = 0.0927°$

30. (a) 32.8 s^{-1} ; (b) 9.8 m/s^2 ; (c) 4.90 m/s^2

32. (a) 51.7 m/s;   (b) 137 m

34. 0.493 m/s^2 ; -0.524 m/s^2; 0.720 m/s^2

36. 37.5 N

38. (a) 0.610 rev/s; (b) 0.766 m/s; 2.93 m/s^2

40. (a) $\sqrt{\pi Rg}$; (b) $m\pi g$

42. (c) $v_{min} = 8.57$ m/s; $v_{max} = 16.6$ m/s

44. $v = \sqrt{gL\sin\theta}$

46. (a) 66.3 N; (b) 36.6 N ; (c) 6.96 N

48. (a) 2.63 m/s^2; (b) 201 m; (c) 17.7 m/s

50. 0.782 m/s

52. (a) 5.19 m/s; (b) 555 N

54. (a) 13.6 m/s

CHAPTER 7

2. 2.93 kJ

4. (b) 0.737 ft·lb

6. (a) 294 kJ; (b) −294 kJ

8. (a) 329 J; (b) −185 J; (c) 0;

   (d) 0; (e) 144 J

10. 4.70 kJ

12. (a) 5.00 ; (b) $\theta = 71.6°$

14. 28.9

16. 16.0

18. 59.0°

20. 83.4°

22. 3.00 J

24. (a) 24.0 J; (b) −3.00 J; (c) 21.0 J

26. (b) −12.0 J

28. (b) $(1000 - 25x)$N; (c) 10.0 kJ

*30. (a) 417 N/m;   (b) 3 J

32. (a) 1.20 J; (b) 5.00 m/s; (c) 6.30 J

34. 2.45×10^{10} J

36. (a) 60.0 J; (b) 60.0 J

38. (a) 1.94 m/s; (b) 3.35 m/s; (c) 3.87 m/s

*40. (a) 22,500 N;   (b) 1.33×10^{-4} s

42. 30.9 m/s

44. (a) 0.791 m/s to the left;

    (b) 0.531 m/s to the left

46. 116 mm

48. (a) 6.34 m/s; (b) 5.52 m/s; (c) 4.10 m

50. 5.18 N

52. (b) −123 J

*54. 9.8×10^6

56. (a) 3920 W; (b) 706 kJ

58. 830 N

60. (a) 30.1 m/s; (b) 44.4 kW

62. (b) 240 W

66. 6.33 km/L

68. (a) 7.37×10^{-13} J; (b) 94.5%

70. (a) = 758 J; (b) −454 J; (c) 0 J;

    (d) −304 J

72. (a) 980 J; (b) −980 J;

    (c) 24.5 J/s *or* 24.5 W

74. (a) $\dfrac{A_x}{A}$

76. (a) 2.80 m/s; (b) 1.96 m/s

*78. 141 kW

80. (a) $\mu = \dfrac{kd}{2mg}$; (b) $\mu = \dfrac{kd}{4mg}$

82. (a) 14.5 m/s; (b) 1.75 kg; (c) 0.350 kg

84. (a) mg^2t; (b) 960 W; 1.92 kW; 0

*88. (a) 2.3 kW;   (b) 62.2 kW

CHAPTER 8

2. (b) 35.0 J

4. (a) $\dfrac{Ax^2}{2} - \dfrac{Bx^3}{3}$; (b) $\dfrac{5}{2}A - \dfrac{19}{3}B$; $-\dfrac{5}{2}A + \dfrac{19}{3}B$

6. (a) 80 J;   (b) -80 J;   (c) 6.32 m/s

8. (a) 22.0 J; $E = 40.0$ J

10. 2.94 m/s

12. (a) 19.8 m/s; (b) -294 J;

   (c) $v_B = (30.0 \text{ m/s}) \, \boldsymbol{i} - (39.6 \text{ m/s}) \, \boldsymbol{j}$

14. (a) 19.6 J;   (b) 2.86 m/s;

   (c) 59.6 N; 0.816 m

16. (a) 19.8 m/s; (b) 78.4 J; (c) 1.00

18. $H = \dfrac{2}{3}h$ $\left(\text{for } H \leq \dfrac{3}{2}h\right)$

20. 1.96 m

22. (a) 9.90 m/s; (b) -14.7 J; (c) -14.7 J

24. 2.00 m/s; 2.79 m/s; 3.19 m/s

26. 1.40 m/s

28. (a) 0.240 J; (b) 0.180 J

*30. 0.344 m

*32. (a)100.5 J;   (b) 0.41 m;   (c) 2.84 m/s

34. 0.102

*36. v=0.537 m/s

38. (a) $-2ax + b$; (b) $\dfrac{b}{2a}$

44. (a) 8.18×10^{-14} J; (b) 3.59×10^{-8} J;

   (c) 1.80×10^{14} J ; (d) 5.38×10^{41} J

46. (a) 0.588 J; (b) 0.588 J; (c) 2.42 m/s;

   (d) 0.196 J; 0.392 J

48. 2940 N/m

*50. 1.45 m

52. 5.05 m/s

*54. 54.2 m/s

56. 0.236 m

58. $\dfrac{3L}{5}$

60. (a) $F = -\dfrac{d}{dx}(-x^3 + 2x^2 + 3x)\boldsymbol{i}$

      $= (3x^2 - 4x - 3)\boldsymbol{i}$;

   (b) 1.87 and -0.535

*62. 10.3 GJ

64. $v = 0.923$ m/s

66. (a) $-2Ax + 3Bx^2$; (b) $x = 0$; $x = \dfrac{2A}{3B}$;

   $x = 0$ is a point of *stable* equilibrium;

   $x = \dfrac{2A}{3B}$ is *unstable*

*68. k = 31.1 N/m

CHAPTER 9

2. 40.0 m/s

*4. 0.732 kg·m/s

6. 2.40 N

8. $-15.0\,\boldsymbol{i}$ N

10. (a) K is quadrupled;

   (b) p increases by a factor of $\sqrt{3}$

*12. (a) 364 kg · m/s; (b) 438 N

14. 5.40 $\boldsymbol{i}$ N·s

16. 23.3 N

18. −6.00 m/s

*20. 2.45 cm

22. (a) 3.33 m/s; (b) −83.4 J Energy lost

24. (b) 0.398 %

26. (a) 2 m/s North ; (b) 5.04 kJ

28. (a) 2.50 m/s ; (b) −3.75 × 10^4 J

*30. 12.5 kN

32. −0.500 m/s ; 2.00 m/s

34. (a) −1.08 m/s ; 4.34 m/s ; (b) $h = 0.240$ m

36. (a) $n \approx 42$ collisions; (b) $n \approx 14$

38. (a) 4.02 m; (b) 2.00 m/s to the right

40. (a) 9.90 m/s $= v_{2i}$; (b) −16.5 m/s;

   +3.30 m/s; (c) 13.9 m; 0.556 m

42. (a) $\dfrac{v_0}{\sqrt{2}}$; (b) 45°; −45°

44. (a) 1.07 m/s; (b) −0.318

*46. (a) $\mathbf{v} = (-34.3$ m/s$)\mathbf{i} - (25.7$ m/s$)\,\mathbf{j}$;

   (b) $E = 7.71$ kJ

48. (a) 20.0 cm/s

50. $\tan \theta_2 = \dfrac{v_1' \sin \theta_1}{v_1 - v_1' \cos \theta_1}$

52. 0.375 m; 1.5 m

54. 1.26 × 10^{-10} m

56. 0.613 m; $y_c = 0$ (by symmetry)

58. (a) (1.43 m/s)$\mathbf{i}$; (b) (10 kg·m/s)$\mathbf{i}$

60. (a) $(3.20\mathbf{i} - 2.00\mathbf{j})$ m/s; (b) $(-4.00\,\mathbf{j})$ m/s^2;

   (c) $(16.\mathbf{i} - 20t\mathbf{j})$ kg·m/s

62. 0.700 m

64. (a) 3.9 × 10^7 N; (b) 3.2 m/s^2

66. (a) 442 metric tons; (b) 19.2 metric tons

70. $R/14$ from center of sphere

72. 1390 m/s

74. (a) 0.188 m/s; (b) 3.44 km

76. 450,000 N; 1.84 g; 2750 m/s (6150 mi/h);

78. 0.215 m/s; 68.2°

80. (a) −3.54 m/s; (b) 1.77 m;

82. (a) $v = \dfrac{m_1 v_1 + m_2 v_2}{m_1 + m_2}$; (b) $(v_1 - v_2)\sqrt{\dfrac{m_1 m_2}{k(m_1 + m_2)}}$

84. $x_{cm} = \dfrac{2}{3}a;\ y_{cm} = \dfrac{1}{3}b$

*86. (a) 6.3 m/s;   (b) 6.17 m/s

CHAPTER 10

2. 16.7 rev

4. (a) $2at + 3bt^2$; (b) $2a + 6bt$

6. 5.00 rad; 53.0 rad; 10.0 rad/s;

   22.0 rad/s; 4.00 rad/s^2; 4.00 rad/s^2

*8. (a) 54.3 rev;   (b) 12.1 rev/s

*10. $\alpha = 25$ rad/s^2

*12. (a) 25 rad/s;   (b) 139.8 rad/s;

   (c) 0.628 s

14. 40.0 rad

16. 158 kJ

*18. 1/160

20. $\dfrac{3}{4}ML^2$; $\dfrac{ML^2}{2}$; $\dfrac{5}{4}ML^2$

24. (a) 29.6 N·m; (b) 35.6 N·m

26. 17.7 kg

28. (a) 21.6 kg·m^2; (b) 3.60 N·m; (c) 52.4 rev

*30. (a) 24 N·m; (b) 0.0356 rad/s^2;

(c) 1.07 m/s^2

*32. 2.36 m/s

34. $\mu = 0.312$

*36. 617 s

38. $\frac{2}{5}mR^2$

42. (a) 9.00 kg·m^2; (b) 10.5 rad/s; 49.3 kJ

(c) 52.4 rad/s; −37.0 kJ

*44. −0.322 rad/s^2

46. $I = Mr^2(\frac{gt^2}{2h} - 1) - \frac{mr^2}{2}$

48. (b) $2g(\frac{M}{m+2M})(\sin\theta - \mu\cos\theta)$

*50. 139 m/s

52. (a) $\omega = \sqrt{\frac{2mg\,d\sin\theta + kd^2}{I + mR^2}}$

(b) 1.74 rad/s

54. (a) 2160 N·m; (b) 439 W

CHAPTER 11

2. 1.05×10^4 J

6. $\frac{15}{14}$; $\frac{15}{14}$

*8. $(-7)\mathbf{i} + (16)\mathbf{j} - (10)\mathbf{k}$

10. (a) $-7\mathbf{k}$ N·m; (b) $11\mathbf{k}$ N·m

*14. (2 N·m)$\mathbf{k}$

*16. (20.4 kg·m^2/s)$\mathbf{k}$

18. (a) $(4dmv)\mathbf{k}$; (b) 0; (c) $(-2dmv)\mathbf{k}$

20. (a) 2.10×10^{10} kg·m^2/s

22. (a) 3.14 N·m; (b) $0.40v$; (c) 7.85 m/s^2

24. (a) 0.36 kg·m^2/s; (b) 0.54 kg·m^{2}s

*28. 7.14 rpm

*26. (a) 0.32 kg·m^2; (b) 0.96 kg·m^2/s;

(c) 4.80 N

30. (a) 9.2 s^{-1}

32. (a) 0.61 rad/s; (b) 0.122 J

34. (a) 3.50 kg·m^2/s; (b) 196 J

38. (a) 12.4 rad/s; (b) −63.1 J

42. (a) $h_{min} = 2.7(R - r)$

48. (a) 3.26×10^7 J; (b) 24.3 min

52. (a) $v_{cm} = \sqrt{\frac{3}{4}g\ell}$, vertically downward

(b) $v_{cm} = \sqrt{\frac{3}{4}g\ell}$, vertically downward.

56. (a) $\sqrt{\frac{10}{7gh}}$; (b) $\sqrt{2gh}$; $\frac{t_1}{t_2} = 1.18$

CHAPTER 12

2.

$$F_y + R_y - W = 0$$
$$-R_x + F_x = 0$$
$$F_y\ell\cos\theta - W\frac{\ell}{2}\cos\theta - F_x\ell\sin\theta = 0$$

4. $x = (\frac{\ell}{2} + d)(\frac{2}{3}\frac{W_1}{W_2} - \frac{1}{3})$

6. 3.01 kN

8. 3.85 cm; 6.85 cm

10. $\frac{2}{3}L$

12. 8.33%

14. 0.643 m

16. 706 N·m

*18. (a) 29.9 N; (b) 22.2 N

20. 2.24 m

*22. $U = 88.2$ N, $D = 58.8$ N

*24. 1.07 mm

26. 9.12×10^{-4} m

*28. 1.097 cm^3

*30. (a) 6.89 mm; (b) No

*32. 3.51×10^8 Pa

34. $1.155Mg$; $0.577Mg$

36. (b) $T = 343$ N; $R_x = 171$ N; $R_y = 683$ N;

   (c) 5.14 m

38. 1.47 kN, 1.33 kN; 2.58 kN

40. 6.47×10^5 N; 1.27×10^4 N; 0

42. $\mu = 0.268$

44. $21.20°$, 1.68×10^3 N; 2.34×10^3 N

*46. $T_1 = T_2 = 1.44$ kN

48. (a) 120 N; (b) 0.30; (c) 103 N; (d) $31°$

*50. $N_C = 634$ N, $N_A = 366$ N

*52. 12.3 kN

*54. (a) 1.04 kN

56. (a) $k = \dfrac{YA}{L}$; (b) $YA\dfrac{(\Delta L)^2}{2L}$

58. 9.85×10^{-5}

60. 4.90 cm

CHAPTER 13

2. (a) $-12\pi \sin(3\pi t + \pi)$ m/s;

  (b) $-36\pi^2 \cos(3\pi t + \pi)$ m/s^2;

  (c) $36\pi^2$ m/s^2; (d) $-12\pi \sin(\pi) = 0$;

  $-36\pi^2 \cos(\pi) = 36\pi^2$ m/s^2

4. (a) 31.6 rad/s; (b) 1.58 m/s

*6. (a) 20 cm; (b) 94.2 cm/s; (c) 17.8 m/s^2

8. 18.8 m/s; 7.11 km/s^2

10. 0.627 s

12. (a) 1.26 s; (b) 0.150 m/s;

  (c) 0.750 m/s^2; $x = -3.00 \cos(5t)$ cm;

  $v = \dfrac{dx}{dt} = 15.0 \sin(5t)$ cm/s;

  $a = 75.0 \cos(5t)$ cm/s^2

14. (a) -1.44 m/s; -3.92 m/s^2

  (b) 1.57m/s; 9.87 m/s^2

*16. (a) 1.19 Hz; (b) 0.21 s; (c) 0.784 N

18. (a) 126 N/m; (b) 0.178 m

*20. 0.384 J

*22. (a) 0.028 J; (b) 1.02 m/s; (c) 12.2 mJ

  (d) 15.8 mJ

*24. (a) 100 N/m; (b) 1.13 Hz; (c) 1.41 m/s;

  (d) 10 m/s^2; (e) 2 J; (f) 1.33 m/s;

  (g) 3.33 m/s^2

26. 6.35 s; 0.158 Hz

*28. $g_{\text{exp}} = 9.85$ m/s^2

30. 1.50 m

32. $\ell = 2R$

*34. $T = 1.42$ s, $L = 0.5$ m

40. (a) 1.00 s; (b) 5.09 cm

44. 6580 N/m

46. 0.357 m

48. 0.302

52. (a) $\dfrac{1}{2}(M + \dfrac{m}{3})v^2$

*56. (a) 38.6 N/m; (b) 1.32 kg

14. (a) 0; (b) 3.86 N/m^2

16. −84.3 N/m^2

20. 10 μW/m^2

22. (a) 3.75 W/m^2;   (b) 0.6 W/m^2

24. 65.3 dB

26. (a) 81.2 dB; (b) 1.316×10^{-4} W/m^2

*28. 1.13 μW

*30. (a) 1.76 kJ;   (b) 108 dB

32. (a) 6.25 Pa; (b) water; (c) 71.2 dB;

    (d) 4.59 Pa

34. 534 m/s

36. (a) 75 Hz; (b) 0.948 m

*38. 18.4 m/s

*40. 19.3 m

42 (a) 3.04 kHz;   (b) 2.08 kHz;

    (c) 2.62 kHz and 2.40 kHz

44. L = 2.34 m

*46. 5.52 μm

48. 1.79 ppm

*52. 67.0 dB

*54. 680 km

56. (a) 1: 4.5: 15.5; (d) 0.331 m; 1.49 m;

    5.14 m; 1.09×10^{-8} m; 1.84×10^{-10} m;

    3.53×10^{-11} m; 2.92×10^{-2} N;

    1.73 N: 9.00 N

*58. (b) 85.9 Hz

60. Bat is gaining at 1.7 m/s

CHAPTER 18

2. (a) 11.6 m

4. (a) 0.34 m; (b) 0.68 m

*6. 91.3°

8. (b) 19,975 Hz

12. 15.7 m; 31.8 Hz; 500 m/s

18. 813 N

20. (a) 0.08 N; (b) 4050 N

*22. 160 N

24. 120 Hz

*28. 800 Hz

30. 3.9%

32. (a) 8.55 m; (b) 4.28 m

*34. 0.253 m, 0.506 m, 0.759 m, ...

36. 0.0858 Hz

*38. (a) 17.0 Hz; 34.0 Hz; (c) 17.6 Hz;

    (d) 35.2 Hz

40. (a) 572 Hz; 1144 Hz; 1716 Hz

    (b) 286 Hz; 858 Hz; 1430 Hz

42. (a) 215 Hz; (b) 1935 Hz

44. (a) 21.4 m, 5,72 mm;

    (b) 10.7 m, 2.86 mm

46. 1.16 m

*50. 5.6 beats/s

54. (a) 261 Hz;   (b) 85 Hz

*56. (a) 34.8 m/s;   0.977 m

58. (a) 4 Hz; (b) −1%

60. 4 Hz

62. 243 Hz

64. 4730 Hz

*68. $(T_B/T_A) = 0.111$

70. (c) 2 kHz;   (d) 0.075 m/s

CHAPTER 19

2. (a) 54.6 mm Hg; (b) 196 mm Hg

4. (a) −251° C; (b) 1.36 atm

6. (a) 1337 K; 2933 K (b) 1596 C°; 1596 K

8. 57.8°C; −88.3°C

10. 40.6°C to −31.6°C

12. 37.0°C; 38.9 C

14. 430 K; 774° F

16. (a) 3.0058 m; (b) $L = 2.9986$ m

*18. 1.000329 m

20. 0.313 m

22. (a) $1.50 \times 10^{-5}(\text{C}°)^{-1}$; (b) −41.7°C

24. (a) −179°C, this is attainable

   (b) −376°C, which is below 0 K

   so it cannot be reached

*26. +0.109 cm^2

*28. 55°C

30. 2.16×10^{-3}

32. 99.8 mL

34. 3.12 atm

*36. 1.5×10^{29} molecules

*38. 1.43 g

40. 884 balloons

42. (a) 2.95 atm gauge $= 4.00 \times 10^5$ Pa (abs.)

   $= 43.4 \, \text{lb/in}^2$ (gauge);

   (b) 50.4 lb/in^2

44. 3.22×10^{11} molecules

46. 22.4 L

48. (a) 2.24 m; (b) 9.16 atm

50. (a) 0.169 m; (b) 1.35×10^5 Pa

52. (a) 9.49×10^{-5} s; (b) 57.4 s lost

54. (a) 0.340%; (b) 0.480%

56. (b) 5×10^{-5} °C^{-1}

58. (a) $\dfrac{\rho g P_0 V_0}{(P_0 + \rho g d)}$; (c) 10.3 m

*60. (a) $\beta = \dfrac{1}{T}$; (b) 3.67×10^{-3}/°C

62. (a) 21.2 kPa; 940 Pa; 32.3 Pa;

   (b) 8.16×10^{-2} m^3; 1.23 kg/m^3;

   (c) 29.0 g/mol

64. $T = 208$°C

66. (a) $h = \dfrac{nRT}{(mg + P_a A)}$; (b) 0.662 m

68. $\bar{\beta} - \dfrac{h_1 - h_0}{h_0 t_c}$

70. (a) 18.44 cm; (b) 3.63%; 6.69 mm;

   (c) 3.20%; 5.90 mm

72. (a) $L_f = L_0 e^{\alpha \Delta T}$; (b) 2.00×10^{-4}%;

   (c) 59%

*54. (a) +3 kJ;   (b) -1 kJ;   (c) +2 kJ

   (d) +1 kJ;   (e) +1 kJ;   (f) 0.333

58. (a) 2.65×10^3 metric tons/day;

   (b) $\$7.74 \times 10^6$/y;

   (c) 8.5×10^8 W; 2.03×10^8 cal/s;

   (d) 4×10^4 kg/s

*60. 0.0144

62. (a) 1.98×10^{-3} m^3; 32.8×10^{-3} m^3;

   11.8×10^{-3} m^3; 5.46×10^{-3} m^3;

   4.17 atm; 6.01 atm;

   (b) 2.98×10^3 J;   (c) 0.333

64. (a) 96.90 W; 8.33×10^4 cal/h;

   (b) 1.19°C/h; 2.14 °F/h

   (c) 284 cal/K · h

*66. (a) 20 °C;   (c) +4.88 J/K